THE NATURE OF
ATOMS AND MOLECULES

EWING C. SCOTT

Professor of Chemistry
International Christian University, Tokyo
Emeritus, Syracuse University

FRANK A. KANDA

Professor of Chemistry
Syracuse University

 HARPER & BROTHERS, PUBLISHERS, NEW YORK

THE NATURE OF
ATOMS AND
MOLECULES

A GENERAL CHEMISTRY

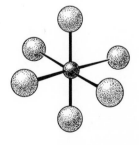

To the memory of my son,

Peter Scott,

who was impelled to reach

the height and depth and

breadth of everything he beheld

E.C.S.

Contents

Preface

This textbook is intended for college students who have a serious interest in chemistry, regardless of whether or not they have had a high school chemistry course. The student who has not studied chemistry previously will find a complete explanation of the subject matter, while the student familiar with chemistry will encounter challenging new ideas from the beginning.

The basic purpose of this book is to offer logical explanations for the behavior of atoms and molecules based upon their electron structures and the implications associated with such structures. Chemistry has grown so much in quantity and complexity that attempts to cover everything which seems pertinent to a general chemistry course results in a task frustrating to both teacher and student. Covering a large area of chemical behavior seems an endless task of learning many isolated reactions and properties of many different substances—a dry, monotonous chore at best. It is no wonder that students raise the criticism that general chemistry seems no more a science than a course in cooking. We should seek systematization of the facts about the chemical properties and behavior of substances in order to make more reasonable the task of learning them.

One common factor to which we can relate a multitude of properties is electronegativity. A glance at the topics indexed under electronegativity will illustrate the use of this approach in the explanation of the chemical nature of substances.

Yet we must remember that no single empirical argument can consistently give absolute answers to questions covering as wide a range of behavior as is observed in chemistry. We feel electronegativity currently suffices to furnish explanations of behavior much as the octet rule did in the past in its dealings with atomic structure.

Since general chemistry primarily deals with inorganic substances in water solution, we stress the ionic nature of these materials; the chemical characteristics of ions, rather than compounds, are generally developed unless the substance is a covalent compound. Thus the student learns at an early stage to regard ionic compounds as substances which display the properties of their ions, which, when learned, are applicable in predicting similar properties of other compounds containing the same ions. By stressing the nature of individual ions which typify classes of ions, we are well on our way to systematize the study of a variety of substances. Ions are molecules and are treated as such; properties which are dependent upon the number of molecules are not treated as being abnormal for ionic substances as is frequently done elsewhere. Since metallic ions in water solutions are usually hydrated and display common unique properties which vary primarily in degree, we do not dodge the existence of ion hydrates but treat them as the normal substances in solution. Only if the property of the hydrated ion is unimportant to the area under discussion do we simplify the ion to the anhydrous form for facility in equation writing or discussion. Instances of this sort are sufficiently qualified so that the student does not lose sight of the fact that the hydrated ions exist.

Pure covalence and electrovalence are treated as extremes of the broad topic of valence. It is stressed that most valence bonding falls somewhere between these extremes, a natural consequence of electronegativity. Thus ionic character of covalent bonds and covalent character in ionic substances are perfectly normal considerations. This allows for the treatment of behavior as a gradual fluctuation between extremes, related to a common factor instead of in terms of isolated characteristics unique to the particular substance under discussion. An example of this is the variation in hydrolysis and volatility of sodium, magnesium, aluminum and phosphorus chlorides with the covalent character of their bonds, which we correlate with the electronegativities.

Electronic structures of atoms and molecules are dealt with in terms of modern orbital concepts. We begin with these early in the book and continue this treatment throughout. A new technique is presented for arriving at logical orbital configurations: we have found this to be highly successful, stimulating and interesting for the students. Through use of the orbital approach, the treatment of complex ions, stability, geometrical configurations, and isomerism is presented on a level understood by beginning students. Furthermore, even certain phases of the unique chemistry of such elements as phosphorus, sulfur, and the halogens, due to an expanded octet and the inert pair of s electrons of some sub-group elements, can be considered as a continuous part of the pattern of electronic structure and chemical behavior. This approach enlivens the interest of students and makes them feel that freshman chemistry is not essentially a repeat of their high school chemistry.

The sequence of the treatment of the metallic elements has been arranged to follow in reverse order one of the standard qualitative analysis procedures. This sequence has much in its favor, introducing the typical metals first and establishing the rather simple aspects of their chemistry. Aluminum serves as a transitory element, naturally following magnesium in chemical characteristics and introducing the student to the amphoteric elements including chromium and zinc. The latter elements lead into the development of the chemistry of the transition and sub-group elements covering complexes, ligands, and the role of d electrons in determining chemical properties.

By bundling together selected elements from the long periods according to their analytical group classifications, we emphasize chemical correlations which are frequently more important than those pertaining to vertical group classifications for these elements. At the end of each chapter which completes a given analytical group of elements, a section which selectively summarizes the pertinent chemical behavior covered in the preceding chapters is devoted to the systematic analytical procedures. For courses in which qualitative analysis is not given, or in which some other analytical scheme is followed, these sections can be readily omitted without detracting from the chemistry to be learned. Detailed treatment of the analysis is reserved for the laboratory manual.

Organic chemistry is treated in this book in a manner unique to beginning texts in chemistry. The classical approach is not followed: this we feel, should be relegated to a formal course in organic chemistry. Instead we treat carbon as another element in the whole family of elements, and continue with the theme of electronegativity, nature of bonds, etc. as previously developed in the book. Early in the chapter the principle of the inductive effect, active groups and "intercommunicating orbitals and bond systems" is introduced to lay the ground work for the behavior and nature of organic molecules. Structural correlations are continued in the following chapter—appropriately entitled "Giant Molecules"— in which carbon is considered with other non-metallic elements capable of displaying a coordination number of four.

We consider the sections devoted to the history of elements or particular compounds, and the economics of production to be an important part of the story of chemistry. True, a lecturer may not wish to devote valuable limited time to these topics, but such sections present interesting simple views about chemistry which the student can readily understand. Students should get into the habit of reading "fringe-area" materials devoted to the subject matter he is studying. We have attempted to make these sections interesting so that the average student will readily read them through his own initiative and learn how names such as "alkali metal," "alkaline earth," and "alumina" were derived, or why certain elements or compounds were "naturals" from the standpoint of their chemical nature for early discovery or development. The awesome production figures, growth and development of chemical industries and their impact in National and World economy, and the effect of international relationships on research and development are all part of the story of our current scientific age and should be included, though briefly, for a wholesome appreciation of the subject of chemistry.

The authors wish to extend their acknowledgement and appreciation to their colleagues in the Department of Chemistry at Syracuse University for their suggestions and criticisms during the preparation of this book. We wish to extend our gratitude to Dr. W. A. Baker for his aid in reading proof and for the many helpful suggestions he made in the course of this work. We also express our appreciation to our secretary, Mrs. Frances Lowe, for her assistance in typing part of the manuscript. We thank our wives for their kindness and patience during the preparation of this book—especially Alberta Kanda who stoically typed part of the manuscript in motels and national parks during a cross country vacation trip. We appreciate the cooperation and efforts of the Harper staff who have worked diligently in close accord with our wishes in the production of this book.

EWING C. SCOTT
FRANK A. KANDA

November, 1961

THE NATURE OF
ATOMS AND MOLECULES

1

Science, energy, matter, and measurement

1.1. Science

"Science is a progressive development of conceptual schemes arising from experiment and observation and leading to new experiments and observations." Thus did J. B. Conant, former president of Harvard University, define science both precisely and adequately. From this it is apparent that a "scientist" is an explorer and discoverer who must judiciously weigh his findings as to their validity and significance. A study of science acquaints us with natural laws and the factors which control the operation of these laws.

A natural law, such as the law of gravity, is not a statute which is enacted to suit the whim of an investigator or the doctrines of a government. It is something that has always existed. It is up to the scientist to uncover it through his probings in the laboratory. The proof of the validity of a law is its ability to fit known facts and to predict new ones. Before a new theory can win acceptance as a law, its predictions in many directions must be carefully verified. It is for this reason that a scientist takes a highly critical attitude toward any newly reported discovery and usually awaits additional evidence before he completely accepts the new concept.

The conscientious, objective type of thinking and reasoning which plays such an important part in the development of science is good for all of us regardless of whether we become scientists. Furthermore, it is almost a necessity to have some knowledge of science today in order to be considered fully educated. We live in a "science age" now; and whether we like it or not, more and more of our everyday life and our individual action will be affected by the scientific nature of this "age." Our newspapers and magazines, radio and television continually make us aware of scientific developments and facts which the lay public usually cannot fully appreciate. We continually hear about sonar, radar, turbojets, high-energy fuels, transistors, fluoridation of water supplies, man-made satellites, H-bombs, A-bombs, Salk vaccine, etc., but what do we know about these? Even the platforms of some of our politicians contain scientific planks of local and international significance. You, as a student, cannot justifiably divorce science from your curriculum; you need at least some exposure to it to appreciate better the world you live in and what is happening around you.

1.2. Chemistry

One of the most important and interesting of the several branches of science is chemistry. It is impossible to segregate one branch of science completely from another; in fact, the names of some divisions—biochemistry, physical chemistry, biophysics, etc.—are indicative of the correlation between branches. Each branch of science contributes knowledge of great importance to other fields of science. It will be evident in our study of chemistry that much of our knowledge about the atom stems from the contributions of the physicist, and that chemistry in turn is one of the foundations of biology, medicine, engineering, geology, etc.

The science of chemistry is primarily concerned with the constitution, properties, and utilization of substances. These terms are actually very broad in scope in connection with chemistry, a fact which will become evident as we develop the subject matter. For example, the "constitution of matter" implies a knowledge not only of the chemical make-up of substances in general but also of how it can be changed in order to enhance or play down certain properties or to increase utilization. Each advance made by chemical research in the broad categories listed above leads to a further understanding of the nature of matter so that the chemist can explain its behavior and devise methods to synthesize materials, such as new fuels, better adapted to modern living.

1.3. Matter and Chemical Constitution

The page of this book and the ink in the print you are reading as well as the water you drink and the air you breathe are forms of matter. Anything possessing a chemical constitution is **matter.** Matter is material substance which already exists. The chemist may simplify and purify it or reconstruct it into something different. For example, a solution of common salt in water, when properly treated by the chemist, yields sodium hydroxide (lye), chlorine, and hydrogen. These were originally combined in a different fashion from that in the end result. As a result of such changes produced in existing matter, a tremendous variety of new substances pours out of laboratories and chemical plants daily. Over a million substances have been made and countless others are still to come.

All matter is composed of simple substances called **elements.** Elements are chemical entities that are incapable of further chemical simplification. You already are familiar with such common elements as gold, carbon, aluminum, iron, oxygen, nitrogen, hydrogen, and sulfur. A total of 103 elements are known. So many are very rare that the average individual, throughout his entire life, comes in contact with no more than 30 or 40 elements in any form or combination. Actually when we consider the varieties of matter which we encounter in the course of a single day, it seems fantastic that they are derived from so few elements.

If matter consisted only of simple mixtures of elements there would not be the tremendous variety of matter which we observe. For example, a mixture of carbon and sulfur would be similar to any other mixture of these elements. One sample might appear more yellow than another because it contains a greater proportion of sulfur. Nevertheless, we could recognize both samples as being mixtures of the same substances. However, chemical elements are able to react with each other to form substances that are entirely different from the original elements. These chemical combinations are **compounds.** For example, when the elements hydrogen and oxygen, which are colorless gases, are mixed and ignited, an explosion results. This is the chemical reaction going on. (Incidentally, contrary to popular belief, relatively few chemical reactions are explosions.) The compound water, a colorless liquid, forms as the product of this reaction. The elements carbon (a black solid), hydrogen, and oxygen are the constituents of many entirely different compounds. Alcohol, acetone, cotton, sugar, starch, and vinegar are a few of the compounds formed from these elements. It is now probably obvious that the vast majority of the substances of which matter is composed are chemical compounds or mixtures of them.

Each chemical compound possesses inherent chemical and physical properties which are usually decidedly different from the properties of the elements which make up the compound. Compare the properties of the compound water with those of the elements hydrogen and oxygen. Even with a limited knowledge of chemistry you can probably make a respectable list of dissimilarities between them.

Any compound can be decomposed into the elements from which it was formed. A compound must contain at least two different elements—for example, water—but it may contain more than two elements—e.g., sugar. Elements and compounds are of prime importance to the chemist and pose many intriguing questions, such as the following: Why do elements form compounds? What characteristics do elements possess which permit specific chemical combinations? Why are the properties of compounds different from those of their elements? Why can more than one compound be formed from the same elements? The answers to these and many other related questions constitute the subject matter of chemistry.

1.4. Matter and Energy

In everyday life we are concerned with energy only in connection with having enough of it to do our work, climb a flight of stairs, or keep warm. We are prone to take energy for granted. It is there when needed. But energy is a very important and significant factor in our normal occupations as well as in the fundamental concepts of science. Exactly what is energy? First of all, we recognize that it exists in various forms. Heat, light, electricity, and the motion of material objects are familiar forms of energy. Why do we say that these are all forms of the same thing—energy? Because they are all manifestations of the ability to do *work,* that is, to produce motion against resisting forces such as friction and gravity. Heat makes steam that runs an engine. A current of electricity runs a motor. Light is converted into heat when absorbed by a dark body, or into an electric current by striking a photoelectric cell. A moving object can set another into motion by means of a collision; falling water can turn a turbine-dynamo combination which produces electric current to heat your toaster, light your house, or pull a train.

It should be obvious from these illustrations that there is a great difference between saying that heat and light are two forms of energy and saying that Buicks and Fords are two forms of car. A Ford cannot become a Buick, but the different forms of energy are interconvertible.

Energy sometimes *seems* to disappear. You may expend a lot of energy pushing an automobile up a hill, and when you halt at the top there is no visible sign of the energy. You know, however, that the energy is somehow there, stored, ready to be released if the car rolls back down the hill again. Stored energy is called **potential energy.**

1.5. Chemical Energy

The most important class of potential energy is **chemical energy.** Chemical energy may be released as any of the forms of energy. Its release is always accompanied by chemical change. One or more substances disappear and new substances appear. Thus coal and air release stored chemical energy in the form of heat and light. Gunpowder liberates heat and light, as well as **kinetic energy** through the motion of the projectile. A dry cell releases its chemical energy in the form of electricity. The reverse process also occurs; that is, energy may be absorbed (hence stored) as a result of a chemical change. The charging of a storage battery does not result in storing electricity but rather in converting the substances produced by discharge back into the original ones. Thus the original chemical energy is available for release again as electrical energy.

1.6. Law of the Conservation of Energy

Theoretically, any form of energy can be transformed into any other form without a gain or loss. Practically, however, this cannot be realized. For example, the current produced in a hydroelectric plant cannot pump all the water back again because some of the energy is converted into heat by friction. But careful measurements show that if one keeps track of *all* the different forms of energy, *no energy is lost or gained while being transformed from one form into another.* This fundamentally important principle is known as the **law of the conservation of energy.**

1.7. Law of the Conservation of Matter

Matter follows the same law of conservation as does energy; that is, *matter can be neither created nor destroyed.* Thus in *ordinary* chemical reactions the total weight of substance used for a reaction is found to be equal to the total weight of products resulting from the reaction.

In recent years some *extraordinary* reactions have been achieved which result in products having less total weight than the original reactants. At first this seems contrary to the law of the conservation of matter; and it would be, were it not for the fact that these reactions liberate an excessive amount of energy to compensate for the "loss of matter." These reactions prove that matter and energy are actually the same thing, but in different forms. Under appropriate but somewhat special conditions matter can be converted into energy and energy can be converted into matter. The late Albert Einstein gave us the equation for the equivalence of matter and energy in 1905; and the first atomic bomb, exploded on August 6, 1945, was awesome proof that

$$E = mc^2$$

where E is the energy available from the disappearance of matter having a mass m, and c is the velocity of light. The property of *mass* is possessed by all matter and is most conveniently measured as *weight*. In view of these facts, the conservation laws can be modified as follows to fit the matter-energy equivalence concept: *Matter-energy can be neither created nor destroyed.*

Reactions in which appreciable amounts of matter are converted into energy, or vice versa (known as nuclear reactions for reasons which will appear later), are easily distinguished from chemical reactions by the enormously larger amounts of energy involved. (The explosion of 1 g. of TNT produces 0.0042 kilowatt-hour of energy, whereas 1 g. of matter, if completely transformed into energy, produces 2.5×10^7 kilowatt-hours, some 6 billion times as much.)

In this textbook we shall not be concerned with matter-energy equivalence except briefly in connection with nuclear energy. Our primary concern with matter will be its chemical constitution, its properties, and the energy relationships associated with chemical and physical phenomena without appreciable gain or loss in mass.

1.8. Physical Nature of Matter

Matter can exist in three forms—or **states** to use the scientific terminology. These three states are **solid, liquid,** and **gas.** Not every substance can exist in all three states, but many do. For example, you can melt ice (solid) and obtain water (liquid) which upon further heating will boil, giving steam (gaseous water). However, when you melt sugar it begins to decompose into carbon and water and therefore it cannot be boiled. Properties of a substance which can be observed without its changing into another substance are called **physical properties.** Certain of these are often useful for identification purposes, e.g., melting and boiling points, density (mass of a substance divided by its volume), color, odor, solubility, etc. Others, such as strength, elasticity, and ability to be drawn into wire or fiber, may determine the industrial usefulness of a substance. All the physical properties of a substance depend upon its fundamental structure, so that a study of the one can frequently throw much light upon the others. **Chemical properties** are those which involve changes into other substances. Attainment of a complete understanding of substances requires the study of both physical and chemical properties. We shall approach our study of chemistry from the physical side because most of us are already familiar with the physical phenomena involved.

1.9. Units of Measure

The scientist at work in the laboratory is frequently faced with the task of making repeated and accurate measurements. Whether or not he is using elaborate equipment to obtain his experimental results, they must be reported in terms of some units. Frequently many units are available to express a given measurement; hence he must be sensible in his selection. A carpenter would no more think of measuring the length of a room in terms of miles than a housewife would consider buying meat for her family in fractions of a ton.

Two systems of measurement are in wide use, the English and the metric. The **English system,** used only in the United States and the United Kingdom, is complicated by the lack of consistency of conversion factors from one unit to another. It requires tremendous memorization of such factors. For example, in linear (length) measurement there are thousandths, hundredths, sixteenths, eighths, and quarters of an inch; 12 inches per foot, 3 feet per yard, and 5280 feet per mile. In the measurement of weight the English system uses two different-sized pounds, each with one or two associated trains of smaller units. An avoirdupois pound = 16 ounces = 256 drams = 7000 grains. A troy pound = 12 ounces = 240 pennyweights = 5760 grains. An apothecaries' pound = 12 ounces = 96 drams = 288 scruples = 5760 grains. Volume and capacity units are equally complicated. No convenient relationship exists between the English units of length, volume, and weight.

In contrast, in the **metric system** all the units are based on decimal multiples or fractions of one fundamental unit for length, one for volume, and one for weight. Furthermore, these three fundamental units are interrelated in simple fashion. The names of the subordinate units are formed by adding prefixes to the names of the fundamental units. A single set of prefixes is used to designate a fraction, whether of length, vol-

TABLE 1.1. Units of Measurement

Length

1000 millimeters (mm.) = 1 meter (m.) = $\frac{1}{1000}$ kilometer (km.)

100 centimeters (cm.) = 1 meter (m.)

1 m. = 39.37 inches

2.54 cm. = 1 inch

Volume

1000 milliliters (ml.) = 1 liter (l.) = $\frac{1}{1000}$ kiloliter (kl.)

100 centiliters (cl.) = 1 liter (l.)

1 l. = 1.057 quarts (U.S. liquid)

1 l. = 1000 cubic centimeters

Weight (Mass)

1000 milligrams (mg.) = 1 gram (g.) = $\frac{1}{1000}$ kilogram (kg.)

454 g. = 1 pound av.

1 kg. = 2.2046 pounds

1 ml. of water at 4° C. weighs 1 g.

ume, or weight units. Another set is used for multiples. Table 1.1 shows
how simple this system is, and how easy it is to change from units of one
size to those of another.

Not listed in Table 1.1 (because it is not needed in elementary laboratory work) is the prefix micro-, meaning one-millionth. The abbreviation for microgram (0.001 mg.) is γ, the Greek letter gamma. A length
of 0.001 mm. is commonly called a micron, because the systematic word
micrometer has another meaning. It is abbreviated μ, the Greek letter
mu. For use in the domain of the extremely small, there are the milli-
cron (mμ) and the Angstrom unit (A.), which is 0.1 mμ. Thus: 10,000
A. = 1000 millimicrons (mμ) = 1 micron (μ) = $\frac{1}{1000}$ mm. X-rays have
wave lengths on the order of 1 A.; visible light, from 400 to 800 mμ. The
smallest particles of matter with which the chemist deals have radii in
the vicinity of 1 A. The solid particles which make up cigarette smoke
may be as large as 200 mμ.

The international metric standards of measurement are maintained at
Sèvres, France. The National Bureau of Standards maintains exact dupli-

cates of these in Washington, D.C. Weights and measures of all sorts will be calibrated (relative to these standards) and certified by the Bureau for a nominal fee. Probably your chemistry department has calibrated and certified weights and measures for its student and research equipment.

1.10. Significant Figures

The object of a scientist who is performing in the laboratory experimental work such as Dr. Conant spoke of, is to make as accurate observations and measurements as possible. To this end it is customary to read an instrument or measuring device to its smallest graduation and then estimate the value of any fraction of a scale division which remains. To minimize the uncertainty involved in this process, the average of several readings may be used; for example:

Reading	1.	2.33
	2.	2.36
	3.	2.35
	4.	2.34
	5.	2.35
	6.	2.33
Total		14.06 ÷ 6 = 2.34 (average)

The "scatter" of the figures in the second decimal place shows that there is some degree of uncertainty regarding the figures; nevertheless, it is better to include it in the reported result than to drop it. The true value is certainly higher than 2.3, and is probably closer to 2.34 than to 2.33 or 2.35. It is standard scientific practice to include one uncertain figure in any result.

A thoughtless student, noting that $14.06 \div 6 = 2.3433333 \cdots$, might be tempted to carry the division several places further than we did in obtaining the above average. It is obvious, however, that no amount of arithmetic will increase the accuracy of the experimental determinations. To report the average as 2.343 implies falsely that the 4 is certain. The final 3 is not a significant figure. **Significant figures** are those which have experimental justification. The number of significant figures in a result has nothing to do with the location of the decimal point; the latter is determined by the size of the unit used. If the above figure was a weight in grams, it might be expressed as 2.34 g. or 0.00234 kg. or 2340 mg., but in each expression there are three significant figures, and only three.

Just as a chain is no stronger than its weakest link, so a result computed from two or more experimental data is no more accurate than the least accurate figure. Suppose we are required to compute the speed of a runner who does the 400-meter dash in 45.1 seconds. If the track has been carefully measured, the distance may be known down to a centimeter; i.e., it may be 400.00 m. Here we have five significant figures, for these zeros do not depend upon the unit of measurement. They actually mean that the distance is more likely to be 40,000 cm. than 39,999 cm. or 40,001 cm. But there are only three significant figures in the time, for the stop watch cannot indicate anything smaller than 0.1 second, and the timer might easily have been that much off in snapping it. Taking the figure as given, we compute the speed as 400.00 ÷ 45.1 = 8.867 m./sec. If the true time was 45.2 seconds, the speed was 400.00 ÷ 45.2 = 8.850 m./sec. If it was 45.0 seconds, the speed was 400.00 ÷ 45.0 = 8.889 m./sec. Since the third figure varies, we see that there are only three significant figures in the result and that the fourth figure is meaningless. This illustrates the general rule that the number of significant figures in any computed result is the same as the number in the least accurate datum used in obtaining it. Rounding the result to three significant figures, we get 8.87 m./sec.

A good experimenter directs his efforts toward improving the least accurate measurement in his work. He does not waste time obtaining great precision in one part of it when another part is unavoidably less precise. For example, he does not weigh to five figures (although this is possible) when his computations must also include a volume measurement that cannot be carried beyond three significant figures.

In computing the results of experiments, superfluous figures should be dropped to save time. (If the figure dropped is 5 or more, the preceding figure should be increased by 1.) Note that using exact integers in a mathematical formula does not bring the number of significant figures in the result down to 1. For example, the volume of a sphere is given by $V = \frac{4}{3}\pi r^3$. There is no uncertainty whatever regarding the ratio 4/3; it was derived by geometric logic and is *exact*. The value of the constant π is known to 200 figures. However, the radius, r, is a measured quantity; hence V will be no more accurate than r. The number of figures used in the computation will depend on the accuracy of r. Thus:

$$V = \tfrac{4}{3}\pi r^3 = (1.3333)(3.1416)(0.015735)^3 = 0.000016281$$
$$= (1.333)(3.142)(0.01574)^3 = 0.00001628$$
$$= (1.33)(3.14)(0.0157)^3 = 0.0000163$$
$$= (1.3)(3.1)(0.016)^3 = 0.000016$$

QUESTIONS AND PROBLEMS

1. State briefly what the study of chemistry is about.

2. What is meant by a law of nature? Give an example.

3. Define and give examples of matter.

4. What is an element? A compound? Give examples of each.

5. State the natural conservation laws and qualify each.

6. Distinguish between kinetic energy, potential energy, and chemical energy. How are they related?

7. What equation postulates the equivalence of matter and energy? What experiment proves this?

8. What are the three states of matter? Name a substance which can exist in all three states, and one which cannot.

9. Distinguish between physical and chemical properties. Give some examples of each.

10. Make the following conversions of measurement:
  a. 12 inches to centimeters; to meters.
  b. Your weight in pounds to grams; to kilograms.
  c. 2 quarts to milliliters; to liters.
  d. 2 mm. = ... cm. = ... μ.

11. What is the weight of 1.5 l. of water at 4° C.?

12. From the following data, calculate the density (weight ÷ volume) of an object to the last significant figure.

Weight	Volume
2.803 g.	1.65 ml.
2.808	1.66
2.810	1.65
2.795	1.61
2.792	1.60

2

The kinetic molecular theory of matter

2.1. Physical States of Matter

All the matter of which the universe is composed is found to be in one of three physical states, **solid, liquid,** or **gas.** When a specimen of matter is in the solid state its volume is determined by the amount of matter present, and its shape by its past treatment. If force is applied to a solid, the solid will resist deformation. If the force does not exceed a certain value (characteristic for each solid) called the **yield point,** the solid will return to its original shape upon removal of the deforming force. When the force exceeds the yield point the solid flows or breaks, depending upon whether it is plastic or brittle; and when the force is removed, the solid has a new shape. When a specimen of matter is in the liquid state its volume is determined by the amount of matter present, but its shape is determined by the shape of the container and by the forces acting upon it, such as gravity. When the liquid does not fill the container, the upper surface of the liquid is approximately flat. The yield point of a liquid is zero; any force whatever causes it to flow. The rate of flow of a liquid under a given force is inversely related to its **viscosity.** If a liquid is very viscous the rate of flow under a moderate force may be imperceptible. A suddenly applied force may then produce elastic deformation or even shattering, as though the substance were solid. When matter is in the gaseous state both its volume and its shape are determined entirely by the shape of the container. Any amount of a gas, however small, will distribute itself evenly throughout any container and exert force upon its walls, trying to expand still further. The amount of *force* which a gas exerts *per unit area* of any surface with which it is in contact is called the **pressure** of the gas.

The same specimen of matter may in general exist in all three physical states under proper conditions. When heat is continually supplied to a solid, its temperature rises. Eventually, if it does not first decompose, it melts to a liquid, but during the melting process the temperature ceases to rise. The heat which flows into a solid during melting, without producing an increase in temperature, is called the **heat of fusion.** If a liquid is put in a cold place its temperature will fall until the liquid begins to freeze. The temperature of the liquid then remains constant while freezing is taking place. The amount of heat energy which flows out of a liquid during freezing is exactly equal to the heat of fusion, and the constant temperature which it maintains is the same as the constant temperature maintained by the solid during melting. This temperature may be called either the **melting point** (m.p.) of the solid or the **freezing point** (f.p.) of the liquid.

Both solids and liquids evaporate into gases. **Evaporation** takes place more rapidly the higher the temperature; it is negligible in the case of solids whose temperatures are far below their melting points. If the gas is colored, like iodine, or has a strong odor, as does camphor, naphthalene (moth balls), or paradichlorobenzene (moth crystals), the evaporation of the solid is easily noticed even though the rate is slow. But if the gas is colorless and odorless, the evaporation may be harder to detect. Many people do not realize, for example, that water vapor evaporates from ice, although people living in a cold, dry climate often see a light snow or thin ice sheet disappear after a few days of cold weather during which the temperature never went as high as the melting point of snow. Evaporation from a solid is called **sublimation;** evaporation from a liquid is called **vaporization.** The term gas and vapor are usually interchangeable; the latter is more likely to be used when we are thinking about a gas and its liquid or solid state at the same time. A gas may condense to a liquid or to a solid, depending upon whether the cold condensing surface is above or below the freezing point of the liquid. Thus moisture in the air condenses as drops of water on the outside of a glass of ice water, but water evaporating from moist food in a refrigerator condenses as frost on the cooling coils. Just as in the case of melting, heat is absorbed in the process of evaporation. The heat of sublimation is greater than the heat of vaporization by the heat of fusion; i.e.,

Heat of fusion + Heat of vaporization = Heat of sublimation

If heat is supplied less rapidly than it is being absorbed by the process of evaporation, the temperature falls, as when you hold your wet hands in a breeze. If heat is supplied more rapidly, the temperature rises, but less rapidly than it would if evaporation were prevented. An open pan of water heats more slowly than a covered one, over the same fire. As the temperature rises, so does the rate of evaporation; hence eventually a liquid evaporates fast enough to prevent any further rise in temperature. If the heat supply is increased, there may be a further rise in temperature; but when the boiling point is reached, so that evaporation is taking place in bubbles within the liquid as well as from the top surface, an increase in the rate of heating merely increases the rate of boiling. The liquid does not get any hotter. When a gas condenses, the heat of vaporization or sublimation is evolved again. Alternatively, part of the energy may be obtained as mechanical work or electrical energy by means of appropriate machinery.

All the facts mentioned in this section are explained and interrelated by the **kinetic molecular theory of the structure of matter.** So also are many others which will be mentioned later. If this theory explained only the physical changes in matter it would be of interest only to physicists. Actually, however, it opened the door to an understanding of chemical changes, i.e., changes of substances into other substances; so a thorough understanding of it is basic to the study of chemistry.

2.2. Basic Assumptions of the Theory

The assumptions of the kinetic molecular theory are implied in its name. In other words, the theory holds that matter is composed of *molecules in motion*. A **molecule** (L., a little mass) is one of the tiny particles into which substances separate when they evaporate or dissolve. According to the theory, molecules are in continual motion, colliding and rebounding elastically from the collisions.

In order for this to be an acceptable theory of matter it must do more than offer a plausible explanation of many observed facts. This further requirement is that no known fact concerning matter shall contradict the theory. This requirement has been met for more than a century. Furthermore, in all that time no other theory has succeeded in connecting all the related phenomena. Therefore, all scientists are now convinced that the kinetic molecular theory provides an accurate description of reality.

When the kinetic molecular theory was being formulated, and for a long time thereafter, all the evidence in its favor was indirect, because molecules are not visible. Nothing can be seen, even through the most powerful microscope, unless it reflects light. The diameter of an ordinary molecule is only about one one-thousandth of the wave length of visible light. Light waves wash over and past a single molecule without any reflection, just as a great sea wave washes unreflected over and past the periscope of a submarine. The indirect evidence for the existence of molecules, consisting largely of the perfect agreement between the predictions of the kinetic molecular theory and the actual behavior of substances, was nevertheless thoroughly convincing. In relatively recent times ways have been found to impart enough kinetic energy to molecules to enable us to see the result of a blow struck by a single invisible molecule, but this direct evidence was not really needed. The following sections will show how the theory explains a great array of experimentally known facts.

2.3. The Pressure of Gases

We said above that any quantity of gas, however small, distributes itself evenly throughout any container into which it is introduced, and exerts pressure upon the walls of the container. In terms of the theory, the molecules travel in straight lines until they reach the walls of the container and rebound. Collisions with one another gradually send them in all possible directions and they become evenly distributed throughout the space. The pressure exerted by the gas is due merely to the myriad blows struck by the molecules. It is constant rather than fluctuating because the individual impacts are tiny and the number upon any appreciable area per second is enormous. The actual value of the pressure agrees perfectly with that calculated by computing the change in momentum occurring when a single molecule of known mass and velocity rebounds from a surface, and multiplying this by the computed collision rate. Furthermore, the introduction into the same container of enough more gas to double the rate of molecular collision actually doubles the pressure. This is true regardless of whether the additional gas is the same as that originally present.

2.4. The Nature of Temperature

When a hot substance is brought into contact with a cold one, so that rapidly moving molecules collide with more slowly moving ones, with resulting equalization of energy, the substances attain the same temperature. This is true, regardless of physical state. When work is done on a substance, as by stirring a liquid or gas or by bending, cutting, or pounding a solid, so that the energy of the molecules should be increased, the substance is found to be hotter than before. The increase in temperature is proportional to the amount of work done. Thus we conclude that temperature is a measure of the kinetic energy of molecules.

Experiments performed in physics laboratories on objects of ordinary size show that kinetic energy is proportional to the mass of the moving object and to the square of its velocity. To state this mathematically:

$$\text{K.E.} = \tfrac{1}{2}mv^2 \qquad\qquad [2.1]$$

According to this equation, molecules that are light should move faster than heavy ones at the same temperature, since they have identical kinetic energies. This is actually the case; a molecule of methane (natural gas) weighs four times as much as a molecule of helium and moves half as fast at the same temperature. The change of momentum (mass × velocity) of the helium molecule, which governs the force it exerts during a collision, is only half as great as that of the methane molecule. The average velocity of the helium molecule is twice that of the methane molecule; so its collision rate is twice as great. Twice as many half-strength blows should and do result in exactly the same pressure. The pressure exerted by a gas is independent of the weight of its molecules, being governed only by their concentration and temperature. An increase in temperature means an increase in the kinetic energy of the molecules. This means (Eq. 2.1) that they travel faster and hit harder and more often; this should and does increase the pressure of a gas.

2.5. Pressure-Volume Relationship; Boyle's Law

An increase in the external pressure exerted upon a liquid or a solid produces only a slight decrease in volume because the molecules are already practically in contact with each other. Gases, on the contrary, are highly compressible. An oxygen cylinder such as you have seen a welder use furnishes two hundred times its own volume of oxygen to the flame. In 1660 Robert Boyle, a pioneer investigator in both chemistry and physics, made some careful measurements of the compressibility of air.

He found that when the temperature is the same at the end of the experiment as it was at the beginning, *the volume of a gas varies inversely with the pressure.* Of course it is assumed that no gas is added or allowed to escape, that is, that the weight remains constant.

This relationship between the pressure exerted by a gas and the volume occupied by it is shown in Fig. 2.1. The temperature is assumed to remain constant during the experiment, as is the weight of gas in the cylinder. Imagine the cylinder to be closed by a weightless, freely movable piston, with nothing to keep the gas from pushing the piston out of the top except a weight or weights which are placed upon it. If the quantity of gas is small, say 0.05 g., a weight of 1 kg. may confine it to a volume of 4 l. The volume of the gas will vary

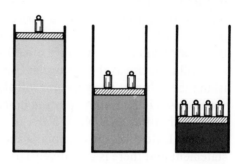

Fig. 2.1. The volume of a gas varies inversely with the pressure (Boyle's law).

with any change in pressure. If you add the weight of your finger to the top of the weight, the piston will sink, and you can feel the increasing pressure of the gas as its volume is reduced. *The gas exerts its pressure equally in all directions.* If the weight is doubled to 2 kg., the pressure exerted on the gas is doubled and the pressure exerted *by* the gas is also doubled. In other words, the greater the pressure applied to a gas, the greater will be the pressure which it exerts upon the walls of a container. But by the time the pressure of the gas has doubled to withstand the doubled weight on top, its volume has decreased to half the original volume. If the weight is increased to 4 kg., the volume will be reduced to 1 l. A weight of 8 kg. will reduce the volume to half a liter, or $\frac{1}{8}$ of the volume. Pressure is expressed in terms of force per unit area. In this case, for convenience, we shall take the unit area as that of the piston; the pressures will then be numerically equal to the respective weights. Thus:

$$4 \times 1 = 4; \quad 2 \times 2 = 4; \quad 1 \times 4 = 4; \quad \tfrac{1}{2} \times 8 = 4$$

Note that in every case the product of any pressure and the corresponding volume has the same numerical value, i.e., is a constant. Expressed mathematically, Boyle's law is:

$$P_1 V_1 = P_2 V_2 \qquad [2.2]$$

THE KINETIC MOLECULAR THEORY OF MATTER 17

The omission of any reference to the temperature or the weight of gas indicates that both are assumed to remain constant. The subscripts refer to initial and final conditions.

The kinetic molecular theory offers a perfectly reasonable explanation of the facts summarized in Boyle's law. If we remember that pressure is pictured as due to the blows struck by colliding molecules against the walls of the container, we can easily see that the greater their *concentration* (that is, the greater the number of molecules per unit volume), the greater will be the number of collisions against the wall. The pressure will then rise as the molecular concentration is increased by diminishing the volume. The pressure will also rise if the concentration of the molecules is increased by putting more molecules into the same space. This is what happens when a tire is inflated. The possibility of either much or little of a gas occupying the same space is explained by the statement that there is a relatively large amount of empty space between the molecules.

2.6. Effect of Temperature on Pressure and Volume of Gases

In Section 2.4 we saw that an increase in temperature causes molecules to move faster and collide with greater impact. The effect of heating a gas is the same as though the number of molecules had been increased. If the volume is kept constant the pressure must rise. If the pressure is to be kept constant the volume must be increased. As early as 1787 the French chemist Charles had noticed that all gases expand equally on heating. In 1802 his countryman Gay-Lussac, continuing the investigation, found that the expansion between 0° C. and 1° C. was $\frac{1}{273}$ of the volume at 0° C., and that for any other 1° rise in temperature the expansion was the same. His results are plotted in the solid portion of the diagonal line in Fig. 2. 2. The fact that this line is straight shows that there is a direct proportionality between the temperature and the volume of a given amount of gas at constant pressure. The statement that

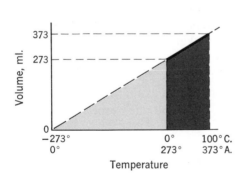

Fig. 2.2. Effect of temperature on volume of a gas. For convenience a volume of 273 ml. at 0° C. was selected. The extrapolated volume at 0° A. is 0 ml. The volume increases 1 ml. for each °A. rise in temperature.

this proportionality exists is known as **Charles' law.** There is, however, an interesting detail to be attended to before this statement can be expressed in simple mathematical terms. To illustrate the point in question, consider the similar statement that railroad fare is proportional to distance. New York City is twice as far from Albany as Poughkeepsie is. Does this mean that a ticket from Montreal to New York will cost twice as much as one from Montreal to Poughkeepsie? Obviously we must measure from where the trips start if the fares are to be proportional. Similarly, if pressures or volumes are to be proportional to temperatures, we must measure from their beginning. Zero pressure and zero volume are simple enough ideas, but zero temperature is not. In fact, we are familiar with *two* temperature zeros, and neither of them is the bottom! The centigrade zero is merely the freezing point of ice. Dr. Fahrenheit took as his zero the lowest temperature in his home town of Danzig in the winter of 1709 during which he invented the mercury thermometer.

2.7. Absolute Zero

If pressure is due to the kinetic energy of molecules, the starting point must be zero kinetic energy. It is not easy to see what might be the limit to coldness, but zero kinetic energy is a perfectly simple idea. It means, simply, no motion. Less than no motion is as obviously impossible as a negative volume, so this zero is called **absolute zero.** By extrapolating the solid line in Fig. 2.2 this zero has been found to be $-273.16°$ C. But precision of temperature measurements to a tenth of a degree is not necessary in most gas law calculations, so this figure is usually rounded off to $-273°$ C.

If T stands for the temperature measured up from absolute zero ($0°$ A.), we can state Charles' law very simply: *The volume of a gas, at constant pressure, is proportional to its absolute temperature.* Hence:

$$V = KT$$

This is the equation of the sloping straight line in Fig. 2.2. K is the slope, or constant of the equation. Thus:

$$\frac{V}{T} = K$$

or
$$\frac{V_1}{T_1} = \frac{V_2}{T_2} \qquad\qquad [2.3]$$

As in Eq. 2.2, it is assumed here that the factors not mentioned—namely, the weight of gas and the pressure—remain constant.

According to Boyle's law (Eq. 2.2), the volume, which increased as a result of raising the temperature of a gas, can be brought back to the original value by a corresponding increase in pressure. We may therefore deduce that

$$P = KT$$

or $$\frac{P_1}{T_1} = \frac{P_2}{T_2}$$ [2.4]

The statement that *the pressure of a gas at constant volume is proportional to its absolute temperature* is called **Gay-Lussac's law.** This law can also be derived directly from Eq. 2.1, from which we see that if the kinetic energy of a given molecule is doubled—i.e., its absolute temperature is doubled—its velocity will be $\sqrt{2}$ times as great as before, and so will its momentum, *mv*. When there are $\sqrt{2}$ times as many impacts per second, each $\sqrt{2}$ times as hard, the pressure is $\sqrt{2} \times \sqrt{2}$ times as great, that is, twice the original pressure.

2.8. Temperature Scales

The reference to the centigrade and Fahrenheit zeros in Section 2.6 brings up the question of temperature scales, and what is meant by a degree. You are already familiar with the **Fahrenheit scale.** This scale is in common use in English-speaking countries—the one used in homes, weather reports, and cooking, and in factories and many engineering calculations. The **centigrade scale** is used in all science laboratories and in homes and factories in non-English-speaking countries. The name centigrade is based on the fact that the scale divides into 100 parts the distance between the two major calibration points upon which it is based. That is, the centigrade scale is defined by stating that the freezing point of water is 0° C., and its boiling point is 100° C. (under standard pressure). These two points are 180° apart on the Fahrenheit scale; hence Fahrenheit degrees are smaller. Nine Fahrenheit degrees equal five centigrade degrees. A Fahrenheit temperature cannot be converted into the equivalent centigrade temperature simply by multiplying it by 5/9, because the zeros on the two scales are different. However, − 40° F. is the same temperature as − 40° C.; so by counting from this common point instead of from the differing zeros conversion in either direction is very simple. The rule is: Add 40°, multiply by the ratio 5/9 or 9/5 as the case requires, and subtract 40°. You will have no difficulty in deciding which form of the ratio to use if you remember that Fahrenheit degrees are smaller and therefore more numerous than centigrade degrees. Expressed mathematically, this rule is:

$$°C. = 5/9(°F. + 40°) - 40° \qquad [2.5]$$
and
$$°F. = 9/5(°C. + 40°) - 40° \qquad [2.6]$$

The freezing point of water can be used as the reference point instead of −40. This leads to the expressions:

$$°C. = 5/9(°F. - 32°) \qquad [2.7]$$
and
$$°F. = 9/5(°C.) + 32° \qquad [2.8]$$

Fig. 2.3 shows the relationships of several temperatures on the Fahrenheit and centigrade scales. The third scale in the figure is the **Kelvin scale.** It is an absolute scale, for it is based on absolute zero and has no negative values. It differs from the centigrade scale only in the location of its zero; the degrees are the same size. For this reason the Kelvin

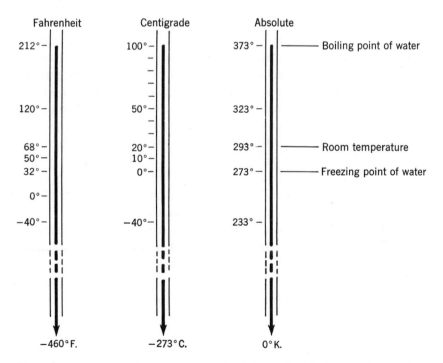

Fig. 2.3. Fahrenheit, centigrade, and absolute centigrade temperature scales.

scale is also called the **absolute centigrade scale** and its degrees are frequently labeled ° A. It is used in all gas law calculations in scientific laboratories. There is also an absolute Fahrenheit scale, called the **Rankine scale**; it is sometimes used by engineers. The two absolute zeros are related to their respective ordinary scales by the equations:

$$°K. = °C. + 273°$$ [2.9]
$$°R. = °F. + 460°$$ [2.10]

2.9. Combined Gas Law Calculations

Generally, gases are subject to simultaneous changes in volume, temperature, and pressure. Hence it is convenient to correlate all these factors in a single mathematical expression called simply the **combination gas law,** to avoid having to make several calculations. This law has the simple form:

$$\frac{P_1 V_1}{T_1} = \frac{P_2 V_2}{T_2}$$ [2.11]

where for a given quantity of a gas one set of conditions (1) is being changed to a second set of conditions (2). It can be seen that if $T_1 = T_2$, Boyle's law (Eq. 2.2) is obtained. Similarly, Charles' law (Eq. 2.3) is obtained if $P_1 = P_2$, and Gay-Lussac's law (Eq. 2.4) if $V_1 = V_2$. A gas law calculation is made by substituting the data in Eq. 2.11 and solving for the unknown. However, errors in algebra are possible with this process. A better method is to set up an expression that is based upon kinetic molecular principles and has already been solved for the unknown. This is done by setting the unknown equal to the original value of the quantity whose final value we want to obtain, and multiplying this by the ratios for the conditions which change.

To illustrate this method, we shall use the following problem. If 156 ml. of gas at 10° C. and 758 mm. of mercury pressure is transferred to a container having a volume of 385 ml. and warmed to 25° C., what is the final pressure? First we write the data in some convenient form, such as the accompanying tabulation, which makes it easy to compare the initial and final pressures, volumes, and temperatures.

Initial Conditions	Final Conditions
$P_1 = 758$ mm.	$P_2 = ?$
$V_1 = 156$ ml.	$V_2 = 385$ ml.
$T_1 = 10°$ C.	$T_2 = 25°$ C.
$\underline{+ 273°}$	$\underline{+ 273°}$
$283°$ K.	$298°$ K.

The first thing to do after listing the data is to check the units. Any units, English or metric, may be used, but they must be used consistently; i.e., *the same units must be used* for P_1 and P_2, V_1 and V_2, T_1 and T_2; furthermore, *an absolute temperature scale must be used.* Now P_2 will be equal to P_1 appropriately corrected for the volume and temperature changes which occur.

$$P_2 = P_1 \times (\text{Correction for volume change})$$
$$\times (\text{Correction for temperature change})$$

The increase in volume decreases the concentration of the molecules and this in turn decreases their collision rate. This means that the pressure is less; so in the first correction factor, which is the ratio of the volumes, the smaller volume must be on top. Now we have:

$$P_2 = 758 \text{ mm.} \times \frac{156 \text{ ml.}}{385 \text{ ml.}} \times (\text{Correction for temperature change})$$

The increase in temperature speeds up the molecules, increasing both the rate and the force of the collisions. This produces an increase in pressure; so in the second correction factor, which is the ratio of the absolute temperatures, the higher temperature must be on top. This gives:

$$P_2 = 758 \text{ mm.} \times \frac{156 \text{ ml.}}{385 \text{ ml.}} \times \frac{298° \text{ K.}}{283° \text{ K.}} = 323 \text{ mm.}$$

Note that the units of measurement cancel out of both correction factors, so that both of them are pure numbers. The answer is accordingly in the same pressure units as P_1.

2.10. Standard Conditions

We have just seen that a given quantity of a gas may occupy almost any volume, depending upon the temperature and pressure. For convenience in making statements about gases comparable, a standard temperature, 273° K. (0° C.), and a standard pressure, 760 mm. (1 atm.) have been universally adopted. The results of experiments are regularly recalculated to these standard conditions, which are conveniently abbreviated S.T.P.

2.11. Dalton's Law of Partial Pressures

In Section 2.4 we saw that the pressure exerted by a gas is independent of the weight of its molecules. Heavy molecules are slow, but what they

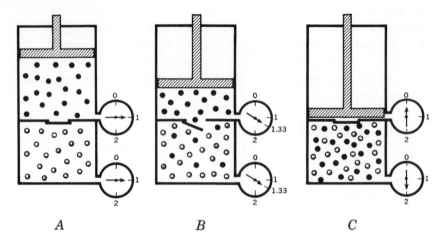

Fig. 2.4. Dalton's law of partial pressures. The examples show that pressure is dependent upon the number of molecules in a container rather than upon the kind of molecule.

lack in collision frequency they exactly make up by their heavier impacts. A pressure gauge registers the average force of all the molecular impacts against it. It does not distinguish between the different molecules of gas which may be present in a container. Each gas in a mixture exerts the pressure it would exert if it alone occupied the space in the container. This is **Dalton's law of partial pressures.** Stated in another way, *the total pressure of a mixture of gases is the sum of the individual (or partial) pressures.* Thus:

$$P_{total} = P_1 + P_2 + \cdots + P_n \qquad [2.12]$$

where P_1, P_2, P_n are the partial pressures of the individual gases in a mixture.

This law can be proved experimentally. In Fig. 2.4*A*, each of two equal-sized cylinders contains a different gas at 1 atm. In *B* the gas in the upper cylinder is being transferred to the lower one by moving the piston. The pressure is still equal in both cylinders, but is greater than the original pressure. In *C* the transfer is complete and the pressure in the lower cylinder is now 2 atm., whereas in the upper cylinder (no gas) it registers zero.

Dalton's law is applied whenever gases are collected by the displacement of water, a frequent laboratory procedure. The force holding the water in the inverted bottle in Fig. 2.5 is the pressure, *P*, of the atmosphere in the laboratory. Thus when the bottle is filled with gas—when the water level is the same inside the bottle and outside—the gas will be at pressure P. However, the gas in the bottle consists not only of the gas which was being collected but also of molecules of water vapor (gas) resulting from evaporation from the surface of the water and the wet inside walls of the bottle. Thus:

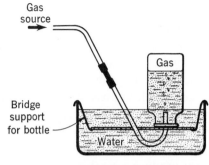

$$P = P_g + P_{\text{water vapor}}$$

or $\quad P_g = P - P_{\text{water vapor}} \quad$ [2.13]

The atmospheric pressure is read from the laboratory barometer; the partial pressure of water vapor is a function of the temperature of the water (Section 2.17) and can be found in reference tables (see Appendix).

Fig. 2.5. Collection of a gas by the displacement of water. In this case the bottle contains a mixture of water vapor and of gas from the gas source.

The following problem illustrates the application of Dalton's law. If 250 ml. of oxygen gas is collected by the displacement of water at 20° C. and a barometric pressure of 740 mm., what is the volume of the *dry* gas at S.T.P.? The vapor pressure of water at 20° C. is 17.5 mm.; the remainder of the atmospheric pressure was furnished by the oxygen. Our data tabulation therefore is:

Initial Conditions	Final Conditions
$P_1 = \quad 740 \quad$ mm.	$P_2 = 760$ mm.
$\quad - \quad 17.5$ mm.	
$\quad \overline{723 \quad}$ mm.	
$V_1 = \quad 250$ ml.	$V_2 = ?$
$T_1 = \quad 20°$ C.	$T_2 = 273°$ K.
$\quad + 273°$	
$\quad \overline{293°}$ K.	

Standard pressure is greater than the partial pressure of the oxygen, so the volume will be reduced as the pressure is increased. In the pressure factor the smaller figure must be above. In going to standard temperature the gas will be cooled; a greater molecular concentration is required to compensate for the lower rate of lighter collisions. In the temperature factor, the smaller figure must be above to reduce the volume sufficiently to maintain the chosen pressure. Therefore:

$$V_{\text{S.T.P.}} = 250 \text{ ml.} \times \frac{723 \text{ mm.}}{760 \text{ mm.}} \times \frac{273° \text{ K.}}{293° \text{ K.}} = 222 \text{ ml.}$$

2.12. Deviation of Real Gases from the Gas Laws

The gas laws, in the simple form in which we have stated them, depend upon the molecules having negligible volume and negligible attraction for one another. In ordinary cases the molecules are so far apart and moving so rapidly that the error caused by neglecting intermolecular attraction is of the order of 1 per cent. Because measurements of gases are difficult to make with great accuracy, this amount of error may often be neglected. The assumption that the whole volume of a gas is free space results in the actual pressure being greater than the calculated pressure by a fraction of 1 per cent. Since the effect of attraction is to make the actual pressure *less* than the calculated pressure, these two sources of error produce a combined effect equal only to their difference. For nitrogen and oxygen, the chief gases in the air, and for hydrogen and helium and many other less familiar ones, the net inaccuracy of the gas laws is less than the probable error of measurement, as long as the temperature and pressure are within limits conveniently obtainable in the laboratory. However, if the pressure is very high or the temperature close to the liquefaction point, serious deviations from the gas laws are observed. Thus the most convincing proof offered by the behavior of gases that the molecular picture has objective reality is furnished, interestingly enough, by the failure of the gas laws in certain cases. This is because these failures are exactly what our picture leads us to expect under extreme conditions.

2.13. Molecular Volume

Our picture of the molecular structure of gases leads us to predict that at extremely high pressures Boyle's law cannot possibly continue to be obeyed. Increasing pressure does not compress the molecules of a gas; it merely brings them closer together, squeezing out the empty space, so to speak. When the empty space is gone, further compression requires tremendous pressures. But the failure of Boyle's law appears long before this point. A liter of a typical gas may, under ordinary conditions, contain 1 ml. of gas molecules and 999 ml. of empty space. If the pressure is doubled, the concentration of the molecules will be doubled; there will be 1 ml. of molecules to 499.5 ml. of empty space, and the new volume will be 500.5 ml. This is 0.1 per cent greater than that predicted by Boyle's law, which is practically perfect agreement. But suppose the initial pressure was 100 atm. instead of 1. The gas would have a volume of 11 ml., composed of 1 ml. of molecules (as before) and 10 ml. of empty space. If the pressure is doubled and the empty space correspondingly halved, the new total volume is $1 + 5 = 6$ ml. This is 9 per cent greater than the prediction by Boyle's law. If the pressure is raised to 400 atm. the error will be 27 per cent. Under such conditions the law is worthless.

2.14. Intermolecular Attraction

Charles' law predicts that the volume of a gas should be zero at 0° K. (Fig. 2.2). According to the kinetic molecular theory, this can never happen, even if the molecules come completely to rest. Only the empty space will disappear; the molecules themselves will retain their original volume. As a matter of fact, it is by no means necessary to deprive the molecules of all kinetic energy in order to get rid of practically all the empty space. All gases, if sufficiently cooled, will condense into liquids because of the attraction of their molecules for one another. The liquid has a volume less than a thousandth that of the original gas, and it is practically incompressible; hence we believe that the molecules are nearly or actually in contact with one another. Like Boyle's law, Charles' law begins to be inaccurate long before it fails completely. As soon as a gas is cooled enough so that the kinetic energy of the molecules is no longer large in comparison with the attractive force between them, the volume begins to diminish more rapidly than the law predicts. The deviations from the law at any given temperature are larger the higher the pressure; for the closer the molecules are to one another, the more they are affected by their mutual attraction.

2.15. Van der Waals' Equation

The so-called **perfect** or **ideal gas** is one which obeys the simple gas law (Eq. 2.11) under all conditions of temperature and pressure. No such gas exists; all gases are **real gases.** An equation which satisfactorily describes the behavior of real gases, even when they are near enough to the liquefaction point to be quite "imperfect," was developed by van der Waals. This equation is fundamentally the same as Eq. 2.11, but includes a correction of the pressure to allow for the effect of intermolecular attraction and a correction of the volume because of the finite volume occupied by the molecules. These corrections are constants for any one gas, but differ from one gas to another. This more elaborate equation will not be used in this book, since the deviations from the simple gas law are negligible within *ordinary* temperature and pressure ranges.

2.16. The Liquid State

The intermolecular attractions mentioned in the two preceding sections are what makes it possible for liquids to exist. There is very little free space within a liquid, so the molecules are continually within the range of one another's attraction. All molecules have the same average kinetic energy at a given temperature, regardless of their physical state; consequently if a substance is in the liquid state the attraction between its molecules must be sufficient to overcome this kinetic energy. If this were not so, the liquid would expand instantaneously to the limits of the container; it would, in fact, be a gas. Since the molecules are attracted equally in all directions by their immediate neighbors, they can move freely in all directions at random, colliding continually with one another. The situation is different at the surface of the liquid. The molecules in the surface of the liquid have no near neighbors above them; hence the force of attraction in the upward direction is negligible, whereas that to each side and downward is as strong as it is anywhere else in the liquid (Fig. 2.6). Every surface molecule is subject to an unbalanced pull which tends to move it into the body of the liquid. The movement of a molecule from the surface to the interior reduces the surface. This process continues until the liquid has attained the shape having the minimum possible surface, a sphere, or until the force producing the pull is balanced by some other force, such as gravity. A liquid thus behaves as though its surface were an elastic skin; the force which produces this effect is called **surface tension.** (However, surface tension does not increase with stretching;

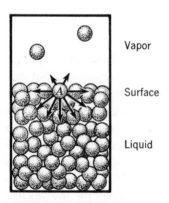

Vapor

Surface

Liquid

Fig. 2.6. Unsymmetrical distribution of attractive forces on surface molecules of a liquid.

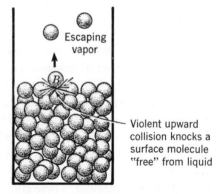

Escaping vapor

Violent upward collision knocks a surface molecule "free" from liquid

Fig. 2.7. Evaporation or boiling of a liquid.

it is constant for a given composition and temperature.) Its magnitude varies with composition, according to the strength of intermolecular attraction. If two kinds of molecules are present, those with the stronger attraction for each other are drawn into the interior, leaving those with the weaker attraction on the surface. The surface tension is then the same as it would be if all the liquid consisted of molecules like those on the surface. The surface tension of water may be reduced from the relatively high value of 80 dynes per cm. to a mere quarter of that by dissolving in the water as little as 0.1 per cent of a detergent. Molecules which tend to be forced to the surface are said to be *surface-active;* the word *surfactant* has been coined to describe substances consisting of such molecules.

2.17. Evaporation

Evaporation from the surface of a liquid is possible because some molecules have more than average energy. (Others, of course, have correspondingly less.) If a molecule in the surface of a liquid happens to receive extra energy and its motion is upward it may escape completely from the attraction of its neighbors (molecule B, Fig. 2.7). Since it received this extra energy at the expense of the molecules which are left behind, the remaining liquid is cooler than it was before the evaporation took place. The molecule which escapes into the gas state may be no "hotter" than the average by the time it is free, its extra energy having been used up in overcoming the attractive forces in the same way that a projectile fired upward from the earth is slowed down by gravity. The energy which disappears in this process is the *heat of vaporization* that was mentioned in Section 2.1. The energy reappears as heat when a molecule of the vapor drifts within the range of the attractive forces and falls back into the liquid with increasing speed. The potential energy of intermolecular attraction is thus converted into heat energy again.

2.18. Specific Heat

When heat energy is put into a substance, only part of it may be effective in raising the temperature, because only part of it appears as kinetic energy of the molecules. Some of it usually goes into the spinning motion of the molecules; and if the substance is in a condensed state—i.e., solid or liquid—part of the energy is used up in producing thermal expansion. As the molecules in a solid or liquid acquire greater kinetic energy and move more rapidly, they jostle each other somewhat farther apart. Since this expansion takes place against the intermolecular attractive forces, the amount of energy used up in this way varies from substance to substance. The total amount of heat energy needed to raise the temperature of 1 g. of a substance 1° C. is called its **specific heat.** (The term specific refers to the fact that the quantity of material and the amount of the temperature rise have been *specified.*) The common scientific unit of heat energy is the **calorie**; this is the specific heat of water at 15° C. Engineers more commonly use the **British thermal unit** (B.t.u.); this is the amount of heat needed to raise the temperature of 1 lb. of water 1° F. One B.t.u. = 252 cal. The total amount of heat needed to raise any amount of a substance a specific number of degrees in temperature is the product of the weight, the temperature change, and the specific heat.

$$\text{(Grams)(Temperature change, °C.)(Specific heat)} = \text{Calories} \quad [2.14]$$

The specific heat of a substance usually varies to some extent over a *large* temperature range, but an average value which is appropriate to the particular temperature range can be used in calculations. The average specific heat of ice is 0.5 cal./g./°C.; hence, to raise the temperature of an ice cube weighing 1 oz. (28.4 g.) from 5° F. (-15° C.) to its melting point, 0° C., will require

$$\text{(28.4 g.)(15° C.)(0.5 cal./g./°C.)} = 213 \text{ cal.}$$

The fact that a good deal of the specific heat of a liquid is used in overcoming the attraction of the molecules for one another means that there is less work to be done against those attractive forces when a molecule evaporates. Consequently, the heat of vaporization varies appreciably with the temperature. The heat of vaporization of water is 596 cal./g. at 0° C., but only 540 cal./g. at 100° C.

2.19. The Solid State

When the forces of attraction between molecules are very large compared with the kinetic energy that corresponds to the temperature, the molecules are unable to move past each other. Instead they vibrate in fixed positions, and the substance they compose is a **solid.** The space occupied by each molecule is slightly larger than the molecule itself, because of the vibration. When a solid is heated, the increased vibrational energy enlarges the space each molecule occupies, and the substance expands. The molecules may acquire rotational as well as vibrational energy.

As the average distance between the molecules increases with increasing temperature, the effect of the intermolecular attractions weakens, because these forces diminish very rapidly with distance. This results in a softening of the solid that is sometimes useful and sometimes inconvenient. It makes forging and welding possible, but sets an upper limit to the operating temperature of a rocket motor or nose cone.

Since diffusion is the result of molecular motion, the rate of diffusion will be increased by an increase in temperature. Although not everyone realizes that diffusion can actually take place through a solid, it can be so rapid as to be of commercial importance if the solid is hot enough to be even slightly soft. The tempering and casehardening of steel involve diffusion. An interesting example of diffusion between solids at room temperature was obtained when a gold bar was left on a sheet of lead. Four years later traces of gold were detected in the lead at a depth of 7 mm.

2.20. Vapor Pressure

When water is exposed to air, there is a good chance that the molecules which evaporate will be thrown back into the liquid when they collide with the molecules of the gases in the atmosphere. Evaporation is rather slow under these conditions. The heat of vaporization which is absorbed from the liquid water during evaporation is readily replaced by heat transfer from the surrounding environment, and the water remains only slightly cooler than the surrounding air. But if the water is allowed to evaporate into an evacuated space, the evaporation will be very rapid indeed and the cooling effect correspondingly more pronounced. This is one method of refrigeration used in air conditioning. Water can actually be frozen in this way. (This procedure is being used in one of the several research projects for obtaining fresh water from sea water. The ice crystals which separate are free from salt.)

If any liquid is introduced into an evacuated container of limited volume, it will boil for an instant; then the temperature falls rapidly, the boiling stops, and the temperature gradually returns to that of the room. At the same time we can observe, by means of a gauge, that the pressure in the container rises, at first rapidly, then more slowly; it finally reaches a constant value which, as long as any liquid remains, depends upon the final temperature but not upon the size of the container. The rise in pressure is due to the evaporation of molecules from the liquid state into the gaseous. But we cannot assume that the rise in pressure eventually ceased because the liquid stopped evaporating, for the nature of the liquid is exactly the same as it was at the start of the experiment. The only possibility is that molecules of the vapor are in some manner being removed as fast as evaporation provides new ones. What happens is that, in the course of their random movement, the vaporized molecules continually strike the surface of the liquid and condense into it. The vapor exerts the same pressure on the surface of the liquid as it does on all the other surfaces, including that of the pressure gauge, but the molecules which strike the liquid do not rebound. The rate of condensation is thus proportional to the pressure, and will rise as long as the pressure rises, i.e., as long as the rate of evaporation is greater than the rate of condensation. Since the rate of evaporation of a liquid is a constant (for a given liquid) at any particular temperature, it will eventually be equaled by the rising rate of condensation.

A steady state which is maintained by two processes that occur at the same rate but in opposite directions is called a state of **dynamic equilibrium.** The pressure of vapor that is in dynamic equilibrium with a liquid is called the **vapor pressure** of that liquid. It depends only upon the nature of the liquid—i.e., the intermolecular attractive forces—and the temperature. The presence of any other gas in the space into which the liquid evaporates delays the attainment of equilibrium, but does not alter the final result. Here the total pressure is the sum of the partial pressure of the other gas (its original pressure) and the partial pressure of the liquid (its vapor pressure). In this case, the gas above the liquid is said to be saturated with the vapor of the liquid. When the atmosphere is saturated with water vapor, there is said to be 100 per cent humidity. "The humidity is 50 per cent" means that the partial pressure of the water vapor in the air is 50 per cent of the vapor pressure of water at that temperature.

2.21. Critical Temperature and Critical Pressure

If a container is partially filled with a liquid, evacuated, sealed, and then heated, the liquid cannot boil. For a liquid to boil, its vapor pressure must *exceed* the pressure upon its surface; but this can never happen in a sealed container because the evaporating liquid is always under its own vapor pressure. With continued heating the density of the vapor increases steadily as the number of vaporized molecules increases. Meanwhile the density of the liquid slowly decreases as a result of the thermal expansion mentioned in Section 2.18. Eventually the two densities become equal. When this happens, the liquid surface abruptly disappears, because the molecules are now evenly distributed throughout the container. The shape and volume of the material now depend solely on those of the container; in other words, the material is a gas. The liquid has ceased to exist. The temperature at which this occurs is called the **critical temperature;** it differs for different substances, being higher the greater the attraction which exists between the molecules. The pressure in the system at this temperature (the vapor pressure of the liquid just as it ceased to exist) is called the **critical pressure.**

At or above the critical temperature the kinetic energy of molecules is so great that it cannot be overcome by the attraction between them even if sufficient pressure is applied to force them into contact with each other. Although the substance would have the density of a liquid or solid it would still be a gas, because any increase in the volume of the container would be accompanied simultaneously by expansion of the substance to fill the space. Below the critical temperature any gas can be liquefied by applying pressure equal to the vapor pressure at the particular temperature. Above the critical temperature a gas cannot be liquefied by any pressure, however great. Table 2.1 lists the critical temperature of several

TABLE 2.1. **Some Critical Temperatures**

Helium	−268° C.	Carbon dioxide	31° C.	Butane	153° C.
Hydrogen	−240° C.	Ammonia	132° C.	Freon	112° C.
Nitrogen	−147° C.	Chlorine	144° C.	Water	374° C.
Oxygen	−119° C.	Sulfur dioxide	157° C.	Mercury	>1550° C.
Carbon monoxide	−139° C.	Ethane	32° C.	Sulfur	1040° C.
Methane	− 83° C.	Propane	96° C.		

more or less familiar substances. Early attempts to liquefy gases by pressure were made at room temperature or by means of a simple ice-salt mixture (− 20° C. at best). In the case of substances with low critical temperatures, such as hydrogen, oxygen, and nitrogen, failure was of course inevitable. Chlorine, sulfur dioxide, and carbon dioxide, which have relatively high critical temperatures, were successfully liquefied. This led to the erroneous conclusion that there was a fundamental distinction between the two classes of substances—between the "permanent gases" and the "condensible vapors." Although this distinction is now known to be only accidental, it is nevertheless of practical importance. For example, refrigerant gases in refrigerators and air conditioners must be liquefied by compression during the operating cycle and hence must have critical temperatures well above room temperature. This is true also of most gases which are to be shipped any distance in steel cylinders; otherwise freight charges become prohibitive.

2.22. Graham's Law of Diffusion

In 1833 Thomas Graham reported that the rate of diffusion of a gas is inversely proportional to the square root of its density. Thus when gas 1 is compared with gas 2,

$$\frac{\text{Diffusion rate of gas 1}}{\text{Diffusion rate of gas 2}} = \sqrt{\frac{\text{Density of gas 2}}{\text{Density of gas 1}}} \qquad [2.15]$$

A typical apparatus for an experiment illustrating Graham's law is shown in Fig. 2.8.

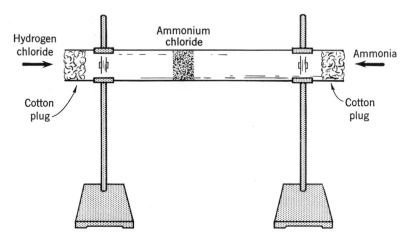

Fig. 2.8. Relative diffusion of hydrogen chloride and ammonia.

A wad of cotton saturated with ammonia solution is inserted in one end of a dry horizontal tube; the other end of the tube is plugged with cotton saturated with hydrogen chloride solution (hydrochloric acid). The two gases evaporate from the cotton and diffuse into the air in the tube. In a few minutes a white ring forms where they meet. The white smoke is ammonium chloride, the salt formed by their reaction. The ring is 1.5 times as far from the ammonia end as it is from the hydrogen chloride end; therefore ammonia diffuses 1.5 times as fast as hydrogen chloride does. The density of ammonia is 0.76 g./l. at S.T.P., and that of hydrogen chloride is 1.66 g./l. Any change in temperature and pressure will affect both gases in the same way; hence the *ratio* of the densities will have the same value. We can therefore check Graham's law as follows:

$$\frac{\text{Velocity of ammonia}}{\text{Velocity of hydrogen chloride}} = \sqrt{\frac{\text{Density of hydrogen chloride}}{\text{Density of ammonia}}}$$

$$= \sqrt{\frac{1.66}{0.76}} = \sqrt{2.19} = 1.5$$

The relationship which is thus experimentally demonstrated to exist between rate of diffusion and density of a gas is exactly the relationship which, according to the kinetic molecular theory, must exist between the average velocities of molecules and their weights. Since all molecules have the same average kinetic energy at the same temperature:

$$\text{K.E. (gas 1)} = \text{K.E. (gas 2), and } \tfrac{1}{2}m_1v_1{}^2 = \tfrac{1}{2}m_2v_2{}^2$$

Rearranging algebraically, we have:

$$\frac{v_1{}^2}{v_2{}^2} = \frac{m_2}{m_1}, \quad \text{so} \quad \frac{v_1}{v_2} = \sqrt{\frac{m_2}{m_1}} \qquad [2.16]$$

But by Graham's law (Eq. 2.15):

$$\frac{v_1}{v_2} = \sqrt{\frac{D_2}{D_1}}$$

therefore

$$\frac{D_1}{D_2} = \frac{m_1}{m_2}$$

Thus the *ratios* of the densities of gases and the weights of their individual molecules are identical.

2.23. Avogadro's Law

The conclusion just drawn can only be true (and it *is* true) if the *same volumes of gases contain the same number of molecules at the same temperature and pressure.* The italicized statement is known as **Avogadro's law.** It is not merely an inescapable conclusion of logic, but an experimentally proved fact. If it still seems strange to you that there should be the same number of heavy as of light molecules in 1 l. of the respective gases under identical conditions, review Sections 2.3 and 2.4. Note particularly that the helium molecules move just enough faster than the methane molecules to compensate for their lighter impacts, thus making unnecessary any increase in their number.

Avogadro's law is one of the most fundamental and important generalizations in chemistry, because it enables the chemist, merely by measuring the volumes of gases which react with each other chemically, to determine the relative numbers of the different kinds of molecules involved.

2.24. Gay-Lussac's Law of Combining Volumes

Avogadro's hypothesis was originally advanced to explain Gay-Lussac's law of combining volumes. In 1808, after many experiments, Gay-Lussac had announced that when two or more gases are used up or produced in a chemical reaction, the relationship between their volumes can be expressed in terms of small, whole-number ratios. For example, 10 ml. of hydrogen will combine with 5 ml. of oxygen, the volume ratio being 2 : 1. The product is water; and if the experiment is begun and finished at room temperature, no gas will take the place of those being used up. If, however, the initial and final temperatures are above the boiling point of water, the water produced will remain in the form of a gas—steam—and its volume will be 10 ml. Neglecting deviations from ideal behavior, we may say that the volume of the hydrogen is to the volume of the oxygen as 2 is to 1; the volume of the hydrogen is to the volume of the steam as 1 is to 1; the volume of the oxygen is to the volume of the steam as 1 is to 2. In the experiment at the higher temperature, fewer molecules will be present in the same volumes, but the ratios will be the same.

Belief in the molecular theory was already fairly general in Gay-Lussac's time, because it explained the gas laws as no other theory could. Avogadro explained the facts summarized in Gay-Lussac's law in terms of the molecular hypothesis as follows: If molecules exist, any reaction between two substances must be between molecules of two kinds. One molecule should be able to react with one or two or three of another kind, but not with 1.036 molecules, or any other odd fraction. Since we expect whole-number molecular ratios and actually find whole-number volume ratios, what more natural than to conclude that these are the same? That is, 1 ml. of any one gas contains the same number of molecules as 1 ml. of any other gas at the same temperature and pressure. This conclusion has since been justified by many diverse and independent experiments and lines of reasoning, and is now regarded as a fundamental law.

2.25. Gram-Molecular Weights and Volumes

Avogadro's law gave the chemist a useful tool which enabled him to work with molecules on a quantitative basis and to deduce molecular relationships in chemical reactions long before he knew the actual weights or numbers of individual molecules in a container of them. For example, if 10 ml. of hydrogen reacts with 10 ml. of chlorine gas at the same temperature and pressure, then as many hydrogen molecules as chlorine molecules are involved in the reaction. Since 20 ml. of hydrogen and 10 ml. of oxygen react together at the same temperature and pressure, *twice* as many hydrogen as oxygen molecules are needed for the reaction. Thus by observing the gas volumes involved in reactions the relative numbers of molecules can be deduced.

Because different volumes of gases at the same temperature and pressure contain different numbers of molecules, it was perfectly natural to select standard reference quantities of gases to represent fixed numbers of molecules. Oxygen, being common as well as reactive with most elements, was arbitrarily selected as the reference material; and 32.0000 g.* of oxygen (22.4 l. at S.T.P.) was adopted as the reference quantity because more than 1 g. of any other known substance would react with that quantity of oxygen. This weight and volume of oxygen are known as its **gram-molecular weight** (g.m.w.) and **gram-molecular volume** (g.m.v.) respectively, and contain a fixed number of molecules, N. Thus by definition the weight of N molecules is the gram-molecular weight of any substance, and will occupy a volume of 22.4 l. as a gas at S.T.P. (Fig. 2.9).

The term gram-molecular weight is often abbreviated to gram molecule or, preferably, **mole.** N, the number of molecules in a mole of substance, is called **Avogadro's number** and its value is 6.023×10^{23}. (Except for precise work, the value is rounded off to 6×10^{23}.) To calculate the weight of an individual molecule we need only divide the gram-molecular weight by N. This information is unnecessary for most chemical considerations because molar quantities are used in virtually all calculations.

---

* It is possible that a new reference standard for atomic weights will be adopted by the International Union of Pure and Applied Chemistry while this book is in press. The new atomic weight scale, called the "unified scale," will be based on the carbon-12 isotope whose mass will be assigned the exact value of 12.0000. The current chemical scale is based on the natural mixture of oxygen isotopes which has been assigned the exact atomic weight of 16.0000 (molecular weight 32.0000). In the unified scale the new atomic weight of oxygen will be 15.9994. When the new scale is adopted, all atomic weights in the chemical scale will be lowered by 0.0037%. Generally this change will be insignificant for most problems and calculations involved in this book.

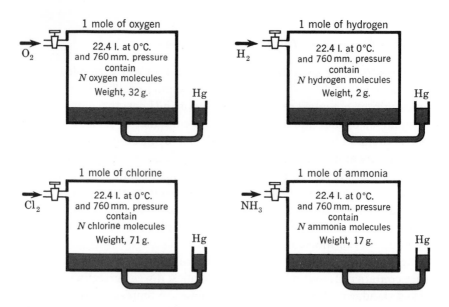

Fig. 2.9. Equal volumes of all gases under the same conditions of temperature and pressure contain the same number of molecules. As shown here, 22.4 l. of any gas at standard conditions contains 6×10^{23} molecules (N), which is a mole of the gas.

Few arbitrary numbers in chemistry need be memorized, for you can find them in reference books when necessary. But because of the continuous usefulness of the mole you should memorize the following: One mole of any gas contains 6.023×10^{23} molecules and occupies the molar volume of 22.4 l. under standard conditions, 760 mm. ($=1$ atm.) and $273°$ K. ($=0°$ C.). It is not necessary to remember the *exact* numerical value of N.

2.26. Finding the Molecular Weight

To find the molecular weight of any gaseous substance it is only necessary to find the volume occupied by some weighed quantity of it under known conditions of temperature and pressure. If this volume is then calculated to standard conditions, the weight of 22.4 l. under the same conditions can easily be obtained from it. Of course 22.4 l. of a gas at S.T.P. is a mole, and the weight of a gas in grams is the molecular weight.

Suppose, for example, that we learn by experiment that an evacuated 100-ml. bulb increases in weight by 0.0688 g. when filled with ammonia at 22° C. and 745 mm. pressure. To compute the molecular weight, it is convenient to set up a table of data such as the following:

Initial Conditions	Final Conditions
$W_1 = 0.0688$ g.	W_2 (weight of 1 mole) = ?
$V_1 = 100$ ml.	$V_2 = 22.4$ l.
$P_1 = 745$ mm.	= 22,400 ml.
$T_1 = 22°$ C.	$P_2 = 760$ mm.
$= 295°$ K.	$T_2 = 273°$ K.

Then the weight of a mole of ammonia is given by:

$$W_2 = W_1 \times \text{Volume factor} \times \text{Pressure factor} \times \text{Temperature factor}$$

The introduction of the weight of a gas into a gas law calculation requires the use of one more correction factor, but does not complicate the reasoning, because the effect of each change in conditions upon the weight is considered separately. Thus we write the volume correction factor with the larger volume in the numerator because a large volume of gas must weigh more than a small volume *at the same temperature and pressure.* Note that the units in which the molar volume is expressed have been changed from liters to milliliters. This is done so that the units will cancel out. Of course the volume of the gas, 100 ml., could just as well have been expressed as 0.100 l. The important thing is that in each ratio both quantities should be expressed in the *same* units. Always check this. Now we have:

$$W_2 = 0.0688 \text{ g.} \times \frac{22,400 \text{ ml.}}{100 \text{ ml.}} \times \text{Pressure factor}$$
$$\times \text{ Temperature factor}$$

Similarly, the pressure correction factor is written with the larger pressure in the numerator because the only way to increase the pressure of a gas *without changing its volume or temperature* is to put in more gas, which will of course increase the weight. This gives us:

$$W_2 = 0.0688 \text{ g.} \times \frac{22,400 \text{ ml.}}{100 \text{ ml.}} \times \frac{760 \text{ mm.}}{745 \text{ mm.}} \times \text{Temperature factor}$$

Finally, the temperature factor must also have the larger number in the numerator, for in order to keep the *pressure and volume constant* when the temperature is lowered, more gas must be added. The final expression is:

$$W_2 = 0.0688 \text{ g.} \times \frac{22,400 \text{ ml.}}{100 \text{ ml.}} \times \frac{760 \text{ mm.}}{745 \text{ mm.}} \times \frac{295° \text{ K.}}{273° \text{ K.}} = 17.0 \text{ g.}$$

The molecular weight of ammonia is therefore 17.0.

2.27. Splitting Molecules by Chemical Reactions

When various examples of the law of combining volumes were studied in the light of Avogadro's law, it became evident that molecules are frequently split into two or more parts by chemical reactions. Consider, for example, the reactions of hydrogen with chlorine and with oxygen, as shown in Fig. 2.10. In accordance with Avogadro's law, each unit volume

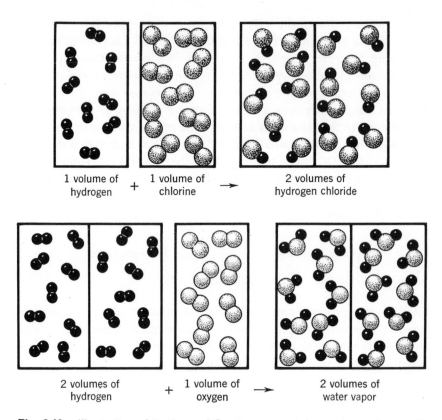

1 volume of hydrogen + 1 volume of chlorine → 2 volumes of hydrogen chloride

2 volumes of hydrogen + 1 volume of oxygen → 2 volumes of water vapor

Fig. 2.10. Illustration of the laws of Gay-Lussac and Avogadro under conditions of constant temperature and pressure.

is diagramed as containing the same number of molecules. Now count the number of hydrogen molecules, and then the number of hydrogen chloride molecules. There are twice as many of the latter as of the hydrogen, yet all the hydrogen chloride molecules are alike and all contain hydrogen. Evidently each hydrogen molecule has split into two parts, one of which goes into the formation of each molecule of hydrogen chloride.

The same statements that have been made about hydrogen hold true for chlorine. Our conclusion is that the net result of a collision between a hydrogen molecule and a chlorine molecule is that each breaks in two and each half-molecule of hydrogen unites with a half-molecule of chlorine to make a hydrogen chloride molecule.

The lower part of the figure shows that oxygen molecules are also divisible into two parts, and that a water molecule contains one of these, together with both parts of a hydrogen molecule. Other experiments show that other molecules can be broken during chemical reactions into even more than two identical pieces. One milliliter of ozone (page 133) will react with three of hydrogen, and if the entire experiment is carried out at 110° C., the product will be 3 ml. of steam (gaseous water). Since all water molecules are alike, each ozone molecule must have split into three parts, each identical with half an oxygen molecule. One of these must have joined with each of three hydrogen molecules to form that number of water molecules. The phosphorus molecule can be split into four identical parts. On the other hand, some molecules cannot be split by any reaction whatever. Helium, neon, argon, and mercury belong to this class.*

2.28. Atoms

Since molecules which can be split by chemical reactions into two or three or four identical parts can never be split into any larger number of parts by collisions of whatever violence with molecules of whatever kind, the parts are appropriately called **atoms** (Gr., not cut). Atoms, then, are the building blocks of molecules. Atoms bear the same relation to molecules as rooms to houses, or cars to trains. Just as a house may have one or many rooms, and a train may consist of a single diesel-motored unit or of many cars, so a molecule may be monatomic or polyatomic. If a diatomic molecule is broken into two separate atoms by a violent collision—i.e., by high temperature—these two atoms are two new and different molecules as long as they remain separate particles.

The number of different kinds of molecules is enormous. Even those whose structure is accurately known are numbered by the hundred thousand. If each of these had to be studied without relation to any of the others, the task would be Herculean, like learning to read Chinese, where

---

* These substances are present in the familiar "neon" sign light tubes. The yellow ones contain helium, the orange ones neon, and the blue both argon and mercury. An excess of the mercury beyond what can remain in the form of a gas at the working temperatures can usually be seen in horizontal portions of blue light tubes as drops of liquid metal.

TABLE 2.2. | Molecular State of Some Elements

Monatomic Molecules	Diatomic Molecules	Polyatomic Molecules
He Helium	H_2 Hydrogen	O_3 Ozone
Ne Neon	F_2 Fluorine	P_4 Phosphorus
Ar Argon	Cl_2 Chlorine	S_8 Sulfur
Kr Krypton	Br_2 Bromine	
Xe Xenon	I_2 Iodine	
Rn Radon	O_2 Oxygen	
Hg Mercury	N_2 Nitrogen	

NOTE: The subscript following the symbol for the element tells how many atoms there are in the molecule. If there is no subscript, 1 is understood.

each word has a separate ideogram. Fortunately, the task is like learning to read English, where half a million words are all composed of only 26 letters, for in all the different kinds of molecules of which the earth is composed, only 103 chemically different kinds of atoms have been observed.

QUESTIONS AND PROBLEMS

1. a. What are the three states of matter?
   b. Name the processes involved in changing from each state to the others.
2. a. Define heat of vaporization; heat of fusion; calorie; specific heat.
   b. How many calories are required to change 10 g. of ice at $-5°$ C. to steam at $100°$ C.?
3. What is the origin of surface tension? Of vapor pressure?
4. Kinetic energy of molecules is a direct measure of which of their properties?
5. What is the fundamental statement of the kinetic molecular theory of matter?
6. Differentiate the modes of the motion of molecules in solids, liquids, and gases.
7. What is the relationship between $°C.$, $°F.$, and $°K.$?
8. What is a real gas? An ideal gas? To which do the simple gas laws exactly apply?
9. Define the following: critical temperature and pressure; vapor pressure; absolute zero; standard conditions; gram-molecular volume; gram-molecular weight; mole.
10. State the following laws: Boyle's gas law; Charles' gas law; Gay-Lussac's gas law; Graham's law of diffusion; Gay-Lussac's law of combining volumes; Avogadro's law; Dalton's law of partial pressures.
11. A gas in a sealed container is heated. What effect has this on (a) the pressure, (b) the force of each molecular impact, (c) the number of molecular impacts per second?

12. A liter each of gases A and B is at S.T.P. The liter of gas A weighs four times as much as the liter of gas B. Compare the following ratios: (a) density of A to B; (b) molecular weight of A to B; (c) velocity of A molecules to that of B molecules.

13. How many molecules of gas A in the preceding problem are there in its container?

14. Express $-25°$ F. in $°K$.

15. What is the volume at S.T.P. of 50 ml. of gas at 20° C. and a pressure of 3 atm.?

16. The pressure of a gas is tripled and its absolute temperature doubled. What is its new volume compared to its original volume?

17. At what temperature C. will 1 l. of gas measured at S.T.P. have a pressure of 1000 mm. of mercury if its volume does not change?

18. Suppose that 250 ml. of oxygen gas is collected by the displacement of water at a laboratory pressure of 740 mm. and a temperature of 25° C. What is its dry volume at S.T.P.?

19. If 1200 ml. of gas X at 25° C. and 770 mm. pressure weighs 2 g., what is its density at S.T.P.? What is its gram-molecular weight?

20. Ten liters of gaseous element X reacts with 30 l. of another gaseous element Y and forms 20 l. of a gaseous compound Z.
    a. How many atoms of X are there in a molecule of X? In a molecule of Z?
    b. How many atoms of Y are there in a molecule of Y? In a molecule of Z?
    c. What is the total number of atoms in a molecule of Z?

3

The electrical nature of matter

3.1. Introduction

We saw in Chapter 2 that the simplest particle of a chemical element which can exist is a monatomic molecule, preferably referred to as an atom. Of what does an atom consist? What makes one atom different from another? If we had to answer that each atom is made of itself, we would be admitting that we had reached the end of knowledge. Happily, that is not the case. Just as a million different kinds of molecules are all built from a hundred or so atoms, so all these atoms are made up of only three component building blocks; these are considered fundamental units of matter. Any one of these subatomic particles taken by itself is entirely different from any of the atoms which can be built up from various combinations of these particles. This is analogous to the fact that we cannot recognize in water any of the characteristics of its constituent elements, oxygen and hydrogen. Since the properties of atoms depend in an understandable way upon their structure, it will be well to consider the nature of the building blocks of which they are composed.

3.2. The Fundamental Units of Matter

In a *chemical* discussion of the atom it is necessary to consider only three fundamental particles: **electrons, protons,** and **neutrons.** All the other "strange particles"—a total of 30—which physicists encounter in atom-smashing experiments, such as positrons, neutrinos, hyperons, mesons of all sorts, and various "anti-" particles, are unstable. Within a tiny fraction of a second they may revert to the more familiar particles, with emission of energy, or react with one of them in an "annihilation reaction" in which the mass of both is converted into radiant energy.

TABLE 3.1. **The Fundamental Units of Matter**

Particle	Relative Weight	Charge	Symbol
Electron	1/1837	−1	− or e^-
Proton	1	+1	+ or p
Neutron	1	0	n

It will be noted from Table 3.1 that although protons and electrons have equal though opposite charges, their weights are very different. In fact, almost 2000 electrons weigh the same as 1 proton (or neutron). Since the number of electrons in an atom is the same as the number of protons, the total weight of all the electrons in an atom is a negligible fraction of the weight of the atom. The weights of these particles in grams (obviously excessively small fractions) are known, but are not necessary for this discussion.

3.3. The Electron

Determining the characteristics of the fundamental units of matter required tremendous effort, patience, and brilliant deduction on the part of many scientists. The study of these particles is not yet finished; on the contrary, the subject still constitutes a very active research area.

The **electron** was the first particle to be studied in detail and to be suggested as a fundamental unit of matter. This was due to the fact that free electrons are so easily obtained. For example, a glowing lamp filament gives off electrons. Sir William Crookes showed as early as 1879 that electrons are particles which have momentum; a stream of them could drive a tiny paddle wheel in an evacuated tube. He also proved that they have a negative electrical charge by observing the direction of the deflection of an electron stream in an electrical or magnetic field. Sir J. J. Thomson concluded in 1891 that all matter contains electrons. He found that when gas molecules are struck by fast-moving electrons they become positively charged molecules which are called positive **ions** (Gr., "on the go"). This could occur only if the original electrically neutral molecules had had negative charges (electrons) knocked off of them (Fig. 3.1). Thomson's work also indicated that atoms contain positive charges which we now know belong to the protons; this accounts for the positive ions that result from the electron collisions.

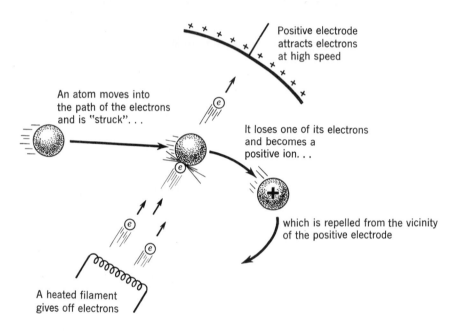

Fig. 3.1. Electron collisions with atoms to form positive ions.

It remained to be proved unequivocally that electrons are discrete, individual particles; hence determination of their mass (weight) and charge became decidedly important. The *ratio* of charge to mass was determined by deflection experiments like that illustrated in Fig. 3.2. When an electron passes between charged plates it is attracted toward the positive plate. An electron which, if there were no electrical field, would strike a photographic plate at *A* will follow a curved path, striking it instead at some point *B*. The radius of curvature of the path depends upon the charge on the deflecting plate, which can be measured, and upon two unknowns, the electron's velocity and its charge-to-mass ratio. A magnetic field at right angles to the electrical field causes a similar deflection in the horizontal plane. When both deflections are allowed to take place, the two mathematical relationships can be solved for the velocity and equated. Thus the only unmeasured quantity in the final relationship would be the ratio of charge to mass.

The absolute value of the charge on an electron was measured by R. A. Millikan in 1909. This made it possible to determine the mass, which is too small to be weighed directly. Millikan produced a cloud of atomized oil droplets between two horizontal metal plates and observed individual droplets with a microscope. The rate of its fall through air of known viscosity enabled him to calculate the weight of each droplet. The lower plate was then made negative and the top one positive, and ionization was produced in the space between by x-ray or radium. Through the microscope Millikan could see what happened when an electron struck an oil droplet and was trapped by it. As the droplet became negatively charged it stopped falling and began to rise, repelled by the negative and attracted by the positive plate. Sometimes a charged droplet would pick up a second or even a third electron, and its rate of motion would change correspondingly, in

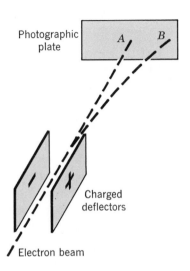

Fig. 3.2. Deflection of electrons by electrical fields. The undeflected beam strikes the photographic plate at **A,** whereas the deflected beam strikes at **B.** The amount of deflection depends upon the mass and velocity of the particles as well as upon the charge on the deflector plates.

spurts. The charge on a drop was computed from the plate charge needed to hold a drop of known weight against gravity. All the charges on thousands of drops were found to be whole-number multiples of the same quantity, which was evidently the charge on one electron, designated as e^-. This is the smallest unit of negative electricity.

Electrons are familiar in modern life. When they pass back and forth through a wire, they constitute an **alternating current.** When they pass steadily from the casing of a dry cell through a light bulb to the central contact of the cell, they constitute a **direct current.** Electrons from the filaments of tubes in radio and TV sets move across the vacuum or halt in accordance with varying voltages from the antennas. When a high-velocity stream of electrons from an electron gun strikes an appropriate

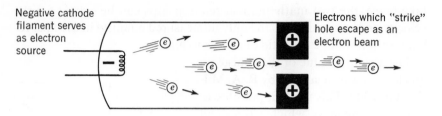

Fig. 3.3. Principle of an electron gun which produces a definite electron beam.

screen, it produces the moving dot of light which traces the curious curves of an oscilloscope and makes the complete TV picture. An electron gun (Fig. 3.3) consists of a hot cathode (negative electrode) and an anode (positive electrode) in which there is a hole. Electrons moving between them are accelerated to such a speed by the high potential difference between them that those which strike the hole shoot through and continue far beyond it. Such a stream of high-speed electrons is also known as a **cathode ray.** Electrons with even higher velocities (up to 95 per cent that of light) are shot out from many radioactive elements such as strontium-90 (notorious in connection with H-bomb fall-out). Streams of electrons thus produced are called **beta rays.**

3.4. The Proton

The positive ions mentioned at the beginning of the preceding section can be accelerated in the same way as electrons (though their greater mass prevents them from attaining comparable velocities) and shot in a beam, through a hole in the cathode in this case (Fig. 3.4). A stream of

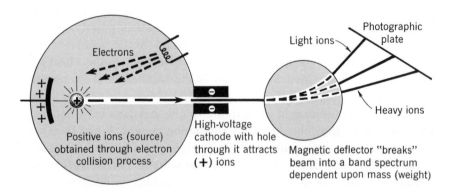

Fig. 3.4. Principal features of the mass spectrograph.

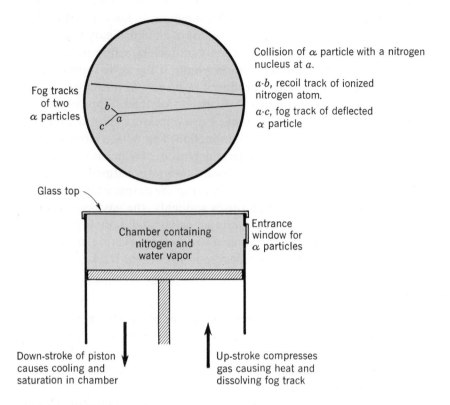

Collision of α particle with a nitrogen nucleus at *a*.

a-b, recoil track of ionized nitrogen atom.

a-c, fog track of deflected α particle

Fog tracks of two α particles

Glass top

Chamber containing nitrogen and water vapor

Entrance window for α particles

Down-stroke of piston causes cooling and saturation in chamber

Up-stroke compresses gas causing heat and dissolving fog track

Fig. 3.5. Principal features of the Wilson cloud chamber, and some typical alpha-particle fog tracks.

positive ions can be investigated by electrical and magnetic deflection just as a stream of electrons can. An instrument for this purpose is called a **mass spectrograph** because it sends the ions to different places on a recording film, depending upon their weights. Unlike electrons, all of which are identical, positive ions vary enormously in weight. However, all these weights prove to be (roughly) whole-number multiples of the weight of the smallest of these ions, the one obtained from hydrogen. It weighs 1837 times as much as an electron. Since it is present in all other atoms it has been named a **proton** (Gr. first). An ordinary, electrically neutral hydrogen atom is composed of one proton and one electron.

One of the instruments used to study high-speed particles is the Wilson cloud chamber (Fig. 3.5). The alpha particles referred to in the figure are helium ions that have a +2 charge and a mass approximately four times that of a proton. They are ejected at high speed during the radioactive decay of radium. Any charged particle, whether it is an electron or a positive ion, leaves a trail of positive ions and loose electrons be-hind it when it moves at high speed through a gas. Such a particle loses energy at each collision, and its collisions in air at ordinary pressure are so frequent that it travels only a few centimeters before its velocity is reduced below that required for ionization. If the air is supersaturated with moisture, the ions thus produced in it serve as nuclei for the con-densation of droplets of water. A hairline "fog track" appears momen-tarily on the path the particle took, like a miniature jet trail, and it can be photographed under strong illumination. The Wilson cloud chamber consists of a glass-topped cylinder, the bottom of which is closed with a piston. When this piston moves upward the gas is warmed by compres-sion and the fog track disappears because of the evaporation of the drop-lets of mist. When the piston drops suddenly, the gas becomes cool; this causes it to become supersaturated again, and more fog tracks ap-pear. A magnetic field can be applied so that the curvature of a fog track indicates the charge of the particle responsible for the track.

3.5. The Neutron

In 1920, Lord Rutherford noted that atoms of all elements except hy-drogen were at least twice as heavy as the sum of their protons. To ac-count for these weight discrepancies, he suggested that neutral particles, which he called **neutrons,** must also be present in atoms. Because, in contrast to electrons and protons, neutrons—even if highly energetic—leave no ion trails, their existence could not be proved directly. Indirect evidence, however, was soon available. It was observed that certain arti-ficially prepared radioactive elements produced no ionizing radiations. Nevertheless, very energetic rays were emitted which manifested them-selves by ejecting fast-moving protons from a target of paraffin (a hydrogen-containing material) when they struck it. These "recoil" pro-tons left characteristic fog tracks from which their energies could be calculated. In 1932, J. C. Chadwick, a British physicist, made the obser-vations and calculations which proved that the uncharged particles that had given rise to the recoil protons weighed the same as the protons, within 0.1 per cent. They were, in fact, the neutrons postulated by Ruth-erford. Chadwick was awarded the Nobel prize for this momentous con-tribution. Rutherford had been so honored in 1908 for his classical work on radioactivity.

Neutrons are now produced in vast numbers in all nuclear energy in-stallations, as well as in atom bombs. They both result from and produce nuclear fission; hence the possibility of chain reactions. Neutrons are also the most effective means of producing artificial radioactivity.

3.6. Distribution of Matter in the Atom

It has been established that the neutrons and protons are concentrated in a tiny central region of the atom, the rest of the atom being occupied solely by electrons. Since the weight of the electrons is negligible, the central region—or **nucleus,** as Rutherford called it—contains practically all the weight of the atom. It was Rutherford who, in 1911, proved this to be true. Two years later Niels Bohr, a Danish physicist, suggested that the electrons in the outer region of an atom must be moving in orbits about the nucleus. Research on atomic structure has been carried on actively ever since and has resulted in continually increasing knowledge of nuclear and electronic structure.

3.7. The Nucleus

Rutherford proved that most of the mass of atoms was concentrated in nuclei by means of his *scattering* experiments, in which he shot positive ions through very thin films of gold, silver, platinum, and copper. Although most of the ions passed straight through without being deflected, the paths of some were bent away from the line of fire and in a few cases were scattered at wide angles or even reflected backward. His projectiles were **alpha particles** which are ejected from radium at a velocity of 10,000 miles per second. The fact that most of the alpha particles were scattered slightly or not at all showed that even dense metals like those he used must consist mostly of empty space. This is shown in Fig. 3.6, which represents two atoms in the thin film of gold in contact with each other; i.e., the nuclei are as close to each other as the electrons allow. Only in case an alpha particle made a direct hit (*A*) on a cluster of protons and neutrons would it be reflected backward. Its close approach to these nuclei would result in more or less significant scattering (*D, E*); but most of the alpha particles pass so far from either nucleus that there is little or no deflection (*B* ··· *C*). Careful mathematical calculation of thousands of deflections showed that the diameters of the nuclei are about 1/10,000 of the distance between them. (The size of the nuclei is obviously exaggerated in the figure. If a nucleus were the size of a period on this page, the nearest nucleus would have to be approximately 10 ft. distant to be in scale.)

3.8. Atomic Number

Rutherford was also able to approximate the value of the positive charge contained in the nuclei of the metals he used in these scattering

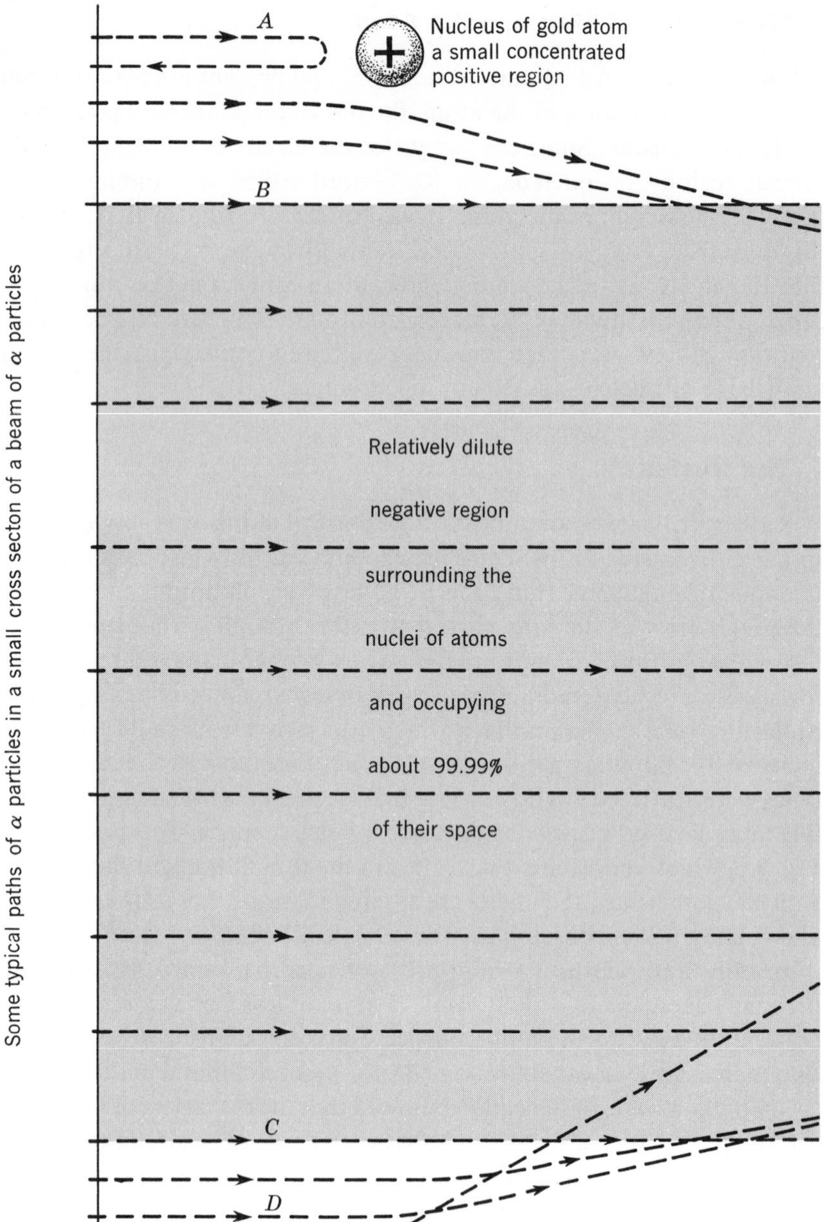

Fig. 3.6. Rutherford's scattering experiment showing some typical deflections of alpha particles caused by two neighboring gold nuclei of high positive charge in a thin section of gold foil.

experiments. This value is known as the **atomic number** (at. no.). The atomic number of many elements was determined accurately in 1913 by the British physicist, H. G. J. Mosely, by means of x-ray measurements. **X-rays** are a form of light; their wave length is even shorter than that of ultraviolet light. Like ultraviolet light, x-rays can be photographed even though they are not visible. When any solid element is bombarded by a stream of high-velocity electrons, some of its own electrons are knocked out of their atoms. These are eventually replaced by other electrons which release energy as they fall, releasing this energy as a pulse of x-rays when they stop. Just as a ball falling to earth releases more energy the farther it falls, so does an electron, the closer it comes to the nucleus. This extra energy can be detected because of the fact that the vibration frequency of the x-rays is greater and the wave length correspondingly shorter. The highest-frequency x-rays emitted by any element are produced by the electrons which have come as close as possible to the nucleus. The larger the positive charge of the nucleus (its atomic number), the closer the electron is to the nucleus and the harder the nucleus pulls on the electron while it is in motion; this accounts for the greater energy in the resulting pulse of x-rays. When Mosely compared the square roots of the highest-frequency x-rays emitted by each member in a series of elements with consecutive atomic weights, he found them related to a series of whole numbers in simple fashion. He correctly assumed these numbers to be the numbers of positive charges in the nuclei of the respective atoms. The elements now known have nuclear charges from 1 through 103.

The number of electrons required to make an atom electrically neutral obviously is equal to the atomic number. We shall see later in this chapter that the chemical properties of any atom depend upon how many electrons it has. This makes it possible to give a precise definition of an element in terms of its atomic number. *An element is a substance all of whose atoms have the same atomic number.*

3.9. Isotopes

We might expect that all atoms of the same element would have the same weight as well as the same atomic number. This is not true because *different* numbers of neutrons can combine with the *same* number of protons to form a nucleus. The total number of particles (neutrons and protons) in a nucleus is called its **mass number.** Atoms having the same atomic and mass numbers constitute an **isotope** of an element. Virtually all elements have isotopic varieties of atoms, those with even atomic numbers displaying the greater variety. Hydrogen, for instance, with atomic number 1, has three isotopes with mass numbers 1 (common), 2 (rare), and 3 (very rare), whereas tin (at. no. 50) has ten isotopes whose mass numbers range from 112 to 124, the least common isotope being 1/100 as abundant as the most common. All the isotopes of hydrogen have 1 electron; only the nuclear structures are different. None of these three isotopes differ in chemical properties, but the heavier isotopes have slightly lower reaction rates, and molecules that contain them diffuse a little more slowly (in proportion to the square roots of the masses). These differences make separating the isotopes possible, but it is tedious and expensive. Thus electrolytic decomposition of water leaves the remaining water richer in "heavy water," the molecules of which contain atoms of "heavy hydrogen"; and fractionation by gaseous diffusion at Oak Ridge separates the lighter, fissionable isotope of uranium from the more common one.

Before World War II no pure isotopes were separated on a commercial basis, though a few experimenters had prepared specimens for research purposes. *Separation* of naturally occurring isotopes is still limited largely to the two mentioned above, but many pure isotopes are now being *manufactured* in quantity in nuclear energy installations as well as being produced in all nuclear explosions. This is done by adding neutrons to the nuclei of naturally occurring isotopes; this will be described in a later chapter. Some of these isotopes are famous and their names are already fairly familiar to the layman. Among them are deuterium (hydrogen of mass number 2), tritium (hydrogen of mass number 3, used in the H-bomb), cobalt-60 (very radioactive; used instead of high-power x-rays industrially and instead of radium in the treatment of cancer), strontium-90 (radioactive and bone-seeking, present in H-bomb fallout), and uranium-235 (produces nuclear power through fission).

3.10. Nuclear Symbols

Obviously the difference between the mass number and the atomic number of an atom states the number of neutrons in its nucleus. Since the two numbers contain all the information necessary to determine all the particles in a neutral atom, they are incorporated in the nuclear symbols of atoms. Some typical atoms are listed in Table 3.2, with their nuclear symbols and the structural information derived from these symbols. In each case the most common isotope is listed first.

Among the other elements, some of those with even atomic numbers have eight or ten isotopes (cadmium, tin, tellurium, xenon), whereas

TABLE 3.2. **Nuclear Data of Some Isotopes**

Element	Chemical Symbol	Nuclear Symbol	Mass. No.	At. No. = Protons = Electrons	Mass No. − At. No. = Neutrons
Hydrogen	H	^1_1H	1	1	0
		^2_1H	2	1	1
		^3_1H	3	1	2
Helium	He	^4_2He	4	2	2
		^3_2He	3	2	1
Lithium	Li	^7_3Li	7	3	4
		^6_3Li	6	3	3
Argon	Ar	$^{40}_{18}\text{Ar}$	40	18	22
		$^{38}_{18}\text{Ar}$	38	18	20
		$^{36}_{18}\text{Ar}$	36	18	18
Potassium	K	$^{39}_{19}\text{K}$	39	19	20
		$^{41}_{19}\text{K}$	41	19	22
Strontium	Sr	$^{88}_{38}\text{Sr}$	88	38	50
		$^{86}_{38}\text{Sr}$	86	38	48
		$^{84}_{38}\text{Sr}$	84	38	46
		$^{87}_{38}\text{Sr}$	87	38	49
		$^{90}_{38}\text{Sr}$	90	38	52
Uranium	U	$^{238}_{92}\text{U}$	238	92	146
		$^{235}_{92}\text{U}$	235	92	143

most of those with odd atomic numbers have only one. Hydrogen-3, potassium-41, and a few other light natural isotopes are radioactive, as are most artificially produced isotopes and all natural isotopes with atomic numbers greater than 83 or mass numbers greater than 209.

3.11. Fractional Atomic Weights

In general, the isotopic distribution in any element is the same wherever its compounds are found in nature. When a chemist determines the atomic weight of an element he obtains a statistical average of the weights of all its naturally occurring isotopes. For example, the atomic weight of chlorine is found to be 35.457 because 22.85 per cent of the atoms in any sample are $^{37}_{17}\text{Cl}$ and the rest are $^{35}_{17}\text{Cl}$. The isotopic composition of an element cannot generally be computed from the fractional atomic weight but must be determined experimentally by means of the mass spectograph or the mass spectrometer.

A beam of positive ions can be separated into a **mass spectrum** by means of magnetic and electrostatic deflection. This was shown digrammatically in Fig. 3.4, which illustrates the essential principle; the actual instrument, however, is more complicated. The light-weight ions in the beam are deflected to the greatest extent. A suitable device records the intensity of the beam of ions in each position. If a photographic plate is used (mass spectrograph), the spectrum is recorded in narrow bands (lines) whose relative intensities depend on the relative abundance of the isotopes. The **mass spectrometer** determines the same data electrically and records them in a line on a moving chart. The geometry of the instrument relates the positions of these lines to the mass numbers of the isotopes. The accuracy of atomic weight determinations with these two instruments has now reached the remarkable reliability of one part per hundred thousand.

In 1943 the mass spectrometer was introduced in commercial laboratories as a means of analyzing the complicated mixtures of gases used in the manufacture of synthetic rubber and high-octane gasoline. In the mass spectrometer the field is progressively altered so as to cause ions of first one weight, then the next, to fall successively upon a fixed collector, where their quantity is measured and recorded by electrical amplifying equipment. When the relative numbers of ionized fragments of various weights produced by the electron bombardment of molecules of the different substances involved have been determined experimentally, the composite spectrum of a mixture can be unraveled. This method gives in minutes the percentage composition of a mixture whose analysis would have required days by older methods, and gives it more accurately. The mass spectrometer, originally invented merely to satisfy a scientist's curiosity, is now a standard control instrument in oil refineries, plants making synthetic rubber, etc.

Very accurate determination of the weights of all the different isotopic species shows that none of them are *exactly* equal to their mass number. This is due to the fact that the amount of energy given off when protons and neutrons combine to form atomic nuclei is so enormous as to have appreciable weight. The amount of matter thus transformed into energy differs from element to element, but is of the order of 0.1 per cent. Less energy is produced in the formation of the lightest and heaviest atoms than in the formation of atoms of intermediate weight. Under very special circumstances light nuclei can be made to unite to form heavier ones (**nuclear fusion**) or certain very heavy nuclei can be split into lighter ones (**nuclear fission**). In both cases a small fraction of the mass is transformed into a large amount of energy. This emission of energy is responsible for the destructive effects of fusion bombs (hydrogen, lithium) and of fission bombs (uranium, plutonium). All "atomic energy" is now derived from controlled nuclear fission. Solar and stellar energy is believed to be produced largely by the fusion of hydrogen into helium, but controlled fusion under terrestrial conditions is as yet only a scientists' dream. *No nuclear changes occur during chemical reactions.*

THE ELECTRONIC STRUCTURE OF ATOMS

3.12. Energy Levels in Atoms

The electrons which thinly populate the outer region of an atom might be expected to fall into the positive nucleus, but this is not the case. Since the only force that can prevent it is centrifugal force, we may represent the electrons as traveling rapidly in curved paths about the nucleus. This is called **orbital motion.** Our earliest knowledge about the behavior of electrons in atoms was obtained by studying the energy of this orbital motion. This could be done because electrons interact with light. An electron can acquire more total energy by absorbing a pulse of light, or it can lose some energy by radiating a pulse of light. This interaction is not confined to visible light, but is true of infrared (low frequency) and ultraviolet (high frequency) light as well as x-rays (very high frequency).

The energy of any form of light is measured by determining its vibration frequency by means of a spectroscope. In a spectroscope the ribbon of light which passes through a narrow slit falls upon a prism or other device that bends it to an extent dependent upon the frequency (Fig. 3.7). If light of two different frequencies (or "colors") is present in the beam, two beams will leave the prism in different directions and make two independent images of the slit on a photographic film. The frequencies are calculated from the position of these **spectral lines.** In 1900 Max Planck conjectured that the energy of any particular pulse of light was proportional to its frequency, and in 1912 Einstein proved this to be true. The following year Bohr applied this relationship to the spectrum of the light obtained by passing an electrical discharge through hydrogen gas (as is now done with neon and other gases in "neon signs").

Since the atomic number of hydrogen is 1, a single electron makes the atom electrically neutral. When hydrogen is ionized by an electrical dis-

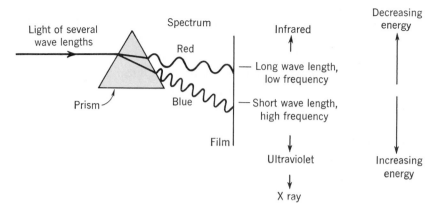

Fig. 3.7. Diagram of the spectroscope and relationship of wave length, frequency, and energy.

charge this electron is knocked off; the positive ion that is left is nothing but the nucleus of the hydrogen atom, a simple proton. When this nucleus succeeds in recapturing an electron, a pulse of light is given out (Fig. 3.8*A*). An electron at a distance from a nucleus has potential energy because it is attracted by the nucleus; but when it is in an orbit around the nucleus it has less energy. The difference between these two amounts of energy is radiated as light. If there were only one possible orbit into which the electron could fall, the amount of energy radiated would always be the same, only one frequency of light would be emitted, and the spectrum of hydrogen would consist of a single line. If orbits could be of any size and shape, there would be an infinite number of energies; the light would have an infinite number of frequencies, and the spectrum would be continuous. Actually the spectrum of hydrogen consists of several series of narrow lines. This, Bohr believed, suggested that only certain orbits are possible. Furthermore, if some of the lines result from electrons falling into various high-energy orbits, it stands to reason that these electrons will presently fall into lower-energy orbits and finally into the orbit of lowest energy. Since energy must be radiated at each drop, many of the lines in the spectrum correspond to quantities of energy which are the *differences* between the energies of two orbits (Fig. 3.8*B*).

Bohr was able to devise a set of energies such that differences between them accounted for the energies corresponding to all the lines in the hydrogen spectrum. His work was extended to the other atoms by Bohr himself and by other spectroscopists. All this work established the fact that each atom has a number of principal **energy levels** which are sepa-

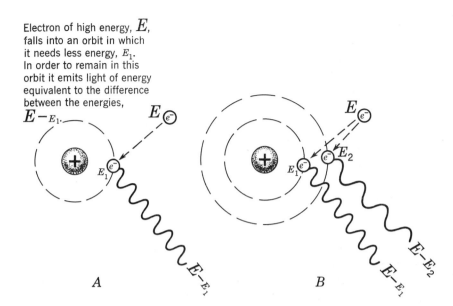

Electron of high energy, E, falls into an orbit in which it needs less energy, E_1. In order to remain in this orbit it emits light of energy equivalent to the difference between the energies, $E - E_1$.

Fig. 3.8. A, The process whereby radiant energy is emitted by an atom as the result of inward shifts of electrons. **B,** The dependence of emitted wave length on orbital energy.

rated from each other by considerable intervals. Each energy level except the lowest was shown to consist of a more or less complex group of closely adjacent sub-energy levels. These facts were of profound importance in interpreting the electronic structure of atoms. An energy level is now believed to result when a number of electrons have orbits which put them at about the same average distance from the nucleus. An energy level is complex because the electron orbits responsible for it are of various shapes and differ somewhat in energy.

Although the word *orbit* is used in relation to the motion of both planets and electrons, the mental pictures in the two cases are vastly different. It is impossible to observe the path of an electron in an atom, but the probability of finding a given electron at any particular point in the atom can be computed mathematically. In effect, what we have is equivalent to a blurred time exposure of a moving electron, dense where the electron passes most frequently and thin and shadowy where it passes infrequently. There is no indication whatever as to its path between any two points. There is no sharp boundary to the region in which an electron may be found; the probability of its being there decreases gradually. Many people find it convenient to think of an electron under these conditions as a diffuse region or cloud of electricity rather than a localized particle. In representing such a cloud diagrammatically, it is customary to have the boundary surface enclose 90 per cent of it and to neglect the diffuse remainder. The mathematical expression by which the electron density at any given point in such a cloud can be calculated is called an **orbital wave function.** (The word wave refers to the fact that in some ways an electron must be treated as though it were a pulse of light.) Henceforth, when speaking of an electron that obeys a particular wave function, we shall say that it occupies a certain **orbital,** in order to indicate that the usual meaning of the word orbit is not intended.

3.13. Electron Shells

When an atom has a number of electrons, the regions of the individual electrons do not constitute a homogeneous cloud that fills the whole volume of the atom evenly. This conclusion follows from the banded structure of the energy levels and is confirmed by modern theory. Mathematical computation shows that a cross section of an atom has this same banded effect. There are no electrons in the nucleus; but as the distance from the nucleus increases, the probability of electrons being present rises to a maximum, then decreases toward zero, rising and decreasing again and again until all the electrons characteristic of that atom have been included. The distance of an electron from the nucleus varies continually, but an electron is most often present in one of the denser regions. All the electrons in such a region are referred to as a **shell of electrons.** The word layer is often used instead of shell.

When the layer effect was first discovered, the shells were designated by capital letters, starting with the middle of the alphabet to allow for the possibility of more shells being found in either direction. It is now known that the K shell is the innermost. However, it is becoming more common to refer to the shells by number, K being given the number 1. The largest atoms have 2 electrons in the seventh shell (Q).

The argon atom, shown in cross section in Fig. 3.9, has the atomic number 18 and therefore has 18 electrons. Two of these are in the first or K shell, 8 in the second or L shell, and 8 in the third or M shell. This may be described more briefly as a 2-8-8 electron arrangement, the first number always referring to the number of electrons in the shell nearest the nucleus. The same information is presented diagrammatically in Fig. 3.10. The figure also indicates the charge in the nucleus (neutrons may or may not be included), the number of shells, and the number of electrons in each shell. Note that diagrams such as this are not drawn to scale, and that the dashed circles do not represent electron orbitals. Each one represents merely a cross section of an electron shell.

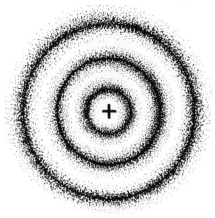

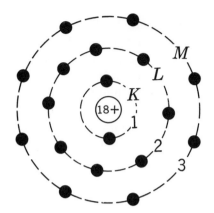

Fig. 3.9. Cross section of an argon atom. There are three shells of electrons. The nucleus, too small to be shown in scale, is indicated by the +.

Fig. 3.10. The three electron shells of the argon atom. The electron content of each shell is shown, as well as the numerical and letter designations of the shells.

3.14. Electron Orbitals

An **electron orbital** is a three-dimensional region in space. This region can be occupied by 1 or at most 2 electrons, or by none at all. The number of orbitals in each shell of electrons is equal to the square of the shell number—1 for the first shell, 4 for the second, 9 for the third, and so on. Since there can be at most 2 electrons to an orbital, it is apparent that in the argon atom in Fig. 3.10 the single orbital of the first shell is full, and so are the four orbitals of the second shell. The third shell, however, contains four full and five empty orbitals.

The present electron cloud picture of an electron orbital was presented by Schrödinger in 1926. The ideas this concept presents have been verified by experimental spectroscopic results in all cases where the computations were not so difficult as to be impossible. Bohr's original concept, formulated in 1913, envisioned simple circular orbits instead of the complex three-dimensional shapes that orbitals are now regarded as having. For this reason Bohr was unable to correlate his proposed electronic structures with spectroscopic evidence for atoms more complex electronically than hydrogen.

3.15. Classes of Electron Orbitals

The existence of several orbital types is required to account for the multiplicity of sub-energy levels found in all electron shells except the simplest one, K. The number of orbital types in a given shell is equal to the shell number; the first shell has one type, the second shell two types, and so on. The different types of orbitals are designated *s, p, d,* and *f* in order of increasing complexity of their shapes (Table 3.3). These letters, which had their origin in spectroscopy before the development of electron theory, may be remembered by means of a student's claim that "*some poor darn fool*" invented them. There are no additional orbital types in shells beyond N because no atom has sufficient electrons to require them.

TABLE 3.3. **Orbital Classifications**

	K	L	M	N
Shell letter	K	L	M	N
Shell number	1	2	3	4
Number of orbital types	1	2	3	4
Orbital type symbols	s	s, p	s, p, d	s, p, d, f
Orbitals of each type	1	1, 3	1, 3, 5	1, 3, 5, 7
Electron capacities	2	2, 6	2, 6, 10	2, 6, 10, 14

The number of orbitals of a given type increases from type to type in accordance with the series of odd numbers 1-3-5-7-. That is, there is one *s* orbital in each shell, three *p* orbitals in each shell beyond K, five *d* orbitals in each shell beyond L, and seven *f* orbitals from N on. Since each orbital can contain 2 electrons, the maximum electron capacity of the K shell is 2, and the single *s* orbital in each of the other shells contributes 2 electrons to the total electron capacity of that shell. The three *p* orbitals can accommodate 6 electrons; hence the capacity of the L shell is 8. In the M shell the *s* orbital can contain 2 electrons, the three *p* orbitals can contain 6, and the five *d* orbitals 10, making a total capacity of 18. The seven *f* orbitals that appear in each shell beyond M add 14 to the electron capacity of that shell, bringing it up to 32.

The shell to which orbitals of a given type belong is identified by a number written before the type symbol, and the number of electrons actually present in orbitals of that type *in that shell* is specified by a superscript following the type symbol. Thus $2p^6$ is a shorthand statement of the fact that there are 6 electrons in *p* orbitals of the second shell. Thus the entire electronic structure of the argon atom diagrammed in Fig. 3.10 may be described by the following brief array of symbols: $1s^2$, $2s^2$, $2p^6$, $3s^2$, $3p^6$. This states that there are 2 *s* electrons in the first shell, 2 *s* electrons and 6 *p* electrons in the second shell, and 2 *s* and 6 *p* electrons in the third shell. It also states that the *d* orbitals in the third shell of this atom are empty.

3.16. Orbital Energies

It takes more energy to raise a satellite from the earth into an orbit 1000 miles out than into a 500-mile orbit. In the same way, an electron moving in a large orbital has more energy than one moving in a smaller orbital of the same type. That is, a *3p* electron is more energetic than a *2p* electron. Not so obvious, but very important, is the fact that within a given shell an electron requires more energy to move in a complicated than in a simple orbital.

The single *s* orbital of a given shell is spherical. The farther we go from the nucleus in *any* direction, the chance of finding an *s* electron increases up to a certain distance and then decreases rapidly. The presence of the inner ring in the cross section (Fig. 3.9) is due almost entirely to the pair of *s* electrons in the 1*s* orbital. Since no other orbital like it is present in the shell, the electron clouds of its 2 electrons are uniformly distributed in the orbital. In a *p* orbital the density of the electron cloud rises and falls as its distance from the nucleus increases, in much the same way as that of an *s* orbital. However, since there are *three p* orbitals which must maintain separate identities but identical energies, it is impossible for them to be spherical. If they were spherical they would constitute a single sphere, hence a single orbital, since their centers and diameters would be common. This would result in 6 electrons occupying the *same orbital,* which cannot occur. Thus they must be non-spherical, but identical in size and shape. A symmetrical distribution of electrons in a system of three identical orbitals of this sort would be realized if the electron clouds were concentrated at the six ends of three mutually perpendicular axes. This is obviously a more complicated and restricted arrangement of electrons than that found in a simple spherical *s* orbital. The successively greater numbers of *d* and *f* electrons are even more restricted as regards orbital shapes and positions, with consequently greater energies. Hence orbital energies in a given shell increase in the order *s, p, d,* and *f.*

The increase in orbital energy due to increasing complexity is comparable to that due to increasing radius. The *d* electrons have more energy than the *s* electrons of the next outer shell—e.g., 3*d* > 4*s*—whereas *f* electrons have greater energy than even the *s* electrons two shells beyond —e.g., 4*f* > 6*s*—but about the same energy as the 6*p* electrons.

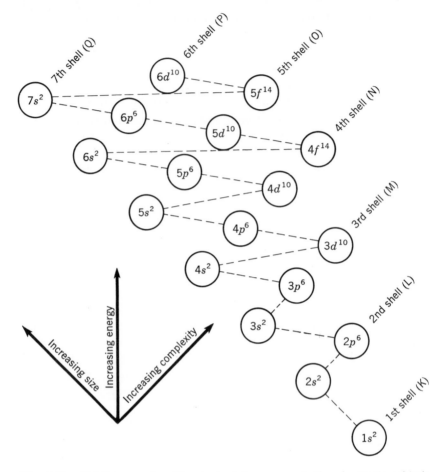

Fig. 3.11. Orbital energies. The dashed line connects the electronic orbitals in the order of their energies.

3.17. The Filling of Electron Shells

No electron can remain in a high-energy orbital if the atom has a lower-energy orbital that either is empty or contains only 1 electron. The electronic structure of any uncombined atom can be deduced by taking a number of electrons equal to the atomic number and assigning them to the lowest-energy orbitals first as far as they go. In Fig. 3.11 the energies are plotted vertically; hence each electron is to be placed as far down the dashed line as there is room for it. The electron capacity of each type of orbital is given by the superscript number. When any one type of orbital is being filled, 1 electron goes into each orbital before a second electron goes into any orbital.

Study of Fig. 3.11 leads to some generalizations* regarding the order in which electron shells are filled as the atomic number increases. After the first shell has its 2 electrons, the second shell starts to fill. Then a new shell starts to fill after each group of p electrons is completed. That is, a new shell starts to fill after 8 electrons have accumulated in any shell regardless of whether or not the latter shell has empty d or f orbitals in it. After 2 electrons are in the s orbital in the new shell, electrons go into empty orbitals in preceding shells. The build-up of electrons from one shell (n) to the next shell ($n + 1$) follows the sequence:

$$ns \underset{2}{} \rightarrow (n - 1)d \underset{1}{} \rightarrow (n - 2)f \underset{14}{} \rightarrow (n - 1)d \underset{9}{} \rightarrow np \underset{6}{} \rightarrow (n + 1)s \underset{2}{}$$

The numbers below the terms indicate the number of electrons to be added for each term before going on to the next. Not all the terms apply in every case.

1. If $n = 1$ the p, d, and f terms are omitted.
2. If $n = 2$ or 3   the d and f terms are omitted.
3. If $n = 4$ or 5   the f term is omitted.
4. If $n = 6$ or 7   all terms remain.

For illustration, let us suppose that enough electrons have been added to start the fifth shell ($n = 5$). Then, according to the first term of the sequence, 2 s electrons start the fifth shell. The second term calls for 1 d electron in the fourth shell. The third term is omitted, so we go on to the fourth term, which calls for 9 more d electrons in the fourth shell, filling it. The fifth term calls for 6 p electrons in the fifth shell. Since that shell now has 8 electrons, the 2 s electrons called for by the last term must start the sixth shell.

In any atom the s electrons in the outer shell are held less tightly than the d or f electrons in the inner shells, even if the latter were reached later in the above sequence formula. This is so because the difference in energy between s, p, d, and f electrons in a given shell decreases as the

---

* The generalizations developed in this section will provide you with the ability to predict *logical* electronic structures for the elements. However, some of the more complex atoms do not follow these generalizations entirely, for reasons that are either unknown or too complicated to be considered in this text. Where the electronic structures are known for such cases, this will be the structure reported; otherwise the predicted structure will be given.

atomic number increases. Thus up through atomic number 20 (calcium) the 4s orbital is lower in energy than the 3d orbitals; hence elements 19 (potassium) and 20 have one and two 4s electrons, respectively. But at atomic number 21 the increasing nuclear charge has brought the energy of the 3d orbitals down below that of the 4s orbital. Accordingly the 19th electron added to an atom with atomic number 21 goes into a 3d orbital. This, however, neutralizes some of the nuclear charge, so that the remaining 3d orbitals are again higher in energy than the 4s orbital; the latter therefore receives the 20th and 21st electrons. Similarly, in element 22, the 19th and 20th electrons go into 3d orbitals before the 21st and 22nd go into the 4s orbital, and in element 23 the 19th, 20th, and 21st electrons go into 3d orbitals before the 22nd and 23rd go into the 4s orbital. The relationship between nd and $(n - 1)f$ orbitals is similar.

In general, each element has one more d electron than the preceding element. However, as will be seen from Fig. 3.12, in the case of chromium (at. no. 24), the addition of the fourth 3d electron still leaves the last 3d orbital lower in energy than the 4s orbital. Accordingly the 23rd

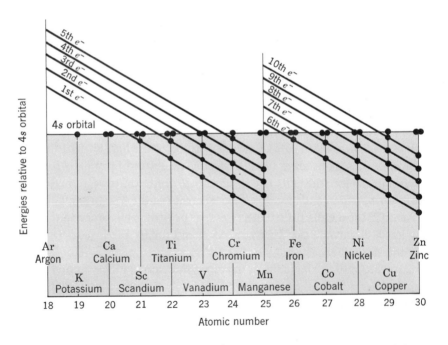

Fig. 3.12. Variation of energies of 3d orbitals relative to the energy of the 4s orbital, at various atomic numbers, as one electron after another is put into the d orbitals. Above atomic number 25 each atom already has the 5 d electrons added previously between 21 and 24. For simplicity these are not shown.

electron also goes into a 3d orbital, leaving only 1 electron for the 4s orbital.

Considerably more energy is required to put a second electron into any orbital because of the repulsion between their charges; this is shown in the right-hand part of Fig. 3.12. Once started, however (at. no. 26), the doubling up proceeds in an orderly manner. The 4s electrons are always higher in energy than the 3d electrons actually present, and in copper (at. no. 29), as in chromium, only 1 electron is left when the 4s orbital is reached.

The actual shell configurations of the atoms are shown in Table 3.5. Comparison of this table with Fig. 3.11 will confirm most of the structures in the table. However, there are a few deviations from the predictions of Fig. 3.11, similar to those in the case of chromium and copper. Most of these deviations result in all the d (or f) orbitals being full (2 electrons in each) or half full (1 electron in each). In most of these cases the energy difference between the predicted and the actual orbital is so small as to have no chemical significance, so it can be disregarded in this book.

3.18. Stable Electron Configurations

An electron in the outermost occupied shell of an atom is not subject to the pull of the entire positive charge on the nucleus. Every electron between it and the nucleus neutralizes one unit of the nuclear charge, so far as this outer electron is concerned. If there is only 1 electron in the outer shell, all the other electrons in the inner shells will shield it from all the nuclear charge except one unit of positive charge. It will be relatively easy to remove the outer electron. If, on the other hand, there are several electrons in the outer shell, each of them will be subject to a much larger positive charge, because the other electrons in that shell will only occasionally come between it and the nucleus. It will be more difficult to remove such an electron. The greatest stability as far as loss of electrons is concerned will thus be shown by the atoms which have the largest number of electrons in their outer shell. Inspection of Fig. 3.11 shows that no atom ever has more than 8 electrons in any shell as long as that shell is the outermost one. After the s and p orbitals in any shell are filled, a new shell is always begun. The one shell of the helium atom contains only 2 electrons, but both of them are so close to the nucleus that they are held more tightly than the outer electrons of any other atom. Table 3.4 summarizes the electronic struc-

TABLE 3.4. **The Inert Gases**

	At. No.	K 1	L 2	M 3	N 4	O 5	P 6
Helium (He)	2	2					
Neon (Ne)	10	2	8				
Argon (Ar)	18	2	8	8			
Krypton (Kr)	36	2	8	18	8		
Xenon (Xe)	54	2	8	18	18	8	
Radon (Rn)	86	2	8	18	32	18	8

tures of these exceptionally stable atoms. The elements listed in the table are known as the **inert gases.**

3.19. Ionization Potentials

An electron can be knocked out of an atom by being hit with a high-speed electron that is shot at it from outside, just as a marble can be knocked out of a ring by being hit with another marble. We saw in Section 3.4 that this is a basic necessity for the operation of the mass spectrograph and the Wilson cloud chamber. If an electron is knocked out of a neutral atom the remainder of the atom will have a charge of $+1$ and will be attracted by a negatively charged plate or repelled by a positively charged one. Because this remainder can thus be made to move through a gas it is called an **ion.** The current in a Geiger counter is produced by ions which result from passing high-energy radiation through atoms of the gas within the counter.

The electrons from an electron gun such as that in a TV picture tube have a velocity that is dependent upon the voltage used to accelerate them. Low-voltage electrons do not produce ionization when they strike atoms. If the voltage is increased gradually, there will be a point, different for each element, at which ionization begins. This voltage is called the **ionization potential;** it measures the tightness of bonding of the atom's highest-energy (i.e., loosest) electron. In Fig. 3.13 this quantity is plotted as a function of the atomic number. The figure shows plainly the exceptional stability of the inert gases. It also shows equally plainly that whenever a new shell is begun, the lone electron in it is held very loosely. The two jogs in the line between Li and Ne mark, respectively, the entry of the first electron into a new type of orbital (p), and the first time a second electron goes into a p orbital which already contains 1 electron. There are similar explanations for the jogs in the other lines.

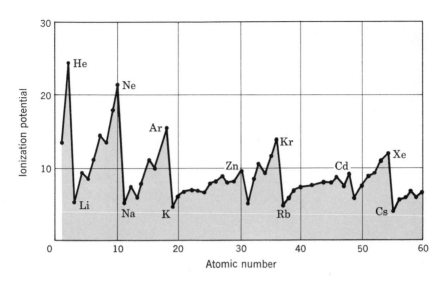

Fig. 3.13. Ionization potentials, in volts, of the first sixty elements.

3.20. Periodicity and Atomic Structure

Nearly everyone is familiar with two types of variation, continuous and periodic. The pressure in a diver's ears increases *continuously* as he goes deeper, but the sun returns *periodically* to the same position in the sky. Similarly, the weights of the atoms increase *continuously* (though somewhat irregularly) with the atomic number, but high and low ionization potentials recur at (increasing) intervals. The periodic variation in ionization potential takes place because the filling of the electron shells has a periodic rhythm, a new shell being started every so often. Thus the atoms of the hundred-odd elements have a variation from only 1 to 8 in the number of electrons in the outer shell. The recurrence of identical outer electronic structures causes a recurrence of similar chemical properties as well as of similar ionization potentials. (Similar but not identical, because these properties are modified by other factors, notably size and the presence of *d* electrons in the next inner shell.)

Chemists find it convenient to correlate the many properties of the periodically varying elements with the continuous variable, the atomic number. This is done by arranging the elements in the order of increasing atomic number in columns in such a way that those with similar electronic structure are in the same column. Such an arrangement is called a **periodic table.** One of the many possible arrangements is shown in Table 3.5. This particular arrangement is commonly called the **long** or **Bohr form** of the periodic table.

TABLE 3.5. Periodic Table of the Chemical Elements, Bohr Form, with Atomic Number and Electron Configurations

GROUP NUMBERS

Period	Levels being filled	VIIIA Inert Gases	IA	IIA	IIIA	IVB	VB	VIB	VIIB	VIIIB	VIIIB	VIIIB	IB	IIB	IIIB	IVA	VA	VIA	VIIA	VIIIA Inert Gases
1 (2 elements)	1 (K) 0→2																		1 H — 1	2 He — 2
2 (8 elements)	2 (L) 0→8	2 He — 2	3 Li — 1 2	4 Be — 2 2	5 B — 3 2											6 C — 4 2	7 N — 5 2	8 O — 6 2	9 F — 7 2	10 Ne — 8 2
3 (8 elements)	3 (M) 0→8	10 Ne — 8 2	11 Na — 1 8 2	12 Mg — 2 8 2	13 Al — 3 8 2											14 Si — 4 8 2	15 P — 5 8 2	16 S — 6 8 2	17 Cl — 7 8 2	18 Ar — 8 8 2
4 (18 elements)	4 (N) 0→8 ; 3 (M) 8→18	18 Ar — 8 8 2	19 K — 1 8 8 2	20 Ca — 2 8 8 2	21 Sc — 2 9 8 2	22 Ti — 2 10 8 2	23 V — 2 11 8 2	24 Cr — 1 13 8 2	25 Mn — 2 13 8 2	26 Fe — 2 14 8 2	27 Co — 2 15 8 2	28 Ni — 2 16 8 2	29 Cu — 1 18 8 2	30 Zn — 2 18 8 2	31 Ga — 3 18 8 2	32 Ge — 4 18 8 2	33 As — 5 18 8 2	34 Se — 6 18 8 2	35 Br — 7 18 8 2	36 Kr — 8 18 8 2
5 (18 elements)	5 (O) 0→8 ; 4 (N) 8→18	36 Kr — 8 18 8 2	37 Rb — 1 8 18 8 2	38 Sr — 2 8 18 8 2	39 Y — 2 9 18 8 2	40 Zr — 2 10 18 8 2	41 Nb — 1 12 18 8 2	42 Mo — 1 13 18 8 2	43 Tc — 1 14 18 8 2	44 Ru — 1 15 18 8 2	45 Rh — 1 16 18 8 2	46 Pd — 18 18 8 2	47 Ag — 1 18 18 8 2	48 Cd — 2 18 18 8 2	49 In — 3 18 18 8 2	50 Sn — 4 18 18 8 2	51 Sb — 5 18 18 8 2	52 Te — 6 18 18 8 2	53 I — 7 18 18 8 2	54 Xe — 8 18 18 8 2

Transition Elements: groups IVB, VB, VIB, VIIB, VIIIB, IB, IIB

Group VIIIB comprises columns 26–28 (Fe, Co, Ni) and 44–46 (Ru, Rh, Pd)

Periodic Table — Periods 6 and 7

Shell-filling notes (Period 6): 6 (P) 0→8; 5 (O) 8→18; 4 (N) 18→32. Period 6 — 32 elements.

Shell-filling notes (Period 7): 7 (Q) 0→8; 6 (P) 8→18; 5 (O) 18→32. Period 7 — 32 elements (incomplete).

Each cell lists the electron-shell populations from the outermost shell down to the innermost (K), with the element symbol placed on its 32-electron (N) shell line.

Period 6

Z	Element	Shell electrons (outer → inner)
54	Xe	8 / 18 Xe / 18 / 8 / 2
55	Cs	1 / 8 / 18 Cs / 18 / 8 / 2
56	Ba	2 / 8 / 18 Ba / 18 / 8 / 2
57–71	Lanthanum and the lanthanides*	
72	Hf	2 / 10 / 32 Hf / 18 / 8 / 2
73	Ta	2 / 11 / 32 Ta / 18 / 8 / 2
74	W	2 / 12 / 32 W / 18 / 8 / 2
75	Re	2 / 13 / 32 Re / 18 / 8 / 2
76	Os	2 / 14 / 32 Os / 18 / 8 / 2
77	Ir	2 / 15 / 32 Ir / 18 / 8 / 2
78	Pt	1 / 17 / 32 Pt / 18 / 8 / 2
79	Au	1 / 18 / 32 Au / 18 / 8 / 2
80	Hg	2 / 18 / 32 Hg / 18 / 8 / 2
81	Tl	3 / 18 / 32 Tl / 18 / 8 / 2
82	Pb	4 / 18 / 32 Pb / 18 / 8 / 2
83	Bi	5 / 18 / 32 Bi / 18 / 8 / 2
84	Po	6 / 18 / 32 Po / 18 / 8 / 2
85	At	7 / 18 / 32 At / 18 / 8 / 2
86	Rn	8 / 18 / 32 Rn / 18 / 8 / 2

Period 7

Z	Element	Shell electrons (outer → inner)
86	Rn	8 / 18 / 32 Rn / 18 / 8 / 2
87	Fr	1 / 8 / 18 / 32 Fr / 18 / 8 / 2
88	Ra	2 / 8 / 18 / 32 Ra / 18 / 8 / 2
89–103	Actinium and the actinides**	

* Lanthanum and the Lanthanides (Rare Earth Metals)

Z	Element	Shell electrons (outer → inner)
57	La	2 / 9 / 18 La / 18 / 8 / 2
58	Ce	2 / 9 / 19 Ce / 18 / 8 / 2
59	Pr	2 / 8 / 21 Pr / 18 / 8 / 2
60	Nd	2 / 8 / 22 Nd / 18 / 8 / 2
61	Pm	2 / 8 / 23 Pm / 18 / 8 / 2
62	Sm	2 / 8 / 24 Sm / 18 / 8 / 2
63	Eu	2 / 8 / 25 Eu / 18 / 8 / 2
64	Gd	2 / 9 / 25 Gd / 18 / 8 / 2
65	Tb	2 / 9 / 26 Tb / 18 / 8 / 2
66	Dy	2 / 8 / 28 Dy / 18 / 8 / 2
67	Ho	2 / 8 / 29 Ho / 18 / 8 / 2
68	Er	2 / 8 / 30 Er / 18 / 8 / 2
69	Tm	2 / 8 / 31 Tm / 18 / 8 / 2
70	Yb	2 / 8 / 32 Yb / 18 / 8 / 2
71	Lu	2 / 9 / 32 Lu / 18 / 8 / 2

** Actinium and the Actinides

Z	Element	Shell electrons (outer → inner)
89	Ac	2 / 9 / 18 / 32 Ac / 18 / 8 / 2
90	Th	2 / 10 / 18 / 32 Th / 18 / 8 / 2
91	Pa	2 / 9 / 21 / 32 Pa / 18 / 8 / 2
92	U	2 / 9 / 21 / 32 U / 18 / 8 / 2
93	Np	2 / 9 / 22 / 32 Np / 18 / 8 / 2
94	Pu	2 / 9 / 23 / 32 Pu / 18 / 8 / 2
95	Am	2 / 8 / 25 / 32 Am / 18 / 8 / 2
96	Cm	2 / 9 / 25 / 32 Cm / 18 / 8 / 2
97	Bk	2 / 9 / 26 / 32 Bk / 18 / 8 / 2
98	Cf	2 / 8 / 27 / 32 Cf / 18 / 8 / 2
99	Es	2 / 9 / 28 / 32 Es / 18 / 8 / 2
100	Fm	2 / 9 / 29 / 32 Fm / 18 / 8 / 2
101	Md	2 / 9 / 30 / 32 Md / 18 / 8 / 2
102	No†	2 / 8 / 32 / 32 No† / 18 / 8 / 2
103	††	2 / 9 / 32 / 32 †† / 18 / 8 / 2

† This element, currently known as Nobelium (No), will probably have its name changed while this book is in press.

†† The name for 103 has not been formally proposed. The name Lawrencium has been suggested by its discoverers in honor of Ernest Lawrence, who founded the Radiation Laboratory of Berkeley where much work has been done on the synthetic actinides.

If the table is read from left to right like lines on a printed page, the atomic numbers (upper right corner of each box) are seen to vary continuously from 1 to 103. Each horizontal row is called a **period**. The vertical columns are called **groups** or **families.** Columns which contain second- and third-period elements are the **main groups**; the others are **subgroups.** In this table the main groups are designated by A and the subgroups by B, but usage varies in this respect; in some tables the groups on the left side are labeled A, those on the right side B. Group VIIIA, the inert gas family, is placed on both sides of the table to show how the electronic structure varies as we approach and leave these gases. Some tables show it only at the right; in others it is called Group 0 and put at the left.

The lanthanides and actinides that are placed horizontally at the bottom of the table actually belong in the boxes marked with one and two asterisks respectively. None of the elements beyond 92 exists in appreciable quantities in nature, but all of the heavier actinides have been synthesized. Some, such as 94, have been prepared in quantity. Only a few atoms of other elements have been made. Up to the time this book went to press no element beyond 103, the last actinide, had been synthesized.

The electronic configurations are given in each box as a series of numbers. The bottom number is the number of electrons in the shell nearest the nucleus; the top one indicates the number of electrons in the outermost shell.

Note the following generalizations about atomic structure and properties relative to the table:

1. The period number corresponds to the number of electron shells in the structure of the atoms in that period. All the elements in the same period have the same number of shells. The period number also corresponds to the number of the particular shell whose s and p orbitals are being filled with electrons ($0 \rightarrow 2$ in period 1, $0 \rightarrow 8$ in the others).

2. Except in the transition elements, the group number indicates the number of s and p electrons in the atom's outermost shell. In the case of the transition elements, the group number (up to VIIIB) indicates the combined number of s electrons in the outer shell and d electrons in the next shell that have been added since the period was begun.

3. The **transition elements** are those which are characterized by partly filled inner shells. In all cases d electrons are present in the shell next to the outside shell. The lanthanides and actinides may have none, one, or more than one such d electrons and, in addition, $0 \rightarrow 14$ f electrons in the third shell in from the outside shell.

4. A comparison of the ionization potentials (Fig. 3.13) with the periodic table shows a general but not smooth increase across each period, from a minimum at Group IA to a maximum at Group VIIIA. They *decrease* down each main group and vary irregularly in the subgroups.

5. All sorts of other physical properties, such as melting point, hardness, compressibility, expansion by heat, etc., vary periodically in the same manner. What is much more important, chemical properties, as will be shown later, can be correlated with the periodic system.

3.21. Short Form of the Periodic Table

The periodic table was first drawn up in approximately its present form by the Russian chemist Mendeleev in 1869. His table was more compact than the Bohr table and is still preferred by many chemists. In the short table, which appears inside the back cover of this book, there are only nine columns. The fourth and succeeding periods are presented in two lines in such a way that main groups and subgroups are in the same column. In addition to being more compact, this form of the table places chemically related elements closer together. The main-group elements are at the left of the boxes on the left side of the table and at the right of the boxes on the right side. The subgroup elements in each case are on the opposite side of their boxes.

In the next chapter we shall see that atoms undergo chemical reactions in an attempt to acquire an electronic structure duplicating that of one of the inert gases. This duplication cannot always be accomplished by the subgroup elements. However, the elements whose symbols appear at the left of their boxes attempt to acquire the electronic structure of the inert gas in the same horizontal row at the left of the table. Those whose symbols are on the right side of their boxes try to acquire the structure of the inert gas at the right of the table.

The elements are arranged in the short form of the periodic table in accordance with the rule that the symbol of each element should be placed in its box on the side nearest to the nearest inert gas. An exception is necessary in the case of carbon, C, and silicon, Si, because they are equidistant from two inert gases. Their symbols are accordingly placed in the center of their boxes. This leaves doubt as to which sequence of the remaining Group IV elements (Ti, Zr, Hf; or Ge, Sn, Pb) constitutes the balance of the main group. The discussion of the Group IV elements in a later chapter will show that the chemical properties of this group of elements also reflect this uncertainty.

QUESTIONS AND PROBLEMS

1. What are the fundamental units of matter? How do they compare in weight, charge, location in an atom, importance in chemical reactions?

2. Which of these particles are deflected in magnetic or electrical fields? Which cause ionization and fog tracks in cloud chambers? Give reasons for your answers.

3. What are some common uses of "flowing" electrons?

4. How can beams of electrons, protons, and neutrons be created and accelerated?

5. Compare the nucleus and the atom that contains it with respect to size, mass, charge, constitution.

6. Why were heavy atoms selected as targets and alpha particles selected as projectiles in scattering experiments? What other highly accelerated common particle might serve equally well in obtaining similar evidence?

7. Distinguish between atomic number and atomic weight. How are x-ray wave lengths related to atomic number and electronic structure?

8. Define an element on the basis of its atomic number. Define an isotope of an element. What part of the structure of the atom and, in particular, what particles vary in the different isotopes of an element?

9. Distinguish between fission, fusion, and radioactivity.

10. What significant structural information is given by the following symbols?

$$^{40}_{20}\text{Ca} \qquad ^{35}_{17}\text{Cl} \qquad ^{55}_{26}\text{Fe}$$

11. By means of nuclear symbols designate a different but reasonable isotope for each atom in the preceding question.

12. Why are atomic weights not simple whole numbers? How can mass spectrometer data give the correct atomic weight?

13. Distinguish between electron layer (level), electron orbital, high- and low-energy layer, high- and low-energy orbitals.

14. Consider the electron orbital types in the order: s, p, d, and f.
    a. Give the number and letter of the shell in which each orbital type first appears.
    b. What is the maximum number of orbitals of each type in any shell in which the orbital appears?
    c. What is the maximum number of electrons in a *single* orbital of each type?
    d. How does the complexity of orbitals vary with type?
    e. How does the energy of the orbitals (electrons) vary with orbital type in the *same* shell?

15. What is the significance of the following: $1s^2$; $4p^3$; $5d^8$?

16. Using energy level and orbital symbols, describe the complete electronic structure of aluminum (at. no. 13); bromine (at. no. 35).

17. Rearrange all the orbital symbols for the electron structures in question 16 so that when read from left to right they will be in order of increasing orbital energy.

18. Stable electron configurations pertain to a consistent characteristic structure of the outer electron shell. What is this structure? What class of elements display it? What single exception is there?

19. Show the complete electronic structure of the following atoms by as many methods (diagrams, shell symbols, orbital symbols, etc.) as you can:

$$_{11}^{22}\text{Na} \qquad _{17}^{35}\text{Cl} \qquad _{38}^{88}\text{Sr}$$

20. What is an ion? What is meant by ionization potential? Which of the elements in question 19 would you predict has the highest and which the lowest ionization potential?

21. How in general does ionization potential vary with increasing atomic number in a horizontal row of the periodic table? In a vertical row?

22. On the basis of the long form of the periodic table, generalize with regard to:
a. Group number and outer electron shell structure.
b. Period number and number of electron shells.
c. Distinction between main and subgroups.

23. In what important ways does the short form of the periodic table differ from the long form?

4

Interaction between atoms

4.1. Valence Electrons

We have seen that an atom consists of a positive nucleus surrounded by negative electrons arranged in a systematic way in successive shells. When the number of electrons in an atom is equal to the number of protons in its nucleus, it is electrically neutral. We might expect a neutral atom to be stable and unalterable except by violent means, but this is usually not so. If it were, there would be only some hundred different substances, one for each kind of atom, and no substance would ever change into anything else. Actually, most kinds of atoms can *react* with other atoms by gaining, losing, or sharing electrons. As a result of these reactions the atoms of our hundred-odd elements *combine* with atoms of the same element to form polyatomic molecules, and with atoms of other elements to form molecules of literally millions of compounds.

Long before much was known about atomic structure, the word **valence** was coined to designate the forces which hold atoms together in compounds. We now know that valence forces involve the transfer or sharing of electrons by atoms. Only certain electron orbitals can enter into these reactions, notably the *s* and *p* orbitals in the outermost shell. For this reason the outer electron shell of any atom is called the **valence shell,** and the electrons in it are called **valence electrons.** Occasionally *d* electrons in the shell next to the valence shell also act as valence electrons, since their energy is close to that of the electrons in the outer shell (Fig. 3.11).

4.2. Atomic Kernels

If an atom is stripped of its valence electrons the structure remaining is referred to as the **kernel** of the atom. It can be seen from the accompanying diagram that the charge on the kernel is always positive and is

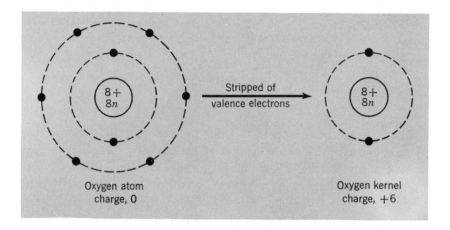

Oxygen atom
charge, 0

Oxygen kernel
charge, +6

equal in magnitude to the number of valence electrons. The kernel structure is important because the ease with which electrons leave or enter the valence shell during chemical reactions depends upon the size of the kernel and its charge. A kernel with a charge of $+6$ will attract electrons more strongly than one with a charge of $+2$ if the kernels are of comparable size.

Table 4.1 shows the atomic and kernel configurations of the elements in the first three rows (series) of the periodic table. Note that from left to right on a horizontal row the charge on each kernel increases successively by 1. In addition, the kernels decrease successively in radius. Both these factors increase the force with which the kernels attract valence electrons. In the vertical columns (similar kernel charge) the radii increase as we go down the column. This decreases the attractive force because the same size of charge is exerted over successively greater distances.

TABLE 4.1. Atomic Kernels of the First Three Series

		IA	IIA	IIIA	IVA	VA	VIA	VIIA	VIIIA
						Group Number			
First Series	Element							H	He
	Atomic configuration							1	2
	Kernel configuration							0	0
	Kernel charge							+1	+2
Second Series	Element	Li	Be	B	C	N	O	F	Ne
	Atomic configuration	2-1	2-2	2-3	2-4	2-5	2-6	2-7	2-8
	Kernel configuration	2-0	2-0	2-0	2-0	2-0	2-0	2-0	2-0
	Kernel charge	+1	+2	+3	+4	+5	+6	+7	+8
	Radius, A.	0.60	0.31	0.20	0.15	0.11	0.09	0.07	0.05
Third Series	Element	Na	Mg	Al	Si	P	S	Cl	Ar
	Atomic configuration	2-8-1	2-8-2	2-8-3	2-8-4	2-8-5	2-8-6	2-8-7	2-8-8
	Kernel configuration	2-8-0	2-8-0	2-8-0	2-8-0	2-8-0	2-8-0	2-8-0	2-8-0
	Kernel charge	+1	+2	+3	+4	+5	+6	+7	+8
	Radius, A.	0.95	0.65	0.50	0.41	0.34	0.29	0.26	0.23

The transition elements in the long periods introduce complexities because the electron configuration of the kernels changes in a given horizontal row instead of remaining constant as in the cases already considered. This is due to the fact that d (and in some cases f) electrons are being *added to the kernel and not to the valence shell.* Therefore, for each proton added to the nucleus an electron is added to the kernel and the kernel charge remains constant (generally $+2$). Only when one or more d electrons are lost (this happens in many cases) does a kernel of a transition element have a charge greater than $+2$.

4.3. Atoms with Complete Valence Shells—The Inert Gases

When two atoms collide with sufficient force so that their valence shells overlap, an electron in the valence shell of one atom may at the same time be in a previously unfilled orbital of the other atom. When the atoms separate, the electron will go with the atom whose kernel attracts it more strongly. The atoms of Group VIIIA never lose any electrons in this manner, because no other atom has a kernel charge of $+8$. (The charge on the helium kernel is only $+2$, but this is more than counterbalanced by the closeness of the valence shell to the nucleus.)

It is as impossible for Group VIIIA elements to take electrons from other atoms as it is for them to lose electrons. The s and p orbitals in their valence shells are full. An additional electron would have to go into the next shell, just as is the case in the Group IA elements that immediately follow the Group VIIIA elements. This would start a new valence shell, and all of the original atom would have to be considered as the kernel. The charge on such a kernel would be 0; hence there would be nothing to hold the electron.

As a matter of fact, Group VIIIA elements form only monatomic molecules and have practically no chemical properties. That is, they form no stable compounds. For this reason they are appropriately named the **inert gases.**

4.4. Electronegativity

The intensity of the attraction exerted by the kernel upon electrons in the valence shell of an atom determines whether the atom will gain or lose electrons when it collides with other atoms. This property of an atom is called its **electronegativity.** Electronegativity values for the elements, measured in *arbitrary* units, range from 0 up to 4.*

The positive charge that is responsible for the electronegativity of an atom is located in its nucleus and is numerically equal to its atomic number. However, each electron in the kernel of the atom screens one unit of that charge from the electrons in the valence shell. (However, *d* electrons screen only 0.85 of a charge each. This is so because a *d* electron ranges so far in and out from its *average* distance that 15 per cent of the time it is actually farther from the nucleus than a valence electron is on the average.) Thus across a series of the periodic table each increase in kernel charge, corresponding to an increase in atomic number, produces a considerable increase in electronegativity. And even though the kernel charge remains constant from one transition element to the next, there is a small increase in electronegativity because the effect of the added nuclear charge is only partially balanced in the valence shell by the added *d* electron.

Another factor which affects the electronegativity of an atom is its size. The smaller the atom the nearer its valence shell is to its nucleus, and the more powerful, therefore, is the attractive force exerted by the nuclear charge upon an electron in the valence shell. For this reason the lithium kernel (radius 0.60 A.) is more electronegative than the sodium kernel (radius 0.95 A.), even though their charges are both +1. The size of the atomic kernels increases as we go down a column, and the electro-

---

* A complete table of electronegativities is given in the appendix.

negativity accordingly decreases in the main groups. In the subgroups the size increases much more slowly and its effect on the electronegativity is more than counterbalanced by an incompletely understood factor, possibly a decrease in the shielding effect of $4d$ and $5d$ electrons as compared with $3d$ electrons. The size of atomic kernels decreases from left to right through any given periodic series. Thus two factors contribute toward increasing the electronegativity of such a series of elements—the decreasing size of the kernel and its increasing charge. These systematic variations in electronegativity may be summarized as follows:

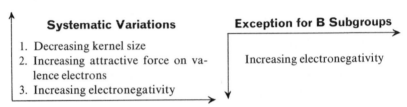

Systematic Variations
1. Decreasing kernel size
2. Increasing attractive force on valence electrons
3. Increasing electronegativity

Exception for B Subgroups

Increasing electronegativity

The least electronegative of the elements is francium. The most electronegative is fluorine. There is a striking difference in appearance between elements with low and high electronegativity; the former are metals, the latter are non-metals. Elements with an electronegativity of around 2 are intermediate in properties. The luster which characterizes metals is due to the relatively loose electrons in the outer shell. We shall see later that the chemical properties of metals are due to the same cause.

4.5. Electron Transfer

When atoms of a typical metal (low electronegativity) collide with atoms of a typical non-metal (high electronegativity) they lose all their valence electrons to the atoms of the non-metal. Each non-metal atom gains enough electrons to satisfy the deficiency in the partly filled p orbitals in its outer shell, and thereby attains the same electronic structure as the inert gas which comes at the end of its series. Fluorine, for example, takes electrons from sodium. When a sodium atom loses its valence electron, the kernel which remains has the same structure as the preceding inert gas, neon, but a charge of $+1$. When a fluorine atom gains an electron it attains the structure of the following inert gas (also neon in this case) but it has a charge of -1. Although Na^+ and F^- have the same electronic structure as neon, they differ from it, as well as between themselves, in both size and charge. These facts are diagrammed in Fig. 4.1.

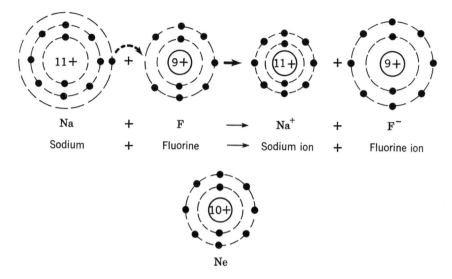

Fig. 4.1. Formation of Na^+ and F^- ions by electron transfer. Both ions have electronic configurations similar to the atom of the inert gas neon.

Note that positively and negatively charged particles (ions) are formed simultaneously, and that by the very nature of the process of formation the total charge on all the negative ions formed must equal the total charge on all the positive ions formed, so that the resultant product as a whole will still be neutral electrically. The positive and negative charges attract each other strongly; hence a solid is formed, instead of a gas like neon.

Except that 2 electrons are involved, so that the resulting ionic charges are $+2$ and -2, the statements that were made about sodium and fluorine apply to magnesium and oxygen.

$$Mg + O \rightarrow Mg^{++} + O^{--}$$

The metal attains the structure of the preceding inert gas (neon) and the non-metal attains that of the following inert gas (also neon). This is typical of non-metals and of metals with kernels of the inert gas type.

This behavior can be made clearer by using diagrams devised by G. N. Lewis, who was the first (1916) to relate the numbers of electrons gained or lost in such reactions to the structure of the inert gases. He let the symbol of the element stand for the kernel, and put around it as many dots as there are electrons in the valence shell. With these dot symbols, typical electron transfer reactions can be diagrammed as follows:

$$\text{Na} \cdot \; + \; :\overset{\cdot\cdot}{\underset{\cdot\cdot}{\text{Cl}}} \cdot \; \longrightarrow \; \text{Na}^+ \; + \; :\overset{\cdot\cdot}{\underset{\cdot\cdot}{\text{Cl}}}:^-$$

$$\text{Mg}: \; + \; :\overset{\cdot\cdot}{\underset{\cdot\cdot}{\text{O}}} \; \longrightarrow \; \text{Mg}^{++} \; + \; :\overset{\cdot\cdot}{\underset{\cdot\cdot}{\text{O}}}:^{--}$$

$$2\text{Al}: \; + \; 3:\overset{\cdot\cdot}{\underset{\cdot\cdot}{\text{O}}} \; \longrightarrow \; 2\text{Al}^{+3} \; + \; 3:\overset{\cdot\cdot}{\underset{\cdot\cdot}{\text{O}}}:^{--}$$

Note that in each case the number of electrons lost by the metal atoms is equal to the number gained by the non-metal atoms. This is essential, for electrons are never created or destroyed in chemical reactions.

4.6. Ions

Atoms which have lost or gained electrons are of course no longer electrically neutral, but have a net positive or negative charge. These charges are indicated in the examples in the preceding section by small superscript plus or minus sign. A *charged atom* is called an **ion.** We shall see below that polyatomic as well as monatomic molecules can become ions.

All the properties of ions except weight are entirely different from those of the atoms from which they were formed. (The weight of the electrons gained or lost is negligible.) The luster of a metal vanishes with the loss of the loose electrons which caused it; so does the ability to lose electrons which characterizes metals chemically. The size of the metal ion is less than that of the neutral atom because the outermost electron shell is no longer present (Fig. 4.1). Similarly, the ability of the non-metal atom to take up electrons is nonexistent in the ion, which now has 8 electrons that completely fill the four low-energy orbitals in its valence shell. The radius of a negative ion is larger than that of the atom from which it was formed (Fig. 4.1) because of the additional mutual repulsion of the larger number of electrons that now occupy the valence shell.

Uncharged atoms have varying degrees of attraction for each other, but ions of like charge repel each other violently. It is possible for a substance to be composed entirely of a single kind of uncharged atom; an example is metallic sodium. But it is absolutely impossible for a substance to be composed of a single kind of ion. On the other hand, oppositely charged ions have a strong attraction for each other; hence actual ionic substances always contain both positive and negative ions in alternating arrangement. The total number of positive charges must be exactly equal to the total number of negative charges, so that the substance as a whole is electrically neutral. Thus for every two Al^{+3} ions there must be three $:\overset{\cdot\cdot}{\underset{\cdot\cdot}{\text{O}}}:^{--}$ ions to produce electrical neutrality.

4.7. Electrovalence

A substance that is composed of different kinds of atoms is a compound; hence the forces that hold oppositely charged ions together are valence forces. For obvious reasons, this kind of valence is called **electrovalence.** An ion is said to have an electrovalence equal in *number* and *sign* to its charge. Thus the ions Li^+ and Na^+ have valences of $+1$, and $:\ddot{F}:^-$ and $:\ddot{Cl}:^-$ ions have valences of -1. All four may be called **univalent** ions. Mg^{++} ion has a valence of $+2$, $:\ddot{O}:^{--}$ ion of -2; both are **bivalent.** Al^{+3} is a **trivalent** positive ion. The electrovalence of any uncharged molecule is zero.

Compounds which display electrovalence are commonly called **ionic compounds.** This is true even when they are composed of polyatomic ions whose atoms are held together by another type of valence that is described in the next section. Nearly all the positive ions are metals, but the negative ions always contain non-metallic atoms. Most of the compounds with which we shall be concerned are of the ionic type. The most important and familiar ionic compound is common salt, composed of sodium and chloride ions. The word "salt" has been generalized until it has become a synonym for ionic compound.

4.8. Electron Sharing

In illustrating electron transfer at the end of Section 4.5 single atoms of chlorine and oxygen were used for the sake of simplicity. As a matter of fact, it is impossible for monatomic molecules of elements with high electronegativity to exist under any ordinary conditions. When two such atoms collide, electrons which have become part of both atoms at the same time are strongly attracted to *both* kernels. The atoms cannot separate because neither kernel will release the jointly held electrons. The result, in the simplest case, is a diatomic molecule.

It is impossible for there to be more than 2 electrons in one orbital. When two atoms of an inert gas collide, there is no interpenetration of the outer electron shells. If any region of space contained filled orbitals of two different atoms at the same time, each orbital would have 4 electrons in it. This is prevented by a violent repulsion that develops. But if two orbitals overlap which contain between them only 2 electrons, we have the situation described in the preceding paragraph. The 2 electrons continue to occupy both orbitals at once. An electron pair under the influence of two nuclei naturally occupies space whose shape differs from what it would be if the electron pair were governed by a single nucleus. A two-center orbital such as this is called a **molecular orbital.**

Fig. 4.2 shows the formation of a molecular orbital. The kernel of each atom is shown, but only one orbital of the valence shell. Note in the last diagram how the electron cloud is condensed because of being attracted by two nuclei instead of only one. This dense electron cloud attracts the

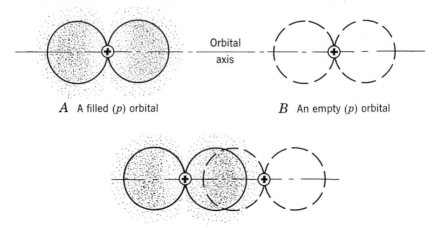

A A filled (*p*) orbital *B* An empty (*p*) orbital

C The two atoms collide along the axes of the *p* orbitals

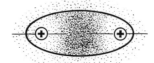

D The electron cloud is drawn down in between the two nuclei

Fig. 4.2. Formation of a molecular orbital. The small circles ⊕ represent kernels of atoms, not to scale. In the formation of molecular orbitals the kernel charges may range from +4 to +7. These figures represent cross sections of three-dimensional electron clouds which are symmetrical about the horizontal axis. The outer lines bound a region large enough to contain 90 per cent of the electron cloud.

two nuclei as strongly as they attract it, and constitutes a strong **bond** between the two atoms. This attraction is much stronger than that between an ion in a crystal and the surrounding oppositely charged ions because the charges are so much closer together.

In Fig. 4.2 one orbital was filled and one was empty. The figure could just as well have shown 1 electron in each orbital instead of 2 in one and none in the other. In that case the distribution of the electron cloud in *A* would have been the same, but only half as dense. *A* and *B* would look exactly like each other, and *D,* the completed bond, would be identical with the D in the figure. A chemical bond requires one orbital in each atom and 2 electrons; how it is formed is immaterial.

4.9. Non-Polar and Polar Bonds

In any chemically uncombined atom each electron is on one side of the nucleus for as long as it is on the other; each orbital is symmetrical about the nucleus. The center of charge of each electron cloud, and therefore of the entire electron system, is in the nucleus—although there is no electron in the nucleus—just as the center of gravity of a tennis ball is at its center, which is empty. The centers of positive and negative charge are thus at the same point. Such atoms constitute a **non-polar molecule.** Inert gas molecules are excellent examples.

In a molecule composed of two identical atoms, such as that of the element chlorine, the center of charge of the bonding electron pair is not at either nucleus, but exactly midway between them (Fig. 4.2D). Since the center of positive charge is at the same point, this molecule is also non-polar. The bond between two identical atoms is called a **non-polar bond.**

Dot symbols are convenient for representing molecules of atoms that are covalently bonded. Each electron pair bond is represented by a pair of dots placed between the symbols of the atoms it joins, thus:

$$:\overset{..}{\underset{..}{Cl}}\cdot\ +\ \cdot\overset{..}{\underset{..}{Cl}}:\ \longrightarrow\ :\overset{..}{\underset{..}{Cl}}:\overset{..}{\underset{..}{Cl}}:$$

In a dot formula all the valence electrons are shown. Since each chlorine atom has 7 valence electrons (Group VIIA), the dot formula of the molecule shows 14 electrons, even though only one pair is used in forming the bond. In the case of an ion, the number of electrons shown differs from the number originally present in the component atoms. There will be one less electron for each positive charge, or one more electron for each negative charge, as the case may be.

If an electron pair bond joins two atoms of unequal electronegativity, the electron distribution in the bond will not be centered between the atoms. The electron cloud will be denser near the more electronegative atom, and its center of charge will be somewhere between the mid-point of the bond and the nucleus of the more electronegative atom (Fig. 4.3). The centers of positive and negative charge will no longer coincide. An electrical field tends to turn such a molecule just as a magnetic field turns a compass needle. The molecule may be said to have a positive and a negative pole just as the compass needle has a north and a south pole.

The molecule is thus a **polar molecule.** The bond is called a **polar bond,** and is said to have some **ionic character.** A pair of oppositely charged ions constitutes the ultimate in polar character. A difference of 1.7 in electronegativity between the atoms of a diatomic molecule results in a bond which is 50 per cent ionic in character, its center of charge being halfway between the midpoint and the nucleus of the more electronegative atom. No distinction between polar and non-polar molecules is made in dot formulas. If the difference in electronegativity is 2.0, the more electronegative atom is best thought of as a negative ion which has been considerably deformed (polarized) by the neighboring positive ion.

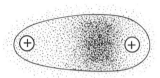

Fig. 4.3. A covalent bond about 40 per cent ionic in character.

4.10. Covalence

An electron pair shared by two atoms constitutes a bond that holds the atoms together in a molecule. The forces in electron pair bonds therefore constitute a second type of valence force. This type of valence is called **covalence** because of its cooperative nature. The covalence of an atom is the number of electron pair bonds it shares with other atoms. Since this cannot be a negative number, it is not necessary to specify the sign. In the molecule : C̈l : C̈l : each atom has a covalence of 1 because one electron pair bond (shown as the pair of dots between the chlorine

atoms) is shared by each atom. In carbon tetrachloride : C̈l : C̈ : C̈l : the

$$: \ddot{C}l :$$
$$: \ddot{C}l :$$

chlorine atoms still have a covalence of 1, but the covalence of the carbon atom is 4.

We saw in Section 4.5 that a non-metal atom takes enough electrons from metal atoms to give its valence shell the regular inert gas configuration of ns^2np^6, where n is the number of the valence shell. These 8 electrons are commonly known as the **octet.** When a non-metal atom reacts with other non-metal atoms, each atom usually *completes its octet* by forming as many covalent bonds as the electrons that are needed to complete the octet. Each atom furnishes 1 electron to each bond. For example, fluorine, chlorine, and iodine, each with 7 valence electrons, need 1 electron to complete the octet; so they each form a single covalent bond with other atoms in order to gain this electron (Fig. 4.4b,c,e,f). Oxygen,

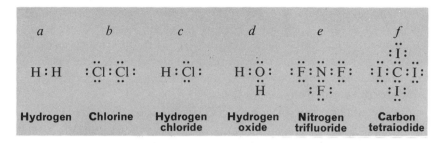

Fig. 4.4. Dot formulas illustrating normal covalence.

with 6 valence electrons, needs 2 electrons to complete the octet and therefore forms two covalent bonds (Fig. 4.4*d*). Nitrogen with 5 valence electrons, and carbon with 4, form three and four covalent bonds respectively (Fig. 4.4*e,f*). It will be seen, then, that the *normal covalence* of a

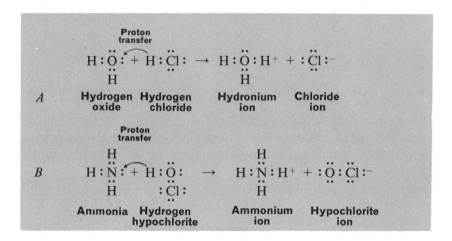

Fig. 4.5 Proton transfer reactions resulting in formation of ions.

non-metal atom is 8 − *v*, where *v* is the number of valence electrons. For hydrogen the normal covalence is 2 − *v*, because the first shell has no *p* orbitals.

4.11. Coordinate Covalence

In compounds of the non-metals in Groups V, VI, and VII, the transfer of a proton (H⁺, the nucleus of a hydrogen atom) from one pair of electrons to another frequently results in a covalence higher or lower than the normal covalence. Note that as the result of this process the molecules in Fig. 4.5 become ions. In that figure the oxygen in hydronium ion has a covalence of 3 (normal covalence is 2), whereas in hypochlorite ion its covalence is 1. Nitrogen (normal covalence is 3) has a covalence of 4 in ammonium ion.

The covalence of an atom may also be increased by an oxygen atom $(:\ddot{O}\,)$ being attached to a "lone" (unshared) pair of electrons in its octet. From one to four oxygen atoms can be attached to the four lone pairs in the chloride ion (Fig. 4.6a). In the new ions resulting from these attachments (b, c, d, e) chlorine has covalences of 1, 2, 3, and 4, respectively.

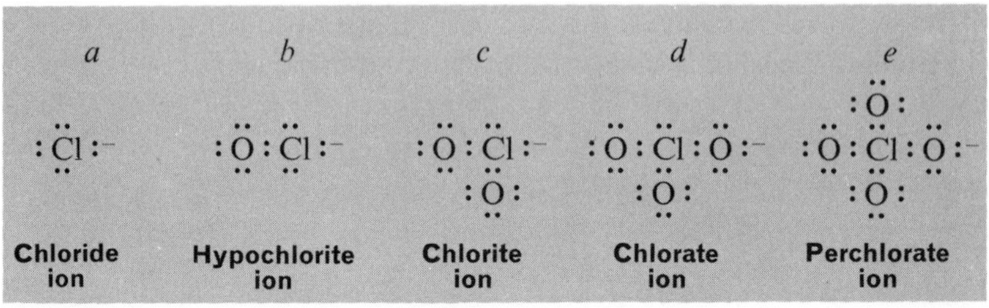

Fig. 4.6. The bonding of oxygen by coordinate covalence on chloride ion.

The addition of an uncharged oxygen atom has no effect on the charge of the ion, which remains -1. The electrovalence of the ions of any series such as this, is the negative of the normal covalence of the central atom, i.e., $v - 8$.

When one atom furnishes both electrons for a covalent bond, the process is called **coordination.** A bond formed by coordination is often called a **coordinate covalent bond,** but is no different from a bond formed in the "normal" manner. The atom which furnishes the electron pair is called the **donor.** Naturally, the higher the electronegativity of an atom, the more reluctantly it acts as a donor, because this means the loss of some of its share of the electron pair it donates for bond formation. On the other hand, a negative charge on the molecule containing the donor atom helps greatly in coordinating a proton (or any positive ion). A molecule which can coordinate a proton is called a **base.** A molecule which can give a proton to a base is called an **acid.**

Compounds in which *only* covalence is displayed, such as water, H_2O, hydrogen chloride, HCl, and ammonia, NH_3, are commonly called **covalent compounds.** Covalence is always shown in the chemical union between non-metal atoms, whether in compounds such as those just mentioned (uncharged) or in polyatomic ions (charged molecules). It also characterizes compounds formed by non-metals with transition metals, many of which display noteworthy ability to coordinate bases.

4.12. Oxidation Number

Commonly included under the general term valence is the **oxidation number** of an atom. This is an extremely useful tool in discussing chemical phenomena. In fact, when a statement is made about the valence of an atom in a molecule, it is always the oxidation number that is meant unless otherwise specified. The oxidation number of an atom is the charge it would have if each covalent bond were broken in such a way as to give the shared electron pair to the more electronegative atom, or 1 electron each to atoms of equal electronegativity. The oxidation number of an atom of a free element is always zero, because any electron pairs that are shared in its molecules obviously are shared by atoms of equal electronegativity and are therefore to be divided equally. If an atom shares no electron pairs (i.e., if the molecule is monatomic), its oxidation number is its actual charge, and therefore the same as its electrovalence. Thus the oxidation numbers of Na^+, He, and Cl^- are $+1, 0$, and -1, respectively.

Since oxidation numbers are assigned on the basis of differences in electronegativity, it is useful to have some idea of the relative electronegativities of the most common non-metals. In the following list the non-metals are arranged in the order of increasing electronegativity, bracketed groups being practically identical: Si, B, [P, H], [C, S, I], Br, [Cl, N], O, and F. By applying the information in this list to the compounds in Fig. 4.5 we see that the oxidation numbers of all the hydrogen atoms are $+1$, and those of all the oxygen atoms are -2. Nitrogen has the oxidation number -3 in both ammonia and ammonium ion, whereas for chlorine it is -1 in chloride ion and $+1$ in hypochlorite ion. The other oxidation numbers of chlorine—$+3, +5, +7$—are evident from Fig. 4.6c, d, e.

Most oxidation numbers may be assigned without referring to a table of electronegativities if the following rules are obeyed:

Rule 1. Since the electronegativity of oxygen is extremely high—3.5 (surpassed only by that of fluorine)—it is safe to assume that oxygen is always more electronegative than any other kind of atom to which it may be bonded covalently, and assign to it the oxidation number -2. (Exception, oxygen fluoride, OF_2.)

Rule 2. Since hydrogen is lower in electronegativity than any of the elements with which it commonly forms covalent bonds, it may regularly be assigned the oxidation number $+1$. (Hydrides of silicon, boron, and phosphorus are rarely encountered.)

Rule 3. The algebraic sum of the oxidation numbers of the atoms in an ion must equal the electrovalence of the ion. Thus without any knowledge of the electronegativity of manganese, we can say that its oxidation number in permanganate ion, MnO_4^-, is $+7$.

TABLE 4.2. **Valences and Oxidation Numbers of Some Elements**

Molecule	Electrovalence	Covalence	Oxidation Number
Cl_2 (chlorine)	0	1 (Cl)	0 (Cl)
N_2 (nitrogen)	0	3 (N)	0 (N)
HI (hydrogen iodide)	0	1 (H)	$+1$ (H)
		1 (I)	-1 (I)
H_2S (hydrogen sulfide)	0	1 (H)	$+1$ (H)
		2 (S)	-2 (S)
H_2O_2 (hydrogen peroxide)	0	1 (H)	$+1$ (H)
		2 (O)	-1 (O)
CO_2 (carbon dioxide)	0	4 (C)	$+4$ (C)
		2 (O)	-2 (O)
ClO_4^- (perchlorate ion)	-1	4 (Cl)	$+7$ (Cl)
		1 (O)	-2 (O)
Na^+Cl^-	$+1$ (Na)	0 (Na)	$+1$ (Na)
	-1 (Cl)	0 (Cl)	-1 (Cl)

Rule 4. The algebraic sum of the oxidation numbers of the atoms in an uncharged molecule must be zero. Thus we have $+6$ sulfur in H_2SO_4, sulfuric acid.

Rule 5. The oxidation number is not affected by any proton transfer.

Test your understanding of the three kinds of valence by computing for yourself all the valence numbers in Table 4.2.

When people talk about covalence they regularly use the specific word "covalence"; but in other cases they may use simply "valence" because the context makes the meaning clear. The only kind of valence an ion can have is electrovalence. A question regarding the valence of an atom in a polyatomic molecule can only refer to its oxidation number; if covalence were meant, that word would be used.

4.13. Multiple Bonds

In Fig. 4.2, two atoms were shown colliding along the line of the axes of a *p* orbital in each atom. The two *p* orbitals met end-on, overlapped, and formed a molecular orbital. This is not the only way two *p* orbitals can collide. They can also collide sideways, with their axes parallel.

Remember that there are *three p* orbitals, with their axes all at right angles to each other. If we think of the axis of the bond in Fig. 4.2 as be-

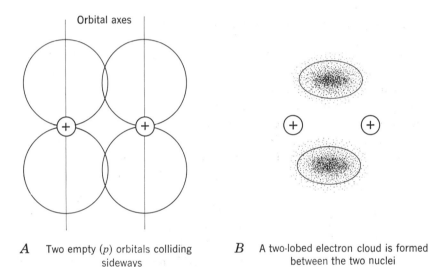

A   Two empty (*p*) orbitals colliding
sideways

B   A two-lobed electron cloud is formed
between the two nuclei

Fig. 4.7.   Formation of a second bond. The bond along the **x** axis (Fig. 4.2**D**) is omitted for the sake of simplicity.

ing the *x* axis of the molecule, then each atom has a second *p* orbital that runs along its *y* axis, and a third orbital, perpendicular to the plane of the paper, along the *z* axis. If the kernels of the atoms are not too large, a pair of these orbitals (one from each atom, in the same plane) will overlap in *two* regions, as shown in Fig. 4.7*A*. If each atom has an electron to contribute, a new kind of molecular orbital will be formed. Because it has two lobes, like a *p* orbital, this second bond is called a π (pi) bond. Similarly, the single-lobed bond along the molecular axis is called a σ (sigma) bond, after the single-lobed *s* orbital.

If the remaining *p* orbital in each atom is not otherwise used, a second π bond can also be formed between the same two atoms, with one lobe above the plane of the paper and one below, both parallel to the *x* axis. A **double bond** consists of one σ bond and one π bond; a **triple bond** consists of one σ bond and two π bonds. A π bond is never present without a σ bond. Multiple-bonded atoms are drawn more closely together and held more tightly than single-bonded atoms because of the larger amount of negative electricity between their positively charged kernels. Multiple bonding is very common between atoms of carbon, nitrogen, and oxygen. It is less common between one of these atoms and an atom in the following (third) period, and seldom occurs between two third-period atoms.

4.14. Determination of Molecular and Crystal Structure

Spectroscopic methods of investigation are utilized for the purpose of determining the structure of molecules and crystals. Bonded atoms can be set into various types of vibration by an impinging light beam, provided the light has wave lengths whose frequencies are compatible with the natural vibrational frequencies of the atoms.* The vibrational frequency which occurs between bonded atoms is dependent upon the type of bond as well as upon the nature of the atoms. For example, the frequency of a C—O bond, $(2.46-2.64)$ × 10^{13} cycles/sec., is different from that of a C=O bond, $(5.13-5.25)$ × 10^{13} cycles/sec.

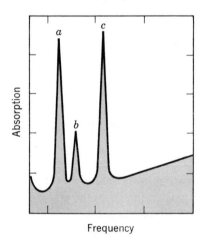

Frequency

Fig. 4.8. An absorption spectrum showing absorption at three frequencies.

The impinging light, covering a limited band of frequencies or wave lengths, strikes the liquid, gas, or solid which absorbs particular frequencies. An analysis of the transmitted light indicates which frequencies (wave lengths) are absorbed. A plot of the results is called an **absorption spectrum** (Fig. 4.8).

The absorption peaks at frequencies *a*, *b*, and *c* indicate the existence of specific bonds whose vibrational frequencies correspond to these.

Infrared (7000 A. to 20μ) and ultraviolet (2500 to 4000 A.) spectra are used in these investigations. Appro-

---

*Wave length is related to frequency according to the equation $\lambda = c/\nu$, where λ is the wave length, ν is frequency, and c is the velocity of light.

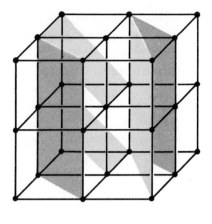

Fig. 4.9. A two-dimensional array of crystal components.

Fig. 4.10. Some planes in a crystal. (Such a crystal extends far beyond the limits of this figure so that the number of possible sets of parallel planes becomes very large.)

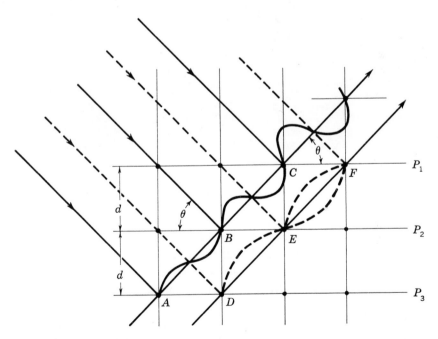

Fig. 4.11. X-ray diffraction in a crystal by atoms **A**, **B**, and **C**, whose waves are in phase. If the wave length is twice as long (atoms **D** and **E**), the waves will be out of phase and will cancel each other.

priate mathematical treatment of the results provides quantitative information regarding both the strength and nature of bonds and the general structure of the molecule.

Investigations of crystal structure furnish information about the size of atoms, ions, and molecules in general, as well as their arrangement relative to each other in crystals. X-ray and electron diffraction techniques are utilized mainly for studies of this sort. An electron beam is similar to an x-ray beam, for an electron is wavelike in nature, its wave length depending upon the voltage used to propel it. The higher the volt-

age the shorter the wave length. X-ray wave lengths are controlled by selecting suitable sources of x-rays, i.e., the element that serves as the target in the x-ray tube. The larger the atomic number, the shorter the wave length that can be obtained. The wave lengths used in these investigations are on the order of atomic diameters in magnitude (up to about 2 A.).

The components in all crystals are arranged in a systematic and symmetrical array. This is shown in two dimensions in Fig. 4.9. The solid lines originate from a point O and pass through points in the crystal that are symmetrically spaced along a given line but differently spaced

Fig. 4.12. X-ray diffraction photographs. (Left) a typical oscillation photograph of a salt; (right) a typical powder photograph of a metallic oxide. ▶

from line to line depending upon the direction through the crystal. The dashed lines parallel to the solid lines have the same symmetry of points as the original lines. However, the distance d between the parallel lines varies as the direction of the lines varies from the origin, O. In three dimensions the lines become sheets or planes (Fig. 4.10). The distance d between parallel planes is called the **interplanar distance** or **spacing.**

When x-rays strike the components of a crystal they radiate rays whose wave length is identical to that of the incident beam. Various results may be observed with these "reflected" rays, depending upon the orientation of planes with respect to the incident beam, the interplanar spacings, and the kinds of atoms and ions which make up the radiation centers in the crystal. The typical situation illustrated in Fig. 4.11 shows an edgewise view of three parallel planes (P_1, P_2, and P_3) with interplanar spacing, d. The incident x-ray beam strikes the crystal at an angle θ and diffracts (reflects) at the same angle provided the necessary conditions for diffraction are present. If the distance between A and B (and therefore between B and C) is one wave length or an integral multiple of one wave length, the waves from A, B, and C will coincide, crest for crest and trough for trough. Waves satisfying this condition are spoken of as being **in phase.** The resultant diffracted wave will be fortified each step of the way by its coincidence in phase with the other waves along its path. However, should the atoms be half a wave length apart or an integral multiple of this—e.g., D, E, F—the waves originating at D and E will be **out of phase** and will cancel each other. Thus the intensities of the diffracted ray may be zero or at a maximum, or fall between these extremes. Photographs registering the reflected waves (Fig. 4.12), properly interpreted and mathematically analyzed, make possible the ultimate determination of the crystal structure.

The preceding discussion embodies only a brief consideration of these methods of investigation. The complete investigation involves many other factors and techniques that are too complicated for presentation in an elementary text.

QUESTIONS AND PROBLEMS

1. Define valence electrons; valence shell; atomic kernel.
2. How do kernel structures of main-group elements vary with horizontal and vertical progression in the periodic system? Describe the effect of this variation on size of kernels and electronegativity.
3. Compare the atomic structures and kernels of atoms with atomic numbers of 5, 7, 9, 11, 12. Which of these elements is the least electronegative? The most electronegative? Which kernel is smallest? Largest?

4. How does the electronegativity of a metal compare with that of a non-metal?
5. Define electrovalence.
6. Diagram the electron transfer reactions between the following atoms, using Lewis dot formulas:

$$Na + Cl \qquad\qquad Al + O$$
$$Mg + F \qquad\qquad Ca + I$$

7. State the electrovalence of each ion in question 6.
8. a. How many electrons are needed per bond?
   b. Describe the role of the orbital in such bond formation and any restrictions upon it.
9. a. What is a polar bond? A non-polar bond?
   b. Give examples of each by means of dot symbols.
   c. What is meant by the "ionic character of covalent bonds"? What role does electronegativity play in this?
10. a. Define the octet rule of normal covalence.
    b. What is the normal covalence of hydrogen, oxygen, nitrogen, chlorine?
    c. Distinguish between normal covalence and coordinate covalence.
11. Illustrate with dot formulas the proton transfer in the following reactions:

$$HCl + NH_3$$
$$HBr + H_2O$$

12. a. In question 11, where is coordinate covalence established?
    b. Which atoms are donors for the coordinate covalence?
    c. Which molecules act as bases?
13. Review all the molecules in questions 1 to 12 and state each oxidation number that is involved. Give reasons for your answer.
14. What are the oxidation numbers of the underlined elements?

$$\underline{P}O_4^{-3} \qquad HN\underline{O}_3 \qquad (\underline{Ba}^{++} + 2Cl^-) \qquad \underline{S}O_3^{--}$$

15. a. What is the difference, electronically, between covalent π bonds and σ bonds?
    b. Which types are present in multiple bonding between atoms? Which bond can exist without the other?

5

Formulas and equations, the language of chemistry

5.1. Introduction

Formulas are the *words* of chemistry. They are of fundamental importance because they specifically describe a molecule. Students frequently confuse formulas with equations. More than one formula is needed to write an equation, just as more than one word is needed to construct a sentence. **Equations** are the *sentences* of chemistry. They use formulas to tell what occurs.

Formulas that describe a molecule may be written in many ways. The particular one selected depends upon what facts are to be illustrated. We may wish to impart structural or electronic information about the molecule, or merely to state its chemical composition. The dot diagrams in Figs. 4.4 and 4.5 are typical electron formulas which designate the element and its valence electron structure. These are especially convenient whenever bonding or electron transfer phenomena are being considered. Ordinarily, however, the electrons are not shown, the symbol standing for the whole atom instead of just its kernel. For example, Cl^- is usually used for the formula of chloride ion instead of $: \overset{..}{\underset{..}{Cl}} :^-$.

5.2. Structural and Common Formulas

A formula that shows which atoms are bonded together is called a **structural formula.** Dot formulas are structural formulas. In a structural formula that is more frequently used, the bonding electron pairs are represented by short lines, one line for each pair of electrons involved in the bonding; the other valence electrons are omitted (Table 5.1).

TABLE 5.1. **Some Structural and Common Formulas**

Structural Formulas		Common Formulas
H:H	H—H	H_2
:Cl̈:Cl̈:	Cl—Cl	Cl_2
H:Ö: H	H—O │ H	H_2O
:Cl̈:Ö:⁻	Cl—O⁻	ClO^-
:Cl̈: :Cl̈:C:Cl̈: :Cl̈:	Cl │ Cl—C—Cl │ Cl	CCl_4
H :N̈:H H	H │ N—H │ H	NH_3

Common formulas make no attempt to show which atoms are connected by bonds. They simply list the atoms present in a molecule (Table 5.1). The symbols are usually written from left to right in order of increasing electronegativity. (NH_3 is an exception to this.) If the molecule contains more than one atom of a given kind, the number is shown by a subscript following the symbol of the element. If the molecule is an ion, its charge must be shown.

Both structural and common formulas tell not only the composition of a molecule, but also the number of atoms in it.

5.3. Molecular Formulas

A formula, structural or common, which describes the composition of an independent molecule is a **molecular formula.** Thus all the formulas in Table 5.1 are molecular formulas. All covalent compounds—e.g., NH_3, CCl_4, H_2O—are described by molecular formulas. Furthermore, all ions, regardless of charge, are molecules and hence are also represented by molecular formulas—e.g., Cl^-, ClO^-, NH_4^+, Al^{+3}. Molecular formulas are regularly used whenever the molecules are independently movable, i.e., when the substance is a gas or liquid or is in solution.

5.4. Empirical Formulas

Every chemical substance can be described by an **empirical formula.** However, this type of formula merely indicates the simplest ratio of the atoms present in the substance and often does not describe the true composition of a molecule. Moreover, an empirical formula can always be used to describe a substance incapable of existing in the form of independent molecules. Some representative examples are given in Table 5.2.

TABLE 5.2. **Some Empirical and Molecular Formulas**

Type of Substance	Empirical Formula	Molecular Formula
1. Elements	H	H_2
	Cl	Cl_2
	P	P_4
	S	S_8
	Na	Na
	Al	Al
2. Covalent compounds	H_2O	H_2O
	CCl_4	CCl_4
	NH_3	NH_3
	HO	H_2O_2
	CH	C_2H_2
	CH	C_6H_6
	HCO_2	$H_2C_2O_4$
3. Ions	Na^+	Na^+
	Ba^{++}	Ba^{++}
	Hg^+	Hg_2^{++}
	ClO^-	ClO^-
	SO_4^{--}	SO_4^{--}
	SO_4^-	$S_2O_8^{--}$
4. Ionic compounds	NaCl	None
	$BaCl_2$	None
	$Al_2(SO_4)_3$	None

Note that all the empirical formulas are expressed in the simplest ratio of atoms possible for the substance. If the substance consists of a single atomic species, the symbol of one atom is sufficient for the empirical formula. When more than one atomic species is present, the ratio of atoms must be numerically equivalent to that in the molecular formula; e.g., HO (ratio 1 : 1) is equivalent to H_2O_2 (ratio 2 : 2). In many cases in chemistry, the same empirical formula applies to more than one molecular formula; e.g., CH (ratio 1 : 1) applies both to acetylene, C_2H_2 (2 : 2), and to benzene, C_6H_6 (6 : 6). Further comparison of the two columns shows that the empirical and molecular formulas of many substances are identical. However, when the molecular and empirical formulas differ, the molecular formula is a simple multiple of the empirical formula.

It is important to note that the ionic compounds differ from all the other substances in the table in that *they do not have molecular formulas.* Ionic compounds can be described only by empirical formulas even though their components, the ions, do themselves have molecular formulas.

The molecular formula is preferred for describing a substance. This will be noted in future discussions dealing with elements, covalent compounds, and ions (classifications 1, 2, and 3 in Table 5.2). Ionic compounds (classification 4) will be described by empirical formulas when they are solids (e.g., NaCl), but will be shown as independent ions, each with its own molecular formula, when melted or in solution (e.g., Na^+ + Cl^-).

5.5. Formulas and Nomenclature

Earlier sections of this book have referred frequently to various formulas and their significance relative to bonding, ions, and oxidation numbers. We now consider formulas of ions with the objective of learning them systematically and deriving from them formulas of compounds and their names, for in order to understand the material presented in succeeding chapters it is essential that we have some command of a "chemical vocabulary."

Table 5.3 lists positive and negative ions, along with their names and valences (oxidation numbers). Although the table is not complete, the majority of the ions commonly dealt with in chemistry are included.

Some of the positive metallic ions have two names. The first one given is preferred in accordance with the modern trend of naming these ions. In this method the ion always has the name of its element, either with or without a Roman number after it. The purpose of the number is to indi-

TABLE 5.3. Names, Formulas, and Valences of Common Ions

Monovalent

	Positive			Negative
H^+	Hydrogen		OH^-	Hydroxide
NH_4^+	Ammonium		H^-	Hydride
Li^+	Lithium		F^-	Fluoride
Na^+	Sodium		Cl^-	Chloride
K^+	Potassium		Br^-	Bromide
Ag^+	Silver		I^-	Iodide
Cu^+	Copper(I) or cuprous		CN^-	Cyanide
Hg_2^{++}	Mercury(I) or mercurous		NO_2^-	Nitrite
			NO_3^-	Nitrate
			ClO^-	Hypochlorite
			ClO_2^-	Chlorite
			ClO_3^-	Chlorate
			ClO_4^-	Perchlorate
			MnO_4^-	Permanganate
			HCO_3^-	Hydrogen carbonate or bicarbonate
			HSO_3^-	Hydrogen sulfite or bisulfite
			HSO_4^-	Hydrogen sulfate or bisulfate
			$C_2H_3O_2^-$	Acetate
			CNS^-	Thiocyanate

Divalent

Mg^{++}	Magnesium		O^{--}	Oxide
Ca^{++}	Calcium		O_2^{--}	Peroxide
Sr^{++}	Strontium		S^{--}	Sulfide
Ba^{++}	Barium		SO_3^{--}	Sulfite
Zn^{++}	Zinc		SO_4^{--}	Sulfate
Cd^{++}	Cadmium		$S_2O_3^{--}$	Thiosulfate
Sn^{++}	Tin(II) or stannous		$S_2O_8^{--}$	Peroxydisulfate
Pb^{++}	Lead(II) or plumbous		CO_3^{--}	Carbonate
Hg^{++}	Mercury(II) or mercuric		CrO_4^{--}	Chromate
Fe^{++}	Iron(II) or ferrous		$Cr_2O_7^{--}$	Dichromate
Co^{++}	Cobalt(II) or cobaltous		$C_2O_4^{--}$	Oxalate
Ni^{++}	Nickel(II) or nickelous		SiO_3^{--}	Silicate
Cu^{++}	Copper(II) or cupric			

Trivalent

Al^{+3}	Aluminum		N^{-3}	Nitride
Bi^{+3}	Bismuth		BO_3^{-3}	Borate
Cr^{+3}	Chromium(III) or chromic		PO_4^{-3}	Phosphate or orthophosphate
As^{+3}	Arsenic(III) or arsenious		AsO_4^{-3}	Arsenate or orthoarsenate
Sb^{+3}	Antimony(III) or antimonous		$Fe(CN)_6^{-3}$	Ferricyanide
Fe^{+3}	Iron(III) or ferric			
Co^{+3}	Cobalt(III) or cobaltic			

TABLE 5.3. Continued

Others			
Positive		**Negative**	
Sn^{+4}	Tin(IV) or stannic	$P_2O_7{}^{-4}$	Diphosphate or pyrophosphate
Pb^{+4}	Lead(IV) or plumbic	$Fe(CN)_6{}^{-4}$	Ferrocyanide
As^{+5}	Arsenic(V) or arsenic		
Sb^{+5}	Antimony(V) or antimonic		

cate which of several oxidation states the element exhibits. For example, copper can have a $+1$ or $+2$ oxidation number. Just calling the ion "copper" tells nothing about its oxidation state. However, copper(I) is informative because it tells us that the ion is copper and has an oxidation state of $+1$. The old method of naming these ions that have multiple oxidation numbers is also given in the table; for example, copper(I) is also called cuprous. Such names are not informative. For instance, without looking at the table can you tell what the oxidation number of cobaltous ion is? Probably not; but the modern numerical system name, cobalt(II), tells you that it is $+2$. Positive ions which have only the name of the element without a number have only the one oxidation number listed. In a few instances there may be other unusual oxidation numbers under particular circumstances. Since the older chemical literature uses the older names and modern literature frequently reverts to them, you still must learn them.

The ion $Hg_2{}^{++}$ is listed in the monovalent class because each mercury in this unique ion displays a $+1$ valence. Compounds containing this ion are often given the wrong formula—e.g., $HgCl$ instead of the correct one, Hg_2Cl_2. The ion consists of two simple $+1$ mercury ions that are bonded together covalently, $^+Hg:Hg^+$.

The monovalent negative ions whose formulas begin with hydrogen —e.g., $HCO_3{}^-$—have the same name as the acid from which they are derived. However, there is no confusion here because chemists always attach the word ion to the name of a negative ion; this sufficiently distinguishes its name from the name of the acid. For example, H_2CO_3 is hydrogen carbonate, whereas $HCO_3{}^-$ is hydrogen carbonate ion. The prefix *bi-*, used by older nomenclature systems in the names of this and other ions similar to it, has no fundamental significance. Whenever a series of negative hydrogen-containing ions can exist—e.g., $H_2PO_4{}^-$, $HPO_4{}^{--}$—they are distinguished by an appropriate prefix attached to the common name, such as dihydrogen phosphate ion and monohydrogen phosphate ion.

Some systematic features in the naming of the negative ions are apparent. Thus the name of an ion consisting of only one element has the suffix -*ide*—O^{--}, oxide; Cl^-, chloride. The main part of the name includes only as much of the name of the element as is necessary to identify the element. A very few -*ide* ions contain more than one element —OH^-, hydroxide; CN^-, cyanide; $Fe(CN)_6^{-3}$, ferricyanide; and $Fe(CN)_6^{-4}$, ferrocyanide.

Names ending with the suffix -*ite* or -*ate* generally denote an ion that consists of an element and oxygen. If only one such ion can exist, the -ate suffix is used—e.g., CO_3^{--}, carbonate. If two combinations are possible, the one with less oxygen has the -ite suffix and the one with the most oxygen the -ate suffix—for example, NO_2^-, nitrite; NO_3^-, nitrate. If more than two combinations are possible, the prefixes *per*- and *hypo*- are used. Per- is used in the name of an -ate ion to denote an ion with an additional atom of oxygen; thus ClO_3^- is chlorate, so ClO_4^- is perchlorate. Hypo- is prefixed to the name of an -ite ion to denote an ion with one less atom of oxygen; thus ClO_2^- is chlorite, so ClO^- is hypochlorite. Historically, the name ending in -ate was always applied to the first oxygen-containing ion of any element that was discovered, regardless of how many atoms of oxygen were present. Thus there is CNO^-, cyanate; $C_2H_3O_2^-$, acetate; ClO_3^-, chlorate; and SO_4^{--}, sulfate. The other names are all applied *relatively* to the -ate names. A few other prefixes are also used in specific cases. For example, *di*- means that the ion contains two atoms of the element for which it is named. *Peroxy*- indicates that there is an oxygen-to-oxygen bond. *Thio*- means that an atom of sulfur has replaced an atom of oxygen. We shall discuss these names later in connection with the chemistry of the individual elements.

Compounds whose formulas begin with hydrogen have two names. When not dissolved in water they are usually named in the way described in the preceding paragraphs. But when dissolved in water, their

TABLE 5.4. **Nomenclature of Acid Compounds and Their Water Solutions**

Formula	Name of Pure Compound	Name of Water Solution
HCl	Hydrogen chloride	Hydrochloric acid
H_2S	Hydrogen sulfide	Hydrosulfuric acid
HNO_2	Hydrogen nitrite	Nitrous acid
HNO_3	Hydrogen nitrate	Nitric acid
H_3PO_4	Hydrogen phosphate	Phosphoric acid

solutions have a common set of properties so important as to warrant a special name. The solutions are called **acids**; the name of an individual acid is based on the name of the negative ion. Some typical examples of this dual nomenclature are listed in Table 5.4.

The following generalizations hold in naming these compounds:

1. Hydrogen ____ide compounds are hydro____ic acids.
2. Hydrogen ____ite compounds are ____ous acids.
3. Hydrogen ____ate compounds are ____ic acids.

5.6. Formulas and Oxidation Numbers

A very important rule which applies to chemical formulas says that *the sum of the oxidation numbers of all the atoms in a formula must equal zero for an electrically neutral molecule, or in the case of an ion must equal the charge on the ion.* (See rules 3 and 4, page 90.) For example, HCl is an electrically neutral molecule in which the oxidation number of H is $+1$ and of Cl is -1. The formula HCl is correct because $+1 + (-1) = 0$. Similarly, $AlCl_3$ is also correct because the oxidation number of Al is $+3$ and of each Cl is -1; therefore the three chlorines have a total oxidation number of -3, and $+3 + (-3) = 0$. A common polyatomic ion, the sulfate ion, SO_4^{--}, has a charge of -2 as shown. The formula of the ion is correct because the oxidation number of S is $+6$ and of each oxygen -2; hence four oxygens will have a total oxidation number of -8. Thus $+6 + (-8) = -2$, which is the charge on the ion.

The oxidation number of an atom or ion can be deduced from the formula, provided the oxidation numbers of all the other atoms or ions in the formula are known. For example, what is the oxidation number of nitrate ion, NO_3, if the formula $Al(NO_3)_3$ is correct? From the preceding paragraph we know that Al is $+3$; therefore the three nitrates must total -3, and each nitrate is -1.

Once oxidation numbers are known, we can apply the rule in reverse and arrive at a correct formula. For example, what is the correct formula of the compound that consists of aluminum and sulfate ions? The solution will be presented in steps.

1. Write the components in proper sequence according to the electronegativity rule (Section 5.2); write the oxidation numbers as superscripts:

$$Al^{+3} \qquad SO_4^{-2}$$

(SO_4^{-2} is often written SO_4^{--}; but since algebraic operations are required, the number is more convenient.)

2. Multiply the oxidation numbers (neglect algebraic signs) to obtain the oxidation number product:

$$3 \times 2 = 6$$

3. Determine the subscript of each ion by dividing the oxidation number product by the oxidation number (again neglect algebraic signs):

$$\text{For } Al^{+3}, \frac{6}{3} = 2 \qquad \text{For } SO_4^{-2}, \frac{6}{2} = 3$$

This gives the resulting formula with appropriate subscripts as $Al_2(SO_4)_3$.

4. Check the formula by adding the oxidation numbers. (This is important because mathematical errors are made even in simple calculations.) Thus $+6 + (-6) = 0$. Therefore the formula is correct.

5.7. Experimental Determination of Formulas

When a chemist synthesizes a new compound or isolates one from some chemical process he usually has to determine the formula by analytical methods. Merely knowing *what* is present and applying simple valence rules does not necessarily mean that he will arrive at the proper formula. For example, the compound may contain iron, sulfur, and oxygen. He cannot conclude that the formula is $Fe_2(SO_4)_3$ (the most common compound containing these elements), because iron forms both Fe^{+2} and Fe^{+3} ions, and sulfur and oxygen can exist as SO_3^{-2}, SO_4^{-2}, $S_2O_3^{-2}$, and $S_2O_4^{-2}$, to mention only a few possibilities. These ions alone would give rise to *eight* different formulas. Which is the correct formula? If the compound has been previously studied and data regarding its chemical properties are available, a few comparisons will identify it and hence its formula will be known. But if the compound is new, it must be purified and analyzed in order to arrive at its formula.

The following consideration of the information provided by a formula will explain how a formula can be derived from analytical data. The formula of water, H_2O, states that this substance contains two atomic weights of hydrogen for each atomic weight of oxygen. The percentages of hydrogen and oxygen in water are thus:

$$\frac{2 \text{ atomic weights of hydrogen}}{1 \text{ molecular weight of water}} \times 100 = \frac{2 \times 1.008}{18.02} \times 100 = 11.19\%$$

$$\frac{1 \text{ atomic weight of oxygen}}{1 \text{ molecular weight of water}} \times 100 = \frac{1 \times 16.00}{18.02} \times 100 = 88.81\%$$

Solving these equations for the number of atoms, we get:

1.
$$\frac{11.19 \times 18.02}{1.008 \times 100} = 2 \text{ atoms of hydrogen}$$

2.
$$\frac{88.81 \times 18.02}{16 \times 100} = 1 \text{ atom of oxygen}$$

Dividing Eq. 1 by Eq. 2 and canceling common factors gives:

$$\frac{\dfrac{11.19 \times \cancel{18.02}}{1.008 \times \cancel{100}}}{\dfrac{88.81 \times \cancel{18.02}}{16 \times \cancel{100}}} = \frac{11.19/1.008}{88.81/16} = \frac{2}{1}$$

Thus if the percentage of each element is divided by its own atomic weight, the ratio of the result shows the ratio of atoms in the compound.

Suppose that a chemist analyzes a 1.50-g. sample of a pure compound and finds that it contains 0.600 g. of carbon, 0.101 g. of hydrogen, and 0.800 g. of oxygen. What is the formula of the compound? The percentage by weight of each element is given by:

$$\%C = \frac{0.600 \times 100}{1.50} \qquad \%H = \frac{0.101 \times 100}{1.50} \qquad \%O = \frac{0.800 \times 100}{1.50}$$

Dividing the percentage of each element by its own gram-atomic weight, we get the relative number of gram-atomic weights of each element.

$$C = \frac{0.600 \times 100}{1.50 \times 12.01} \qquad H = \frac{0.101 \times 100}{1.50 \times 1.008} \qquad O = \frac{0.800 \times 100}{1.50 \times 16.00}$$

To obtain the necessary atomic ratios we divide each of these by the smallest one.

$$C = \frac{\dfrac{0.600 \times \cancel{100}}{\cancel{1.50} \times 12.01}}{\dfrac{0.600 \times \cancel{100}}{\cancel{1.50} \times 12.01}} \qquad H = \frac{\dfrac{0.101 \times \cancel{100}}{\cancel{1.50} \times 1.008}}{\dfrac{0.600 \times \cancel{100}}{\cancel{1.50} \times 12.01}} \qquad O = \frac{\dfrac{0.800 \times \cancel{100}}{\cancel{1.50} \times 16.00}}{\dfrac{0.600 \times \cancel{100}}{\cancel{1.50} \times 12.01}}$$

But the factor 100, and the weight of the compound, 1.50, used in obtaining the percentages, cancel out. This leaves:

$$C = \frac{\dfrac{0.600}{12.01}}{\dfrac{0.600}{12.01}} = 1 \qquad H = \frac{\dfrac{0.101}{1.008}}{\dfrac{0.600}{12.01}} = 2 \qquad O = \frac{\dfrac{0.800}{16.00}}{\dfrac{0.600}{12.01}} = 1$$

The empirical formula is thus CH_2O.

Whenever the percentage by weight of each element is given, instead of grams as in the above problem, the percentage values can be treated as the grams of each element. This is so because we can consider the weight of the compound to be 100 g. Thus, a compound which consists of 40 per cent calcium by weight is one which contains 40 g. of calcium per 100 g. of compound. Since, as noted in the above calculations, the weight of the compound cancels out, any weight at all can be taken. Working with percentages simply amounts to taking 100 g. of the compound. If any weight of an element is divided by its gram-atomic weight, the result is *the number of gram-atomic weights,* just as dividing any number of eggs by 12 (the number of eggs in a dozen) will give the number of dozens. The number of atoms in a gram-atomic weight is the same for all elements—namely, Avogadro's number, N. In view of this fact it is not surprising that the ratio of the number of gram-atomic weights is the same as the ratio of the number of atoms.

If an arbitrary quantity of material is used, the actual number of gram-atomic weights, or of atoms, is of no interest, only their ratios. If the *simplest whole-number ratio* is used, the *empirical formula* of the compound will be given. If instead of some arbitrary quantity like 100 g. we use 1 gram-molecular weight of the material, the number of gram-atomic weights of each element in it will be identical with the number of atoms of each element in a molecule of it. This is so because there are N molecules in a gram-molecular weight. Accordingly, using 1 gram-molecular weight of a compound gives the *molecular formula* directly, without using any ratios. Ordinarily, experimental error in the figure for the molecular weight will necessitate subscripts in the formula which are not integers but in most cases can be rounded off with assurance.

The molecular formula of any substance except a salt (a salt has no molecular formula) can be obtained by multiplying the empirical formula by the proper integer such as 1, 2, 3, etc. The correct integer for this purpose is determined by dividing the molecular weight of the compound by the formula weight obtained from the empirical formula. (One method of determining molecular weights was described in Section 2.26 in connection with gases; other methods will be discussed in Section 8.17 on solutions.) To illustrate, suppose that the molecular weight of the substance CH_2O is found by experiment to be about 180. We divide this by the empirical formula weight of CH_2O, 29, to get the multiplier: $180 \div 29 = 6$ (rounded off to the nearest whole number). The true molecular formula is obtained by multiplying the empirical formula by 6:

$$CH_2O \times 6 = C_6H_{12}O_6$$

5.8. Formula Weights, Molecular Weights, and Moles

The sum of the gram-atomic weights of all the atoms shown in a formula is the formula weight of the substance in grams. This quantity is also known as a **mole** of the substance. The word mole was originally adopted as a contraction of gram-molecular weight, but unfortunately it no longer has exactly this meaning because it is also applied to ionic substances. For example, compare the covalent compound H_2SO_4 (which consists of H_2SO_4 molecules) and the ionic compound Na_2SO_4 (which consists of Na^+ ions and SO_4^{--} ions):

H_2SO_4	Na_2SO_4
$2H = 2 \times 1.008 = 2.016$ g.	$2 Na = 2 \times 22.997 = 45.994$ g.
$1 S = 1 \times 32.066 = 32.066$	$1 S = 1 \times 32.066 = 32.066$
$4 O = 4 \times 16.000 = 64.000$	$4 O = 4 \times 16.000 = 64.000$
98.082 g.	142.060 g.

H_2SO_4 98.082 g. $= 1$ gram-formula wt. $= 1$ mole $= 1$ gram-molecular wt.
Na_2SO_4 142.060 g. $= 1$ gram-formula wt. $= 1$ mole
            $= 2$ gram-molecular wt. $(Na^+) + 1$ gram-molecular wt. (SO_4^-)

Note that there is no gram-molecular weight for Na_2SO_4.

To summarize: For a substance that has a molecular formula, the term mole is synonymous with formula weight and means 1 gram-molecular weight of the substance. But for a salt, the term mole, although still synonymous with formula weight—that is, the empirical formula, since there is no molecular formula—means as many moles of each ion as the formula calls for.

5.9. Chemical Equations

A chemical equation serves a twofold purpose in chemistry. First, it describes a chemical reaction or change by indicating what substances are used for the reaction and what products are obtained from it. Second, it determines the exact quantities of reactants and products involved in the reaction. From the point of view of this second purpose, the chemical equation is in the category of **stoichiometry.**

5.10. Descriptive Aspects of the Equation; Balancing

Fundamentally all chemical equations state the following:

$$\text{Reactants} \rightarrow \text{Products}$$

The reactants are written on the left side of the arrow and the products on the right side. The arrow indicates the direction in which the reaction proceeds. The reactants and products may be either elements or compounds, or both.

To be more specific, consider the decomposition of mercury(II) oxide into mercury and oxygen.

$$\text{Mercury(II) oxide} \rightarrow \text{Mercury} + \text{Oxygen}$$
$$HgO \rightarrow Hg + O_2$$

The compound and elements are stated as formulas which appropriately and correctly describe them. This is the first step in writing an equation.

The second step involves balancing the equation, that is, accounting for all the atoms on both sides of the arrow. Inspection of the above equation shows that there are twice as many atoms of oxygen on the right side as are available on the left. Since matter can be neither created nor destroyed by a chemical reaction, a material balance of components is necessary. At first it may seem plausible to achieve this balance in either of the following ways:

$$HgO \rightarrow Hg + O$$
$$HgO_2 \rightarrow Hg + O_2$$

Neither of these is correct because the formulas O and HgO_2 are not correct. *Never change a formula for convenience in balancing an equation.*

The correct procedure is to take twice as much HgO to obtain the required amount of oxygen.

$$2HgO \rightarrow Hg + O_2$$

Now, however, there is more mercury on the left than there is on the right. This is rectified by doubling the amount on the right. That is:

$$2HgO \rightarrow 2Hg + O_2$$

The equation is now balanced. Note that free non-metal elements such as oxygen generally appear in reactions as diatomic molecules—

X_2 (F_2, Cl_2, Br_2, H_2, N_2)—whereas free metallic elements are mon-atomic.

It is common to include additional information in the equation, generally by means of symbols, in order to clarify the conditions necessary for the reaction to take place. It is also important to designate the states of the substances. This particular reaction requires heat if it is to occur. This is shown by putting a Δ over the arrow. The mercury(II) oxide is a solid, the mercury is a liquid, the oxygen a gas. This information is indicated as follows:

$$\underline{2HgO} \xrightarrow{\Delta} 2Hg \text{ (l)} + \overline{O_2}$$

Usually only the solid and gas states are indicated. If neither of these is shown, the assumption is that the substance is a liquid or in solution. Solids and gases are also indicated by arrows, thus: HgO↓ and O₂↑. In this book we shall underline <u>solids</u> and overline gases.

5.11. Quantitative Aspects of the Balanced Equation; Stoichiometry

Earlier chapters stressed the fact that the formulas of molecules and the symbols of the elements represent distinct quantities of material. Thus HgO means a gram-formula weight of mercury(II) oxide, Hg a gram-atomic weight of mercury, and O_2 a mole of oxygen. Therefore we can state quantitatively, on the basis of the balanced equation:

$\underline{2HgO}$ → $2Hg$ $+ \overline{O_2}$

2 gram-formula wts. mercury(II) oxide yield 2 gram-atomic wts. mercury + 1 mole oxygen

$2(201 + 16)$ g. → $2(201)$ g. $+ 2(16)$ g.

434 g. → 402 g. + 32 g. or 22.4 l.

These quantities, derived from the balanced equation, establish the reaction on a weight basis. If the amount of any substance actually used or produced differs from that given in the equation, the amount of every other substance will differ proportionately. In solving stoichiometric problems it is convenient to use a table as we did with the gas law problems. For example, we wish to calculate the quantities of mercury and oxygen produced by the decomposition of 100 g. of mercury(II) oxide.

Equation	Problem
434 g. HgO	100 g. HgO
402 g. Hg	? g. Hg (1)
32 g. O_2	? g. O_2 (2)

The amount of each produced can be obtained by multiplying the amount given in the equation by the ratio $\dfrac{\text{g. HgO in problem}}{\text{g. HgO in equation}}$; this is a pure number.

1. $402 \text{ g. Hg} \times \dfrac{100 \text{ g. HgO}}{434 \text{ g. HgO}} = 92.6 \text{ g. of mercury produced}$

2. $32 \text{ g. O}_2 \times \dfrac{100 \text{ g. HgO}}{434 \text{ g. HgO}} = 7.4 \text{ g. of oxygen produced}$

If we want to determine the volume of oxygen instead of its weight we need only to express the amount of oxygen in the equation in terms of volume instead of weight, since the problem/equation ratio is a pure number. The molar volume, 22.4 l. S.T.P., can be substituted for the gram-molecular weight of *any* gas. We have then, in this case:

Equation	Problem
434 g. HgO	100 g. HgO
22.4 l. O_2	? l. O_2 (3)

3. $22.4 \text{ l. O}_2 \times \dfrac{100 \text{ g. HgO}}{434 \text{ g. HgO}} = 5.16 \text{ l. of oxygen (S.T.P.)}$

Note that the same problem/equation ratio was used in all three of these calculations.

A technique called the **factor label method** is invaluable in checking the mathematical setup of all kinds of chemical problems. Its use was implied in our treatment of both gas law and stoichiometric problems by the statement that the various ratios by which initial quantities are multiplied must be pure numbers. We may state the factor label method explicitly as follows: If all the factors in a setup are labeled completely and words that appear in both numerator and denominator are canceled, those that remain describe the answer correctly. If the word answer does not correspond to what was desired, there was an error in the setup. We shall check the preceding calculation (3) by this method. Completing the labeling, we have:

$$22.4 \text{ l. of O}_2 \text{ at S.T.P. in equation} \times \dfrac{100 \text{ g. of HgO in problem}}{434 \text{ g. of HgO in equation}} = \text{ans.}$$

We have already called attention to the fact that "g. of HgO" can be canceled; the words "in equation" also cancel. That leaves:

$$22.4 \text{ l. of O}_2 \text{ at S.T.P.} \times \dfrac{100}{434} \text{ in problem} = \text{ans.}$$

which is correct. If the problem/equation ratio had been inverted in error, the answer would have read:

$$22.4 \text{ l. of } O_2 \text{ at S.T.P. in equation} \times \frac{434 \text{ in equation}}{100 \text{ in problem}}$$

which does not make sense. The abbreviation S.T.P. in the factor label check shows that if a problem calls for the volume of a gas under any other than standard conditions, a separate calculation involving the combination gas law must be made to allow for the necessary conversions. For example, if in (3) above, we wanted the yield of oxygen from the decomposition of 100 g. of HgO at 20° C. and 740 mm. pressure, an additional calculation to the one shown would be necessary. We found that 5.16 l. of oxygen would be obtained at S.T.P. Therefore, under the new conditions the following volume would be obtained:

$$V = 5.16 \text{ l.} \times \frac{760 \text{ mm.}}{740 \text{ mm.}} \times \frac{293° \text{ A.}}{273° \text{ A.}}$$
$$= 5.70 \text{ l.}$$

5.12. Reaction Predictions

Once the principles underlying chemical equations are presented to students they become unduly concerned over their ability to predict how, or if, X will react with Y and what the products will be. You cannot predict a chemical reaction and all the factors inherent in it until you understand the nature of the elements, ions, and compounds involved in it. This is a stepwise job; and as you step deeper into the study of chemistry your experiences will give you a broader knowledge and appreciation which in turn will expand your ability to understand and hence predict chemical behavior.

For the present, have as your objective the ability to write formulas correctly and to balance equations when given the reactants and products. In the next chapter you will study the chemistry of oxygen and some of its compounds. You should then know something about the chemical behavior of oxygen and its compounds and be able to predict reactions in this area of chemistry. When you study a specific element and its compounds, be curious about the principles which dictate the pattern of its chemical behavior. Learning an isolated chemical reaction is not learning chemistry. Consider each reaction in relation to (1) why it occurs, (2) the nature of the element or compound that allows the behavior it manifests, and (3) whether it is typical of a class of elements or compounds from which similar behavior should be expected. For example, you may be studying about the thermal decomposition of the compound, sodium peroxide, Na_2O_2. This particular reaction is typical of the peroxide ion in this compound. In this case the sodium ion is unimportant. Hence any compound containing peroxide ion should behave similarly and liberate oxygen when heated. The equation

$$2Na_2O_2 \xrightarrow{\Delta} 2Na_2O + \overline{O_2}$$

should express the reaction of all peroxides when heated. In other words, do not learn this as the reaction of sodium peroxide but rather as *the reaction of peroxides.*

After a discussion such as this, your instructor can legitimately expect you to write an equation showing the behavior of calcium peroxide when heated. Can you do it?

QUESTIONS AND PROBLEMS

1. Distinguish between formula and equation. Give an example of each.
2. For three substances, write common, structural (dot and bond type), empirical, and molecular formulas.
3. What class of chemical substances can be represented only by empirical formulas? Why?
4. Write correct formulas for the following:
   a. Calcium carbonate
   b. Hydrogen sulfite
   c. Chromium(III) nitrate
   d. Iron(III) sulfide
   e. Sulfuric acid
   f. Hydrochloric acid
5. Name the following compounds and give the oxidation number of the underlined component.
   a. $Na_3\underline{P}O_4$
   b. $Cd\underline{Cr}O_4$
   c. $\underline{Co}(NO_3)_2$
   d. $H\underline{Cl}O_3$
   e. $Zn\underline{S}O_4$
   f. $\underline{Hg}_2O$
6. Wherever necessary, add appropriate subscripts to make the formula correct. Name the compounds.
   $\qquad$ AgS $\qquad$ BaHCO$_3$ $\qquad$ MgSiO$_3$ $\qquad$ BiO
7. What are the formula weights of:
   $\qquad\qquad$ AgNO$_3$ $\qquad$ H$_3$PO$_4$ $\qquad$ Fe$_2$(SO$_4$)$_3$
8. Calculate the percentage by weight of oxygen in each formula in question 7.
9. Derive the simplest formula which will satisfy the following analyses:
   a. K $\quad$ 44.8% $\qquad$ S $\quad$ 18.4% $\qquad$ O $\quad$ 36.8%
   b. As $\quad$ 65.2% $\qquad$ O $\quad$ 34.8%
   c. H $\quad$ 2.25% $\qquad$ P $\quad$ 34.8% $\qquad$ O $\quad$ 62.9%

10. What is the molecular formula of each of the following compounds:

C = 92.3%	C = 40.0%	C = 26.6%
H = 7.68%	H = 6.7%	H = 2.24%
Mol. wt. = 78	O = 53.3%	O = 71.1%
	Mol. wt. = 60	Mol. wt. = 90

11. Balance the equations:

a. $Fe_2O_3 + \underline{C} \overset{\Delta}{\rightarrow} Fe + \overline{CO}$

b. $Ca(OH)_2 + HCl \rightarrow CaCl_2 + H_2O$

c. $KClO_3 \overset{\Delta}{\rightarrow} KCl + \overline{O}_2$

d. $P + \overline{O}_2 \rightarrow P_2O_5 + \Delta$

e. Aluminum + Hydrochloric acid → Aluminum chloride + Hydrogen

f. Barium + Bromine → Barium bromide

g. Sodium oxide + Water → Sodium hydroxide

h. Hydrogen sulfide + Copper(II) chloride → Copper(II) sulfide + Hydrogen chloride

12. How many grams of $CaCl_2$ form from 50 g. of $Ca(OH)_2$? (See question 11b.)

13. How many liters of oxygen are obtained at S.T.P. from 100 g. of $KClO_3$? (See question 11c.)

14. How many grams of P_2O_5 form from 10 l. of oxygen at 25° C. and 2 atm.? (See question 11d.)

15. How much iron is produced by 10 g. of Fe_2O_3 and 1 g. of C? (See question 11a.)

16. In the following tables, write the correct name and formula in each block according to the ions in the vertical and horizontal rows.

Names and Formulas of Compounds

		Oxide O^{--}	Chloride Cl^-	Nitrate $NO_3{}^-$	Sulfate $SO_4{}^{--}$	Carbonate $CO_3{}^{--}$	Phosphate $PO_4{}^{-3}$
Ammonium	$NH_4{}^+$						
Potassium	K^+						
Silver	Ag^+						
Sodium	Na^+						
Lithium	Li^+						
Copper(II)	Cu^{++}						
Mercury(I)	$Hg_2{}^{++}$						
Mercury(II)	Hg^{++}						
Barium	Ba^{++}						
Calcium	Ca^{++}						
Lead(II)	Pb^{++}						
Magnesium	Mg^{++}						
Nickel	Ni^{++}						
Strontium	Sr^{++}						
Zinc	Zn^{++}						
Cadmium	Cd^{++}						
Chromium(III)	Cr^{+3}						
Cobalt(II)	Co^{++}						
Manganese(II)	Mn^{++}						
Iron(II)	Fe^{++}						
Iron(III)	Fe^{+3}						
Tin(II)	Sn^{++}						
Tin(IV)	Sn^{+4}						
Aluminum	Al^{+3}						
Bismuth	Bi^{+3}						
Antimony(III)	Sb^{+3}						
Arsenic(III)	As^{+3}						
Cerium(III)	Ce^{+3}						
Cerium(IV)	Ce^{+4}						

Names and Formulas of Compounds

	Chlorate ClO_3^-	Hydroxide OH^-	Permanganate MnO_4^-	Sulfide S^{--}	Chromate CrO_4^{--}	Dichromate $Cr_2O_7^{--}$	Borate BO_3^{-3}
NH_4^+							
K^+							
Ag^+							
Na^+							
Li^+							
Cu^{++}							
Hg_2^{++}							
Hg^{++}							
Ba^{++}							
Ca^{++}							
Pb^{++}							
Mg^{++}							
Ni^{++}							
Sr^{++}							
Zn^{++}							
Cd^{++}							
Cr^{+3}							
Co^{++}							
Mn^{++}							
Fe^{++}							
Fe^{+3}							
Sn^{++}							
Sn^{+4}							
Al^{+3}							
Bi^{+3}							
Sb^{+3}							
As^{+3}							
Ce^{+3}							
Ce^{+4}							

6 Oxygen

6.1. Occurrence of Oxygen

Oxygen is the most abundant of all the elements. Water is 89 per cent oxygen, air 21 per cent; the igneous rocks in the earth's crust contain 46.6 per cent of this element. You probably don't realize that your own body is two-thirds oxygen. Table 6.1 lists the percentages of several of the more important elements in the earth's crust and in the body.

TABLE 6.1. **The More Abundant Elements—Weight Percentage Distribution**

Element (Non-metallic)	% In Rocks	% In Body	Element (Metallic)	% In Rocks	% In Body
Carbon	0.032	17.22	Aluminum	8.13	Trace
Chlorine	0.03	0.01	Calcium	3.63	2.5
Hydrogen	Present	9.17	Iron	5.0	0.01
Nitrogen	0.005	2.5	Magnesium	2.09	0.07
Oxygen	46.6	67.20	Manganese	0.1	Trace
Phosphorus	0.118	1.14	Potassium	2.59	0.01
Silicon	27.72	Trace	Sodium	2.83	0.01
Sulfur	0.052	0.14	Titanium	0.44	Trace

No other single element amounts to as much as 0.1 per cent of the weight of rocks; all the others together amount to only 0.63 per cent.

Many elements that are present in the body in only minute quantities are nevertheless essential.

Oxygen has a fundamental role in chemistry. Many salts, most acids and bases, and thousands of organic compounds contain it. It is essential for the combustion of wood, coal, gasoline, etc. As we shall see in later chapters, oxygen is the type element for the entire class of non-metals; moreover, in nearly every case, the compounds that an element forms with it are among the most important ones we shall study. Naturally enough, oxygen is likely to be the first element prepared in a beginning laboratory course.

6.2. Discovery of Oxygen

Joseph Priestley, who is usually credited with the discovery of oxygen, was born near Leeds, England, in 1733. His sympathy for the American Revolutionists resulted in the destruction of his church, home, and equipment. He moved from England to the United States in 1794.

In 1774 Priestley conducted some experiments on the decomposition of substances placed in an inverted tube above mercury. Heat was obtained by converging the sun's rays on the top of the tube by means of a lens, or burning glass as it was called. He found that mercuric oxide liberated a gas in which substances burned brilliantly. Mice placed in the gas became livelier, and he himself felt exhilarated when he breathed it. He did not recognize the gas as a new element, but considered it only another kind of "air."

Priestley was not the first man to discover this gas, but because his results were *published first* he is credited with its discovery. In 1771 a Swedish drug clerk named Scheele heated potassium nitrate, silver carbonate, mercuric carbonate, and other salts and from several of them obtained a gas which he described as having the same properties as the gas which Priestley later obtained from mercuric oxide. Both men recognized that this gas was present in air.

Antoine Laurent Lavoisier, son of wealthy French parents, was a keen student of mathematics, physics, and chemistry. After Priestley had visited him in Paris and told of preparing an "air" from mercuric oxide, Lavoisier repeated Priestley's experiments and obtained a gas which he investigated thoroughly. He named it **oxygen** (Gr., acid former) because he thought that it was a constituent of all acids. Although this is not true, his other conclusion, that ordinary combustion involves the combination of substances with oxygen, was correct. He proved this by showing that the weight of the products of combustion was always equal to the sum of the weight of the substance burned and of the oxygen consumed. Lavoisier is sometimes called the "father of modern chemistry," for his textbook, *Traité Elémentaire de Chimie* published in 1789, was the first book written in the language chemists use today. He coined the word oxide, explained combustion, and served the king as comptroller of munitions and tax collector. Although in sympathy with the poor, his loyalty to the Royalists brought him to the guillotine.

6.3. Preparation of Oxygen

By heating compounds. Oxygen can be obtained by heating any peroxide, some oxides, and some salts. Lavoisier proved that the reaction between mercury and oxygen is reversible.

$$2Hg + \overline{O_2} \rightarrow 2HgO$$

and
$$\underline{2HgO} \xrightarrow{\Delta} 2Hg + \overline{O_2}$$

All elements except the inert gases will combine either directly or indirectly with oxygen to form oxides. Some elements combine with oxygen to form several oxides because of the variable valence of the element. If an element forms more than one oxide, it is often easier to decompose the one containing the larger amount of oxygen and obtain oxygen than to decompose the other. This is shown in Table 6.2.

TABLE 6.2. **Melting Point of Oxides in °C**

Substance	Melting Point	Substance	Melting Point
FeO	1420	MnO	1650
Fe_2O_3	1560 Dec.*	MnO_2	535 Dec.
PbO	888	Mn_2O_3	Dec.
Pb_2O_3	370 Dec.	Mn_2O_7	Explodes
PbO_2	290 Dec.	I_2O_5	300 Dec.
Cu_2O	1235	Oxides of chlorine	Explode
CuO	1026 Dec.	Ag_2O	300 Dec.

* Dec. = decomposes.

Some higher oxides can be decomposed and the lower oxides produced. The equation for the decomposition of MnO_2 is:

$$\underline{3MnO_2} \xrightarrow{535°C} \underline{Mn_3O_4} + \overline{O_2}$$

Most oxides are too stable to be decomposed in the Bunsen flame because the maximum temperature for heated objects seldom reaches 1000° C.

Peroxides are oxygen compounds in which pairs of oxygen atoms are covalently bound together. Some metals combine directly with oxygen to form peroxides. Thus if air is passed over sodium which is warmed, the reaction is:

$$2Na + \overline{O_2} \rightarrow \underline{Na_2O_2}$$

All peroxides are quite unstable. They readily decompose upon heating.

$$2\underline{Na_2O_2} \xrightarrow{\Delta} 2\underline{Na_2O} + \overline{O_2}$$

$$2\underline{BaO_2} \xrightarrow{\Delta} 2\underline{BaO} + \overline{O_2}$$

$$2\underline{H_2O_2} \xrightarrow{\Delta} 2\underline{H_2O} + \overline{O_2}$$

The general reaction of a peroxide is:

$$\text{Peroxide} \xrightarrow{\Delta} \text{Normal oxide} + \text{Oxygen}$$

Some peroxides will liberate oxygen even on the addition of water. The other product is a hydroxide. The equation for the reaction between Na_2O_2 and water is:

$$2Na_2O_2 + 2H_2O \rightarrow 4Na^+ + 4OH^- + \overline{O_2}$$

A convenient method of producing oxygen in the laboratory is by decomposing certain salts which contain it. However, not all salts which contain oxygen will liberate it on being heated. One that does may liberate either part or all of its oxygen. This behavior is like that of oxides.

If potassium nitrate, KNO_3, is placed in a test tube and heated to 400° C., oxygen is liberated and potassium nitrite, KNO_2, is formed. The equation for the reaction is:

$$2\underline{KNO_3} \xrightarrow{400°\,C.} 2\underline{KNO_2} + \overline{O_2}$$

Nitrates of all metals in Group IA behave similarly. The nitrates of other metals also give oxygen as a decomposition product, but mixed with another gas, nitrogen dioxide, NO_2.

$$2\underline{Pb(NO_3)_2} \xrightarrow{\Delta} 2\underline{PbO} + \overline{4NO_2} + \overline{O_2}$$

This method of preparation involves the separation of one gas from another, an inconvenience to be avoided in simple laboratory procedures.

The salt, potassium chlorate, $KClO_3$, loses all its oxygen on being heated.

$$2KClO_3 \xrightarrow{400°\,C.} \overline{2KCl} + \overline{3O_2}$$

The reaction temperature required for the decomposition of $KClO_3$ can be lowered by adding a **catalyst.** A catalyst may be regarded as a substance whose presence speeds up a chemical reaction but whose composition is not affected by the reaction. Students working in the laboratory often add a little manganese dioxide, MnO_2, or ferric oxide, Fe_2O_3, to one portion of $KClO_3$ and compare the rate of evolution of oxygen with that in a control sample containing no catalyst. Oxygen is liberated much more rapidly even at 200° C. with MnO_2 than it is at 400° without the catalyst. All chlorates, perchlorates, and analogous salts of bromine and iodine decompose as $KClO_3$ does. Care is necessary in handling molten salts that are capable of liberating oxygen, because they are highly reactive toward combustible materials and may produce an explosion on contact with them.

By using an electric current.   If the two terminals of a direct current are dipped in water containing a little sulfuric acid so that the solution will conduct the current, oxygen gas is liberated at one terminal and hydrogen at the other. The gases can be kept separate. Other substances such as sodium hydroxide may be used instead of sulfuric acid. Although the process is expensive, it is used if very pure oxygen is desired. The equation for the reaction is:

$$2H_2O \xrightarrow{\triangle} \overline{2H_2} + \overline{O_2}$$

The symbol $\triangle$ is placed over the arrow in all reactions involving electrolysis. Since hydrogen is required in large volume by industries, the process is sometimes used commercially. The detailed chemistry of electrolytic reactions will be discussed in a later chapter.

By using liquid air.   The unlimited supply of oxygen that is available in the atmosphere can be obtained on a commercial scale by liquefying air and then subjecting it to fractional distillation. Since the boiling point of nitrogen is $-195°$ C. and that of oxygen is $-183°$ C., these two elements can be readily separated (fractionated) from the solution (liquid air) that contains them. Manufacturers of oxygen frequently install plants right on the premises of large users of it, in this way delivering the gas or liquid by pipeline at the point of consumption. For most purposes 96 per cent pure oxygen suffices, and is considerably cheaper. Liquid oxygen can be shipped in insulated tank trucks. Small users buy the gas under 100 atm. pressure in steel cylinders. The energy required for obtaining oxygen by the liquefaction of air is less than that required by the electrolysis of water or by any process involving the formation and decomposition of chemicals. Our annual production of oxygen from the air is about 105 billion cu. ft. and is rapidly increasing. This does not include government uses which may amount to as much as 15 billion cu. ft.

6.4. Physical Properties of Oxygen

The weight of a liter of oxygen is 1.429 g. at S.T.P. This value need not be remembered. You can always obtain it in a moment by dividing the weight of a mole by 22.4. A liter of dry air at S.T.P. weighs 1.293 g. This is less than the weight of a liter of oxygen because nitrogen, the chief constituent of air, has a lower molecular weight (28) than oxygen does. At 0° C., 4.89 ml. of oxygen will dissolve in 100 ml. of water. This solubility is greater than that of nitrogen (2.35 ml. at the same temperature).

TABLE 6.3. **Data on Oxygen**

Atomic number	8
Valence electrons	6
Atomic weight	16
Covalent radius	0.74 A.
Radius of O^{--}	1.40 A.
Melting point	$-218.4°$ C.
Boiling point	$-183°$ C.
Electronegativity	3.5

6.5. The Oxygen Molecule

Monatomic molecules composed of a single oxygen atom do not exist under ordinary conditions. If we say of a compound, "It contains oxygen," we mean that there are one or more oxygen atoms in each of its molecules. Ordinary atmospheric oxygen is diatomic; its formula is O_2. This is what is meant when we say "oxygen" without qualification. The triatomic molecule O_3 is formed from oxygen by the action of ultraviolet light or an electrical discharge. This is **ozone.** It is an entirely different substance from oxygen. It is 50 per cent denser, has a characteristic strong smell, and is much more reactive. At its boiling point, $-183°$ C., oxygen is *polymerized* to some extent into still another different substance, O_4. A molecule which is a multiple of another is said to be a **polymer** of the latter. O_4 is pale blue and non-magnetic. It readily breaks down again into O_2, which is colorless and magnetic.

$$2O_2 \rightleftarrows O_4$$

6.6. Reactions of Oxygen with Elements

The electronegativity of oxygen, 3.5, is higher than that of any other element except fluorine. Oxygen therefore reacts energetically with most elements; it takes electrons completely away from elements that have low electronegativity, and the major share of an electron pair from elements of moderate electronegativity in forming a covalent bond. The resulting compounds are called oxides in both cases. The only elements which do not react with oxygen are the "noble" metals—silver, palladium, gold, and platinum—the halogens (Group VIIA), and the inert gases (Group VIIIA). All of these except the last can be united with oxygen by indirect methods.

In spite of its high electronegativity, oxygen is relatively inactive at room temperature. The reason is that the atoms in the oxygen molecule are held together by multiple bonds; they share more than one electron pair. A piece of paper, wood, or coal can remain exposed to the air for years or even centuries with little change; a diamond, forever. This is because oxygen molecules do not collide with sufficient force to break their bonds. But at higher temperatures the molecules have enough kinetic energy so that the bonds are partially broken on collision, and reaction occurs. Water catalyzes the reaction of oxygen with a number of metals. For example, iron remains bright indefinitely in dry air, but in moist air it rapidly *rusts, corrodes,* or *oxidizes,* forming the yellow-to-red oxide, Fe_2O_3.

If metals with very low electronegativity such as lithium, sodium, potassium, barium, strontium, and calcium (in none of these is the electronegativity above 1.0) are exposed to air, they react with oxygen very quickly. Potassium reacts at such a rate that it is melted by the liberated heat. The increase in temperature, in turn, speeds up the reaction and soon the metal bursts into flame. The other five metals are less active than potassium, but even in them the silvery luster of a freshly cut surface dulls almost the instant the air reaches it.

$$4Li + \overline{O_2} \rightarrow \underline{2Li_2O} + \Delta$$

$$2Ca + \overline{O_2} \rightarrow \underline{2CaO} + \Delta$$

Magnesium has an electronegativity of only 1.2, but it merely tarnishes quickly, remaining indefinitely thereafter without further change. This is not due to any reluctance to unite with oxygen, as will be evident if a strip of magnesium ribbon is held in a match flame. The strip ignites and burns with a dazzling white light.

$$2Mg + \overline{O_2} \rightarrow \underline{2MgO} + \Delta$$

(Flash bulbs contain magnesium—or aluminum, or an alloy of the two —in pure oxygen.) The reason the magnesium remains unaltered after tarnishing is that the layer of magnesium oxide, MgO, that forms first soon becomes impervious to oxygen and protects the metal just as a coat of paint would. Aluminum also protects itself by a tightly adhering transparent layer of oxide.

$$4Al + \overline{3O_2} \rightarrow \underline{2Al_2O_3} + \Delta$$

The aluminum oxide becomes impervious while it is still so thin as to be invisible. Chromium behaves similarly, but iron oxide is porous or it cracks and flakes off, exposing the iron to further corrosion.

Some elements form more than one oxide. If steel wool is ignited and plunged into oxygen it burns to the black magnetic oxide, Fe_3O_4, rather than to the Fe_2O_3 which is formed at low temperature. The oxide, Fe_3O_4, is also formed when iron burns after being heated by a cutting torch, when extra oxygen is turned on, or when a white-hot steel billet is passing through a rolling mill. In most cases in which more than one oxide of a given element may form, the quantity of oxygen available for the reaction may determine which oxide will form. Students in the laboratory test for the presence of oxygen by lowering a glowing splint into a bottle of the gas. If the concentration is high, the splint bursts into flame and burns to carbon dioxide.

$$\underline{C} + \overline{O_2} \rightarrow \overline{CO_2} + \Delta$$

But if the supply of oxygen is limited, the carbon dioxide formed first may be reduced to carbon monoxide by further contact with hot charcoal.

$$\underline{C} + \overline{CO_2} \xrightarrow{\Delta} \overline{2CO}$$

Carbon monoxide is combustible, and in the presence of oxygen it will burn to the higher oxide, CO_2.

$$\overline{2CO} + \overline{O_2} \rightarrow \overline{2CO_2} + \triangle$$

In still other cases the amount of oxygen which can combine may be limited by the tendency of the oxide to decompose on heating. Sulfur burns readily in air and brilliantly in oxygen; but if any of the higher oxide, SO_3, is formed, it decomposes in the heat of the flame. In order to form the trioxide in useful quantities, it is necessary to keep the temperature below 450° C., and at this temperature a catalyst is needed in order for the reaction to proceed with reasonable speed.

$$S + \overline{O_2} \longrightarrow \overline{SO_2} + \triangle$$

$$\overline{2SO_2} + \overline{O_2} \xrightarrow[\text{catalyst}]{450°} \overline{2SO_3} + \triangle$$

The elements mentioned thus far in this section are only a few of the many that burn in oxygen. Another one that deserves special mention is hydrogen. This gas burns in oxygen with a virtually colorless but extremely hot flame. A mixture of the two gases is dangerous; if ignited, the mixture will not merely burn but will explode with a detonation more powerful than that of the same weight of dynamite, shattering not only glass bottles but even small-bore glass tubing. Explosion occurs over a wide range of $H_2 : O_2$ ratios. The product of the reaction is the oxide, water.

$$\overline{2H_2} + \overline{O_2} \rightarrow \overline{2H_2O} + \triangle$$

6.7. Reactions of Oxygen with Compounds

The most important reactions of oxygen with compounds are those that occur when the compounds of carbon and hydrogen which we use for fuels are burned. They furnish most of the heat used in buildings and in the generation of steam, and all the energy for gasoline, diesel, and jet engines. A typical example of such a reaction is furnished by the combustion of methane (the major constituent of natural gas).

$$\overline{CH_4} + \overline{2O_2} \rightarrow \overline{CO_2} + \overline{2H_2O} + \triangle$$

Methane is burned in Bunsen burners, household gas ranges and furnaces, and industrial furnaces and kilns. More complex hydrocarbons such as gasoline, kerosene, diesel and fuel oil, and coal burn similarly, the same products resulting. Liquid-fuel rockets may burn kerosene or alcohol with liquid oxygen. "Exotic" fuels such as hydrides of boron and nitrogen have recently been tried because of the greater amount of energy produced by the combustion of a given weight of fuel. The following equations are typical:

$$\overline{B_2H_6} \text{ (diborane)} + \overline{3O_2} \rightarrow \overline{B_2O_3} + \overline{3H_2O} + \Delta$$

$$\overline{N_2H_4} \text{ (hydrazine)} + \overline{O_2} \rightarrow \overline{N_2} + \overline{2H_2O} + \Delta$$

Oxygen may also react with oxides and oxygen-containing salts, the result being an increase in their oxygen content. The carbon monoxide and sulfur dioxide reactions were mentioned in a preceding section. Other examples are:

$$4FeO + \overline{O_2} \rightarrow \underline{2Fe_2O_3}$$

$$2Na_2SO_3 + \overline{O_2} \rightarrow \underline{2Na_2SO_4}$$

In each of the examples used in this section the oxidation number of one atom in the compound increased (algebraically). The carbon in CH_4 went from -4 to $+4$, the hydrogen in B_2H_6 from -1 to $+1$, the nitrogen in N_2H_4 from -2 to 0, the iron in FeO from $+2$ to $+3$, and the sulfur in Na_2SO_3 from $+4$ to $+6$. All these changes are examples of oxidation. In each the valence of oxygen was reduced from 0 to -2 (per atom).

6.8. Oxidizing and Reducing Agents

Although non-metals do not give up electrons completely to oxygen as metals do, the electrons which they share with oxygen are really largely lost, for their average position is much nearer the strongly electronegative oxygen atoms. The action of oxygen on both classes of elements is therefore similar, a taking away of electrons from them. Oxygen is the earliest known and most important of the electron-takers, but the effect upon the electron-loser is the same when the electron-taker is chlorine or any other electronegative molecule. The process of electron loss was named **oxidation** when it was studied with oxygen as the de-electronating agent, and that name is now used for it regardless of the identity of the **oxidizing agent.** Thus chlorine is properly described as a strong oxidizing agent.

The case of chlorine shows that it is not necessary for an oxidizing agent to contain oxygen; neither is it necessary for it to be an element.

All that is necessary is that two strongly electronegative atoms be covalently bonded. Thus all chlorine-oxygen compounds are oxidizing agents. But oxygen compounds with slightly electronegative non-metals are not oxidizing agents. Silicon dioxide is 56 per cent oxygen, but those who recognize it as the main constituent of common sand will know that it is not an oxidizing agent!

Whenever an oxidizing agent gains electrons it is said to have been **reduced,** and the substance which was oxidized is called the **reducing agent.** From what has been said, it should be possible to deduce that the active metals and the less electronegative non-metals are reducing agents. Very important among them are hydrogen and carbon, and their compounds.

6.9. Combustion

Electron transfer reactions usually involve relatively large amounts of energy. At room temperature or even somewhat above it, however, they are usually slow enough so that the energy which is evolved escapes as fast as it is produced and the temperature does not rise. All chemical reactions increase in speed as the temperature is raised, and usually quite rapidly. A temperature is presently reached in many cases at which the heat evolved by the reaction can no longer be dissipated; the reaction accordingly speeds up, the temperature shoots up of its own accord, and the mixture glows or bursts into flame. The temperature at which this occurs is called the **kindling point.** Any chemical reaction which takes place with the emission of both light and heat is called **combustion.** If one of the reactants is a gas into which the other reactant is introduced in any form but in relatively small quantities, the gas is said to support the combustion of the other substance. In the case of two gases, which one is said to support the combustion of the other obviously involves an arbitrary choice of experimental conditions. Combustion in air is the most familiar example of this phenomenon. If a substance is said to be combustible, without particularization, the implication is that it will burn in *oxygen.* Similarly, if a gas is said to support combustion, without specifying what, it is taken for granted that it supports the combustion of the familiar list of ordinary combustibles. The word combustion is synonymous with one meaning of "burning" but is preferred in scientific discussions because it has only one meaning. By way of contrast, we speak of "burning love," the "burning taste" of tabasco sauce, or "burning the toast" when actually no combustion occurs.

Ordinarily fuels burn at a moderate speed, governed by the rate at which atmospheric oxygen can reach the combustible substance. If the air supply at the base of your Bunsen burner is shut, some of the gas may have time to rise 10 to 20 cm. above the top of the tube before air reaches it, so the flame is long. When some air is admitted at the base, it does not take as long for the remainder of the needed oxygen to reach the burning gas, and the flame is correspondingly short. (Since the same amount of heat is produced in both cases, the *temperature* of the more concentrated flame is higher.) If *all* the needed oxygen is mixed with the gas before ignition, the mixture burns in a small fraction of a second, i.e., it *explodes*. Some combustible gases form explosive mixtures with air even when the proportions are considerably different from those required for perfect combustion. Acetylene, C_2H_2, is notoriously dangerous in this way.

The combustion of solid fuel can be speeded up by blowing air into the fuel bed, or by mixing with it a solid oxidizing agent such as ammonium perchlorate, NH_4ClO_4. Dividing the fuel more finely so as to offer greater surface in contact with the air or other oxidizing agent is also effective. Excelsior burns faster than logs, if the supply of air is sufficient. It is also much easier to ignite, since it is easier to raise a small piece of material to the kindling point. The extreme case in subdividing a solid is reached with *dust*.

Because of the rapid rate at which small particles (with a relatively great proportion of their mass exposed as surface) can be oxidized, combustible dusts are a serious industrial hazard. If you have ever gone through a large flour mill you know that precautions are taken to keep dust at a minimum because a spark in dusty air may mean an explosion. As many coal mine explosions have been caused by dust as by gas. If there is coal dust on the floors of a mine a small gas explosion at a working face can raise a cloud of it. This, ignited by the first explosion, produces a larger one which can in turn be similarly propagated throughout the mine. Powdered coal is blown into the fireboxes in many great central power stations and burned just like gas. Powdered metals and certain non-metals—e.g., boron—show promise as solid-fuel propellants for rockets. After the cartridges have been soaked in liquid oxygen, powdered charcoal is used instead of dynamite in some mining operations.

6.10. Uses of Oxygen

All animal energy is derived from oxidation processes that use atmospheric oxygen (in the case of fish, this has first been dissolved in water). Warm-blooded animals require energy even when not moving or exerting themselves in any way. Our bodies would soon cool to the surrounding temperature were it not for oxidation reactions which produce energy. The evaporation of water from our bodies in hot weather is nature's provision for combating excess heat. Waste body tissues are oxidized to soluble compounds and CO_2 and thus eliminated. Entire courses in chemistry, known as physiological chemistry, are devoted to the study of reactions in the body.

Far more complicated than most of us realize is the process by which molecular oxygen dissolves in the moisture in lung tissue, diffuses into the blood stream, reacts with hemoglobin to produce red oxyhemoglobin (the coloring material in the blood), is released from this compound and from the oxidation of products resulting from the food we eat, and forms carbon dioxide, which diffuses back through the lung tissue and thence into exhaled breath. Failure of one step in this series of complicated reactions means that we cannot survive. If fats, proteins, or carbohydrates are burned in a crucible, they must be heated to high temperatures. These same materials, or compounds produced from them, "burn" in the body at its temperature of about 37° C. Catalysts called enzymes play an important role in making this oxidation possible. The energy which is necessary for physical exertion is supplied at the moment needed by the reaction:

$$C_6H_{10}O_5 + H_2O \rightarrow 2C_3H_6O_3$$
$$\text{Glycogen} \qquad\qquad\quad \text{Lactic acid}$$

This is followed by a complex series of reactions in which some of the lactic acid is oxidized to carbon dioxide and water; part of the energy from this reaction is used to convert the rest of it back into glycogen. If the exertion is severe, the lactic acid accumulates faster than it can be oxidized and the sensation of fatigue results. An athlete acquires, in training, the ability to tolerate relatively high concentrations of lactic acid. In running a 100-yard dash, which is often done without taking a single breath, a sprinter may produce 30 g. of it. He thereby incurs an "oxygen debt" which may require half an hour of deep breathing to make up.

Oxygen is used in an oxygen tent to enrich the air breathed by pneumonia patients and others with impaired breathing capacity. When oxygen is used in resuscitation apparatus it is mixed with 5 per cent CO_2 to stimulate the breathing reflex. Oxygen is mixed with gaseous anesthetics, such as nitrous oxide, N_2O, or cyclopropane, C_3H_6, because a patient must have oxygen even though he is unconscious.

Of the many chemical industries which require oxygen, the most important one is the metal industry. If the cheap reducing agent, carbon, is heated with naturally occurring metal oxides, the metal and oxides of carbon are formed.

$$\text{Some metal ores} + C \rightarrow \text{Metal} + \text{Oxides of carbon}$$

Exact equations for these reactions are given in the chapters dealing with the metals. The temperature necessary for the reduction of the ore is obtained by burning some carbon compound or coke with a blast of air. When air is used, the nitrogen in it is raised to the same temperature as the burning fuel; this involves a great waste of heat. "Pure" oxygen reacts more violently than air because it is a concentrated reactant instead of a diluted one. Very recently the steel industry has begun to enrich with oxygen the air used in some furnaces in order to make steel and alloys more quickly and cheaply. Oxygen-fed torches are used in scarfing white-hot steel ingots (i.e., cutting off an unsound end) before rolling them. In 1960 the steel industry used 500 cu. ft. of oxygen for each ingot ton of steel produced, an increase in oxygen consumption of 250 cu. ft. per ton of steel within two years. It is predicted that by 1970, 1500 cu. ft. of oxygen will be used per ton of steel produced. This tremendous growth of the oxygen industry in conjunction with steel production resulted in an annual production in 1960 of 120 billion cu. ft. from 360 oxygen-producing plants in the United States. The use of oxygen-enriched atmospheres in steel production has resulted in a 35 per cent increase in capacity of production using existing facilities. There is no visible evidence of a tapering off of the oxygen industry. In fact, in the first four months of 1960, 39 new oxygen plants were slated for construction, their total daily capacity to be 5228 tons of gaseous and 872 tons of liquid oxygen. The Armed Forces are consuming unpublished tonnages of liquid oxygen as the oxidizer in rockets; in their vernacular it is called "lox." In some parts of the country, "lox" tank trucks and mobile "lox" plants are almost as common as gasoline tank trucks.

6.11. Properties of Oxides in the Presence of Water

All oxides can be divided into two groups: metal oxides and nonmetal oxides. The chemical properties of oxides in these two classes are strikingly different. This is best shown by allowing them to react with water; in the case of a metal oxide the product is a base, and in the case of a non-metal oxide it is an acid. The reason for this difference is that the metal oxides contain a free oxide ion, whereas in the oxides of non-metals the non-metal atom is covalently bonded to the oxygen.

Many metal oxides are not soluble enough to react with water to any great extent. Those that are sufficiently soluble react with water because the oxide ion is an extremely strong base and water is an acid, although an exceedingly weak one. When the oxide ion takes a proton from water, the result is two hydroxide ions.

$$:\ddot{O}:^{--} + :\ddot{O}:H \rightarrow :\ddot{O}:H^- + :\ddot{O}:H^-$$
$$\qquad\qquad\quad H$$

The oxides of the metals sodium, potassium, calcium, and barium are soluble in water and so are the resulting hydroxides. (The oxides of all the less active metals are insoluble in water.) Typical equations are:

$$\underline{Na_2O} + H_2O \rightarrow 2Na^+ + 2OH^- \text{ (sodium hydroxide)}$$

$$\underline{CaO} + H_2O \rightarrow Ca^{++} + 2OH^- \text{ (calcium hydroxide)}$$

The hydroxide ion is a very strong base; therefore solutions of these hydroxides are strongly basic and will injure the skin and clothing. If spilled, they should be rinsed away with plenty of water and the remaining solution neutralized with dilute acetic acid.

If a non-metal oxide reacts with water—and most of those that are sufficiently soluble do—it is for a quite different reason. Since the oxygen atom has only 6 valence electrons, any non-metal oxide will contain at least one oxygen atom which is sharing two electron pairs. Test this out, remembering that each non-metal atom, including oxygen, must be surrounded by a complete octet of valence electrons. Oxygen, one of the most electronegative of all elements, does not like to have to share electrons with other non-metal atoms which are also electronegative. It wants to have the whole valence octet to itself, or at least shared only with hydrogen, which is only slightly electronegative. The oxygen atom which has a covalence of 2 in a non-metal oxide can remedy this situation if the oxide combines with a molecule of water. Thus chlorine monoxide, Cl_2O, reacts with water according to the equation:

$$:\ddot{C}l:\ddot{O}: + :\ddot{O}:H \rightarrow 2:\ddot{C}l:\ddot{O}: \text{ (hypochlorous acid)}$$
$$\quad :\ddot{C}l: \qquad H \qquad\qquad H$$

In sulfur dioxide, SO_2, the di-covalent oxygen atom is sharing both electron pairs with the *same* sulfur atom. Here again, reaction with water produces a substance in which no oxygen atom has to share two pairs of electrons with a strongly electronegative atom.

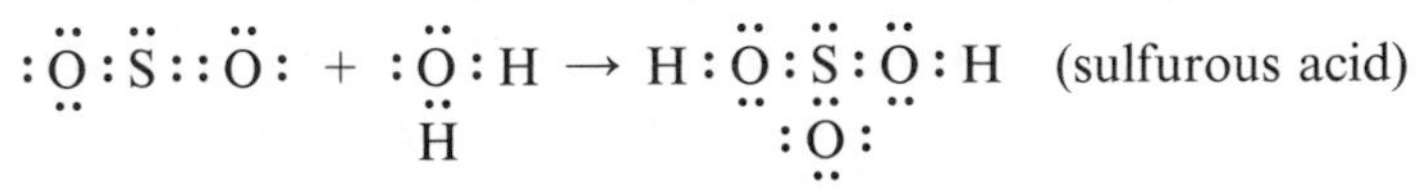

$$:\overset{..}{\underset{..}{O}}:\overset{..}{S}::\overset{..}{\underset{..}{O}}: \; + \; \overset{..}{\underset{..}{\underset{H}{O}}}:H \; \rightarrow \; H:\overset{..}{\underset{..}{O}}:\overset{..}{\underset{\underset{..}{:\overset{..}{O}:}}{S}}:\overset{..}{\underset{..}{O}}:H \quad \text{(sulfurous acid)}$$

The conventional equations for these reactions are:

$$\overline{Cl_2O} + H_2O \rightarrow 2HClO$$

$$\overline{SO_2} + H_2O \rightarrow H_2SO_3$$

Several reactions of this type are of commercial importance. Among them are:

$$\overline{SO_3} + H_2O \rightarrow H_2SO_4 \text{ (sulfuric acid)}$$

$$\overline{CO_2} + H_2O \rightarrow H_2CO_3 \text{ (carbonic acid)}$$

$$\underline{P_2O_5} + 3H_2O \rightarrow 2H_3PO_4 \text{ (phosphoric acid)}$$

Because metallic oxides, as shown above, react with water to form basic solutions, they are frequently called **basic anhydrides.** Similarly, non-metallic oxides, which react with water to form acids, may be called **acid anhydrides.**

The contrast between the basic nature of metal oxides and the acid-forming properties of non-metal oxides is so great and so important that metals are frequently referred to as basic elements and non-metals as acidic elements. It will be seen, however, that oxygen is the key element in both cases. Neither metals nor metal ions are themselves bases; the metals simply turn oxygen into the strong base, the oxide ion, by their willingness to give up electrons completely to the oxygen. Non-metals, by insisting on sharing electrons with oxygen, lower its basic strength to a level that permits the easy escape of protons if they are present. In other words, the plain oxide ion is a stronger base than any ion containing oxygen and another non-metallic element.

6.12. Ozone

In addition to ordinary oxygen, O_2, oxygen atoms can form the molecule O_3. When two different substances are both composed of one single kind of atom they are said to be **allotropic** modifications of the element. If two allotropic forms of an element have identical molecules, merely arranged in different patterns in their crystals, they may not differ very much from each other. If the molecules are different, the two forms may resemble each other only in giving the same products after a chemical reaction has taken place. This is the case with O_2 and O_3, so it is natural that the latter has been given a name of its own, **ozone.** It comes from the Greek word meaning to smell. The strong, peculiar smell of ozone is familiar to all who have been in the vicinity of big electrical machinery or strong ultraviolet lights. A trace of ozone as small as one part in 10,000,-000 can be detected in air by this odor. Ozone is noticeably blue (the liquid is dark blue), 1.5 times as dense as oxygen, and has a boiling point 71° higher.

Chemically, not only is ozone much more active than molecular oxygen, it is one of the most powerful oxidizing agents known. Such metals as silver and mercury, although not tarnished by O_2, are quickly covered with a coating of oxide in the presence of O_3. A spectacular demonstration consists in tying a weight to a rubber band and hanging the band in front of the outlet of an ozone machine. It is only a matter of seconds until the band breaks. The probable lasting quality of rubber goods exposed to the sunlight and air can thus be predicted in a few minutes with such a test, for ozone accomplishes in a few seconds or minutes changes which would require a much longer time under ordinary conditions. A piece of paper moistened with a solution of potassium iodide is only very slowly affected by molecular oxygen. Ozone liberates iodine quickly. A little starch applied to the paper is turned blue by the free iodine.

Ozone is formed by the addition of an oxygen atom to an oxygen molecule, the added atom sharing one of the previously unshared electron pairs in the O_2 molecule. This appears to be permitted by the O_2 only with some reluctance, for the third oxygen atom is rather easily broken off again. This accounts for the greater reactivity of ozone as compared with oxygen. It also accounts for the fact that a large amount of energy is used up in the formation of ozone from oxygen. Much more energy is used up in breaking the multiple bonds of an O_2 molecule than is given out when the resulting atoms combine with other O_2 molecules.

6.13. Formation of Ozone

Some chemical reactions produce traces of ozone as a by-product. The "smell of phosphorus" which is observed when yellow phosphorus is exposed to air is at least partly due to ozone formed during the slow oxidation of the phosphorus. The Los Angeles smog owes a considerable part of its irritating and deleterious properties to the presence of a few parts per million of ozone, produced during the light-induced oxidation of incompletely burned hydrocarbons in automobile exhaust gases.

It is not practicable to prepare ozone by high temperature, for thermal collisions break O_3 molecules apart far faster than they do the more stable O_2 molecules. Oxygen molecules absorb ultraviolet light, with resulting dissociation and formation of ozone. This process, taking place on a large scale in the outer reaches of the earth's atmosphere, removes from the incoming sunlight all but the very near ultraviolet and is probably responsible for the fact that we cannot see ultraviolet light. No appreciable amounts of the ozone produced either in this way or by lightning persist for any length of time; the ozone decomposes spontaneously into ordinary oxygen, or reacts with oxidizable impurities in the air.

The only practical method of making ozone is by passing cold, dry oxygen through a **silent discharge.** The apparatus consists essentially of a condenser, between whose charged plates the oxygen can be passed. Large numbers of gaseous ions are always present in any gas from which they have not been intentionally removed; they are produced continuously by passage of cosmic rays, etc. These ions are driven back and forth through the oxygen by an alternating potential of several thousand volts applied to the condenser plates. They dissociate molecules which they strike, or at least "excite" them to a reactive state. The yield of ozone may be better than 10 per cent at room temperature and is almost 100 per cent when the apparatus is cooled with liquid air. The liquid ozone which is produced in the latter case is dangerously explosive because its decomposition is exothermic.

6.14. Uses of Ozone

Ozone, being much more reactive than oxygen, has some specialized uses. For most industrial reactions, 2 per cent ozone in oxygen is used. This mixture can be stored and shipped in liquid form, or adsorbed in containers filled with silica gel. Certain selective oxidations of organic compounds can be accomplished only with ozone. Air and water can be purified by ozonizing processes. Ozone readily attacks anaerobic bacteria, and destroys odors that are not affected by chlorination, or may even be due to it. Liquid ozone is receiving some consideration as a possible rocket fuel. The blue liquid boils at $-112.4°$ C. and is less bulky than "lox," but its explosiveness is a great drawback. The tricky problems involved in handling and dispensing ozone as well as the installation and operating costs of ozonators have hampered the expansion of its use in industry. It is nevertheless anticipated that ozone will be produced and used by the chemical industry in large quantities in the near future.

6.15. Peroxides

Very reactive metals, like those in Groups IA and IIA of the periodic table, with electronegativities of less than 1.0, can give electrons to an oxygen molecule without breaking it up. The result is the peroxide ion, O_2^{--}. The electronic formula is $:\ddot{O}:\ddot{O}:^{--}$. With only a single covalent bond to hold the two atoms together, this ion is much more reactive than the O_2 molecule.

Many metal peroxides are prepared for various commercial uses; the most common in the laboratory are those of sodium and barium. All peroxides react with water or stronger acids to produce hydrogen peroxide, a very weak acid. In the case of Na_2O_2, which is easily soluble, the reaction is very rapid and produces a dangerous amount of heat. Thus moisture in the air can easily cause Na_2O_2 to ignite paper that is in contact with it. For this reason the material should not be poured from the bottle onto pieces of paper nor should any that is left over be thrown into waste jars. The equation for the reaction with water is:

$$Na_2O_2 + H_2O \rightarrow 2Na^+ + 2OH^- + H_2O_2$$

If barium peroxide, BaO_2, is treated with sulfuric or phosphoric acid the product other than H_2O_2 is insoluble and can be removed by filtration.

$$BaO_2 + H^+ + HSO_4^- \rightarrow BaSO_4 + H_2O_2$$
$$3BaO_2 + 2H_3PO_4 \rightarrow Ba_3(PO_4)_2 + 3H_2O_2$$

This was until recently the commercial method for the preparation of H_2O_2. The product is a 3 per cent solution and is usually sold in drugstores under the designation "ten-volume." This means that the solution will yield ten times its volume of oxygen when the H_2O_2 in it decomposes. Attempts to concentrate this solution by the evaporation of water result only in decomposing the H_2O_2 unless it is very pure and the conditions are carefully controlled.

In addition to the metallic peroxides, which contain the peroxide ion, it is possible to prepare a long list of compounds in which one or both of the peroxide oxygens share an electron pair with some other non-metallic atom. Some organic reducing agents resemble the active metals in their ability to form peroxides by reaction with molecular oxygen. Other covalent peroxy compounds are produced by electrolytic oxidation. A simple example is peroxymonosulfuric acid,

$$
\begin{array}{c}
:\overset{\cdot\cdot}{O}: \\[2pt]
H:\overset{\cdot\cdot}{\underset{\cdot\cdot}{O}}:\overset{\cdot\cdot}{\underset{\cdot\cdot}{S}}:\overset{\cdot\cdot}{\underset{\cdot\cdot}{O}}:\overset{\cdot\cdot}{\underset{\cdot\cdot}{O}}:H \\[2pt]
:\overset{\cdot\cdot}{O}:
\end{array}
$$

All of them react with water or acids to give H_2O_2, but more slowly than do the metallic peroxides, because a covalent bond has to be broken. Each has individual properties which are responsible for many special uses.

6.16. Commercial Preparation of H_2O_2

The most important of all peroxides is peroxydisulfuric acid. When moderately concentrated sulfuric acid or ammonium hydrogen sulfate, NH_4HSO_4, is electrolyzed (details of electrolytic reactions are given in Chapter 22), the anode removes an electron from one of the oxygen atoms, thus:

$$
H^+ \text{ (or NH}_4{}^+) + \left[\begin{array}{c} :\overset{\cdot\cdot}{O}: \\ H:\overset{\cdot\cdot}{\underset{\cdot\cdot}{O}}:\overset{\cdot\cdot}{\underset{\cdot\cdot}{S}}:\overset{\cdot\cdot}{\underset{\cdot\cdot}{O}}: \\ :\overset{\cdot\cdot}{O}: \end{array} \right]^- \xrightarrow{\text{\tiny anode}} H^+ \text{ (or NH}_4{}^+) + \left[\begin{array}{c} :\overset{\cdot\cdot}{O}: \\ H:\overset{\cdot\cdot}{\underset{\cdot\cdot}{O}}:\overset{\cdot\cdot}{\underset{\cdot\cdot}{S}}:\overset{\cdot\cdot}{O}. \\ :\overset{\cdot\cdot}{O}: \end{array} \right]^{\circ} + e^-
$$

The electron immediately discharges a proton at the cathode. Two of the uncharged sulfuric acid fragments then join to form a molecule of peroxydisulfuric acid in the same way and for the same reason as two chlorine atoms combine to form Cl_2. The formula of the product:

$$
\begin{array}{c}
:\overset{\cdot\cdot}{O}: \qquad :\overset{\cdot\cdot}{O}: \\[2pt]
H:\overset{\cdot\cdot}{\underset{\cdot\cdot}{O}}:\overset{\cdot\cdot}{\underset{\cdot\cdot}{S}}:\overset{\cdot\cdot}{\underset{\cdot\cdot}{O}}:\overset{\cdot\cdot}{\underset{\cdot\cdot}{O}}:\overset{\cdot\cdot}{\underset{\cdot\cdot}{S}}:\overset{\cdot\cdot}{\underset{\cdot\cdot}{O}}:H \\[2pt]
:\overset{\cdot\cdot}{O}: \qquad :\overset{\cdot\cdot}{O}:
\end{array}
$$

plainly shows the peroxide linkage in the middle. The ammonium salt of this acid is a valuable, strong oxidizing agent. The name is commonly shortened to ammonium persulfate, $(NH_4)_2S_2O_8$. When steam is passed through a solution containing either $(NH_4)_2S_2O_8$ or $H_2S_2O_8$, H_2O_2 is formed and distills over, and the original hydrogen sulfate ions are regenerated.

$$2NH_4^+ + S_2O_8^{--} + \overline{2H_2O} \rightarrow 2NH_4^+ + 2HSO_4^- + \overline{H_2O_2}$$

This is the chief method at present for the preparation of H_2O_2.

In the electrolytic method it will be observed that -2 oxygen is oxidized to the -1 state. In the newest commercial method for manufacturing H_2O_2, the valence of atmospheric oxygen is *reduced* from 0 to -1. The reducing agent is a complex organic substance known as an alkylanthrohydroquinone, which we may represent as H—O—(R)—O—H, where (R) stands for the rest of the molecule. When air is bubbled through a solution of this reducing agent in an organic solvent, it transfers the two hydrogen atoms to an oxygen molecule.

$$H—O—(R)—O—H + O_2 \rightarrow O{=}(R){=}O + H_2O_2$$

The H_2O_2 is extracted from the organic solvent by means of water, and then purified and concentrated. By passing hydrogen through the organic solution, the O—(R)—O (alkylanthroquinone) is reduced back to the starting material and thus can be reused indefinitely.

6.17. Concentrated H_2O_2

Electrolytic H_2O_2 is much purer than the filtrate obtained with BaO_2. This fact led to the discovery that pure H_2O_2 could be concentrated by evaporation (its boiling point is $52°$ higher than that of water) without serious decomposition. Before World War II, a 30 per cent solution of H_2O_2 was a standard commercial product, shipped in tank-car lots. In 1944 it was found that the Germans had been using the reaction between an 80 per cent solution and a concentrated sodium permanganate solution to generate a mixture of steam and oxygen that would drive the fuel pump of the V-2 rocket, which had to deliver a ton or two of fuel in a few seconds.

$$2Na^+ + 2MnO_4^- + 3H_2O_2 \rightarrow 2Na^+ + 2OH^- + 2MnO_2 + \overline{3O_2} \overline{} \overline{2H_2O}$$

$$2H_2O_2 \overset{MnO_2}{\rightarrow} \overline{2H_2O} + \overline{O_2}$$

When our War department asked for H_2O_2 of this concentration for experimental purposes, it was only a short time before an American manufacturer, paying special attention to the problem of purity, was able to produce a 95 per cent concentration.

Whereas the old 3 per cent solution was mainly a bottled item sold in drugstores, concentrated H_2O_2 has opened a wide new field for itself. It is used to bleach paper pulp and cotton cloth, to develop vat dyes (an oxidative process), and as a powerful oxidizing agent in chemical industries. A particular point in favor of its use as an oxidizing agent is that it leaves no residue, and any excess can be decomposed catalytically into oxygen and water as shown in the above equation. The bulk of the current production is shipped as 35 and 50 per cent solutions, but a 90 per cent solution is regularly available. In addition to the advantages naturally accruing from its high concentration, the 90 per cent solution is soluble in organic liquids. When stored below 30° C. it decomposes at the rate of less than 1 per cent a year, but will ignite soiled clothing or wooden floors if spilled. Pure H_2O_2 is stable enough to withstand the shock of a bullet or even a detonator, but the presence of a slight trace of organic impurity makes it behave more like nitroglycerin. MnO_2 is only one of many substances which can catalyze the decomposition of H_2O_2. A bottle of the latter should always be pointed away from the face while being opened, because a dangerous pressure of oxygen may have developed in it. Acids and some organic compounds such as acetanilide deactivate many catalysts (which may be present as trace impurities) and are used as preservatives.

Dilute H_2O_2 is used in the laboratory as a mild oxidizing agent. For example, it oxidizes black lead sulfide, PbS, to white lead sulfate, $PbSO_4$; hence old paintings containing lead pigments can be brightened with it.

$$\underline{PbS} + 4H_2O_2 \rightarrow \underline{PbSO_4} + 4H_2O$$

White manganese(II) hydroxide, $Mn(OH)_2$, is oxidized to black manganese dioxide, MnO_2.

$$\underline{Mn(OH)_2} + H_2O_2 \rightarrow \underline{MnO_2} + 2H_2O$$

Free iodine is liberated from solutions of iodides.

It is not always possible to tell from the formula of a compound whether or not it is a peroxide. Knowing that barium, manganese, and lead all form divalent cations, we might jump to the conclusion that BaO_2, MnO_2, and PbO_2 are all peroxides. That this is false in the case of the last two can be proved by a simple experiment in *qualitative analysis*. Any peroxide will yield H_2O_2 if treated with dilute H_2SO_4.

$$\underline{Na_2O_2} + H^+ + HSO_4^- \rightarrow 2Na^+ + SO_4^{--} + \underline{H_2O_2}$$

After the salt in question has been thus treated, the acid solution can be tested for the presence of H_2O_2 by adding a little very dilute potassium dichromate, $K_2Cr_2O_7$, and then ether, which will float on top of the solution. When the test tube is shaken and the ether is allowed to float back to the top it will be colored blue by the perchromic acid it has extracted from the solution if any H_2O_2 was present in the first place. The formula of the unstable perchromic acid has not been determined. The failure of this test with MnO_2 and PbO_2 shows that these compounds are dioxides rather than peroxides. That is, the metals have an oxidation number of $+4$, whereas the oxygen has the normal oxidation number of -2. The unusual valence for the metals is confirmed by the fact that lead dioxide will dissolve in cold acetic acid, $HC_2H_3O_2$, to form lead(IV) acetate, $Pb(C_2H_3O_2)_4$, and MnO_2 in cold HCl to form manganese(IV) chloride, $MnCl_4$.

QUESTIONS AND PROBLEMS

1. The highest temperature that can be obtained by heating objects in the Bunsen flame is about 1000° C. Which oxides completely or partly decompose under these conditions? Write balanced equations for each reaction.

2. Illustrate the preparation of oxygen with balanced equations for the following:
   a. A metal peroxide + heat.
   b. A non-metal peroxide + heat.
   c. A peroxide + water.
   d. A salt + heat.

3. Salts containing which negative ions are suitable for the preparation of oxygen by thermal decomposition?

4. How does oxygen compare with other non-metals in electronegativity? With which elements will it not combine directly? At all?

5. Is heat liberated or absorbed by the direct union of oxygen with elements? What visible evidence can you cite for this? Are these reactions exothermic or endothermic?

6. Explain why the very reactive metals, magnesium and aluminum, do not continuously corrode in oxygen, whereas the less active metal, iron, does. Why does stainless steel contain chromium?

7. Contrast the chemical nature of the oxide ion of a soluble metal oxide with that of covalently bonded oxygen in a non-metal oxide.

8. Write balanced equations for the reaction of oxygen with four metals and four non-metals.

9. Which of the compounds in question 8 are acid anhydrides? Basic anhydrides? Soluble in water?

10. What is an oxidizing agent? A reducing agent? What is the role of electronegativity in connection with these? Name four elements that are good oxidizing agents and four that are good reducing agents.

11. List several uses of oxygen. What is "lox"? How is it made? Name several solid fuels and state specific uses of each. Define combustion.

12. What are the allotropic forms of oxygen, and under what conditions do they exist?

13. Show by balanced equations how H_2O_2 can be prepared from metallic peroxides, from organic peroxides, by electrolysis.

14. What are some of the important properties and uses of H_2O_2? What part does its concentration play in some of its uses?

15. What factors affect the stability of H_2O_2?

16. How many grams of sodium chlorate must be decomposed to produce 45 g. of oxygen?

17. What volume of oxygen collected by the displacement of water at 30° C. and under a barometric pressure of 720 mm. would be obtained from the thermal decomposition of 25 g. of calcium peroxide?

7

Hydrogen

7.1. Discovery of Hydrogen

Records are incomplete prior to 1650, when Turquet de Mayerne reported that an inflammable gas could be obtained from iron and sulfuric acid. In 1766, Sir Henry Cavendish (1731–1810), an English scientist, proved that the gas obtained from the reaction of a metal with an acid was an individual substance; he called it "inflammable air." He found that it would react with oxygen to produce water. His one mistake regarding this gas was the fact that he thought it came from the metal and not the acid. Lavoisier gave this gas its present name, **hydrogen,** meaning water former.

7.2. Occurrence of Hydrogen

Hydrogen is found in unimportant quantities in some gaseous emanations from the earth such as the *solfataras* of Iceland, the petroleum fields of Pennsylvania and Ohio, some volcanoes, jets of steam in Tuscany, and salt beds in Stassfurt. It is also occluded in certain meteorites, minerals, and clays. Some metals absorb large volumes of hydrogen, and wherever these metals are found free in nature hydrogen may be found associated with them. The most important of these metals are iron, cobalt, nickel, platinum, and palladium. Hydrogen is a normal product of anaerobic decomposition and is found in the intestinal gases of many animals, in the gases escaping from septic tanks, and in sewage sludge gas. Its concentration in the atmosphere, never above 0.02 per cent, may have been produced by the anaerobic decomposition of organic matter. Spectroscopic observations show that hydrogen completely surrounds the sun. Photographs of the sun's chromosphere show flames of incandescent hydrogen 300,000 miles high and over 100,000 miles wide. Other stars are also composed mainly of hydrogen.

In the combined state hydrogen is abundantly distributed throughout nature. It forms one-ninth the weight of water and one-quarter the weight of natural gas (methane), and is an essential constituent of cellulose, sugar, starch, fats, proteins, oils, petroleum, and all hydrocarbons. In fact, *nearly all organic compounds contain hydrogen.* It is a constituent of acids and bases. In smaller quantities it occurs in combination with phosphorus, sulfur, boron, and nitrogen (as ammonia). In some mineral springs it is liberated as the gas hydrogen sulfide, H_2S. Water and natural gas are the cheapest sources of hydrogen.

7.3. Preparation of Hydrogen

When any new substance is discovered, it remains a laboratory curiosity until some use for it is found. The uses to which hydrogen could be put were a long time in coming, but they are increasing steadily. Old expensive methods of preparing hydrogen have given way to cheaper commercial processes, and several procedures are now available.

Hydrogen from water. The cheapness of the raw material makes water the most important source of commercial hydrogen. The gas is prepared in three ways: by the reaction of *metals with water,* the reaction of *non-metals with water,* and the *electrolysis of water.* The second of these is by far the most important.

The metals can be divided into three groups according to the ease with which they react with water and liberate hydrogen. Some react at room temperature with no application of external heat, others must be heated, and still others will not react at all. The alkali metals (Group IA) react vigorously, even violently. *Never under any conditions drop more than a very small piece of sodium or potassium into water.* Potassium dropped on water catches fire and burns. A small piece of sodium skims around over the surface with a sizzling noise. The reaction between sodium and water is:

$$2Na + 2H_2O \rightarrow 2Na^+ + 2OH^- + \overline{H_2} + \Delta$$

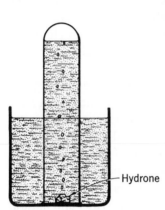

Fig. 7.1. Hydrogen gas collected by displacement of water.

To decrease the speed of this reaction and thus the hazard, some laboratories use an alloy of lead and sodium (65 per cent Pb, 35 per cent Na) called hydrone. It is heavy enough to sink readily. Hydrogen is collected in an inverted tube, as shown in Fig. 7.1. If samples of all the metals are added to water, only the alkali metals and the heavier alkaline earth metals (Group IIA), starting with calcium, are found to liberate hydrogen at room temperature.

A strip of magnesium placed in water produces no visible evolution of hydrogen, but it liberates hydrogen from steam. A suitable apparatus is shown in Fig. 7.2. Water is first heated to boiling to drive the air from the flask; then a spoon with magnesium ribbon wrapped around it is held in a flame until the magnesium ribbon ignites, and the connection is quickly fitted in place. Hydrogen is caught in the inverted bottle.

$$Mg + \overline{H_2O} \rightarrow MgO + \overline{H_2} + \Delta$$

At the temperature of this reaction the magnesium oxide does not react with water to form magnesium hydroxide.

A commercial process, developed in 1861 and formerly important, involved the reaction between iron or iron turnings (greater surface exposed) and steam at 550° to 800° C. The equation for this reaction is:

$$3Fe + \overline{4H_2O} \xrightarrow{\Delta} Fe_3O_4 + \overline{4H_2}$$

The fact that many hot metals liberate hydrogen from steam is the reason why one should never attempt to put out metal fires with water. The resultant hydrogen may cause an explosion that has a far worse effect than the fire.

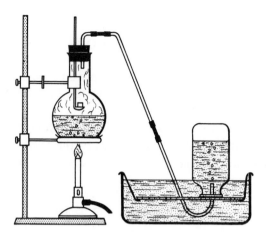

Fig. 7.2. Preparation of hydrogen by the reaction between magnesium and steam.

Cheaper than any method involving the use of metals is the decomposition of water by means of electricity, a process called **electrolysis.** H_2SO_4, Na_2SO_4, or NaOH is added to the water to make it a conductor. A substance added for this purpose is called an **electrolyte.** The most modern commercial electrolytic units use alkaline electrolytes. When a direct current is passed through the solution, oxygen is liberated at one electrode and hydrogen at the other:

$$2H_2O \overset{\text{\tiny⚡}}{\rightarrow} \overline{2H_2} + \overline{O_2}$$

The equation shows that 2 volumes of hydrogen are liberated per volume of oxygen.

One reaction of great commercial importance is the **water gas process,** in which steam is passed over the non-metal, carbon (coke at 1000° C.). The resultant mixture of carbon monoxide and hydrogen can be burned as a fuel.

$$\underline{C} + \overline{H_2O} \xrightarrow{1000° C.} \overline{CO} + \overline{H_2}$$

A blast of air is forced through coke until it is white-hot; the air is then shut off and steam is forced through the coke. When the temperature has fallen to such a point that the reaction is no longer efficient, the steam is shut off and the remaining coke is again heated to 1000°. If the only end product desired is hydrogen, the mixture of H_2 and CO is passed with additional steam at a more moderate temperature over catalysts of thorium, chromium, and iron oxides until the CO is converted into CO_2.

$$\overline{CO} + \overline{H_2O} \xrightarrow{500° C.} \overline{CO_2} + \overline{H_2}$$

The carbon dioxide can be efficiently removed by passing the mixture of gases, at high pressure, through cold water. The solubility of hydrogen is very low.

A mixture of CO and H_2 that contains a much larger percentage of the latter than water gas does is produced by the reaction of steam with natural gas. Natural gas is mainly methane, CH_4. The equation for its reaction with steam is:

$$\overline{CH_4} + \overline{H_2O} \xrightarrow{\Delta} \overline{CO} + \overline{3H_2}$$

This is the most important commercial process for producing hydrogen in the United States at present.

Hydrogen from acids. Metals are frequently divided into two groups: those which react with acids and liberate hydrogen, and those which do not. The reaction of metals with water, which has just been described, falls into this class, for water has weak acid properties. Sodium and potassium will displace hydrogen from stronger acids too, of course. (Do not try the experiment. It is explosively violent.) Less active metals, such as iron and zinc, which do not liberate hydrogen from water at room temperature with appreciable speed, will do so at a reasonable rate from ordinary acids. Such a process is of no commercial importance because the materials are expensive; but it is excellent in the laboratory, for the reaction will take place at room temperature and the rate of the evolution of gas can be easily controlled by regulating the concentration of the acid. A salt is always the other product of the reaction between an acid and a metal. The following equations illustrate reactions between metals and acids:

$$\underline{Mg} + 2HC_2H_3O_2 \rightarrow Mg^{++} + 2C_2H_3O_2^- + \overline{H_2}$$

$$\underline{2Al} + 3H^+ + 3HSO_4^- \rightarrow 2Al^{+3} + 3SO_4^{--} + \overline{3H_2}$$

If you add samples of several metals to hydrochloric acid, you will find quite a difference in the rate of liberation of hydrogen. This is because of the difference in the ease with which they give up electrons, for the reaction with acids is essentially the reduction of protons. The **electrochemical series** of the metals, which is shown in part in Table

TABLE 7.1. Electrochemical Series (Metals and Hydrogen)

Name	Symbol	Notes
1. Lithium	Li	
2. Potassium	K	1. Elements 1–6 liberate hydrogen from cold water.
3. Barium	Ba	$2\,Na + 2\,HOH \rightarrow 2Na^+ + 2OH^- + \overline{H_2}$
4. Strontium	Sr	2. Elements 1–13 liberate hydrogen from steam.
5. Calcium	Ca	$Mg + \overline{H_2O} \rightarrow \underline{MgO} + H_2$
6. Sodium	Na	3. Elements 1–17 liberate hydrogen from acids.
7. Magnesium	Mg	$\underline{Zn} + 2H^+ + 2Cl^- \rightarrow Zn^{++} + 2Cl^- + \overline{H_2}$
8. Aluminum	Al	4. Elements 1–23 react with oxygen and form oxides.
9. Manganese	Mn	$4Al + 3\overline{O_2} \rightarrow \underline{2Al_2O_3}$
10. Zinc	Zn	5. Elements 24–26 form oxides by indirect methods.
11. Chromium	Cr	$\underline{AuCl_3} + 3K^+ + 3OH^- \rightarrow$
12. Iron	Fe	$\qquad Au(OH)_3 + 3K^+ + 3Cl^-$
13. Cadmium	Cd	$2Au(OH)_3 \xrightarrow{\Delta} \overline{Au_2O_3} + \overline{3H_2O}$
14. Cobalt	Co	6. If heated, the oxides of elements 23–26 decompose
15. Nickel	Ni	to form metals and oxygen.
16. Tin	Sn	$2\underline{HgO} \xrightarrow{\Delta} 2Hg + \overline{O_2}$
17. Lead	Pb	7. Oxides of elements 1–11 are not reduced by hy-
18. Hydrogen	H	drogen to produce metals.
19. Copper	Cu	$\underline{MgO} + \overline{H_2} \rightarrow$ no reaction
20. Bismuth	Bi	8. Oxides of elements 12–26 can be reduced by hy-
21. Arsenic	As	drogen.
22. Antimony	Sb	$\underline{Fe_3O_4} + \overline{4H_2} \xrightarrow{\Delta} 3Fe + \overline{4H_2O}$
23. Mercury	Hg	9. Oxides of metals below hydrogen are *easily* re-
24. Silver	Ag	duced.
25. Platinum	Pt	$\underline{CuO} + \overline{H_2} \rightarrow Cu + \overline{H_2O} + \Delta$
26. Gold	Au	

7.1, indicates the order in which some of the metals will replace each other from water solutions of their compounds. Notice that the metals and hydrogen are set free by reduction. In general, *any element in the series will displace any element below it* from water solutions of its compounds. Thus all the elements above hydrogen will displace it from acids; those below will not. On the basis of this series we should expect iron to replace copper ions in solution. This can be shown to be the case, for an iron nail placed in a solution of copper sulfate is quickly coated with copper. Magnesium will replace lead and lead will replace mercury. The closer any two elements are to each other in the electrochemical series (frequently abbreviated E.C.S.), the less probable it is that the higher metal will, under all conditions of concentration, replace the lower from its compounds. The E.C.S. is more accurate the farther apart the metals are.

The E.C.S. table should be consulted in regard to every metal which is studied in the laboratory. The elements listed are arranged nearly but not quite in order of increasing electronegativity. The differences take into account the varying energies with which the ions attach water molecules to themselves. This is why the E.C.S. applies specifically to water solutions. In the absence of water the order of reactivity is the order of decreasing electronegativity.

Hydrogen from solutions of hydroxides. Several elements liberate hydrogen vigorously from water if the water contains enough sodium or potassium hydroxide to react with the product other than hydrogen. Among these are the metals zinc and aluminum and the non-metal silicon. When zinc starts to react with plain water, the hydroxide is produced, as in the case of sodium, but zinc hydroxide is insoluble. It coats over the surface of the metal and stops the reaction.

$$\underline{Zn} + 2H_2O \rightarrow \underline{Zn(OH)_2} + \overline{H_2}$$

Zinc, however, is one of a considerable class of metals which show some characteristics of non-metals; for example, $Zn(OH)_2$ is a weak acid as well as a base. To call attention to this, the formula may be rewritten H_2ZnO_2. If a sufficient amount of a soluble hydroxide is present it will dissolve the $Zn(OH)_2$ as fast as it is formed, according to the equation:

$$\underline{H_2ZnO_2} + 2Na^+ + 2OH^- \rightarrow 2Na^+ + Zn(OH)_4^{--}$$

This permits the evolution of hydrogen to continue rapidly. The two equations may be added together; the H_2ZnO_2 and $Zn(OH)_2$ being the same substance, they cancel out.

$$\underline{Zn} + 2Na^+ + 2OH^- + 2H_2O \rightarrow 2Na^+ + Zn(OH)_4^{--} + \overline{H_2}$$

The ion $Zn(OH)_4^{--}$ is called the zincate ion; here also the zinc shows a behavior characteristic of a non-metal, for it is part of a negative ion.

Aluminum is ordinarily prevented from reacting with water by a coating of Al_2O_3, but this substance behaves not merely as a metallic oxide would behave, but also as though it were a non-metallic oxide. It reacts with NaOH to form the soluble salt, sodium aluminate, $NaAl(OH)_4$, thus:

$$\underline{Al_2O_3} + 2Na^+ + 2OH^- + 3H_2O \rightarrow 2Na^+ + 2Al(OH)_4^-$$

In a sodium hydroxide solution, then, the surface of the aluminum is immediately cleaned so that the active metal can liberate hydrogen from water in accordance with the prediction of the E.C.S. Aluminum hydroxide is not actually precipitated, however, because it reacts even more readily with the hydroxide ion than does the corresponding oxide. The over-all reaction with the metal is thus:

$$\underline{2Al} + 2Na^+ + 2OH^- + 6H_2O \rightarrow 2Na^+ + 2Al(OH)_4^- + \overline{3H_2}$$

The ability of some elements to form compounds in which they act as metals and others in which they act as non-metals is so important that it will be discussed in a special chapter. These elements are called **amphoteric** elements.

The non-metal silicon reacts with sodium hydroxide solutions in a similar manner, yielding sodium silicate and hydrogen.

$$\underline{Si} + 2Na^+ + 2OH^- + H_2O \rightarrow 2Na^+ + SiO_3^{--} + \overline{2H_2}$$

Here too we may imagine an acidic hydroxide as an intermediate step. Since it does not behave like a base, it is called silicic acid and written H_4SiO_4 or, after losing water, H_2SiO_3. A hydrogen-generating kit used during World War II contained silicon (in the form of an alloy with iron called ferrosilicon) and dry sodium hydroxide. The addition of water quickly caused the production of enough H_2 to inflate a small balloon which carried a radio aerial aloft for emergency broadcasting.

Hydrogen by other methods. Hydrogen is produced by oil refineries during the "cracking" of petroleum hydrocarbons in manufacturing gasoline and other products. Some of it is recombined with particular products for special purposes; more of it is burned as fuel. Some is piped to adjacent plants for chemical uses.

Ammonia is also cracked.

$$\overline{2NH_3} \xrightarrow[\text{catalyst}]{600°\,C} N_2 + \overline{3H_2}$$

The gas mixture produced is 25 per cent nitrogen by volume, but this rather inert gas is as effective as hydrogen in such uses as excluding oxygen from metals in annealing ovens. To those who know that ammonia is prepared from hydrogen and nitrogen in the first place, it may seem uneconomic to reverse the process. The explanation lies in the fact that ammonia is easily liquefiable. Enough of it to produce 3000 cu. ft. of hydrogen can be shipped in a single light-walled cylinder.

Other substances than those mentioned can react with water to produce hydrogen. Among them are boron hydrides and the hydrides of the metals 1 to 6 in the E.C.S., such as sodium hydride, NaH.

7.4. Laboratory Preparation of Hydrogen

A simple apparatus used in preparing small amounts of hydrogen is shown in Fig. 7.3. The acid is poured through the thistle tube and quickly comes in contact with the metal. Two precautions are necessary. The reaction is exothermic; therefore add the acid gradually, for otherwise the hydrogen will be liberated so rapidly that it may force the acid out of the thistle tube because of the back pressure produced. Keep all flames away from the gas escaping from the bottle until you are certain that no oxygen is mixed with the hydrogen; for such a mixture, if ignited, may explode with sufficient force to blow the bottle to bits. The best test of the purity of hydrogen is to collect the gas by displacement of water and then bring a test tube full of it near a flame. Quiet burning indicates pure hydrogen, but a "pop" shows that oxygen is mixed with the hydrogen. (Why should the test tube be kept inverted while it is being brought near the flame?) Mossy zinc and hydrochloric acid are frequently used in a hydrogen generator such as this.

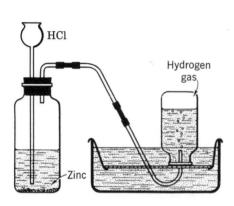

Fig. 7.3. Preparation of hydrogen.

7.5. Physical Properties of Hydrogen

Pure hydrogen gas is colorless, odorless, and tasteless. Any odor detected as it is prepared in the laboratory comes from impurities in the gas. It is the lightest of all gases, one liter weighing $\frac{2.016}{22.41}$ or 0.08996 g. at S.T.P. The solubilities of hydrogen, nitrogen, and oxygen in ml. per 100 ml. of water at 0° C. are 2.1, 2.35, and 4.89 respectively. Hence hydrogen is the least soluble of these three gases. The thermal conductivity of hydrogen gas is seven times that of air. The gas can be liquefied under a pressure of 180 atm. if cooled sufficiently. Liquid hydrogen is colorless; it boils at −252.8° C., and has the greatest specific heat (6.4) of any liquid known. In the liquid state hydrogen is a non-conductor of electricity. If liquid hydrogen is cooled by rapid evaporation under reduced pressure, some of it solidifies to a transparent solid which melts at $-259.14°$ C.

The absorption of hydrogen by some metals, particularly if they are in a finely divided state, is frequently called **occlusion.** One milliliter of palladium will absorb over 900 ml. of hydrogen gas. One important property of hydrogen when absorbed by palladium is its great chemical activity. Oxygen and hydrogen do not react at room temperature, but this reaction occurs when the hydrogen is absorbed by palladium. The hydrogen occluded in palladium is thought to be in the monatomic state and hence more active.

$$\overline{H_2} \rightarrow \overline{2H}$$

Some reactions involving the use of hydrogen commercially take place at a rapid rate only if certain metals are present. These metals may be responsible for converting some molecular hydrogen into the monatomic form.

Hydrogen, the lightest of all gases, diffuses the most rapidly. This constitutes a real problem in its use for balloon ascensions. Great improvements have been made during recent years in coating fabrics so that they are both flexible and reasonably resistant to the diffusion of hydrogen. Bottles filled with the gas should be kept inverted until ready for use.

7.6. Chemical Properties of Hydrogen

In the electrochemical series hydrogen was placed with the metals. Its electronegativity, 2.1, puts it near the middle of the electronegativity range. It is not a metal, but it does show some of the chemical behavior of metals. In substitution reactions it displaces some metals, and other metals displace it from compounds.

$$\overline{H_2} + \underline{CuO} \rightarrow \underline{Cu} + \overline{H_2O} + \Delta$$
$$\underline{Zn} + 2H^+ + 2Cl^- \rightarrow Zn^{++} + 2Cl^- + \overline{H_2} + \Delta$$

The apparatus shown in Fig. 7.4 can be used to illustrate both reactions. Zinc is placed in the bottle, the bottle is filled about one-third with water, and hydrochloric acid is added through the thistle tube. Any water in the hydrogen escaping from the generator is removed by means of a tube filled with calcium chloride, which has a great affinity for water but none for hydrogen. After the small amount of air has

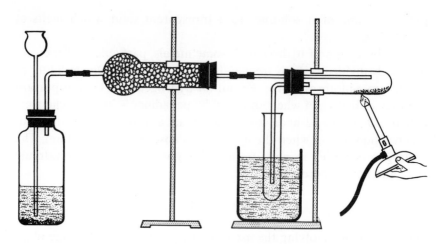

Fig. 7.4. Preparation of hydrogen and reduction of copper oxide.

been swept out of the generator by the stream of hydrogen, the black copper oxide in the test tube is heated gently. The flame can be removed as soon as the reaction starts because the reaction is exothermic. This is easily observed, for the material suddenly begins to glow and will continue to do so as long as the reaction is in progress. The water which is produced can be condensed in another test tube immersed in an ice bath. Be careful to see that all the oxygen is removed from the apparatus before you light the Bunsen burner. Why? This reaction illustrates the very important *reducing property* of hydrogen. Considerable quantities of hydrogen are used to reduce several metal oxides in the production of fine metallic powder for powder metallurgy. All the tungsten powder and a good deal of copper and iron powders are produced by this method.

Hydrogen will burn in the presence of oxygen over a wide range of concentrations of the two gases. They combine very slowly at temperatures below 400° C. Above 600° C. the reaction is rapid, and it is explosive if there is between 5 and 70 per cent of hydrogen in the mixture. If hydrogen is mixed with half its volume of oxygen, ignition of the mixture will produce an extremely violent explosion.

$$\overline{2H_2} + \overline{O_2} \rightarrow \overline{2H_2O} + \Delta$$

Hydrogen burns with a colorless flame. Any color observed when it is burning is due to impurities in the air or to some substance that vaporizes from the tip from which the gas is escaping. Hydrogen burning from a glass tip always has the characteristic yellow color of a sodium flame because of the sodium compounds in glass.

Hydrogen reacts with many other non-metals besides oxygen. The Haber process for producing ammonia on a commercial scale consists of passing nitrogen and hydrogen at high pressure and temperature over a suitable catalyst. Chlorine will burn in hydrogen, and vice versa. A mixture of the two reacts slowly at room temperature in diffused light but explodes in sunlight. The product is hydrogen chloride, HCl. The water solution of this gas is called hydrochloric acid.

$$\overline{H_2} + \overline{Cl_2} \rightarrow \overline{2HCl} + \Delta$$

Less electronegative non-metals may require indirect methods to form hydrogen compounds. Among such compounds are hydrogen sulfide, H_2S; phosphine, PH_3; arsine, AsH_3; and the similar but less stable gas, stibine, SbH_3. All four of these gases have characteristic bad odors and are moderately to extremely poisonous. Hydrogen compounds of this class are all flammable.

Hydrogen is unique in being the first and at the same time the last (active) element in its period. It may thus be considered to be the first element in Group IA in the periodic system, and at the same time the first element in Group VIIA. The resemblance to the metals in Group I is largely formal. Hydrogen loses electrons; but the proton, which is all that is left when a hydrogen atom loses an electron, is too small to exist as an independent ion, a cation, like Li^+. Instead, it promptly shares an electron pair belonging to the octet of some non-metallic atom in the vicinity. For example, in the reduction of copper oxide, the hydrogen atoms lose electrons to the Cu^{++} ion, changing it to metallic copper and themselves to protons. The protons then attach themselves to the oxide ion, converting it into H_2O. Thus, although the hydrogen has acquired a valence of $+1$, it is an oxidation number, not an electrovalence.

The resemblance of hydrogen to the elements in Group VIIA is much stronger than its resemblance to those in Group IA. In all its compounds with the non-metals hydrogen completes its valence layer, acquiring the structure of the following inert gas, by forming one covalent bond, just as do fluorine, chlorine, bromine, and iodine. Hydrogen can also attain the helium structure by outright capture of an electron from a sufficiently active metal (Nos. 1 to 6 in the E.C.S.), forming the monovalent anion, H^-, called the hydride ion.

$$\underline{2Na} + \overline{H_2} \rightarrow \underline{2NaH}$$

Sodium hydride is a salt, but reacts with water, liberating hydrogen.

$$\underline{NaH} + H_2O \rightarrow Na^+ + OH^- + \overline{H_2}$$

The hydrides are excellent research and commercial reducing agents. The compounds of hydrogen and carbon constitute one large group of hydrogen compounds. These substances, called **hydrocarbons,** are important and will be discussed in detail later.

Some organic compounds such as liquid fats will combine with hydrogen and form solids. This process is called **hydrogenation.** The compounds which are capable of adding hydrogen are said to be **unsaturated.**

7.7. "Atomic" Hydrogen

When Irving Langmuir (General Electric Co.) discovered that hydrogen at reduced pressure in an incandescent lamp conducted heat away from the filament faster than he had expected, he attributed this to the fact that some of it was in the form of monatomic molecules. Believing that the hot tungsten of the filament had produced the reaction:

$$\overline{H_2} + \Delta \rightarrow \overline{2H}$$

he proved this by blowing a stream of hydrogen through an arc between tungsten electrodes. Although the H atoms which were produced rapidly recombined with each other, their presence could be detected at a considerable distance from the arc by their ability to react at room temperature with many substances which react with hydrogen only at high temperatures. H cannot be preserved; the reaction

$$\overline{2H} \rightarrow \overline{H_2} + \Delta$$

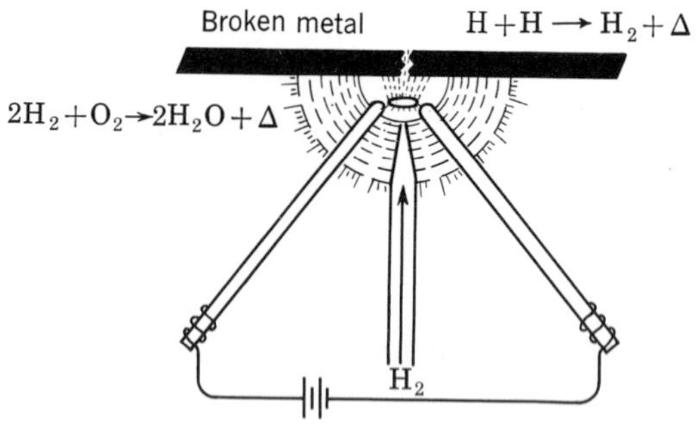

Fig. 7.5. High temperatures are produced with the atomic hydrogen torch.

takes place almost immediately. The amount of heat liberated is enormous—103,400 cal. per mole of hydrogen. It was found that the recombination reaction could be accelerated by playing the blast of gas upon a metallic surface. The practical application of this was obvious. If the blast is played upon metals which are to be welded, the heat from the formation of hydrogen can be used for the welding. The commercial apparatus, the general plan of which is shown in Fig. 7.5, is known as the atomic hydrogen torch; temperatures of 4000° to 5000° C. may be attained with it. The inner cone of the flame is due to the recombination of hydrogen atoms to form molecules, and the outer cone is due to hydrogen molecules burning in the oxygen of the air. The heat of formation of H_2 from 2H is about 1.5 times that of H_2O from H_2; therefore the inner zone is the hotter.

7.8. Uses of Hydrogen

Hydrogen was once the only gas used to fill balloons and dirigibles. It has been replaced by helium in the United States, the only country in which helium occurs in quantity. The use of hydrogen offers some advantage in lifting power, but this is more than offset by the enormous fire hazard. The many disasters which have been caused by hydrogen catching on fire can be prevented only if an inert gas is used; helium is the only other possibility.

The *reducing power of hydrogen* makes it valuable in converting some metal oxides into metals. In the manufacture of tungsten filament lamps a regular supply of hydrogen is required to prepare the reducing atmosphere in which the filaments are heated during the final drawing of the wire. In general, hydrogen can be used whenever a non-oxidizing or reducing atmosphere is necessary in preparing and annealing alloys. If oxygen does come in contact with a metal at high temperatures and an oxide is formed, hydrogen reduces the metal to its metallic state and steam escapes from the furnace.

The oxyhydrogen blowpipe does not give as high a temperature as the atomic hydrogen torch, but it is more economical to operate. It is

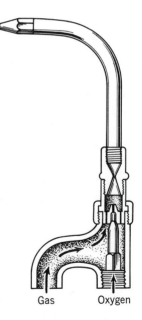

Gas   Oxygen

Fig. 7.6. Sectional view of oxyhydrogen blowpipe. (Courtesy, Hoke, Inc.)

used for the autogenous welding of metals (uniting pieces of metal by fusing them without solder) when a reducing atmosphere is necessary, and in the working of platinum metals. The design of an oxyhydrogen blowpipe is shown in Fig. 7.6. Note that oxygen is forced into the center of the gas cone so that the burning will involve pure oxygen and hydrogen as much as possible. The same type of equipment is used in the more common oxyacetylene torch, used in cutting and welding steel. (Acetylene, a hydrocarbon gas, is discussed in Chapter 23.)

Hydrogen is an important raw material in the production of many important chemicals. Until 1925 methanol (wood alcohol), CH_3OH, was prepared by the destructive distillation of wood. The vastly larger quantity now produced is almost entirely synthetic. In the synthetic process carbon monoxide and hydrogen are passed over catalysts such as finely divided CuO and ZnO.

$$\overline{CO} + \overline{2H_2} \rightarrow CH_3OH$$

Formaldehyde, HCHO, another substance once obtained from wood, is synthesized by the same type of process.

$$\overline{CO} + \overline{H_2} \rightarrow HCHO$$

The synthesis of ammonia is discussed in Section 12.4. The synthesis of gasoline by the "liquefaction" of coal, which is based on the reaction of coal with hydrogen, provided much badly needed gasoline for Germany during World War II. This process is known as the Bergius process.

Hardening of liquid fats with hydrogen is another important achievement of chemistry. Cottonseed, coconut, and other oils are heated under pressure at about 175° in the presence of a catalyst such as finely divided nickel. Hydrogen adds on and the product solidifies at room temperature. Some hydrogenation tanks will hold 15 tons of oil at one charge. In the wet process a nickel salt, such as nickel formate, is added; hydrogen reduces this salt, producing metallic nickel which serves as the catalyst. During hydrogenation some hydrogen is allowed to escape so that any carbon monoxide or carbon dioxide which has been produced can be removed. The process requires a pressure of about 60 p.s.i. and several hours for the reaction. Filter presses are used to separate the catalyst from the finished product, and the catalyst can be used again. As the temperature drops, the hydrogenated product solidifies.

7.9. The Equivalent Weight

One of the earliest and most fundamental quantitative discoveries in chemistry was the **law of chemical equivalence.** This states that the (different) quantities of two substances which are equivalent to each other in one reaction will be equivalent to each other in other reactions. For example, 22.991 g. of sodium is equivalent to 20.04 g. of calcium in reacting with water; in each case 1.008 g. of hydrogen is produced. Therefore, according to the law of equivalence, both should (and do) react with the same amount of chlorine, which is 35.457 g. But if 1.008 g. of hydrogen is equivalent to 35.457 g. of chlorine in reacting with 22.991 g. of sodium, the same quantities of these elements should react with each other, with no residue of either. This is actually the case.

The reason for this series of relationships is clear. The quantity of hydrogen just mentioned, 1.008 g., is 1 gram-atomic weight of that substance, or N atoms (Avogadro's number). In setting free that amount of hydrogen, a metal must give 1 electron to each hydrogen atom. Evidently 22.991 g. of sodium is the amount of sodium which can give up N electrons, and 20.04 g. of calcium is the amount of calcium which can furnish the same number of electrons. Obviously, then, 35.457 g. of chlorine is the amount of chlorine which can and does take up N electrons from 22.991 g. of sodium, 20.04 g. of calcium, or 1.008 g. of hydrogen. The amount of any substance which is associated with N electrons is called **1 gram-equivalent weight** of that substance or, more commonly, 1 equivalent of it. The expression "associated with" includes both giving up and receiving electrons. Since any atom may gain or lose one or more electrons, 1 equivalent of any element may be N atoms, N/2 atoms, N/3 atoms, etc., depending upon the number of electrons gained or lost per atom. Since N atoms is 1 gram-atomic weight, the gram-equivalent weight can be obtained by dividing the gram-atomic weight by the number of electrons gained or lost per atom. Because the latter number also indicates what oxidation number an atom may acquire, it may be called the **valence factor.** (In cases when an atom may have more than one valence, it may also have more than one equivalent weight and valence factor. In such cases the particular reaction must be specified.) If the atomic weight instead of the gram-atomic weight is divided by the valence factor, the result obtained is the equivalent weight instead of the gram-equivalent weight, but the numerical value is the same.

Although equivalent weights are now computed from the atomic weights (which are determined easily and accurately by the mass spectrometer) and the valence factor (which can be obtained by glancing at the periodic table), they were determined experimentally before the periodic system or the mass spectrometer was even thought of. In fact, Mendeleev based his periodic system on atomic weights which had been worked out from experimentally determined equivalent weights.

The first table of equivalents that was drawn up was not based upon the amounts of substances associated with N electrons, for neither Avogadro's number nor electrons had been heard of. Instead, it listed the amounts of the substance which were equivalent to an arbitrarily chosen amount of one particular substance. Thus, if the amount of hydrogen chosen is assigned the number 1, oxygen will be 7.937; if the amount of oxygen chosen is 8, hydrogen will be 1.008. If the latter figure is used, the other equivalent weights will be much nearer to whole numbers than with the first; hence the latter was eventually agreed upon universally. The equivalent weights of the active metals are conveniently determined by means of their reaction with an acid.

$$Na + HCl \rightarrow NaCl + H$$
$$Ca + 2HCl \rightarrow CaCl_2 + 2H$$
$$Al + 3HCl \rightarrow AlCl_3 + 3H$$

(The empirical instead of the molecular formula of hydrogen is used in balancing these equations, to simplify the arithmetic in the following discussion.) Since an equation which is balanced may be multiplied or divided throughout by a common factor and still remain balanced, we can rewrite the above equations as follows:

$$\frac{Na}{1} + \frac{HCl}{1} \rightarrow \frac{NaCl}{1} + \frac{H}{1}$$

$$\frac{Ca}{2} + \frac{2HCl}{2} \rightarrow \frac{CaCl_2}{2} + \frac{2H}{2}$$

$$\frac{Al}{3} + \frac{3HCl}{3} \rightarrow \frac{AlCl_3}{3} + \frac{3H}{3}$$

Each equation now involves 1 mole of hydrogen chloride and 1 gram-atomic weight of hydrogen and fractions of gram-atomic and formula weights of the other substances. If we define 1 gram-atomic weight of hydrogen as being 1 gram-equivalent weight of hydrogen, all the other quantities in the equations are also gram-equivalent weights of their respective substances. The gram-equivalent weight of sodium $= \frac{Na}{1}$, of

calcium $= \frac{Ca}{2}$, of aluminum chloride $= \frac{AlCl_3}{3}$, etc. These divisors are related to the valences of the substances. Aluminum has a valence of $+3$ in the reaction; so its gram-equivalent weight is the gram-atomic weight divided by 3. The divisor used to calculate the gram-equivalent weight of $AlCl_3$ is also 3. To what valence is this related? In the compound, aluminum has a valence of $+3$, whereas the three chloride ions have a total valence of -3. Thus either can be used, since they are of equal numerical magnitude. Of course, as we have seen, this is true of any compound because the sum of the positive and negative valences must be zero. The following equation

$$\frac{\text{Gram-atomic weight}}{\text{Valence factor}} \quad \text{or} \quad \frac{\text{Formula weight}}{\text{Valence factor}} = \text{Gram-equivalent weight}$$

holds where the valence factor is the valence of the element or, in the case of a compound, the total positive or the total negative valence. The gram-equivalent weight of hydrogen is $\frac{H}{1}$; hence this is the same quantity as $\frac{H_2}{2}$. Thus it is apparent that the gram-equivalent weight of hydrogen is $\frac{1}{2}$ gram mole of hydrogen. Half a gram mole of any gas occupies 11.2 l. at S.T.P., a fact which is included in the following definition: *The gram-equivalent weight of a substance is the weight that will react with, displace, or in any other way be equivalent to 1.008 g. of hydrogen, or 11.2 l. of hydrogen at S.T.P.*

Although this is the classical definition of gram-equivalent weight, it does not mention either atomic weights or valences, for neither of them were known at that time. Eventually, however, as we shall see later, ways were devised for obtaining a good idea of the atomic weights of various elements. Valences were then determined by dividing the atomic weights by the equivalent weights which had previously been determined by the displacement of hydrogen or some other means. The equivalent weight of a substance can be related to other elements as well as to hydrogen. Since $\frac{H}{1}$ is equivalent to $\frac{Cl}{1}$ is equivalent to $\frac{O}{2}$, chlorine and oxygen are convenient substitutes for hydrogen in experimental determinations of equivalent weights. Actually, once the accurate equivalent weight of any substance is known, it can be used as a reference standard in determining the equivalent weights of other substances.

7.10. Use of Equivalent Weights in Computations

Use of the equivalent weight principle makes it unnecessary to write a balanced chemical equation in determining quantities of reagents consumed or products produced.

For example, how many grams of H_2SO_4 will react with 20.0 g. of aluminum? How many grams of $Al_2(SO_4)_3$ will be produced, and how many liters of hydrogen (at S.T.P.)?

Determine the value, in terms of equivalents of aluminum, of 20.0 g. of aluminum. This number of equivalents will apply to all the other substances.

$$\frac{\text{Grams of Al}}{\text{Gram-eq. wt. of Al}} = \text{No. of equivalents of Al, } H_2SO_4, Al_2(SO_4)_3, H_2$$

$$\frac{20.0}{\frac{26.98}{3}} = 2.22 \text{ equivalents}$$

$$\text{Gram-eq. wt. of } H_2SO_4 \times 2.22 = \text{Grams of } H_2SO_4$$
$$98.1/2 \times 2.22 = 109 \text{ g. of } H_2SO_4$$

$$\text{Gram-eq. wt. of } Al_2(SO_4)_3 \times 2.22 = \text{Grams of } Al_2(SO_4)_3$$
$$342/6 \times 2.22 = 123 \text{ g. of } Al_2(SO_4)_3$$

$$\text{Gram-eq. vol. of } H_2 \times 2.22 = \text{Liters of } H_2 \text{ (S.T.P.)}$$
$$22.4/2 \times 2.22 = 24.9 \text{ l. of } H_2$$

7.11. Exact Atomic Weights from Equivalent Weights

Modern chemists use an atomic weight table and the relationship described in Section 7.9 to compute any equivalent weights they need, but most atomic weights were first computed from experimentally determined equivalent weights. These computations depended upon several assumptions, all of which have been justified by the fact that the results obtained with them were confirmed without exception when direct determination of atomic weights by means of the mass spectrometer became possible.

The equation for calculating valence is:

$$\frac{\text{Atomic weight}}{\text{Equivalent weight}} = \text{Valence}.$$

We know from theory that the valence has to be a *whole number*. If we can obtain a rough approximation of the atomic weight, we can use this with the equivalent weight to calculate the valence. Even though the equivalent weight is accurate, the valence thus obtained will not be a whole number, because of the inaccuracy of the atomic weight, but we can round it off with perfect confidence. Then we replace the inaccurate value of the atomic weight by x and solve the equation, using the accurate equivalent weight and the rounded-off valence.

7.12. Approximate Atomic Weights

As soon as Avogadro's law became known and accepted, it was easy to determine reasonably accurate atomic weights for any gaseous element. It was only necessary to find what weight of the element was present in 1 mole of it, and divide that by the number of atoms in the molecule. (The number of atoms in a molecule of a gaseous element can be determined by applying Avogadro's law to reactions in which the element is produced or consumed; see Section 2.27.) The result thus obtained is as accurate as the experimental data from which it was derived. A mole of the element contains N molecules, and $n \times$ N atoms of the element, where n is the number of atoms of it in each molecule. So if we divide the total weight of the element in 1 mole (weight of $n \times$ N atoms) by n, we will obtain the weight of N atoms, the atomic weight; thus the definition, N atoms = 1 gram-atomic weight—or **gram atom,** for short.

It is also possible to determine the approximate atomic weight of an element by finding the smallest weight of it that is present in 1 mole of any of its gaseous compounds, even though the number of atoms in a molecule is not known. Since there must be one, two, three, or four atoms of an element in each molecule of any of its compounds, there must be one, two, three, or four gram-atomic weights of it in a gram-molecular weight of the compound. If several compounds are analyzed, there will surely be one that contains only a single atom of the element per molecule and thus only a single gram atom per mole (some molecules will differ by only one atom of the element), for the simplest molecules are the easiest to synthesize. The experimental difficulties in making accurate measurements of gases, coupled with uncertainties in the gas law corrections necessary, make difficult any high degree of accuracy in atomic weight determinations made by this method. It has, however, been of great value in ascertaining the *approximate atomic weight*.

Many elements, particularly metals, do not form any stable gaseous compounds. Fortunately, as early as 1819, Dulong and Petit discovered that, with very few exceptions, 1 gram atom (N atoms, you will remember) of any *solid* element has approximately the same heat capacity (at ordinary temperatures) as 1 gram atom of any other solid element. This means that it takes the same amount of energy to raise the temperature of that many atoms the same amount. (This is definitely not true in the case of gases, for differing amounts of the energy, depending on the shape of the molecules, impart to them rotational and vibrational energy as well as kinetic energy.) It has been found that on the average 6.4 cal. of heat energy will raise the temperature of 1 gram-atomic weight of a solid 1° C. This is called the **gram-atomic heat capacity.**

Let us determine the accurate atomic weight of iron. The specific heat of iron (heat capacity per gram) is found to be 0.112 cal. per degree; therefore:

$$\frac{\text{Gram-atomic heat capacity}}{\text{Specific heat}} = \text{Approx. at. wt.} = \frac{6.4}{0.112} = 57 \text{ g.}$$

The true atomic weight may be several units more or less than this because of the approximate nature of the law. The next bit of information needed, in order to refine the value of the atomic weight, is the equivalent weight of iron. Analysis shows that a *pure* oxide of iron contains 69.95 per cent iron and 30.05 per cent oxygen. Thus, according to the law of equivalence:

$$\frac{\text{Grams of O}}{\text{Gram-eq. wt. of O}} = \frac{\text{Grams of Fe}}{\text{Gram-eq. wt. of Fe}} = \text{No. of equivalents}$$

$$\frac{30.05}{8.000} = \frac{69.95}{\text{Gram-eq. wt. of Fe}}$$

or

$$\text{Gram-eq. wt. of Fe} = 69.95 \text{ g. of Fe} \times \frac{8.000 \text{ g. of O}}{30.05 \text{ g. of O}} = 18.62 \text{ g. of Fe}$$

The valence is:

$$\frac{\text{Approx. at. wt.}}{\text{Eq. wt.}} = \frac{57}{18.62} = 3.06$$

Obviously, the true valence of iron in this compound is 3. Continuing, we have:

$$\text{Eq. wt.} \times \text{Valence} = 18.62 \times 3 = 55.86 = \text{At. wt. of Fe}$$

These methods were invaluable in calculating the atomic weights Mendeleev used in setting up the periodic table. Once the table had been formulated, the atomic weights of the remaining undiscovered elements could be estimated from those of their neighbors with sufficient approximation to serve as a starting point for calculating the exact atomic weight. It was necessary only to place the element in the table on the basis of its properties. The discovery of the x-ray method for determining atomic numbers eliminated any possibility of error in placement.

7.13. Water

Since water is the most abundant single compound of the elements hydrogen and oxygen which we have been studying, it is worthy of special consideration here. It is such a common and familiar substance that it is a little difficult to realize that it is a very peculiar one. If water is compared with other substances which are liquids at room temperature it is found to have the highest specific heat, heat of fusion, heat of vaporization, and dielectric constant. Water is the only substance, liquid at room temperature, which expands on freezing. It is strange, in fact, that it *is* a liquid, for other substances of similar molecular weight have boiling points two to three hundred degrees lower than that of water. These peculiarities of water are of extreme practical importance. The high specific heat (1 cal./g.) accounts for the moderating influence that the oceans have upon climate. The high heat of fusion (80 cal./g.) makes ice the most efficient refrigerating agent, pound for pound. The high heat of vaporization (540 cal./g.) makes water the best cooling agent within its temperature range. The high dielectric constant is responsible for the solvent properties of water upon salts (Chapter 8) and for the possibility of the electronic heating of water-containing substances, as in diathermy (artificial fever) and the seemingly magical transformation of a package from a deep-freezer into a steaming hot meal in a matter of seconds. When water in minute crevices freezes into ice, the expansion which takes place tears down cliffs and splits rocks into sand, altering the face of the earth. But for the fact that ice floats on water, our rivers and seas would be like the Siberian tundras, solid ice except for a few feet that melt in summer. Curiously enough, skating would be impossible. The slipperiness of ice depends upon the fact that it melts a trifle under pressure, which tends to reduce its volume to that corresponding to liquid water.

7.14. Hydrogen Bonding

The structure of the water molecule is responsible for the remarkable properties of water. The important thing about this structure is that it is unsymmetrical, both geometrically and electrically. The two electron pairs which the oxygen atom shares with the hydrogens in a water molecule make use of p orbitals of the oxygen atom. These p orbitals are at right angles to each other; so the molecule is not the linear H : Ö : H which was naïvely taken for granted a generation ago, but angular:

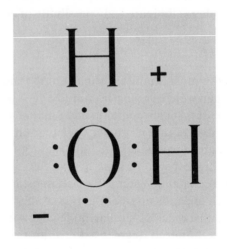

The H—O—H angle is actually a little larger than 90° because the hydrogens repel each other. The electronegativity of oxygen is 1.4 units higher than that of hydrogen; so the oxygen atom gives each hydrogen atom hardly more than a quarter of each shared electron pair. The oxygen atom thus has about half a unit of extra negative charge, and each hydrogen a quarter of a unit of unneutralized positive charge. Thus we see that the water molecule is as unsymmetrical electrically as it is geometrically. The left side, as shown above, is found to consist of a cloud of electrons, whereas on the right side are the two positively charged protons.

For many purposes the water molecule is satisfactorily described as an object that is negative on one end and positive on the other, i.e., an electrical dipole. Actually, however, the molecule has two positive corners and two negative corners. The positive corners are the two protons; the negative corners are the two unshared electron pairs. (The orbitals of these unshared pairs make about the same angle with each other as do those shared by the protons, but are in a plane at right angles to the H—O—H plane.) A positive corner of one water molecule is strongly attracted to a negative corner of another water molecule,

thus: H : Ö : H : Ö : . It is held there by the attractive force between the
　　　　H　　H

two opposite charges. This force is less than one-tenth of the force that holds the proton to its own oxygen atom, but far greater than the ordinary van der Waals forces between non-polar molecules. Accordingly there is an *association* of the two water molecules into a single molecule of double the size. Linus Pauling (California Institute of Technology) and W. H. Rodebush (University of Illinois), who have developed this idea and proved it in many interesting ways, call a hydrogen atom a **hydrogen bond** when it is thus holding two other atoms together. Only the atoms which do not give hydrogen a fair share of the electrons in a covalent bond can be held together in this fashion.

7.15. Expansion on Freezing

The thermal motions of molecules tend to keep a certain amount of empty space between them, even in the case of liquids and solids. The quantity of empty space diminishes as the temperature falls; therefore substances regularly contract as they cool. Water does so at first, but at a continually increasing rate there are formed molecules not merely of

$$H : \ddot{O} : H : \ddot{O} : ,$$
$$H \quad\quad H$$

but also of

$$H : \ddot{O} : H : \ddot{O} :$$
$$H \quad\quad H$$
$$\quad\quad : \ddot{O} : H$$
$$\quad\quad H$$

and even of

$$: \ddot{O} : H : \ddot{O} : H$$
$$H \quad\quad H$$
$$H : \ddot{O} : H : \ddot{O} :$$
$$H \quad\quad H$$

Although these formulas do not accurately represent the shapes of these three-dimensional molecules, they do suggest that it is impossible to pack them as closely as individual H_2O units could be packed, and experiments with scale models show this to be the case. By the time the temperature has fallen to 4° C., the increase in volume due to the loose packing of these larger molecules equals the decrease in volume due to lessening thermal motions, and below that temperature the increase exceeds the decrease. Water therefore expands slightly as it is cooled further, down to its freezing point, 0° C. In the process of freezing, molecules of a liquid ordinarily fall into the positions corresponding to the closest possible packing (the remaining thermal motion being converted into vibration about those positions), but in the case of water, hydrogen bonding prevents this. The process illustrated in the formulas goes to completion. Every hydrogen atom forms a hydrogen bond and the entire crystal becomes a gigantic molecule occupying nearly 10 per cent more volume than the water from which it forms. When ice melts, hydrogen bonds are broken, which takes much energy; hence ice has a higher heat of fusion than does any substance held together only by van der Waals forces. More such bonds are broken as water warms up and evaporates; so the specific heat and the heat of vaporization are also abnormally large.

Additional properties of water—its role as a solvent and its properties in solutions of acids, bases, and salts—will be considered in other chapters where they are more pertinent.

QUESTIONS AND PROBLEMS

1. Show, by balanced equations, as many *different* reactions as you can for the preparation of hydrogen. Which of these are of commercial importance?
2. a. What is an amphoteric metal?
   b. With what reagent can it react to produce hydrogen, in contrast to non-amphoteric metals?
   c. Where are these metals located in the periodic table?
3. Relative to the top, middle, and bottom of the electrochemical series:
   a. Where are the metals which react with cold water and produce hydrogen?
   b. Which metals do *not* displace hydrogen from acids?
   c. Which metals are the strongest reducing agents?
   d. Which metals form thermally stable oxides?
4. What are some unusual or special physical properties of hydrogen?
5. a. What is the outstanding chemical property of hydrogen?
   b. Illustrate this property with balanced equations involving both elements and compounds.
6. a. What is the hydride ion?
   b. How is it formed?
   c. Compare it with the proton.
7. What are some of the important commercial uses of hydrogen?
8. Define equivalent weight. What other elements may be conveniently used to

determine equivalent weights on the basis of their combination with metals and non-metals?

9. What are the equivalent weights and volumes of hydrogen, oxygen, chlorine, HCl gas?

10. What are the equivalent weights of:
    a. $AlCl_3$ d. Cu^{++}
    b. $Fe_2(SO_4)_3$ e. PO_4^{-3}
    c. $Na_2SO_4 \cdot 10H_2O$ f. Zn

11. If 0.042 g. of a metal liberates 16.3 ml. of H_2 over water at 21° C. and 752 mm. pressure, what is the equivalent weight of the metal? What is the metal?

12. The equivalent weight of a hypothetical element is 12.0. If 10 g. of it reacts with HCl to liberate hydrogen:
    a. How many grams of HCl are consumed?
    b. How many grams of metal chloride are produced?
    c. What volume of hydrogen is produced at S.T.P.?

13. The specific heat of an element X is 0.093 cal./°C. Chemical analysis of its chloride gives 47.3 per cent X and 52.7 per cent chlorine. What is the atomic weight of X? Which element is X?

14. 5.00 g. of a metal displaces 6.88 l. of dry hydrogen from HCl at 20° C. and 740 mm. pressure. The approximate atomic weight of the metal is 26. Calculate its equivalent weight, its valence, its accurate atomic weight.

15. a. What is a hydrogen bond?
    b. What conditions favor its formation?
    c. What effect would you expect it to have on boiling and freezing points of substances, in contrast to the values obtained if there were no hydrogen bonding?
    d. Would crystals be stronger or weaker if hydrogen bonding occurred in them?

8

Solutions

8.1. Importance of Solutions

When separate molecules of one substance are scattered around among the molecules of another substance the resulting mixture is *homogeneous* and is called a **solution.** Everyone is familiar with innumerable solutions. Examples include all sorts of clear, transparent beverages (milk is white because of particles far larger than molecules which are suspended in the solution), the gasoline we burn in our cars, and the air we breathe. Air is an example of a solution in a gaseous state. All mixtures of gases form solutions because their molecules are already separate from each other; liquids and solids often have limited solubilities in each other. Solutions may be solid, liquid, or gaseous.

The importance of solutions in chemistry cannot be overemphasized. Substances in a state of molecular dispersion may show properties which cannot be discerned when they are in the solid state; they react readily and quantitatively, whereas the corresponding solids are inert or react only superficially. Other substances which react too violently when brought together in the pure state may be so moderated by dilution with an inert solvent that the reaction is no longer hazardous. By measuring the effect of substances upon the boiling and freezing points of liquids in which they have been dissolved it is possible to find out how many molecules were added and thus determine the molecular weight. Equivalent weights, equally important in chemistry, are commonly determined on the basis of reactions that occur in solutions. Solutions are used in most chemical analyses.

Some of the important features of solutions will be explored in this chapter. Additional properties and characteristics will be considered in later chapters. In fact, solutions and reactions that take place in solutions will be referred to constantly throughout this book.

8.2. Constitution of Solutions

A simple solution is made up of two components, the **solute** and the **solvent.** The solute is the substance which is dissolved; the solvent is the substance in which the dissolving takes place. It is quite common for solutions to contain several solutes dissolved in a common solvent; sea water, for example, contains sodium, potassium, magnesium, and calcium chlorides, sulfates, and bromides, as well as many other substances, all dissolved in water. Not so common, at least in inorganic chemistry, are solutions in mixed solvents, but they are well known in the food and beverage industries. Alcoholic drinks and flavoring extracts contain various substances dissolved in mixtures of alcohol and water.

The distinction between solute and solvent is somewhat arbitrary. For example, when we consider air, a solution of nitrogen and oxygen, nitrogen can be considered to be dissolved in oxygen as well as oxygen to be dissolved in nitrogen. Or, in a solution of alcohol and water, which is the solute and which the solvent? Whenever the two components of the solution are in the same state—both gases, liquids, or solids—the one which is more abundant is usually referred to as the solvent. If a solid or a gas and a liquid form a solution, the latter is regularly considered to be the solvent. Since most of the solutions used by chemists are liquid, most of our discussion will concern this type.

8.3. Liquid Solvents

Water is the most common liquid solvent. This is true because we live in a water system. Most chemical processes of living organisms take place in or involve water solutions; so it is natural that we drink

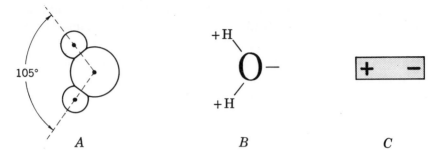

Fig. 8.1. Representations of a water molecule.

water and use solutions of it extensively. The commonness of this solvent has led to its being called "the universal solvent," but this is a misnomer; there are many substances which are not soluble in water. Often other solvents must be used in separations and to obtain the solutions needed in chemical reactions. Benzene, ether, alcohol, carbon tetrachloride, and acetone are examples of a few solvents commonly used with organic compounds. Certain gases, when cooled and liquefied, have important commercial uses as solvents; examples include ammonia and sulfur dioxide.

Liquid solvents fall into two main classes, **polar** and **non-polar.** Which of these classes a solvent is in depends upon the structure of its molecules. If the molecules are polar, the properties of the solvent will be very different from those of a solvent with non-polar molecules. The most important polar molecule is the water molecule. The fact that a water molecule has a positive and a negative end may be represented in several ways. In Fig. 8.1, *A* represents a cross section of a molecule, to scale, with the H—O—H angle correctly shown as 105°. The structural formula in *B,* to which charge signs have been added, is commonly used in print to indicate the shape of the molecule. For many purposes the fact that the molecule has an unsymmetrical charge distribution, and therefore an electrical dipole moment, may be satisfactorily represented by the simpler diagram in *C,* in which the + sign represents the mid-point between the two hydrogens. Many non-polar solvents are hydrocarbons, that is, compounds containing only carbon and hydrogen. Their molecules are non-polar because the difference in electronegativity between these two elements is so small that electron pairs shared between them are evenly distributed. Others contain elements that differ considerably in electronegativity, so that each covalent bond is polar; but the bonds are arranged so symmetrically that the "center of gravity" of all charges is in the center of the molecule. Carbon tetrachloride, CCl_4, is an example of this class; the four relatively negative chlorines are arranged in a regular tetrahedron (triangular pyramid) with the relatively positive carbon atom in the center.

Polar solvents readily dissolve polar solutes but not non-polar ones, whereas the reverse is true of non-polar solvents. The great majority of inorganic compounds are ionic and therefore represent the extreme in polar character. It is for this reason that water is so widely used as a solvent for inorganic compounds. Virtually all the solutions discussed in this book are solutions in water.

8.4. Dissolving Action of Water

Crystals composed of ions, such as those of common salt, Na^+Cl^-, are strong and hard. The electrostatic forces of attraction between oppositely charged ions are responsible for this. A whole crystal of sodium chloride may almost be regarded as a single giant molecule, with every Na^+ ion "bonded" to the six Cl^- ions which surround it, and vice versa. This is illustrated by the symmetrical array of ions shown in Fig. 8.2. Note that each Na^+ ion is surrounded by four Cl^- ions. The ions above and below the layer shown are staggered so that there is one Cl^- ion above, and one Cl^- ion below, each Na^+ ion.

$$
\begin{array}{l}
Na^+Cl^-\ Na^+Cl^-\ Na^+Cl^-\ Na^+Cl^- \\
Cl^-\ Na^+Cl^-\ Na^+Cl^-\ Na^+Cl^-\ Na^+ \\
Na^+Cl^-\ Na^+Cl^-\ Na^+Cl^-\ Na^+Cl^- \\
Cl^-\ Na^+Cl^-\ Na^+Cl^-\ Na^+Cl^-\ Na^+ \\
Na^+Cl^-\ Na^+Cl^-\ Na^+Cl^-\ Na^+Cl^- \\
Cl^-\ Na^+Cl^-\ Na^+Cl^-\ Na^+Cl^-\ Na^+
\end{array}
$$

Fig. 8.2. One layer of a crystal of NaCl

It is really rather astonishing that a crystal such as this, that has high mechanical strength and can barely be melted in the Bunsen burner flame, readily disintegrates by dissolving when immersed in water. The abnormally high **dielectric constant** of water contributes to this remarkable behavior. The force of attraction between charged bodies such as Na^+ and Cl^- is expressed by the equation:

$$ F = \frac{C_{Na^+} \times C_{Cl^-}}{\varepsilon r^2} $$

where C is the charge on the ion, r is the distance between them, and ε is the dielectric constant of the substance between the ions. *The dielectric constant is a measure of the ability of a substance to neutralize electrical charges and thereby reduce electrical attractive force.*

In a crystal nothing exists between two neighboring ions; hence the dielectric constant of a vacuum, which is 1, goes into the equation. Under these conditions the force of attraction, F, between the ions is at a maximum. When the crystal is put into water, the water molecules adjacent to it line up on the crystal surfaces because of their polarity (Fig. 8.3). Their charges neutralize to some extent the opposite charges of the ions they touch and thereby weaken the attraction of these ions for those inside. This effect is particularly strong at projecting ridges and promontories where the ions are more nearly surrounded by water molecules. The dielectric constant of water is 80, so this loosening effect is very large. Since the ions are vibrating in the crystal lattice with the same kinetic energies that gas molecules have at the same temperature, some of them will be vibrating vigorously enough to overcome the relatively weak attractive forces now in existence. If the solution is warmed, more ions will have energy enough to break loose, and the rate of dissolving will rise. Increasing the surface of a solid by grinding it to powder also raises its rate of dissolving.

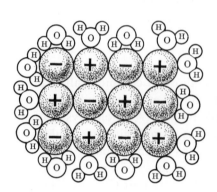

Fig. 8.3. Alignment of polar H_2O molecules on the surface of an ionic crystal.

When an ionic substance resists dissolving in water, it means that the forces of attraction between the surface ions, even though 1/80 of normal, are still sufficiently strong to resist any vibrational breaking loose. As is evident from the equation for the forces of interionic attraction, these forces are greater the higher the charges and the smaller the diameters of the ions. The strength of a crystal, its **lattice energy,** may also be greatly increased by the establishment of some degree of covalent bonding between its ions. The tendency of a cation (positive ion) to form covalent bonds is increased by high charge, small size, and the presence of d electrons in its surface. The willingness of an anion (negative ion) to permit a cation to acquire a share in one of the electron pairs in its valence shell, thereby forming a partially covalent bond, is greater the more loosely these outer electrons are held. It is therefore greater the larger the ion and the larger its negative charge.

8.5. Ion Clusters

When an ionic crystal dissolves, little chunks of crystal may break away from the crystal. The more concentrated a solution, the more abundant such ion clusters in it. They display a variety of charges, depending upon the number and kind of individual ions which make up the cluster. Some typical ion clusters found in a calcium chloride solution might be:

$$[Ca^{++}Cl^-]^+, \quad [Cl^-Ca^{++}Cl^-]^0, \quad \begin{bmatrix} Cl^- \\ Cl^-Ca^{++}Cl^- \\ Cl^- \end{bmatrix}^{--} \quad \text{etc.}$$

Clusters of this sort are constantly growing by gaining ions from the solution, and diminishing by losing ions to it. Although they vary from moment to moment in both size and charge, these particles are molecules; they have the same average kinetic energy as do any of the other molecules (H_2O, Ca^{++}, and Cl^- in this case) in the solution. "Solution molecules" we may call them. The denser the ion population in the solution, the larger the number of ion clusters and the larger they are. As the solvent is allowed to evaporate, clusters become so large as to be visible. Since each particle still has the same kinetic energy as, for example, a monatomic ion, molecular agitation can no longer keep them suspended. They settle out, but continue to grow through attachment of ions from the solution. We say that the solute is crystallizing out.

The relationship between crystals, ion clusters, and individual ions in solution may be represented as in the accompanying diagram for calcium chloride, where CaCl$_2$ represents solid crystals, $[Ca^{++}2Cl^-]$ represents ion clusters, and Ca^{++} + $2Cl^-$ are the individual free ions. The

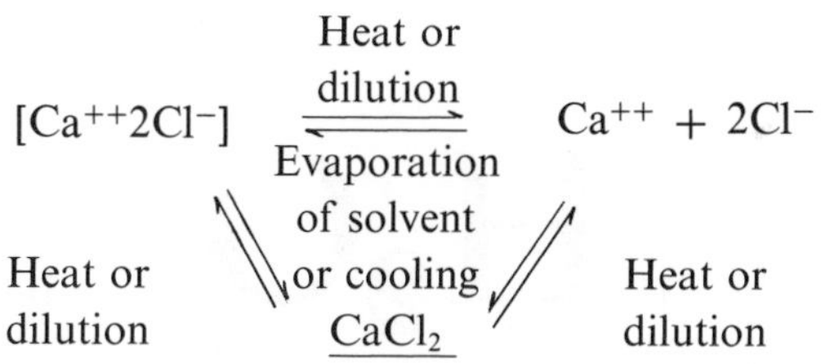

$$[Ca^{++}2Cl^-] \quad \underset{\text{Evaporation}}{\overset{\substack{\text{Heat or} \\ \text{dilution}}}{\rightleftharpoons}} \quad Ca^{++} + 2Cl^-$$

Heat or dilution $\diagdown$ of solvent or cooling $\diagup$ Heat or dilution

CaCl$_2$

solid solute, which is not in solution and therefore cannot affect the properties of the solution, can be eliminated from any discussion of solution molecular species. Thus the simplified version:

$$[Ca^{++}2Cl^-] \rightleftharpoons Ca^{++} + 2Cl^-$$

is sufficient to represent the species in solution. The double arrows indicate that the situation in a solution is dynamic; individual ions are continually dissolving from both solid crystals and ion clusters, and likewise continually rejoining them. At any given temperature a state of equilibrium is reached in which the crystals (if any are left) are dissolving and growing at the same rate; the same is true of the ion clusters. When this state is reached, the concentrations of ion clusters and free ions no longer change with time.

8.6. Formation of Ions

When typical metals and non-metals react with each other, ions are formed by direct transfer of electrons and are present in the solid salt before it is dissolved. Compounds of non-metals with each other, on the other hand, are covalent, but many of them react with water to form ionic compounds. Acids constitute the most important class of covalent compounds which behave in this manner. All acids react with water, some extensively, others slightly, forming in each case hydronium ion, H_3O^+, and another ion which differs for each acid. The hydronium ion is responsible for the sour taste which is characteristic of all but very weak acids. An acid which reacts almost completely with water is called a **strong acid**; a **weak acid** is one which reacts only slightly with water.

Strong acid:

$$\text{HCl} + \text{H}_2\text{O} \rightleftharpoons \text{H}_3\text{O}^+ + \text{Cl}^-$$

Weak acid:

$$\text{HC}_2\text{H}_3\text{O}_2 + \text{H}_2\text{O} \rightleftharpoons \text{H}_3\text{O}^+ + \text{C}_2\text{H}_3\text{O}_2^-$$

The relative sizes of the symbols in these equations indicate the relative proportions of the molecular species in the solution at equilibrium, but not to scale. In dilute solutions containing the same molecular amounts of HCl and $HC_2H_3O_2$, about 100 per cent of the former and approximately 3 per cent of the latter are present in ionic form. A solution of a strong acid is essentially the same as a solution of a salt (including the ion clusters); a solution of a weak acid contains uncharged molecules almost exclusively.

8.7. Saturated Solutions, Solubilities

A solution in which the solute concentration is such that it is in equilibrium with undissolved solute is called a **saturated solution.** If a solute has a high rate of solution and a low tendency to crystallize out, the solution may have to become very concentrated before the rate of crystallization will equal the rate of solution and equilibrium results. However, there is a limit to the solubility of almost every solid solute in liquid solvents at ordinary temperatures. For some solutes this limit is very low. Table 8.1 lists the solubilities of several substances to illustrate how widely they vary. The solubility of a substance is commonly defined as *the number of grams of solute required to reach saturation in 100 grams of solvent.* A simple test for saturation is to drop a crystal of the solute into the solution. If the crystal remains unchanged, the solution is saturated; if it dissolves, the solution is unsaturated.

TABLE 8.1. **Solubilities of a Few Substances**

Substance	Solubility at 20° C. g./100 g. H_2O	Substance	Solubility at 20° C. g./100 g. H_2O
AgCl	0.0001	HCl	76
O_2	0.0043	$NaNO_3$	85
$MgCO_3$	0.05	NaOH	100
H_2S	0.34	Sugar	204
NaCl	36	$LiClO_3$	325

All solids dissolve more rapidly at higher temperatures, but in a few cases the rate of crystallization increases even more rapidly, with a resultant decrease in solubility. The effect of temperature on the solubilities of several salts is shown in Fig. 8.4. Whenever an abrupt change in the solubility curve appears, it indicates a change in composition of the solute. Thus the solubility curve of $Na_2SO_4 \cdot 10H_2O$ takes a sharply different direction at 36° C. because at that temperature the crystals of the decahydrate lose water and decompose into anhydrous sodium sulfate.

All solutes make the solution warmer or cooler as they dissolve. If the solution becomes warmer, so that heat flows out from it into the surroundings, the solute is said to dissolve **exothermically.** Most solutes dissolve **endothermically;** i.e., the solution becomes cooler, and heat flows into it from the surroundings. The amount of energy involved, the **heat of solution,** is the difference between two larger quantities of opposite sign. Just as kinetic energy is used up in putting a satellite into orbit against the gravitational attraction of the earth, so it is used up in separating the ions from the crystal lattice against the attraction of their oppositely charged neighbors. This is called the **lattice energy.** Kinetic energy is produced when the negative ends of water molecules come into contact with the cations, and their positive ends into contact with the anions. This is called the **heat of hydration.** (Cations are responsible for most of it, because they are much smaller than anions and hence the water molecules can get closer to them.) If the lattice energy is greater than the heat of hydration, solution takes place endothermically; if the reverse is true, the action is exothermic. A solute which dissolves endothermically in its almost saturated solution always increases in solubility with an increase in temperature, and vice versa.

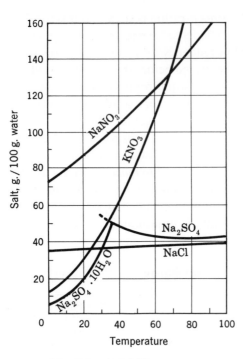

Fig. 8.4. Solubility curves.

8.8. Supersaturated Solutions

If a solvent is saturated with solute at one temperature and the solution is then carefully cooled (without introducing into it any particles of dust, dirt, solute, or salt isomorphous to the solute), the temperature can sometimes be lowered several degrees before any crystallization occurs. Crystallization never takes place until the first nucleus for it appears; thereafter it is usually quite rapid. If some water is saturated with sodium thiosulfate, $Na_2S_2O_3$, at 50° C. and the solution is filtered hot, it can be cooled to room temperature without forming any crystals. This is a **supersaturated solution**; in it crystallization, if once started, will be much more rapid than solution until all the excess solute has crystallized. The remaining solution will be just saturated at whatever temperature it was raised to by the heat liberated by the crystallization.

In Fig. 8.4 the portion of the Na_2SO_4 curve at the left of its intersection with the $Na_2SO_4 \cdot 10H_2O$ curve represents a solution which is saturated with respect to the anhydrous salt and supersaturated with respect to the decahydrate.

8.9.   Liquid Solutes

The solubility of one liquid in another varies over as wide a range as the solubility of a solid in a liquid. In general, as with solids, solubility increases with temperature. In the case of a few liquids, however, the solubility is also increased by lowering the temperature. Many liquids have unlimited solubility in each other; they are said to be **miscible.** Two liquids which have limited solubilities in each other (or practically none) are **immiscible.** Phenol (carbolic acid) and water are immiscible at room temperature, but miscible at elevated temperatures. When a clear, hot 50 per cent phenol-water solution is cooled, it turns milky as tiny droplets of water-in-phenol and phenol-in-water separate. This **emulsion** soon separates, droplets of like kind coalescing; and two layers of clear (liquid) solutions result, the lighter one floating on the denser. Even if both liquids are colorless, the interface between them is easily observable because of the difference in refractive index.

8.10.   The Colloidal State

An emulsion very commonly consists of ultramicroscopic droplets of one liquid, called the **dispersed phase,** suspended in another liquid, called the **continuous medium** or **phase.** Emulsions are most often prepared by mechanical agitation. An **emulsifying agent** may be added to stabilize the emulsion by preventing the droplets of the dispersed phase from coalescing. The molecules of such an agent must be polar at one end and non-polar at the other, so that one end, but not the whole molecule, is soluble in each of the immiscible liquids. Milk is an emulsion of droplets of butterfat oil in a water solution of milk sugar, etc., and the emulsifying agent is calcium butyrate, $Ca^{++} + 2CH_3 \cdot CH_2 \cdot CH_2COO^-$. The Ca^{++} ions and the negatively charged oxygen ends of the butyrate ions are soluble in water but not in oil, whereas the reverse is true of the hydrocarbon "tails" of the butyrate ions. As a result, all of the emulsifying agent is found at the oil-water interface, the hydrocarbon end in the oil droplets, the salt end in the water. The coating of the emulsifying agent on the surface of the droplets prevents oil-to-oil contact when the molecules collide, so the droplets cannot coalesce. Tiny solid particles may serve the same purpose. The total volume of the dispersed phase may be much greater than that of the continuous phase, making flow difficult or impossible. Mayonnaise, for example, has some 16 volumes of oil dispersed in 1 volume of flavored water. When home-made mayonnaise fails to thicken, it is because the emulsion has *inverted* to one of water-in-oil. This can easily be verified by noting the taste, which is oily instead of tart and salty.

An emulsion is an example of a **colloidal suspension.** Other examples include smoke and muddy water. They are not true solutions (even though the dispersed particles may be so small as to settle out only extremely slowly if at all), because they are heterogeneous mixtures of at least two different phases. The term colloidal solution is sometimes used, but it is incorrect and should be avoided. A true solution consists of a single phase; i.e., there is no bounding surface between two regions of different composition. In a solution the solute—sugar, salt, or alcohol in water, for example—is *molecularly* dispersed. Colloidal particles, such as smoke particles or fog droplets in the air, gas bubbles in a foam, or nickel sulfide particles in a solution being analyzed, are like molecules in having the same kinetic energy, but unlike them in being as much as a million times as large (Table 8.2). They are big enough to have a *surface*.

TABLE 8.2. **Particle Size**

1 A.	5 mμ	200 mμ	∞
True Solution Range	Colloidal Range		Micro to Macro Range
Molecules	Colloidal particles		Crystals and aggregates
Upper limit of giant molecular size ⎫→		←⎧ Lower limit of microscopic visibility	

A true solution is **homogeneous;** no light is scattered sideways from a beam of light passing through it. A colloidal suspension is **heterogeneous;** the path of a light beam which traverses it is visible from the side because the particles scatter the light. Although colloidal particles are below the limit of visible microscopy, this scattering of light enables them to be "seen" just as a pilot at four miles' altitude "sees" a pocket mirror held by someone on the ground when it reflects sunlight.

Colloids constitute a large and important subject, but their treatment in any detail is beyond the scope of this book. Consideration of one small facet of the subject, however, is frequently forced upon the elementary chemistry student in connection with analytical chemistry. When ions of an insoluble salt are brought together in solution, the first particles of precipitate formed are always colloidal in size. Ordinarily they rapidly grow large enough to be filtered or centrifuged out. But in the case of certain extremely insoluble compounds, practically all the material separates out at once in an enormous number of particles which fail to grow above colloidal size because no dissolved material remains. These particles can grow to manageable size only by clumping, but this is sometimes prevented by their tendency to acquire a charge of a given sign. Sulfide particles commonly make themselves negative by attaching excess sulfide ions to themselves, whereas the very insoluble hydroxides of trivalent cations tend to become positive by taking up protons from the solution. The remedy in both cases is to provide the solution with a large supply of ions (any kind which will not interfere with the analysis), thus forcing the charged particles to take up enough of the oppositely charged ions to become electrically neutral.

This process takes place in nature, often with undesirable effects. The deltas of fresh-water rivers—e.g., the Mississippi, the Colorado, and the Amazon—are due to the fact that colloidally suspended mud in the fresh water becomes electrically neutralized by the adsorption of suitable ions when it comes in contact with the ocean at the river's mouth; the result is that vast tonnages of mud are dumped.

8.11. Solutions of Gaseous Solutes

When gases dissolve in liquids they obey a law which does not apply to solutions considered thus far. This law, which is called **Henry's law,** states that *the amount of gas dissolved by a given volume of liquid, at constant temperature, is proportional to the partial pressure of the gas.* Thus gases behave as though a liquid solvent merely provides a certain amount of space, which the dissolved portion of gas occupies, there being free communication between it and the undissolved portion of gas. According to Boyle's law, doubling the pressure of the undissolved gas doubles its concentration; so the concentration of the dissolved gas will also be doubled. (Standard pressure of 1 atm. is implied for the gas solubilities in Table 8.1.) According to Charles' law, increasing the temperature of a gas at constant pressure causes it to expand. Hence, the gas concentration is less so the solubility is less. This effect is superimposed on the temperature-solubility relationships described in Section 8.7. Thus gases show the same molecular concentration relationships in liquid solutions as they do in the pure gas state; that is, the molecular concentration in a given volume is increased by an increase in pressure and a decrease in temperature.

Unless a gas reacts chemically with a liquid, the volume of gas dissolved is only a small fraction of the volume of the liquid. Henry's law cannot be simply applied to any gas which reacts extensively with a liquid, because the amount of solvent does not remain constant but diminishes. A number of gases do react extensively (though reversibly) with water. Thus 1 l. of water at 15° C. will dissolve *and react with* 568 l. of ammonia at the same temperature.

$$\overline{NH_3} + H_2O \rightleftharpoons NH_4OH$$

The volume of the resulting solution is 1.6 l. Each liter contains nearly 525 g. of ammonium hydroxide (15 moles), some ammonia, and only about 355 g. of water. Similarly, the reaction of hydrochloric acid with water, mentioned in Section 8.6, produces a solution which contains a greater weight of $H_3O^+ + Cl^-$ (hydronium chloride, or hydrochloric acid) than of water. These are regularly called ammonium hydroxide and hydrochloric acid solutions respectively, rather than ammonia and hydrogen chloride solutions. This is obviously appropriate, even though the original gases can readily be obtained from them by heating the solutions, the reaction going to the left.

A bottle of carbonated beverage illustrates nicely the role of pressure and temperature in the solubility phenomena of a gas. When the bottle is sealed, it is saturated with carbon dioxide at 5 atm. pressure. When the chilled bottle is opened and the pressure drops to 1 atm., the solution is supersaturated and promptly begins to effervesce, losing carbon dioxide. If the bottle is partly emptied and then restoppered, the liquid will continue to lose the gas until a sufficient partial pressure of it has been built up in the bottle to reestablish equilibrium. If the beverage is allowed to become warm, further transfer of the carbon dioxide from the solution to the gas phase accompanies the diminishing solubility because of the increasing temperature.

Our blood is always saturated with nitrogen, the unreactive gas which forms 78 per cent of the air. If the pressure is rapidly lowered, as when a diver rises too quickly from a great depth, the blood becomes supersaturated with nitrogen and bubbles of it are produced which block circulation in the capillaries. The excruciating cramps which result, called the bends, may be fatal. The condition may be relieved by repressurization in a pressure chamber to force the bubbles back into solution. This is followed by suitably slow decompression which permits the excess nitrogen to diffuse from the blood into the lungs. Blood leaving the lungs is also saturated with oxygen, but this creates no trouble because the oxygen is used up in the body. Sudden loss of pressure in the cabin of a high-flying plane may also produce the bends. By using helium, the least soluble of all gases, instead of nitrogen, as the diluent of oxygen, an artificial atmosphere of lower total solubility can be prepared which greatly reduces the danger of the bends.

8.12. Concentrations of Solutions

Solutions may be described qualitatively as dilute, concentrated, saturated, or unsaturated, but the concentration must be expressed quantitatively for many important calculations. This can be done in many ways, all of which are based on the following fundamental relationships:

 A. Amount of solute per *weight* unit of *solvent.*
 B. Amount of solute per *volume* unit of *solution.*
 C. Amount of solute per *weight* unit of *solution.*

For calculations involving physical properties of solutions, including molecular weight determinations, concentrations are usually expressed in accordance with A. If chemical reactions are involved, the calculations are based on concentrations expressed in terms of B.

When a solute is a definite chemical compound, its amount can be expressed not only in weight units but also in moles or equivalents. For example, 98 g. of H_2SO_4 can equally well be expressed as 1 mole or 2 equivalents of H_2SO_4. The same choice of units is available for expressing the weight of solvent in A.

Concentrations are commonly expressed in terms of A in two cases: (1) in the listing of solubilities, and (2) in calculations involving physical properties of dilute solutions. In Table 8.1, for example, the solubilities are given in grams of solute per 100 g. of water. The physical properties of dilute solutions, such as freezing and boiling points, depend upon the number of solute molecules present, not upon their weight; so when calculations involve such properties it is convenient to state the concentrations in terms of *moles of solute per 1000 g. of water.* When concentration is expressed this way it is called **molality** (abbreviated *m*). Molality may be expressed mathematically as follows:

$$\text{Molality} = m = \frac{\dfrac{\text{Weight of solute}}{\text{Formula weight of solute}} \times 1000}{\text{Weight of solvent}}$$

where the fraction in the numerator is obviously the number of moles of solute.

To illustrate this formula we will calculate the molality of a solution consisting of 25.0 g. of H_2SO_4 dissolved in 250 g. of water.

$$m = \frac{25.0/98.1 \times 1000}{250} = 1.02$$

The weight of H_2SO_4 divided by its formula weight, 98.1, gives the number of moles of H_2SO_4. When this is divided by 250, the result is the number of moles of H_2SO_4 per gram of water; multiplying this by 1000 gives the number of moles in 1000 g. of water, or the molality. The solution is 1.02 molal (1.02 m).

Concentrations are commonly expressed in terms of B when we want to find the amount of one substance which will react with a given amount of another substance. Here also we are interested in the number of moles, not the weight, of the reagent; but the amount of water is of no interest to us. If we use B to express the concentration, we can find the number of moles of reagent used simply by measuring the volume of the solution which is used. When concentration is expressed in terms of *moles of solute per liter of solution,* it is called **molarity** (abbreviated M). Mathematically this is:

$$\text{Molarity} = M = \frac{\dfrac{\text{Weight of solute}}{\text{Formula weight of solute}}}{\text{Volume of solution in liters}}$$

If 100 ml. of a solution contains 50 g. of H_2SO_4, what is its molarity? Substituting the appropriate numbers, we have:

$$\text{Molarity} = M = \frac{50/98}{0.100} = 5.1$$

The solution is 5.1 molar (5.1 M).

The density of a 0.100 M solution of H_2SO_4 solution at 25° C. is 1.025. Since 1 l. of it weighs 1025 g. and contains 9.81 g. of H_2SO_4, it contains 1015 g. of water. The molality is then $\dfrac{0.1 \times 1000}{1015}$, or 0.0985. A similar computation for 0.1 M Na_2SO_4, density 1.011, shows that it contains

997 g. of water and is 0.1003 m. Other dilute solutions also contain very nearly 1000 g. of water per liter of solution and therefore their molalities are almost the same as their molarities. Although molalities and molarities can be interchanged in the case of dilute solutions without introducing much error, they must not be confused when solutions of any considerable concentration are involved; for example, 10 M H_2SO_4 is almost 28 m.

A mole of one substance may react with more than 1 mole of another substance, but 1 equivalent of one substance always reacts with 1 equivalent of another. Computations can frequently be simplified if concentrations of solutions are expressed in terms of *equivalents per liter* instead of moles per liter. Concentration expressed in this way is called **normality** (abbreviated N). The mathematical definition is:

$$\text{Normality} = N = \frac{\dfrac{\text{Weight of solute}}{\text{Equivalent weight of solute}}}{\text{Volume of solution in liters}}$$

The normality is either identical with the molarity or an integral multiple of it. The multiplier is, in fact, the valence factor used in calculating the equivalent weight of the solute.

$$N = M \times \text{Valence factor}$$

The valence factor for H_2SO_4 is 2; so the 5.1 M H_2SO_4 mentioned above is 10.2 N. This can be checked by inserting the equivalent weight of H_2SO_4, together with the given amounts of acid and water, in the normality formula. The result differs from that for molarity only by the valence factor 2. When the valence factor is 1 there is no difference at all, and M and N are numerically identical. This is the case, for example, with solutions containing such solutes as HCl, NaOH, NH_4OH, and NaCl.

When we want to find the number of moles of solvent in a solution as well as the number of moles of solute, it is convenient to express concentration in terms of **mole fractions,** that is, in terms of relationship C above. The mole fraction of a substance in a solution is obtained by dividing the number of moles of that substance by the total number of moles of all substances present.

Mole fraction of substance A =

$$\frac{\text{Moles of substance A}}{\text{Moles of substance A} + \text{Moles of substance B} + \cdots}$$

The sum of all the mole fractions for a given solution, including that of the solvent, must be 1. In a solution containing 1 mole (342 g.) of sugar and 99 moles (1782 g.) of water the mole fraction of sugar is 0.01 and that of water is 0.99. In such a solution the vapor pressure of the water is 0.99 of that of pure water, a fact which illustrates the type of case in which mole fractions are useful.

Commercially the concentration of a solution is frequently given in terms of C, using ordinary weight units, not moles. The figure most commonly used is the weight of solute per 100 g. of solution. This is called the **per cent,** and is represented by the sign %. Thus:

$$\frac{\text{Weight of solute} \times 100}{\text{Weight of solute} + \text{Weight of solvent}} = \frac{\text{Weight of solute} \times 100}{\text{Weight of solution}}$$

$$= \% \text{ solute by weight}$$

Substituting 1000 for 100 in the above expression gives the concentration in *parts per thousand,* represented by the sign $^o/_{oo}$. In expressing the concentration of a very dilute solution, as in water analysis, *parts per million* (abbreviated p.p.m.) is usually used to avoid fractions.

If, in the above equation for per cent, the amount of solution is 1 ml., the denominator states the **density** of the solution. (Density is defined as weight per unit volume.) Rearranging the equation, we have:

$$\text{Weight of solute (per ml.)} = \frac{\% \text{ Solute by weight} \times \text{Density}}{100}$$

The specific gravity (sp. gr.) of a solution is the ratio of its density to that of water at 4° C.* This is numerically equal to the density when the latter is expressed in metric units (but not when in English units, such as lb./gal.). Tables in the various chemical handbooks state the relationship between percentage composition and density for solutions of many common reagents. If either of these quantities is given on the label of a stock bottle the other can be found in such a table; it is then easy to compute the molarity (or normality) of the solution. For this it is convenient to consider a volume of 1 ml. The definition of molarity then takes the form:

---

* Sometimes the density of water at some other temperature than 4° C. may be used. The temperature at which the density of the solution is measured must be specified if great accuracy is desired. The symbol d^{20}_4 or d^{20}_{20} may be used for specific gravity; the upper number is the temperature at which the density of the liquid in question was measured, the lower number the temperature of the water. Since d^{20}_4 for water is 0.99823, d^{20}_4 and d^{20}_{20} for other liquids differ by less than $2^o/_{oo}$.

$$M = \frac{\text{Weight of solute per ml.} \times 1000}{\text{Formula weight of solute}}$$

But the weight of solute per milliliter is given by the expression:

$$\frac{\% \text{ Solute by weight} \times \text{Density}}{100}$$

Substituting this in the equation defining molarity, we have:

$$M = \frac{\% \text{ Solute by weight} \times \text{Density} \times 1000}{100 \times \text{Formula weight}}$$

Thus we find that the molarity of a 60 per cent H_2SO_4 solution, with a corresponding specific gravity of 1.498, is:

$$\frac{60 \times 1.498 \times 1000}{100 \times 98.1} = 9.17 \; M$$

8.13. Concentrations of Ions

The concentrations of the ions in a solution can be computed very easily if the molar concentration of the parent salt is known. It is only necessary to multiply the molarity of the salt by the subscript of the ion in the formula of the salt. Thus a 2 M $AlCl_3$ solution is 2 M with respect to Al^{+3} ions and 6 M with respect to Cl^- ions. In order to determine the normality of the ions we multiply the molarity of the salt by the valence factor (Section 7.9), which is the product of the subscript number of *either* ion multiplied by its valence (the sign is disregarded). Notice that although the ions of a salt may have different molarities, they have the same normality. This is illustrated in Table 8.3, in which V.F. stands for valence factor, M is molarity, and N normality.

8.14. Concentration-Volume Calculations

The concentration-volume relationship of solutions which contain the same amount of a given solute is directly analogous to the pres-

TABLE 8.3. **Concentrations in 1 M Salt Solutions**

	Compound	Positive Ion	Negative Ion
	$M \times$ V.F. $= N$	$M \times$ V.F. $= N$	$M \times$ V.F. $= N$
NaCl	$1 \times 1 = 1$	$1 \times 1 = 1$	$1 \times 1 = 1$
$CaCl_2$	$1 \times 2 = 2$	$1 \times 2 = 2$	$2 \times 1 = 2$
$Al_2(SO_4)_3$	$1 \times 6 = 6$	$2 \times 3 = 6$	$3 \times 2 = 6$

sure-volume relationship of samples of gas containing the same number of molecules. You will recall from Boyle's law, $P_1V_1 = P_2V_2$, that when the volume of a gas is doubled the pressure is halved. Thus the pressure of a gas is a measure of its molecular concentration. If the volume is doubled there are half as many molecules per milliliter of space as there were originally. Similarly, if we start with a volume V_1 of a solution of concentration C_1 and add enough water to double the volume, so that $V_2 = 2V_1$, we may apply a product law similar to Boyle's law, $C_1V_1 = C_2V_2$; note that the concentration has been halved.

As in the case of gases, it is convenient to solve this expression for the unknown quantity before making any computations. In the above case we would have:

$$C_2 = C_1 \times \frac{V_1}{V_2} = C_1 \times \frac{1}{2} = \frac{C_1}{2}$$

In other words, to find the new concentration when water is added to or removed from a solution, we simply multiply the old concentration by the ratio of the volumes. Common sense will tell us which volume to use as the numerator.

For example, what is the final molarity of HCl if 5 drops of 6 M HCl is mixed with 5 drops of pure water and 5 drops of $CuSO_4$ solution? The concentration of the $CuSO_4$ solute is not given because it is irrelevant; no amount of this solution has anything to do with the concentration of HCl. Applying the above equation, we have:

$$C_2 = 6\ M \times \frac{5\ \text{drops}}{15\ \text{drops}} = 2\ M$$

A "drop" may seem curious as a unit of volume, but it makes no difference what units of volume are used in the ratio (as long as both are the *same*), because they cancel out. Since the ratio is a pure number, the new concentration will be expressed in the same units as the old concentration.

It was stated at the beginning of this section that the product CV is a constant for all solutions containing a given amount of a solute. As a matter of fact, that constant *is* the amount of solute. If C is given in molarity and V in liters, CV is the total number of moles in that number of liters. If V is in milliliters, CV is the number of millimoles. Thus 2.5 l. of 4 M HCl contains 10 moles of HCl, and 2.5 ml. of 4 M HCl contains 10 millimoles of HCl. By the same reasoning, if the concentration is expressed in terms of normality, CV is the amount of solute in equivalents or millequivalents respectively.

This provides us with a powerful tool for reaction calculations involving solutions. Since in any reaction, such as

$$A + B \rightarrow C$$

the amounts of all the reactants are *equivalent,* the products of their normalities and the volumes of the solutions which contained them must be equal.

$$\text{Equivalents of } A = \text{Equivalents of } B = \text{Equivalents of } C$$
$$N_A \times V_A \quad = \quad N_B \times V_B \quad = \quad N_C \times V_C$$

For example, 20 ml. of 0.2 N HCl solution reacts with just 50 ml. of NaOH solution. What was the normality of the NaOH solution? Since the number of equivalents is the same for the two quantities of solution, this problem may be treated in exactly the same way as a concentration-volume problem.

$$C_{\text{NaOH}} = C_{\text{HCl}} \times \frac{20}{50} = 0.2 \times \frac{20}{50} = 0.08 \ N$$

Note that if the concentration of any product of a reaction is to be calculated, the volume used must be the sum of the volumes of the reactants. The NaCl produced by the above reaction is:

$$0.2 \ N \times \frac{20}{70} = 0.057 \ N$$

The weights of substances involved in a reaction can readily be calculated from the normality-volume data for either of the reactants. The number of equivalent weights of a solute in a solution is:

$$\text{Normality} \times \text{Volume (in } \textit{liters}) = \text{Equivalent weights}$$

Thus for the problem above:

$$0.2 \ N \quad \times \ 0.02 \ 1. = 0.004 \text{ equivalent of HCl}$$
$$0.08 \ N \ \times \ 0.05 \ 1. = 0.004 \text{ equivalent of NaOH}$$
$$0.057 \ N \times 0.07 \ 1. = 0.004 \text{ equivalent of NaCl}$$

Hence the product of the volume (liters) and normality for *one* reactant establishes the equivalents involved for *each* reactant.

The weight of each reactant (in grams) is obtained by multiplying the number of equivalents by the weight of each equivalent, thus:

$$\text{Equivalents} \times \text{Weight per equivalent} = \text{Grams}$$

0.004	×	36.5	= 0.15 g. of HCl
0.004	×	40.0	= 0.16 g. of NaOH
0.004	×	58.5	= 0.23 g. of NaCl

The over-all expression which is used to derive the weight of a reactant from volume-normality data of *any* reactant in the reaction is:

$$N \times V \text{ (liters)} \times \text{Equivalent weight} = \text{Grams}$$

Since volumes are frequently measured in milliliters, a similar expression is used for weight in milligrams:

$$N \times V \text{ (ml.)} \times \text{Equivalent weight} = \text{Mg.}$$

8.15. Titration

Data such as those used toward the end of the preceding section are obtained by a process called **titration.** This involves determining the exact volume of one solution that is needed to react completely with a definite amount of another solution. The volumes of the solutions are commonly measured by means of burettes (see Fig. 8.5). The point at which the reaction is complete is called the **equivalence point.** There must be some means of telling when it has been reached.

In some cases one of the reagents may have a strong enough color to serve this purpose. In other cases, however, both reagents are colorless; this is commonly true of acids and bases. In these reactions a small quantity of an **indicator** must be added. An indicator is a substance which shows the equivalence point of a titration by a sharp color change. In acid-base work (**acidimetry**) the indicator is usually a dye that is also a weak acid; on losing a proton, its bonds are rearranged and it changes color. If an acid is being titrated, the indicator acid will remain undissociated as long as any of the stronger acid is present. When the last of this has been neutralized, the next drop of base that is added will neutralize the indicator acid and change the color.

Indicator acids differ in strength. Some ionize considerably even in a somewhat acid solution; others are so weak that the solution must be fairly basic before they lose protons and change color. For example, the indicator phenolphthalein loses its red color and becomes colorless when a strongly basic solution becomes more weakly basic. On the other hand, the indicator methyl orange is straw-yellow in a weak acid solution and reddish-orange in a strong acid solution. Proper selection of an indicator is important. The degree of acidity or basicity of a solution at the beginning and end of neutralization must be compared, for the indicator must change color between these extremes. A single drop of a 1 M solution of hydrochloric acid added to 50 ml. of water or a neutral salt solution will increase the acidity 10,000-fold; a drop of a 1 M solution of sodium hydroxide will decrease the acidity to the same extent. Many indicators change color within this range, and any of them can be used without causing an error greater than one drop.

In the setup shown in Fig. 8.5, one burette is filled with a solution of known normality, e.g., HCl acid. A known volume of base, e.g., NaOH, is measured into the beaker from the other burette. A few drops of indicator, e.g., phenolphthalein, are added to the base. The indicator imparts a red color to the solution because of its strong basicity but becomes colorless when enough acid has been added to the base so that the equivalence point is reached. While the acid is being added the solution is stirred continuously. As the equivalence point is approached, the indicator begins to pale or even completely decolorizes briefly in the vicinity of the added acid. The acid is now added dropwise until

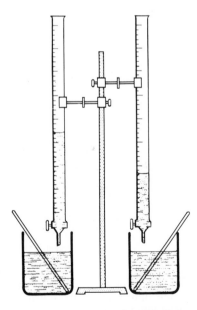

Fig. 8.5. Burettes for titration.

one additional drop produces permanent total decolorization. This is the equivalence point of the titration. To compute the normality of the base, the volume of acid needed for the equivalence point, its normality, and the volume of base used for the titration are substituted in the expression:

$$V_A N_A = V_B N_B.$$

8.16. Vapor Pressure, Freezing and Boiling Points of Solutions

The vapor pressure of a liquid increases with rising temperature until it reaches atmospheric pressure, whereupon the liquid boils. The upper curve in Fig. 8.6 shows this variation for a typical liquid. Thus, for standardization, the boiling points of liquids are defined as **standard boiling points** relative to 760 mm. pressure (standard pressure). The solid solvent also has a vapor pressure curve which starts from zero at 0° K.; it rises faster than that of the liquid solvent and eventually reaches

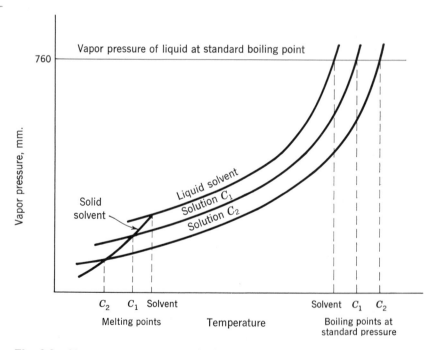

Fig. 8.6. Vapor pressure curves, boiling and melting points of pure solvent, solute, and solutions of concentration C_1 and C_2. The scale is magnified at the lower temperatures.

but does not cross it. The vapor pressure curve of the solid ends at this point, the **melting point,** because the solid melts. The melting point of a solid is the same as the freezing point of its liquid form; thus ice melts at 0° C., water freezes at 0° C. Although a solid cannot be heated *above* its melting point, a liquid can be cooled below that temperature if no solid is present. A liquid which has been cooled below its freezing point is said to be **supercooled.** From the foregoing it is clear that the freezing and boiling points of a liquid will be altered by any factor that alters its vapor pressure. Dissolving any substance in a liquid brings about a change in its vapor pressure.

Evaporation from a liquid takes place when one of the molecules on the surface acquires an upward velocity sufficiently great to enable it to escape. If 1 mole of any solute is dissolved in 99 moles of water, 99 out of every hundred molecules will be water molecules and 1 will not. If any given molecule on the surface of the solution receives an upward blow that would enable a water molecule to evaporate, 99 times out of a hundred the molecule will *be* a water molecule and will evaporate; but the hundredth time it will not be a water molecule and whether it *evaporates* or not will have nothing to do with the vapor pressure of *water.* In such a solution the rate of evaporation of water is 99 per cent of that of pure water. Accordingly the vapor pressure of the water will be 99 per cent of the vapor pressure of pure water. Since evaporation is entirely a matter of energy, the weight of the dissolved molecule is of no importance. It can even be an ion; the result will be the same.

In 1881 Raoult proved experimentally that many properties of solutions depend upon the number of moles of solute added to a solvent. Raoult's law may be stated: *Any property of a substance in a solution is shown to an extent proportional to the mole fraction of that substance in the solution.* In the example just given, the mole fraction of water in the solution is 0.99, that of the solute 0.01. Applying Raoult's law to the solute, we can predict that the *lowering* of the vapor pressure of the solution will be twice as great in a solution containing 2 moles of solute to 98 of water as it is in this case.

Raoult's law is obeyed only by "ideal" solutions, those in which the solute molecules show no tendency either to clump together or to combine with the solvent. In the case of electrolytes the law is precise only for dilute solutions. In dilute solutions the mole fraction is given with sufficient accuracy by:

$$\text{Mole fraction} = \frac{\text{Moles of solute}}{\text{Moles of solvent}}$$

The small quantity, moles of solute, in the denominator is neglected. But when this approximation is made, the concentration is actually being expressed in terms of A (Section 8.12); so it can be recalculated into *molality*. Thus we can restate Raoult's law, less precisely: *The extent of variation of the properties of a dilute solution is proportional to its molality.*

The vapor pressure curves of two solutions are plotted in Fig. 8.6. Solution C_2 has a higher concentration than C_1. Since the vapor pressure of the solvent is *lowered* when a solute is added, the freezing points (melting points) of the solutions are *lower* than that of the solvent and the boiling points are *higher*. The boiling of a solution depends upon the total vapor pressure, not just upon that of the solvent; so this statement about the elevation of the boiling point assumes that the solute is nonvolatile. If the solvent is water, this excludes substances that boil below 200° C.

Experiment has shown that the depression of the freezing point of water is 1.86° C. per mole of solute dissolved in 1000 g. of water, and the elevation of the boiling point is 0.52° C. These quantities are called the **molal freezing-point depression constant** (K_f) and the **molal boiling-point elevation constant** (K_b) respectively. Thus the freezing point of a water solution is given by:

$$\text{f.p.} = 0° \text{ C.} - m(1.86° \text{ C.})$$

and the boiling point by:

$$\text{b.p.} = m(0.52° \text{ C.}) + 100° \text{ C.}$$

For example, what are the freezing and boiling points of a solution consisting of 50.0 g. of ethylene glycol, $C_2H_4(OH)_2$ (a permanent type of antifreeze), dissolved in 250 g. of water?

$$\text{Molality} = \frac{\dfrac{\text{Grams of solute}}{\text{Formula weight of solute}} \times 1000}{\text{Grams of solvent}} = \frac{50.0 \times 1000}{62.1 \times 250} = 3.23 \ m$$

$$\text{b.p.} = (3.23)(0.52°) + 100° = 101.68° \text{ C.}$$
$$\text{f.p.} = -(3.23)(1.86°) = -6.06° \text{ C.}$$

More than one kind of solute molecule may be present in a solution. In that case the freezing and boiling points will depend upon the total molality of *all* solute molecules present.

What is the freezing point of a 0.20 m CaCl$_2$ solution that is 80 per cent free ions and 20 per cent ion clusters averaging CaCl$_2$?

$$\begin{array}{ccc} \text{Ion clusters} & & \text{Free ions} \\ (Ca^{++}, 2Cl^-) & \rightleftharpoons & Ca^{++} & + & 2Cl^- \\ 0.20 \times 0.20\ m & & 0.80 \times 0.20\ m & + & 0.80 \times 0.40\ m \end{array}$$

Total molality $= (0.20 + 0.80) \times 0.20 + 0.80 \times 0.40 = 0.52\ m$

f.p. $= -m(1.86°\ C.) = -0.52(1.86°\ C.) = -0.97°\ C.$

8.17. Molecular Weight Determinations

One of the most important applications of this type of solution studies is the experimental determination of the molecular weights of non-volatile substances which cannot be determined by gas density measurements. A weighed sample of the unknown compound is dissolved in a known quantity of solvent. The freezing-point depression (or boiling-point elevation) is carefully measured with a thermometer calibrated in hundredths of a degree. From these data the molecular weight is readily calculated.

For example, 50 g. of a non-ionic compound is dissolved in 200 g. of water. The resultant solution freezes at $-5.06°$ C. What is the molecular weight of the compound?

$$\text{f.p.} = -m(1.86°\ C.) = -5.06°\ C.$$

Therefore: $\qquad m = \dfrac{5.06°}{1.86°} = 2.72$

But

$$m = \dfrac{\dfrac{\text{Grams of solute}}{\text{Formula weight of solute}} \times 1000}{\text{Grams of solvent}} = 2.72 = \dfrac{50 \times 1000}{\text{Formula weight} \times 200}$$

Therefore: $\qquad$ Formula weight $= \dfrac{50 \times 1000}{200 \times 2.72} = 92$ g.

Since this substance is not a salt, this is the actual molecular weight as well.

Solutions in other liquid or easily melted solvents can be studied in the same manner. Each solvent has its own K_b and K_f; these constants are given in tables in the various handbooks. The computations follow the principles just outlined. It should also be obvious that the extent to which a salt exists as free ions can be determined from the freezing or boiling point of a solution if its molality is known. This fraction, known as α, is frequently called the apparent degree of dissociation.

QUESTIONS AND PROBLEMS

1. List some *true* solutions which you use around the home.
2. Define solute; solvent. What types of each are there? Give some examples.
3. What roles do molecular configuration and electronegativity play in the physical character of solvents?
4. a. Describe the physical aspects of an ionic compound dissolving in water.
   b. What unique property does water possess which makes it a particularly good solvent for ionic compounds?
   c. What explanation is offered for the insolubility of some ionic compounds in water?
5. a. What is meant by ion clusters or solution molecules?
   b. Write typical formulas to describe the molecular species in a solution of barium nitrate.
6. a. Distinguish between strong and weak acids.
   b. HF is a weak acid and HNO_3 a strong acid. How do their ionic reactions in water differ?
7. Distinguish between unsaturated, saturated, and supersaturated solutions. If a crystal of solute were dropped in each of these solutions, what would happen?
8. When crystals of calcium chloride are added to water the resultant reaction is accompanied by the liberation of heat. Explain.
9. What procedures would you usually follow to increase the rate of solution of solids or liquids? To increase the quantity of solute dissolved?
10. Distinguish between a colloidal suspension and a true solution.
11. How does the solubility of a gas in a liquid conform to some of the simple gas laws?
12. Define molarity; molality; normality. Under what conditions may any of these be equivalent?
13. A solution contains 10 g. of NaCl in 500 g. of H_2O. What is its molality?
14. Fifty grams of H_2SO_4 are present in 500 ml. of solution. What is the molarity? The normality?
15. A solution of $Al_2(SO_4)_3$ is 3 N in aluminum ion. What is the molarity of Al^{+3}; of SO_4^{--}; of $Al_2(SO_4)_3$? What is the normality of SO_4^{--} and of $Al_2(SO_4)_3$?
16. How many grams of $Al_2(SO_4)_3$ are dissolved in 250 ml. of solution in question 15?
17. If the density of the solution in question 15 is 1.1 g./ml., what is its molality?
18. If 250 ml. of 2 M H_2SO_4 is diluted to a volume of 1 l., what is the final molarity? What are the initial and the final normality?

19. If 25 ml. of 0.30 N NaOH reacts with 40 ml. of H_2SO_4, what is the normality of the H_2SO_4? How many grams of NaOH and H_2SO_4 were consumed in the reaction? How many grams of Na_2SO_4 were formed in the reaction?

20. A solution of H_2SO_4 has a specific gravity of 1.73 and is 80 per cent H_2SO_4 by weight. Calculate:

a. Its molarity, normality, and molality.

b. The volume of 2 M $Ba(OH)_2$ solution required to neutralize 1 l. of the H_2SO_4 solution.

21. What is the mole fraction of $C_2H_4(OH)_2$ in a solution consisting of 25 g. of it in 100 g. of water?

22. What are the freezing and boiling points of the solution in question 21?

23. A solution consisting of 5 g. of solute in 25 g. of H_2O boils at 102.08° C. Find the molecular weight of the solute.

24. The apparent degree of dissociation of a 2 m solution of $BaCl_2$ is 80 per cent. What is the freezing point?

25. Assuming the electrolytes to be 100 per cent in the form of free ions, what is the freezing point of a solution resulting from mixing 1000 g. of H_2O containing 10 moles of NaOH with 1000 g. of H_2O containing 10 moles of HCl?

9

The halogen family

9.1. Introduction

The elements which immediately precede the inert gases form a closely related group known as the halogen family. They are the main group in Group VII of the periodic table and are characterized by having 7 electrons in the valence shell. The term halogen means salt former. The family was so named because of the strong resemblance of its sodium and potassium compounds to common salt, sodium chloride, NaCl. A number of the physical properties of these elements are listed in Table 9.1.

Note that even the least electronegative halogen, iodine, is above the middle (2.0) of the electronegativity scale. This means that an element in this family will always complete its valence shell through chemical reaction. If possible, it does this by gaining 1 electron per atom, forming a halide ion of the type X^-. If there is no metal atom from which to take electrons, a halogen atom completes its octet by sharing an electron pair with some other non-metal atom in a covalent bond. Because of the high electronegativity of the halogens, the halogen atom regularly "owns" more

TABLE 9.1. **Properties of the Halogens**

	Fluorine	Chlorine	Bromine	Iodine
Atomic weight	19.00	35.457	79.916	126.92
Molecular formula	F_2	Cl_2	Br_2	I_2
Color	Pale yellow	Greenish yellow	Red-brown	Violet
Melting point, °C.	−223	−102	− 7	114
Boiling point, °C.	−187	− 35	59	184
Density, g./ml.	1.1 (l)	1.56 (l)	3.12 (l)	4.93 (s)
Electronegativity	4.0	3.0	2.8	2.5

than half of a shared electron pair and is assigned an oxidation number of −1. Only when combined with oxygen, nitrogen, or a more reactive halogen is chlorine, bromine, or iodine assigned a positive oxidation number. Fluorine is never positive, for it is the most electronegative of all atoms.

With 7 electrons already in the valence shell, the formation of a *single* covalent bond is all that is needed to complete the shell. A halogen molecule therefore has the simple structure represented by a dot formula of the type : $\ddot{X}$: $\ddot{X}$: . The multiple bonding which made the O_2 molecule abnormally unreactive is not present.

9.2. Discovery of the Halogens

The halogens were discovered during the period 1811–1886, and were identified as elements in the following order: chlorine, iodine, bromine, and fluorine. Chlorine was prepared by Scheele in 1774 by the reaction between manganese dioxide, MnO_2, and HCl. He described its characteristics correctly, but believed that it was an oxide of some type. Sir Humphry Davy concluded that it was an element, for all his efforts to decompose it failed. It is interesting to note that chlorine, bromine, and iodine were all discovered accidentally, whereas the isolation of fluorine was the result of arduous and dangerous work.

The discoverer of iodine was a French saltmaker, Bernard Courtois, who made a living by extracting salts from brown algae and seaweed. He was particularly interested in the recovery of potassium salts and used H_2SO_4 to "destroy" certain sulfur compounds present in the mother liquor. One day in 1811 he must have added more H_2SO_4 than usual, for beautiful clouds of violet vapor escaped from the container. The vapor, which had an odor similar to that of chlorine, condensed readily on cold objects and formed dark crystals almost metallic in character. After making a few observations, he turned this work over to two of his friends, Desormes and Clément, for more thorough study. Two years later Clément described the properties of iodine in great detail.

The French chemist, Balard, discovered bromine in 1826 when, while treating Montpellier salt brine (which contained bromides) with chlorine gas, he distilled a dark red liquid which boiled at 47° C. He named this substance bromine because of its "bad odor." (The names chlorine and iodine refer to the color of these elements.)

With the discovery of bromine, iodine, and chlorine, it was clear to chemists that there was an undiscovered element above chlorine in the periodic table. The fluorides and hydrogen fluoride, HF, were known for many years before anyone was able to obtain the element fluorine in the free state. Davy, Gay-Lussac, Thenard, George Knox and his brother Thomas nearly lost their lives from breathing the fumes of HF, and Louyet and Nicklés died. Finally, in 1886, Moissan, the famous French chemist, prepared fluorine by electrolyzing a solution of dry potassium acid fluoride, KHF_2, and anhydrous HF in a platinum electrolytic cell with platinum-iridium electrodes.

9.3. Sources of Fluorine

Fluorides of polyvalent cations are usually insoluble owing to the small size of F^- ion, which results in high lattice energy (Section 8.4). Because of this fact, natural deposits of fluorides have not been washed into the sea by rain water, but remain as rocks. Three of these minerals constitute the commercial source of F^- ion. They are calcium fluoride, CaF_2, commonly called fluorspar; sodium fluoaluminate, Na_3AlF_6, called cryolite; and $Ca_5(PO_4)_3F$, known as fluorapatite to geologists but usually called phosphate rock. Fluorspar is the main source of F^- ion at present. Cryolite is used in the manufacture of aluminum; but the natural deposits no longer meet the demand, so it is now synthesized. Phosphate rock is by far the most abundant. It is the raw material for one section of the great fertilizer industry. In making the phosphate ion, PO_4^{-3}, available for plant use, the undesirable F^- ion is removed as HF. This by-product of the fertilizer industry, once wasted, may eventually become our main source of F^- ion. Not only fluorine but all fluorine compounds are prepared from this ion.

9.4. Preparation of Fluorine

Because of the expense of preparing it and the difficulty and danger involved in using such a violently reactive substance, fluorine was a rare chemical curiosity until a sudden large-scale demand for it developed during World War II. Fortunately, some research that had continued resulted in important improvements in Moissan's process for preparing it.

By pooling their efforts, several chemical companies in the United States developed a variety of cells constructed of cheaper materials than the noble metals used by Moissan; various operating conditions

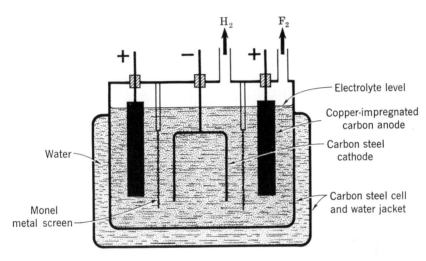

Fig. 9.1. Electrolytic production of fluorine (and hydrogen). Fluoride ions give up electrons to the positive anode; hydrogen ions receive electrons from the negative cathode. Low concentrations of these ions are in equilibrium with HF_2^- ions. The inlet for HF is not shown.

for the electrolytic production of fluorine were also made possible. A typical cell is illustrated in Fig. 9.1. Ordinary carbon steel can be used for the cell body, water jackets, feed lines, and cathode. Although the anode may be constructed of various materials, copper-impregnated graphite has worked very well. A Monel metal screen between the anode and cathode is used to prevent any mixing of the gases produced. Several modifications of this cell are now in use; they have been found to function for a year or more before repairs are necessary.

The electrolyte consists of a solution of potassium fluoride, KF, dissolved in anhydrous HF. The melting point of the electrolyte depends upon the KF : HF ratio. A composition corresponding to KF : 2HF generally is used; the resultant electrolyte becomes molten over the operating range of 80 to 120° C. A higher KF content raises the operating range. KF $\cdot$ HF (or KHF_2) melts at 250° C. The electrolyte can be considered to produce K^+ and HF_2^- ions in the molten condition. A small amount (1 to 3 per cent) of lithium fluoride, LiF, is added to the electrolyte. It facilitates the wetting of the anode by the molten electrolyte and also prevents polarization of the electrodes.

In operation, the electrodes are connected to a source of electric current which pulls electrons out of the graphite electrode and pushes them onto the iron electrode. The iron electrode, negatively charged because of its excess of electrons, is called a **cathode.** The graphite electrode, positive because it has lost electrons, is called an **anode.** When the potential difference between the electrodes reaches a sufficient value, HF_2^- ions in contact with them begin to react. At the cathode they take up some of the excess electrons and hydrogen is liberated.

$$2HF_2^- + 2e^- \xrightarrow{\triangle} \overline{H_2} + 4F^-$$

At the same time the HF_2^- ions in contact with the anode lose electrons and fluorine is produced.

$$2HF_2^- \xrightarrow{\triangle} 2HF + \overline{F_2} + 2e^-$$

The F^- ions and HF molecules produced by these reactions remain dissolved in the melt; and as fast as diffusion brings them together they combine, forming HF_2^- ions.

$$2HF + 2F^- \rightarrow 2HF_2^-$$

The two electrode reactions above must take place simultaneously and to an exactly equal extent, for every electron that is pulled out of the anode must be pushed on to the cathode. Hence it is legitimate to combine all the above reactions in one equation. Canceling molecules and electrons common to both sides of the equations gives the over-all equation:

$$2HF_2^- \rightarrow \overline{H_2} + \overline{F_2} + 2F^-$$

It is necessary only to add more HF to restore the melt to its original composition, and this is done. Essentially, then, HF is split into hydrogen and fluorine by means of the electric current; consequently this process is called **electrolysis** (*lysis* means splitting). The K^+ ions remain unchanged during electrolysis because they have so much less tendency to take up electrons than combined hydrogen does. This is indicated by the electronegativities—2.1 for hydrogen as against 0.8 for potassium.

9.5. Nature of the HF$_2^-$ Ion

The acid fluoride ion, HF$_2^-$, is a notable example of the hydrogen bonding which was described in connection with water (Section 7.14). The difference in electronegativity between hydrogen and fluorine is so large that the HF molecule is very polar. Its hydrogen end is even more positive and its negative end more negative than is the case with H$_2$O. As a result, it has an outstanding ability to form hydrogen bonds. In HF$_2^-$ the electrostatic attractive force between the proton and one F$^-$ ion is possibly one-tenth as strong as the covalent bond that holds the proton to the other F$^-$ ion. The force is strong enough so that even at 250° C., the operating temperature of a 2000-ampere F$_2$ cell, little HF breaks loose to be carried off in the gases leaving the cell. Any HF gas that escapes in either the hydrogen or the fluorine can be easily removed by passing the gas stream through cold crystalline KF.

$$\overline{HF} + \underline{KF} \rightarrow \underline{KHF_2}$$

9.6. Properties of Fluorine

When two atoms share an electron pair between them in a covalent bond, an orbital in each atom is occupied. The fluorine molecule, : F̈ : F̈ :, has no room for more electrons. But if, as in this case, both atoms are strongly electronegative, a great deal of energy will be released if the bond is broken and one electron is added to each atom; then each atom will have, in the orbital in question, a whole electron pair all to itself instead of only a half-share of an electron pair. Since a substance which can take up electrons is an oxidizing agent, we can generalize and say that *any molecule in which two highly electronegative atoms share an electron pair is a good oxidizing agent.* Because fluorine is the most electronegative of all atoms, it is the strongest of all oxidizing agents. It is not only a stronger oxidizing agent than oxygen, but a much more reactive agent. This greater readiness to react is due to the fact that only 31 per cent as much energy is needed to break the single bond in the F$_2$ molecule as is required to break the multiple bond in the O$_2$ molecule.

Fluorine can take electrons from any molecule not protectively covered with F$^-$ ions except those of the inert gases and nitrogen (the latter has a triple bond). If the substance is of low or moderate electronegativity the reaction is likely to be explosive, because these atoms give up electrons readily. Hydrogen, boron, carbon, silicon, phosphorus, arsenic, antimony, bromine, iodine, sulfur, selenium, tellurium, and potassium ignite in fluorine and burn to fluorides. Silver, magnesium, zinc, aluminum, tin, manganese, and iron burn in it when heated.

When fluorine oxidizes elements that have electronegativities of 2.0 or more, they do not necessarily lose the electrons completely. Thus fluorine may liberate O_2 or O_3 when it attacks water, but when a slow stream of it is bubbled through NaOH solution the reaction is:

$$\overline{2F_2} + 2Na^+ + 2OH^- \rightarrow 2Na^+ + 2F^- + \overline{OF_2} + H_2O$$

OF_2 is oxygen fluoride, not fluorine oxide; it contains $+2$ oxygen and is the only stable compound in which oxygen shows a positive valence. Similarly, fluorine oxidizes Cl^- to Cl_2, and itself becomes F^-.

$$\overline{F_2} + \underline{2NaCl} \rightarrow \underline{2NaF} + \overline{Cl_2}$$

But when heated with chlorine it combines to form chlorine fluoride, ClF, or chlorine trifluoride, ClF_3.

9.7. Partial Ionic Character of Bonds

In hydrogen fluoride, HF, carbon tetrafluoride, CF_4, oxygen fluoride, OF_2, chlorine trifluoride, ClF_3, and other compounds fluorine forms with elements of similar electronegativity, each fluorine atom leaves an electron pair partly in possession of the other atom, constituting a covalent bond. The center of the bonding electron cloud in such cases is not midway between the two atoms, as in a pure covalent bond, but more or less displaced toward the fluorine. If the electron could be further displaced so that it was completely owned by the fluorine atom, an F^- ion would result; hence a lopsided covalent bond such as this is said to have partial ionic character (Section 4.9).

9.8. Uses of Fluorine

One particular use was responsible for initiating the large-scale production of fluorine, namely, the production of uranium hexafluoride, UF_6. This molecule is compact, electrically neutral, and, because of its symmetry, non-polar. Therefore, even though it is fairly heavy, it sublimes at 56° C. (No other compound of uranium is volatile.) Heavy gas molecules can be separated from lighter ones by multiple fractional diffusion. In the case of uranium, the molecules containing the rarer fissionable isotope, ^{235}U, diffuse faster than those containing the more abundant heavier isotope, ^{238}U, and can be separated from the latter to

Fig. 9.2. The Oak Ridge gaseous diffusion plant (K-25) operated by the Union Carbide Corporation for the U.S. Atomic Energy Commission is the largest known industrial plant in the world. Here ^{235}U atoms are separated from ^{238}U. (U.S.A.E.C. photo.)

any desired degree. Since these molecules differ only slightly in weight, acres of ground are necessary to accommodate the many diffusion units required to effect the separation so that the product will have a high degree of purity (Fig. 9.2). The first nuclear bomb was made from ^{235}U, and uranium rich in that isotope enables the use of much smaller, cheaper nuclear energy installations than are possible with natural uranium.

As soon as fluorine became available, other uses were developed. Most of them involved the preparation of fluorine derivatives of complex carbon compounds. Some of these derivatives can be prepared from fluorides alone, but many require the simultaneous presence of an oxidizing agent and a source of F^- ion. Fluorine itself satisfies both requirements, but its enormous reactivity is sometimes a great disadvantage. This disadvantage is overcome by using fluorine to prepare compounds in which the first element is in an unusually high state of oxidation, which makes it a powerful oxidizing agent. Such compounds include silver fluoride, AgF_2, gold fluoride, AuF_3, lead fluoride, PbF_4, antimony fluoride, SbF_5, cobalt fluoride, CoF_3, and chlorine trifluoride, ClF_3. Except in the case of ClF_3, so much of the available energy of the fluorine is set free in the formation of such compounds that their reactions are more moderate. ClF_3 is nearly as reactive as fluorine itself. One research worker described it as being "merely fluorine which has been tricked into liquefying." The most recent addition to this class of compounds is the gas, perchloryl fluoride, ClO_3F. It is remarkably stable, withstanding a temperature of 500° C., and resisting hydrolysis by water and cold alkalies. In cold, neutral solution it is fairly weak as an oxidizing agent, but it becomes much stronger as the temperature and acidity are increased. It supports combustion as readily as pure oxygen does.

Fluorine is supplied for experimental purposes in small nickel cylinders under a pressure of 400 p.s.i. (pounds per square inch). For heavy consumers, liquid fluorine is supplied in insulated tank trucks.

9.9. Commercial Preparation of Chlorine

The manufacture of chlorine constitutes one of our largest and most important chemical industries. Fig. 9.3 (a) indicates both the size of the industry and its remarkable rate of growth, which as yet shows no sign of tapering off. This great increase since 1948 can be attributed mainly to new synthetic organic chemicals and to continually expanding uses of them. Although the bulk of this tremendous output is produced by the electrolysis of solutions of NaCl, the simplest electrolytic method of producing chlorine is to pass the current through fused NaCl. Accordingly this will be described first, even though it accounts for less than 10 per cent of the total output.

9.10. Electrolysis of Fused Salt

In a crystal of common salt two kinds of electrically charged molecules are present—sodium ions, Na^+, and chloride ions, Cl^- (Fig. 9.4). Each of these has as much kinetic energy as a molecule of any liquid or gas at the same temperature. But the attractive forces between the oppositely charged ions are so strong that they pull the ions tightly together and hold them in an ordered solid in which they merely vibrate in fixed equilibrium positions. Each ion is surrounded by six ions of

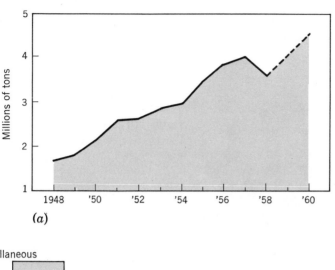

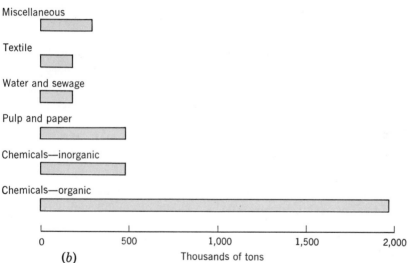

Fig. 9.3. (a) Production of elemental chlorine in the United States. The 1957-1958 recession accounted for the production lag. The general trend of production predicted beyond 1958 leads to an estimated 5 million tons in 1961.

(b) End uses of the 3.6 million tons of chlorine produced in 1958. Elemental chlorine is used only in the manufacture of pulp and paper, in sanitation, and in the textile industry. Chlorine compounds are involved in the other uses listed.

the opposite charge—one on each side, one in front and one in back, one above and one below. Thus every pair of cations has an anion between them which holds them together by the attraction exerted by opposite charges for each other. Similarly, every pair of anions is held together by a cation. The strong electrostatic attraction makes the crystals hard and strong. A temperature of over 800° C. is required to melt NaCl. This is in striking contrast to the behavior of a substance that is composed of small uncharged molecules. Other salts consist of other ions which may be packed in different patterns, but the salts are characteristically hard, high-melting crystals.

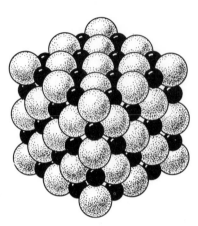

Fig. 9.4. Cubic ionic crystal lattice of NaCl. Small spheres represent Na^+, the larger spheres Cl^-.

A salt melts when its ions have been given sufficient kinetic energy so that the attraction between them can no longer confine them to fixed positions. If oppositely charged electrodes are inserted in the melt, the motion of the ions will cease to be completely random and chaotic. Instead, there will be a steady drift of cations toward the negatively charged cathode and of anions toward the positively charged anode (Fig. 9.5).

If the line voltage is low, say 1 v., a state of equilibrium will soon be reached. There will be a few extra Cl^- ions near the anode that will give this part of the melt a negative charge which will stop both the approach of more anions and the departure of the remaining Na^+ ions. Similarly the slight excess of Na^+ ions around the cathode will give that part of the melt a positive charge which will stop the movement of cations toward it and of anions away from it. For the same reason no current will flow through the wires; no more electrons will be pulled away from the anode or pushed onto the cathode. But if the potential difference in the line is raised to some 5 v., chemical reactions will begin at the electrodes. An electron will be jerked out of each Cl^- ion that touches the anode, and the resulting neutral atoms will unite to form Cl_2 molecules.

$$2Cl^- \xrightarrow{\triangle} Cl_2 + 2e^-$$

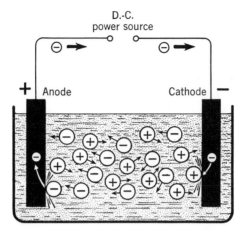

Fig. 9.5. Electrolysis of molten NaCl. Cl⁻ ions, on the average, move toward the anode; the net motion of Na⁺ ions is toward the cathode. One of each kind of ion is being discharged in the diagram.

At the cathode, electrons will flow onto Na^+ ions, converting them into neutral atoms of metallic sodium.

$$2Na^+ + 2e^- \xrightarrow{\triangle} \underline{2Na}$$

Since a generator is needed to move electrons from the anode to the cathode to keep up the voltage, a current flows through the wire connecting them. Also, Na^+ and Cl^- ions move continuously through the melt to replace those discharged. Because electrons flow continuously onto one electrode and off the other in equal numbers, the melted salt is said to conduct the electric current. This type of conduction, involving oppositely charged ions moving in both directions and being oxidized and reduced respectively at the electrodes, is called **electrolytic conduction.** The melt or solution in which the ions move is called an **electrolyte.** (A salt that is added to a solvent to produce a conducting solution is also called an electrolyte.)

Fig. 9.6 shows how the electrolysis of fused NaCl is carried out so as to keep the products separate. The melting point of the NaCl can be lowered by adding another electrolyte. However, the additional ions which are introduced must be more difficult to discharge than Na^+ or Cl^- ions. Potassium ion, K^+, fluoride ion, F^-, or carbonate ion, CO_3^{--}, for example, can be added without contaminating the products. But even

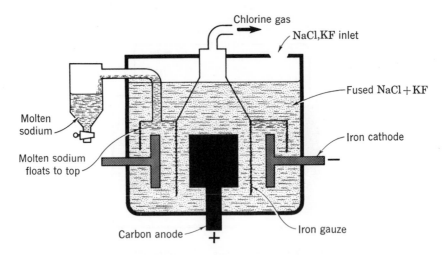

Fig. 9.6. A Downes cell for the electrolysis of fused NaCl. The Cl$_2$ gas liberated at the central graphite anode rises into the bell above it and is led into the collecting pipe. Metallic sodium, liquid at the operating temperature, is trapped above the ring-shaped iron cathode. Since it is lighter than the melted salt, the sodium is forced up into the rise and overflows into storage.

so, the lowest practicable operating temperature is still high enough to make this method much more expensive than the electrolysis of NaCl solution, described in the next section. Therefore, it is used only to the extent necessary to supply the demand for metallic sodium (not much over 150,000 tons per year). The chlorine is only a by-product; it constitutes about 7 per cent of our annual production.

9.11. Electrolysis of NaCl Solution

The electrolysis of a salt solution is complicated by the fact that the solution contains the ions of water as well as those of the salt. True, the concentrations of H$^+$ ion and OH$^-$ ion are very low (only 10^{-7} M), but these ions are discharged relatively easily. In the brine used in the manufacture of chlorine the ions of the salt are some fifty million times as concentrated as those of the water. This largely compensates for the fact that it is considerably easier to remove an electron from an OH$^-$ ion than from a Cl$^-$ ion; so the anode reaction is fundamentally:

$$2Cl^- \xrightarrow{\triangle} \overline{Cl_2} + 2e^-$$

However, some OH$^-$ ions are also discharged and decomposed.

$$4OH^- \xrightarrow{\triangle} 2H_2O + \overline{O_2} + 4e^-$$

At the cathode, where Na^+ ions and H^+ ions are competing for electrons, the concentration of Na^+ ion exceeds that of H^+ ion as much as the concentration of Cl^- ion exceeds that of OH^- ion at the anode. However, the result is different because H^+ ion is discharged so much more easily than Na^+ ion. (The difference between H^+ and Na^+ is much greater than in the case of OH^- and Cl^- ions.) Even the 50,000,000-fold concentration of the Na^+ ions over the H^+ ions is not enough to cause the discharge of many of the Na^+ ions. Furthermore, H_2O may react directly at the electrode.

$$2H_2O + 2e^- \xrightarrow{\triangle} H_2 + 2OH^-$$

Any metallic sodium that is produced reacts immediately with water, liberating hydrogen and reverting to Na^+ ion.

$$2Na + H_2O \rightarrow 2Na^+ + 2OH^- + \overline{H_2}$$

The net result is the same as though the hydrogen had been discharged directly. To all intents and purposes, then, the only reaction at the cathode is:

$$2H^+ + 2e^- \xrightarrow{\triangle} \overline{H_2}$$

During electrolysis an electron must be taken from the cathode for every one deposited on the anode; that is, an H^+ ion must be discharged for every Cl^- or OH^- ion. The *concentration* of H^+ ions is extremely low, but the *supply* is unlimited; for as fast as they are discharged, more water dissociates. We may combine the equations for the dissociation of water and the discharge of H^+ ions thus:

$$2H_2O \rightleftharpoons 2H^+ + OH^-$$
$$\underline{2H^+ + 2e^- \xrightarrow{\triangle} \overline{H_2}}$$
$$2H_2O + 2e^- \xrightarrow{\triangle} \overline{H_2} + 2OH^-$$

Canceling the H^+ ions which appear on both sides gives the total reaction at the cathode. Similarly, if we combine the anode and cathode reactions and cancel the electrons, we have

$$2H_2O + 2Cl^- \xrightarrow{\triangle} \overline{H_2} + \overline{Cl_2} + 2OH^-$$

as the over-all equation for the electrolysis. Since the Na^+ ions remain

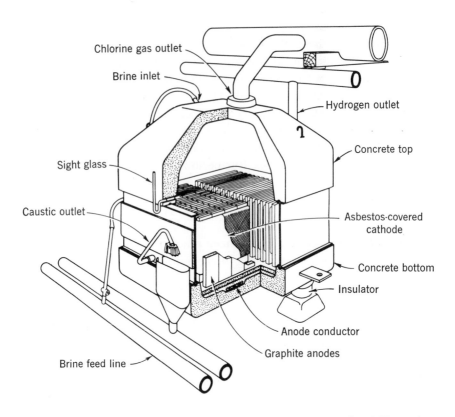

Fig. 9.7. Hooker type of S-3B cell. When this cell is operated at 3.85 v. using a current of 27,000 amperes, its daily output is 1814 lb. of chlorine, 2047 lb. of NaOH, and 9480 cu. ft. of hydrogen. These quantities vary with differences in operating conditions. (Courtesy, Hooker Chemical Corporation.)

unchanged, this amounts to saying that the electrolysis of an aqueous solution of NaCl produces a solution of NaOH.

9.12. Diaphragm Cells

It is just as necessary to keep the chlorine away from the OH⁻ ion in the electrolysis of NaCl solution as it is to keep it away from the metallic sodium in the fused salt process. Fig. 9.7 shows how this is done in a modern chlorine-producing plant. Each cell contains a large number of closely interleaved anodes and cathodes. The short distance between them economizes electrical power by minimizing the resistance. Each cathode is encased in a porous asbestos diaphragm with two exit tubes;

one permits the escape of NaOH solution, the other leads the hydrogen off. The OH⁻ ions which are formed at the cathodes move away from them, along with the Cl⁻ ions, because of their charges; but fresh brine is fed continuously into the top of the cell and seeps through each diaphragm at the exact rate that will counterbalance the movement of the anions in the opposite direction. The effluent from the cathode compartments is thus a solution of Na⁺ and OH⁻ ions, only slightly contaminated with Cl⁻ ions. The rated total daily capacity of the cells shown in Fig. 9.8 is 100 tons of Cl_2, 110 tons of NaOH, and 1 million cu. ft. of H_2 (at S.T.P.). About 75 per cent of our total output of chlorine is produced in diaphragm cells.

Fig. 9.8. Cell room in Hooker Chemical Corporation plant in North Vancouver, British Columbia. It contains a total of 116 type S-3B electrolytic cells. (Courtesy, Hooker Chemical Corporation.)

9.13. Mercury Cathode Cells

Extremely pure NaOH can be produced directly, in any desired concentration, by a modification of the diaphragm cell process which has been widely adopted since 1945. When mercury instead of steel is used as the cathode, no H^+ ions are discharged until the voltage is well above that normally required for the production of H_2. (Perhaps this is due to the fact that mercury is a poor catalyst for the reaction: $2H \rightleftharpoons H_2$.) In this particular case, it is actually possible to discharge Na^+ ions without any considerable amount of H_2 being produced. The sodium is not destroyed by the water in the brine because it dissolves in the mercury, forming an alloy called an **amalgam.** An essential part of the process depends on the amalgam not being allowed to become concentrated. The dilute amalgam is constantly pumped to "strippers" where, as the result of a catalyst and a higher temperature, it reacts completely with pure water.

$$2Na \text{ (in Hg)} + 2H_2O \rightarrow 2Na^+ + 2OH^- + \overline{H_2}$$

The purified mercury is returned to the cell. Or the amalgam may be used as a powerful reducing agent in some other chemical manufacturing process carried on in the plant. The cost of the sodium in the amalgam is only about one-fifth that of pure solid sodium. Approximately 16 per cent of our output of chlorine is produced in mercury cathode cells.

The other 1 per cent or so of our output of chlorine is produced as a by-product in the manufacture of sodium nitrate, $NaNO_3$ (page 333), in which NaCl, the cheapest source of Na^+ ion, is oxidized with nitric acid, HNO_3. Here again, as in the electrolysis of fused NaCl, the use of this process is limited by the demand for the main product. But even in the electrolysis of brine, the production of chlorine is tied up with that of NaOH. The NaOH and Cl_2 produced by this process are really co-products, similar in amount and in value. If the demand for either product increases disproportionately, its price must increase and the price of the other decrease until consumption is in balance again. If there is an excess of NaOH, another alternative which can help restore the balance is the fact that when the price is low enough, electrolytic NaOH will begin to displace the impure NaOH produced by causticization of soda ash (see page 415).

9.14. Laboratory Preparation of Chlorine

In teaching fundamentals of chemistry, the convenience and theoretical interest of the laboratory procedures selected are usually far more important than the cost of the materials. Therefore the commercial methods of producing chlorine are not used in the laboratory, nor is chlorine obtained in liquid form in the steel cylinders that are available commercially. Instead, students prepare chlorine from $NaCl$ by oxidizing the Cl^- ion with a chemical oxidizing agent. This provides not only a convenient method of preparing chlorine, but a good opportunity for students to learn fundamentals of chemistry and to become familiar with complex reactions involving reduction and oxidation, called **redox reactions** for short.

Equations for reactions in which a pair of ions crystallize from solution (precipitation reactions) or a proton is transferred from an electron pair on one atom to an electron pair on another atom (acid-base reactions) are usually simple enough to be written by inspection. This is also true of equations for reactions between elements and simple decompositions. In most redox reactions, however, O^{--} and H^+ are involved as well as the elements between which electron transfer occurs. This complicates matters to the extent that some systematic procedure is necessary in order to balance the equations quickly and correctly. Although several procedures are used, in the case of reactions that take place in water solutions the **ion-electron method** is generally simplest and most closely represents the actual mechanism of the reaction.

9.15. Balancing Redox Equations

When a substance is oxidized or reduced there is no certain method of predicting what the products will be. Only experiment can supply this information. *You will be expected to know the redox products only if you have found out the experimental facts yourself in the laboratory or been given the results of experiments done by others.* But if the formulas of the oxidizing and reducing agents and their products are given to you, you should be able to balance a redox equation by proceeding systematically through the steps given below.

The reaction of $KMnO_4$ and HCl, a convenient laboratory method for the preparation of chlorine, will be used as an example, and each step in the process will be considered in detail. The amount of space devoted here to this is necessarily greater than that required, once the process has become familiar.

To balance a redox equation, we must know the reactants that are oxidized and reduced, and the formulas of the products of the reaction which contain the oxidized or reduced elements. Hence in our example we must know that $KMnO_4$ solution is a good oxidizing agent; that in acid solution the permanganate ion, MnO_4^-, is reduced to the manganous ion, Mn^{++}; and that some of the Cl^- ion from the HCl is oxidized to free chlorine, Cl_2. With the above information, the steps are as follows:

1. Write as much of the reaction in ionic form as is possible. (Un-ionized or very slightly ionized substances, gases, and solids are represented by molecular or empirical formulas.)

$$(K^+ + MnO_4^-) + (H^+ + Cl^-) \rightarrow \overline{Cl_2} + Mn^{++}$$

Other products will be determined automatically when the redox reaction is completed.

2. Write a **half-reaction** for each ion, molecule, or atom whose oxidation number is changed. Show its form both originally and in the final state. There will always be two such half-reactions.

$$MnO_4^- \rightarrow Mn^{++} \quad \text{(reduction half-reaction)}$$
$$Cl^- \rightarrow Cl_2 \quad \text{(oxidation half-reaction)}$$

3. Balance the atoms on each side of the half-reaction. The chlorine half-reaction is easily balanced.

$$2Cl^- \rightarrow \overline{Cl_2}$$

However, the permanganate ion reduction involves oxygen and there are special rules for balancing the oxygens. In *acidic solution,* add water molecules to the side requiring oxygens, and the proper number of H^+ ions to the other side. In the following reaction:

$$MnO_4^- \rightarrow Mn^{++}$$

four oxygens are needed on the right, so *four* H_2O molecules are added to the right side.

$$MnO_4^- \rightarrow Mn^{++} + 4H_2O$$

To balance the hydrogen atoms on the right side, write eight H^+ ions on the left.

$$8H^+ + MnO_4^- \rightarrow Mn^{++} + 4H_2O$$

Both half-reactions are now balanced as far as *atoms* are concerned.

4. Balance the electrical charges on both sides of the half-reactions by adding electrons to or subtracting them from the left side. In the chlorine half-reaction:

$$2Cl^- \rightarrow \overline{Cl_2}$$

the algebraic sum of the charges on the molecules on the right side is zero. Therefore the algebraic sum of the charges on the left side must also equal zero. The total on the left side is -2, so two negative charges must be subtracted from the left side.

$$2Cl^- - 2e^- \rightarrow \overline{Cl_2}$$

The algebraic sum of the charges on the left side of the reaction:

$$8H^+ + MnO_4^- \rightarrow Mn^{++} + 4H_2O$$

is $+7$, that on the right side is $+2$. In order to make the left side also total $+2$, 5 negative charges (electrons) must be added to the left side.

$$8H^+ + MnO_4^- + 5e^- \rightarrow Mn^{++} + 4H_2O$$
$$+8 \ + \ -1 \ + \ -5 = \ +2$$

5. The number of electrons subtracted in the oxidation reaction must equal the number added in the reduction reaction. But 5 were added and 2 subtracted. Therefore, after canceling any common factor, multiply each half-reaction completely through by the number of electrons in the other half-reaction so that the number of electrons in each half-reaction will be the same:

$$5(2Cl^- - 2e^- \rightarrow \overline{Cl_2})$$
$$2(8H^+ + MnO_4^- + 5e^- \rightarrow Mn^{++} + 4H_2O)$$

6. Adding the half-reactions gives the complete redox equation.

$$10Cl^- - 10e^- \rightarrow \overline{5Cl_2}$$
$$\underline{16H^+ + 2MnO_4^- + 10e \rightarrow 2Mn^{++} + 8H_2O}$$
$$10Cl^- + 16H^+ + 2MnO_4^- + \cancel{10e^-} - \cancel{10e^-} \rightarrow \overline{5Cl_2} + 2Mn^{++} + 8H_2O$$

7. To obtain the complete over-all equation, the missing ions not involved in the oxidation and reduction must be supplied. Consequently, insert next to each kind of ion on the left side the ions which were used to bring it into the reaction. Add the same ions on the right side in any convenient order, since all these ions and neutral molecules are completely independent and thoroughly mixed in solution.

$$2(K^+ + MnO_4^-) + 16(H^+ + Cl^-) \rightarrow$$
$$\overline{5Cl_2} + 2Mn^{++} + 2K^+ + 6Cl^- + 8H_2O$$

9.16. Redox Reactions in Alkaline Solutions

The general principles discussed in the preceding section, with a modification in one step, are utilized for balancing redox reactions in alkaline solution. Whereas H^+ ion was added to form water (step 3) with the oxygen from the oxidizing ion in acid solution, water can be added to combine with the oxygen to form hydroxide ion in alkaline solutions. This will be shown in step 3 of another redox example given below. Other differences may be due to the different half-reaction behavior of the oxidizing and reducing agent in acid and in basic solution. For example, MnO_4^- ion can oxidize Cl^- ion to chlorine in acid solution but does not attack Cl^- ion in alkaline solution. Table 9.2 lists typical half-reactions of some common oxidizing agents in both types of solutions.

Although ions of the halogens which contain oxygen will be discussed later, we shall refer to them in discussing redox reactions which take place in alkaline solution.

Permanganate ion, MnO_4^-, attacks *easily* oxidized substances in alkaline solution and forms MnO_2, an insoluble solid. Chlorite ion, ClO_2^-, is readily oxidized in alkaline solution to chlorate, ClO_3^-, or perchlorate, ClO_4^-, ion. Which one appears depends upon the alkalinity, temperature, and concentration of the reactants. Whenever more than one oxidation or reduction product of the same element can be formed, separate equations must be written for each product. We shall consider the equation for the production of ClO_4^-.

1. The ionic form of the reaction is:

$$MnO_4^- + ClO_2^- \rightarrow \underline{MnO_2} + ClO_4^-$$

2. The separate half-reactions are:

$$MnO_4^- \rightarrow MnO_2 \text{ (reduction half-reaction)}$$

$$ClO_2^- \rightarrow ClO_4^- \text{ (oxidation half-reaction)}$$

3. Balance these atomically, adding OH⁻ ions to the side requiring oxygen. Add twice as many OH⁻ ions as there are oxygen atoms needed. To the other side, add half as many water molecules as OH⁻ ions.

$$MnO_4^- + 2H_2O \rightarrow \underline{MnO_2} + 4OH^-$$

$$ClO_2^- + 4OH^- \rightarrow ClO_4^- + 2H_2O$$

4. Balance the half-reactions electrically.

$$MnO_4^- + 2H_2O + \quad 3e^- \rightarrow \underline{MnO_2} + 4OH^-$$
$$-1 \quad + \quad 0 \quad + (-3) = \quad 0 \quad + (-4)$$

$$ClO_2^- + 4OH^- - 4e^- \rightarrow ClO_4^- + 2H_2O$$
$$-1 + (-4) - (-4) \quad = \quad -1 + \quad 0$$

5. Multiply the equations by factors to make the electrons the same in each; then add the half-reactions.

$$4(MnO_4^- + 2H_2O + 3e^- \rightarrow \underline{MnO_2} + 4OH^-)$$
$$3(ClO_2^- + 4OH^- - 4e^- \rightarrow ClO_4^- + 2H_2O)$$
$$4MnO_4^- + 8H_2O + 3ClO_2^- + 12OH^- + \cancel{12e^-} - \cancel{12e^-} \rightarrow \underline{4MnO_2} + 16OH^- + 3ClO_4^- + 6H_2O$$

Since OH⁻ and H_2O appear on both sides, cancel 12OH⁻ and $6H_2O$.

$$4MnO_4^- + 2H_2O + 3ClO_2^- \rightarrow \underline{4MnO_2} + 4OH^- + 3ClO_4^-$$

6. Now add the positive ions of the original permanganate and chlorite ions to complete the over-all reaction. These may be any suitable positive ions (not H⁺, because this is a basic solution); for example, Na⁺:

$$4(Na^+ + MnO_4^-) + 3(Na^+ + ClO_2^-) \rightarrow$$
$$\underline{4MnO_2} + 7Na^+ + 4OH^- + 3ClO_4^-$$

In describing a reaction it is common to state whether it takes place in an acidic or basic solution. This information tells us whether to use H⁺ or OH⁻ ions to balance the half-reactions.

9.17. Some Common Oxidizing Agents

The high electronegativity of chlorine makes Cl^- ion very difficult to oxidize. Oxidizing agents which are strong enough to oxidize this ion are strong enough to oxidize most other oxidizable substances; so a list of the most common agents is valuable for ready reference. Table 9.2 is such a list; it also shows the reduction products on the assump-

TABLE 9.2. **Half-Reactions for Some Strong Oxidizing Agents**

Permanganate ion, MnO_4^-	$MnO_4^- + 8H^+ + 5e^- \rightarrow Mn^{++} + 4H_2O$
Manganese dioxide, MnO_2	$MnO_2 + 4H^+ + 2e^- \rightarrow Mn^{++} + 2H_2O$
Nitrate ion, NO_3^-	$NO_3^- + 2H^+ + e^- \rightarrow \overline{N}O_2 + H_2O$
(as conc. HNO_3)	
Hydrogen peroxide, H_2O_2	$H_2O_2 + 2H^+ + 2e^- \rightarrow 2H_2O$
Peroxydisulfate ion, $S_2O_8^{--}$	$S_2O_8^{--} + 2e^- \rightarrow 2SO_4^{--}$
Hypochlorite ion, ClO^-	$ClO^- + 2H^+ + e^- \rightarrow \frac{1}{2}Cl_2 + H_2O$
Chlorite ion, ClO_2^-	$ClO_2^- + 4H^+ + 3e^- \rightarrow \frac{1}{2}Cl_2 + 2H_2O$
Chlorate ion, ClO_3^-	$ClO_3^- + 6H^+ + 5e^- \rightarrow \frac{1}{2}Cl_2 + 3H_2O$
Perchlorate ion, ClO_4^-	$ClO_4^- + 8H^+ + 7e^- \rightarrow \frac{1}{2}Cl_2 + 4H_2O$
(only at high temperature)	
Bromate ion, BrO_3^-	$BrO_3^- + 6H^+ + 5e^- \rightarrow \frac{1}{2}Br_2 + 3H_2O$
Periodate ion, IO_4^-	$IO_4^- + 8H^+ + 7e^- \rightarrow \frac{1}{2}I_2 + 4H_2O$
Dichromate ion, $Cr_2O_7^{--}$	$Cr_2O_7^{--} + 14H^+ + 6e^- \rightarrow 2Cr^{+3} + 7H_2O$

tion that the agents react with a poor reducing agent, such as Cl^- ion, in *acid* solution. Br^- and I^- ions react similarly, but F^- ion resists attack even by these reagents. Peroxides of metals, such as sodium peroxide, Na_2O_2, are very powerful oxidizing agents. They are not included in Table 9.2 because they must be used only in alkaline solution. The half-reaction characteristic of these compounds is typified by sodium peroxide.

$$Na_2O_2 + 2H_2O + 2e^- \rightarrow 2Na^+ + 4OH^-$$

The half-reaction for any given oxidizing agent that is being reduced to a given product is the same regardless of the reducing agent being used. This is true also of the half-reaction for the oxidation of any reducing agent.

9.18. Properties of Chlorine

Chlorine is diatomic and a strong oxidizing agent for the same reasons that fluorine is. It is not as strong an oxidizing agent as fluorine, or even oxygen, because of its lower electronegativity (3.0). But it is much more readily available than fluorine, and the fact that it is a weaker oxidizing agent is in many cases an advantage. For example, it can be used in water solution, since it liberates oxygen only very slowly; furthermore, it rarely ignites hydrocarbons. Chlorine is a far more reactive oxidizing agent than oxygen. Most combustible substances must be heated before they will burn in oxygen—i.e., there must be a great deal of energy in the collisions between the molecules if they are to react—whereas phosphorus and powdered antimony, for example, ignite spontaneously in chlorine. Most substances which can react at all with chlorine do so at a moderate rate at room temperature; but this is not the case with oxygen. One reason for this is the extraordinarily tight bond in the O_2 molecule. The $: \ddot{O} : \ddot{O} :^{--}$ bond in peroxides is only 20 percent stronger than the similar bond in $: \ddot{C}l : \ddot{C}l :$, the Cl_2 molecule, but the multiple bond in the O_2 molecule is twice as strong. The other reason is that the valence shell of each atom in the O_2 molecule is full, whereas there are five empty d orbitals in the valence shell of a chlorine atom. Therefore, before an O_2 molecule can react, a bond must be broken, whereas one atom in a Cl_2 molecule can accept an electron pair from a reducing agent, first forming an unstable intermediate compound by means of the d orbitals, then readjusting by releasing a Cl^- ion. If $R :$ represents a reducing agent:

$$R : + : \ddot{C}l : \ddot{C}l : \rightarrow R \overset{.}{\underset{.}{:}} \ddot{C}l : \ddot{C}l : \rightarrow R : \ddot{C}l :^+ + : \ddot{C}l :^- \rightarrow R^{++} + 2 : \ddot{C}l :^-$$

9.19. Binary Compounds of Chlorine

Chlorine combines directly with most of the elements (other than the inert gases), the notable exceptions being carbon, nitrogen, and oxygen; with these it combines indirectly. Since, as we have seen, only oxygen and fluorine are more electronegative than chlorine, in all its binary compounds with elements other than these two, chlorine has an oxidation number of -1. If the other element has a rare gas type of kernel with not too high a charge in proportion to its size, a completely ionic compound will result. This is the case with all the alkali metals (Group IA), the alkaline earth metals (Group IIA) after beryllium, the

Group IIIA metals after aluminum, and thorium. Kernels with high charge and small size and those with *d* electrons in their surface can more easily compel anions to share electron pairs with them, forming covalent bonds. These compounds are all called chlorides, regardless of the covalent character of the bonds, as long as the chlorine has an oxidation number of -1. Each Cl^- ion in NaCl (Fig. 9.4) is surrounded by and equally attracted by six Na^+ ions. In chlorides of elements with higher valences the proportion of Cl^- ions is larger; eventually it reaches the point where each of these ions is in contact with and attracted to only one oppositely charged atom, the latter still being surrounded by Cl^- ions. Such a cluster of atoms, with a positively charged center and a negatively charged surface, constitutes a molecule which has little attraction for other molecules of the same kind. An example is carbon tetrachloride, CCl_4 (Fig. 9.9), in which the

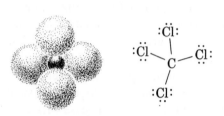

Fig. 9.9. Tetrahedral CCl_4 molecule, showing packed sphere and line-bond diagrams of the same molecule.

$+4$ carbon atom in the center is almost completely concealed by the four chlorine atoms. The structure of this molecule explains the fact that CCl_4 is a volatile liquid instead of a hard solid like NaCl. It was once believed that high melting and boiling points proved a crystal to be ionic, and that low melting and boiling points proved that the bonding was covalent. It is obvious, however, that the nature of the bonding is indecisive. If each atom is held strongly by two or more neighbors (either by the electrostatic attraction between oppositely charged ions or by bonds of any degree of covalent character, even up to 100 per cent), the crystal will be strong; if the atom is thus held by only one neighbor, the crystal will be weak.

9.20. Hydrolysis of Chlorides

Strongly electronegative atoms like chlorine have a strong tendency to develop an octet of unshared electrons in the valence shell whenever possible. Any sharing of electron pairs that such an atom is forced into takes electrons away from it to a greater or lesser extent, depending on how completely covalent the bond is. When two very electronegative atoms share an electron pair, each atom is still unsatisfied. A molecule that has a covalent bond between two electronegative atoms reacts with a base because the molecule of the base has an electron pair which it is willing to share. Even a weak base like water can usually attack such a molecule and split it up. The reaction is called **hydrolysis** (water splitting). A typical and very important example is the hydrolysis of chlorine. In the first step in this reaction one of the atoms in a Cl_2 molecule pulls an electron pair from water into one of its empty d orbitals as a result of this unsatisfied electronic state:

$$H : \overset{..}{\underset{..}{O}} : \; + \; : \overset{..}{\underset{..}{Cl}} : \overset{..}{\underset{..}{Cl}} : \; \rightarrow \; H : \overset{..}{\underset{..}{O}} : \overset{..}{\underset{..}{Cl}} : \overset{..}{\underset{..}{Cl}} :$$
$$H H$$

But the formation of the bond with oxygen neutralizes enough of the kernel charge of the chlorine atom so that the other chlorine atom can capture complete control of the shared electron pair and escape as a Cl^- ion. At the same time one of the protons of the attached water is transferred to a neighboring H_2O molecule.

$$H : \overset{..}{\underset{..}{O}} : \; + \; H : \overset{..}{\underset{..}{O}} : \overset{..}{\underset{..}{Cl}} : \overset{..}{\underset{..}{Cl}} : \; \rightarrow \; H : \overset{..}{\underset{..}{O}} : H^+ \; + \; : \overset{..}{\underset{..}{O}} : \overset{..}{\underset{..}{Cl}} : \; + \; : \overset{..}{\underset{..}{Cl}} :^-$$
$$H H H H$$

The proton transfer takes place because the necessity of sharing an electron pair with chlorine makes the oxygen atom pull more closely to itself the electrons it was sharing with the protons, thus weakening its hold upon the protons. Even after losing one proton the HOCl molecule which remains is a stronger acid than the original water molecule, because the chlorine atom is more electronegative than the hydrogen it replaced. HOCl is known as hypochlorous acid; it ionizes very slightly in accordance with the equation:

$$H_2O + HOCl \rightleftharpoons H_3O^+ + OCl^-$$

The hydrolysis of chlorine is conveniently summed up in the equation:

$$\overline{Cl_2} + 2H_2O \rightleftharpoons H_3O^+ + Cl^- + HOCl$$

This is usually abbreviated:

$$\overline{Cl_2} + H_2O \rightleftharpoons H^+ + Cl^- + HClO$$

The slight ionization of HClO is ordinarily not shown explicitly.

The double arrow calls attention to the fact that the above three reactions are reversible. H^+, Cl^-, and HClO react rapidly to form Cl_2 and

H$_2$O; so when chlorine is dissolved in water it is never completely used up. The solution soon reaches a state of dynamic equilibrium in which Cl$_2$ is formed as fast as it is consumed. If a strong base such as OH$^-$ is added, the reaction goes practically to completion. The OH$^-$ attacks the Cl$_2$ more rapidly than H$_2$O does. It also prevents the reverse reaction by neutralizing both the H$_3$O$^+$ and the HClO. The conventional equation:

$$2OH^- + \overline{Cl}_2 \rightarrow H_2O + Cl^- + ClO^-$$

actually represents a series of reactions:

$$2H:\overset{\cdot\cdot}{\underset{\cdot\cdot}{O}}:^- \; + \; :\overset{\cdot\cdot}{\underset{\cdot\cdot}{Cl}}:\overset{\cdot\cdot}{\underset{\cdot\cdot}{Cl}}: \; \rightarrow \; H:\overset{\cdot\cdot}{\underset{\cdot\cdot}{O}}:^- \; + \; H:\overset{\cdot\cdot}{\underset{\cdot\cdot}{O}}:\overset{\cdot\cdot}{\underset{\cdot\cdot}{Cl}}:\overset{\cdot\cdot\cdot}{\underset{\cdot\cdot}{Cl}}:^- \; \rightarrow \; H:\overset{\cdot\cdot}{\underset{\cdot\cdot}{O}}:^- \; +$$

$$H:\overset{\cdot\cdot}{\underset{\cdot\cdot}{O}}:\overset{\cdot\cdot}{\underset{\cdot\cdot}{Cl}}: \; + \; :\overset{\cdot\cdot}{\underset{\cdot\cdot}{Cl}}:^- \; \rightarrow \; H:\overset{\cdot\cdot}{\underset{\underset{\textstyle H}{\cdot\cdot}}{O}}: \; + \; :\overset{\cdot\cdot}{\underset{\cdot\cdot}{O}}:\overset{\cdot\cdot}{\underset{\cdot\cdot}{Cl}}:^- \; + \; :\overset{\cdot\cdot}{\underset{\cdot\cdot}{Cl}}:^-$$

Note that all except the last step in this series are of the same form as the reaction series at the end of Section 9.18, if H : O : is substituted for R:. The difference is that a reducing agent *gives up* electrons completely, but a base only *shares* them. (Also of interest is the fact that a reducing agent gives up one electron at a time much more commonly than two, whereas a base always shares an electron pair.)

Phosphorus trichloride, PCl$_3$, formed by burning phosphorus in chlorine, hydrolyzes in a similar manner, for the same reason.

$$H:\overset{\cdot\cdot}{\underset{\underset{\textstyle H}{\cdot\cdot}}{O}}: \; + \; :\overset{\overset{\textstyle :\overset{\cdot\cdot}{Cl}:}{}}{\underset{\underset{\textstyle :\overset{\cdot\cdot}{\underset{\cdot\cdot}{Cl}}:}{}}{P}}:\overset{\cdot\cdot}{\underset{\cdot\cdot}{Cl}}: \; \rightarrow \; H:\overset{\cdot\cdot}{\underset{\underset{\textstyle H}{\cdot\cdot}}{O}}:\overset{\overset{\textstyle :\overset{\cdot\cdot}{Cl}:}{}}{\underset{\underset{\textstyle :\overset{\cdot\cdot}{Cl}:}{}}{P}}\cdot\overset{\cdot\cdot}{\underset{\cdot\cdot}{Cl}}: \; \rightarrow \; H:\overset{\cdot\cdot}{\underset{\cdot\cdot}{O}}:\overset{\overset{\textstyle :\overset{\cdot\cdot}{Cl}:}{}}{P}:\overset{\cdot\cdot}{\underset{\cdot\cdot}{Cl}}: \; + \; H:\overset{\cdot\cdot}{\underset{\cdot\cdot}{Cl}}:$$

This process is then repeated, with the loss of the second and third chlorine atoms and the production of HPO(OH)$_2$, phosphorous acid, more often written H$_3$PO$_3$.

$$H_2O + HOPCl_2 \rightarrow (HO)_2PCl + \overline{HCl}$$
$$H_2O + (HO)_2PCl \rightarrow H_3PO_3 + \overline{HCl}$$

In this example the second proton from each water molecule is shown as being taken up by a Cl$^-$ ion and escaping as hydrogen chloride gas, HCl. This can happen only if no water is left after the hydrolysis; for HCl dissolves and ionizes in excess water.

This behavior is typical of the chlorides of non-metals, such as sulfur monochloride, S_2Cl_2, iodine monochloride, ICl, iodine trichloride, ICl_3, sulfuryl chloride, SO_2Cl_2, etc. In all cases the molecule that is left after the addition of H_2O and the loss of Cl^- is an acid whose strength depends on the electronegativity of the element to which the H_2O is attached. If this is high, the acid will be very strong and one or even both protons of each combined H_2O will be lost to adjacent free water molecules.

$$SO_2Cl_2 + 5H_2O \rightarrow HSO_4^- + 3H_3O^+ + 2Cl^-$$

Even HSO_4^- is a strong enough acid to have a very strong reaction with water.

If the electronegativity is only moderate, the acid will be weak and the first proton may be lost to water only to a slight extent. This is true of the di- and tri-chlorides of the metals from titanium through gallium. These elements are metals, but their ions have some ability to form covalent bonds. This ability increases with the number of d electrons present and also with the valence. (When the element has a valence of $+4$ or more, the bond with chlorine is usually predominantly covalent and the compound belongs to the class described in the preceding paragraph.)

Not all binary halides with covalent bonds undergo hydrolysis readily. For example, CCl_4 is remarkably stable even at high temperatures. Even more stable are such compounds as nitrogen trifluoride, NF_3, carbon tetrafluoride, CF_4, and dichlorodifluoromethane, CF_2Cl_2 (trade name, Freon-12). Apparently stability is favored by the lack of d orbitals in fluorine (in all the other halogens d orbitals are available for the formation of intermediates; see Sections 9.18, 9.19) or by the halogen atoms being packed tightly around the central atom (CCl_4) so that d orbitals cannot be used because of lack of space. Sulfur hexafluoride, SF_6, armor-plated, so to speak, with inert F^-, and with F^- electrons already occupying the d orbitals by means of which it would ordinarily be possible to attack the sulfur, is one of the most inert compounds known. Many kinds of covalently bonded fluorine-coated molecules have commercial uses because of a similar inertness.

9.21. Uses of Chlorine

Chlorine has almost innumerable uses, only a few of the most important of which can be described here. Liquid chlorine is shipped in 55-ton tank cars and in barges that hold four 150-ton tanks. It sells for about

3 cents per pound in bulk shipments. In a few cases, heavy users of it have located their plants near chlorine production plants so that chlorine gas can be delivered directly to them by pipeline.

The most familiar of the uses of chlorine is in the sterilization of water, both for drinking and in swimming pools. This involves the killing of microorganisms by oxidation. Chlorination of city water supplies helped greatly to wipe out typhoid fever, which at one time was responsible for the death of thousands of people a year.

The largest single use of elemental chlorine (Fig. 9.3B) is in the bleaching of wood pulp for paper. The bleaching action consists in the removal, by oxidation, of colored impurities in the pulp. Fortunately these impurities are less resistant to oxidation than is cellulose, which is the main constituent of the pulp. Since cotton is almost pure cellulose, cotton cloth can also be bleached by chlorine; but silk and wool would be badly oxidized.

In both of these uses of chlorine it is actually the HClO produced by the hydrolysis of the chlorine that does the work. HClO not only is a stronger oxidizing agent than chlorine, but is much more reactive and can bleach more rapidly at room temperature. For this reason chlorine is used in the presence of water when the desired reaction is to take place at a moderate temperature. An example of the reaction mechanism by which HClO brings oxidation about is the preparation of ethylene oxide from ethylene.

| Ethylene | Ethylene chlorohydrin | Ethylene oxide |

Ethylene oxide is an intermediate from which valuable solvents, plasticizers, and emulsifying agents are manufactured. A direct air-oxidation process that has recently been invented is used in virtually all new ethylene oxide plants, but the chlorine oxidation process still ranks second among the large single uses of chlorine in this country.

It is interesting that the power of chlorine as an oxidizing agent accounts for its two largest uses, for in both of these chlorine may eventually be supplanted by reagents that do not require electrical power (H_2O_2 in the case of wood pulp). This is not the case with many inorganic oxidations that are carried out by chlorine, e.g.:

$$Au \rightarrow AuCl_3 \qquad Sn \rightarrow SnCl_4 \qquad Fe \rightarrow FeCl_3$$

The bulk of our enormous chlorine production goes into the manufacture of chlorine compounds. In most of these the chlorine is combined with either oxygen or carbon. The oxyhalogen compounds will be discussed later.

The carbon compounds are mostly produced either by the *substitution* of chlorine for hydrogen in a **hydrocarbon** (hydrogen-carbon compound) or by the *addition* of chlorine to members of a subclass of hydrocarbons called **unsaturated hydrocarbons**—those in which at least one pair of carbon atoms are doubly or triply bonded and share more than one electron pair.

9.22. Substitution

One of the most important substitution reactions occurs in the chlorination of methane, $H : \overset{\cdot\cdot}{\underset{\cdot\cdot}{C}} : H$. When a chlorine molecule absorbs light energy, an electron may be displaced to a higher-energy orbital, or the molecule may be torn apart into two chlorine atoms, each with only 7 electrons. At room temperature a Cl_2 molecule can collide with a CH_4 molecule without any reaction; there is not sufficient energy in the collision to excite the molecules into a reactive state. But a chlorine atom will react with the first CH_4 molecule it touches.

$$\overline{Cl} + \overline{CH_4} \rightarrow \overline{CH_3Cl} + \overline{H}$$

The hydrogen atom which is produced has an odd electron and will react with the first Cl_2 molecule it encounters

$$\overline{H} + \overline{Cl_2} \rightarrow \overline{HCl} + \overline{Cl}$$

This is an example of a **chain reaction**. A chain can be ended by the combination of H and H, Cl and Cl, or H and Cl, but only if a third molecule (or the wall of the container) is present to absorb the energy produced by the combination. It is characteristic of chain reactions that the temperature gradually rises to the point where dissociation is produced by thermal collisions. This multiplies the number of chains rapidly and explosion results. Careful cooling enables the chlorination of methane to be kept under control—in fact, to such an extent as to yield almost any desired proportions of methyl chloride, CH_3Cl, methylene chloride, CH_2Cl_2, and chloroform, $CHCl_3$.

Carbon tetrachloride, CCl_4, is produced more economically by the reaction of chlorine with carbon disulfide. The sulfur monochloride, S_2Cl_2, produced simultaneously is also useful.

$$CS_2 + \overline{3Cl_2} \rightarrow CCl_4 + S_2Cl_2$$

Many hydrocarbons more complicated than methane can be chlorinated in a similar way.

9.23. Addition

Ethylene, $\overset{\displaystyle H}{\underset{\displaystyle H}{\cdot}}\overset{..}{C} :: \overset{..}{C}\overset{\displaystyle H}{\underset{\displaystyle H}{\cdot}}$, is a typical unsaturated hydrocarbon. Addition of Cl_2 converts it into a dichloroethane, $\overset{\displaystyle H\ \ H}{:\overset{..}{\underset{..}{Cl}}:\overset{..}{\underset{..}{C}}:\overset{..}{\underset{..}{C}}:\overset{..}{\underset{..}{Cl}}:}\underset{\displaystyle H\ \ H}{}$. Half a billion pounds of the latter are used annually, principally in the manufacture of Ethyl antiknock fluid. The equation for the reaction is:

$$\overline{Cl_2} + \overline{C_2H_4} \rightarrow C_2H_4Cl_2$$

Chlorinated hydrocarbons of many kinds, each with its own slightly different properties, are used by the hundred thousand tons as industrial solvents. Others, such as DDT and Gammexane, have proved to be invaluable as insecticides. Vinyl chloride, C_2H_3Cl, is used as a building block in the giant molecule of a chemically resistant plastic. Fluorine ignites hydrocarbons, but reacts at a moderate rate with fully chlorinated hydrocarbons, liberating chlorine and producing fluorocarbons. (Curiously, the corresponding term chlorocarbons is not used.) From one of these fluorocarbons, tetrafluoroethylene, C_2F_4, Teflon is made; it is a plastic that is inert to all chemical reagents except melted sodium, at temperatures up to 400° C. A mixed chloro-fluoro- series provides non-flammable, non-toxic working gases with any desired boiling point, which have made possible the vigorous ($2 billion) air-conditioning and refrigeration industry. A typical example is dichlorodifluoromethane, CCl_2F_2, whose trade name is Freon-12.

9.24. Displacement Reactions

A reaction in which one element combines and another is set free is frequently called a **displacement reaction.** Such a reaction is merely a special case of a redox reaction. Thus in the manufacture of fluorocarbons, chlorine is displaced by fluorine. Similarly, chlorine can displace the less electronegative bromine and iodine, particularly from their salts. In fact, these displacement reactions provide standard commercial methods for manufacturing bromine and iodine, and constitute another important use of chlorine.

9.25. Sources of Bromine

Wherever Cl^- ion is found in nature, Br^- ion is also found, but in far smaller quantities. When ancient seas were drying up and forming salt beds, nearly all the NaCl crystallized from the solution before the Br^- ion was sufficiently concentrated to saturate the remainder with NaBr, KBr, or $MgBr_2$; hence the portions of such deposits that crystallized last are much richer in Br^- ion than other portions.

Before 1925 all the bromine produced was obtained from salt wells which happened to strike the bromine-rich portions of salt beds, or from sea water in which the impurities had been similarly concentrated during its evaporation to salt. Since then, however, the demand for bromine has exceeded the amount available as a by-product of the production of salt; as a result, important quantities are now produced directly from unconcentrated sea water. A ton of sea water contains about 32 lb. of Cl^- ion, but scarcely 2 oz. of Br^- ion. Nevertheless, the process described below permits the production of bromine from this inexhaustible source for less than 35 cents per pound. One sea-water plant in the United States is operated by Ethyl-Dow at Freeport, Texas; another by Westvaco on San Francisco Bay. The first such plant was built by Ethyl-Dow at Cape Fear, N.C., but was dismantled in 1956 because it was within the area of a government munitions dump.

9.26. Preparation of Bromine

The bromide-containing brine is first slightly acidified to prevent hydrolysis of either Cl_2 or Br_2; then Cl_2 is added to oxidize the Br^- ion to bromine.

$$\overline{Cl_2} + 2Br^- \rightarrow Br_2 + 2Cl^-$$

The bromine thus displaced is picked up from the brine by air, and sulfur dioxide, SO_2, is added. This mixture is bubbled through water. The reaction is:

$$\overline{SO_2} + \overline{Br_2} + 2H_2O \rightarrow 3H^+ + HSO_4^- + 2Br^-$$

The air is recirculated and a portion of the strongly acid solution is continuously drawn off and chlorinated. The Br_2 is easily driven out of this fairly concentrated solution by heating, and is then condensed to a liquid. The sulfuric acid is not wasted but is used in the acidification of the brine.

Bromine production in this country—less than 1000 tons in 1925—increased sevenfold in each of the following two decades, and is still increasing, though at a slower rate. In 1960 about 100,000 tons were produced.

9.27. Properties of Bromine

Bromine and chlorine are more alike than chlorine and fluorine are because their electronegativities are similar. Bromine is nearly as strong an oxidizing agent as chlorine; it ignites powdered antimony. It reacts with hydrogen, but without explosion; the heat of reaction is only half that between chlorine and hydrogen. Its reactions with hydrocarbons are similar to those of chlorine, but milder and more easily controlled. Bromine readily displaces iodine from iodides, just as chlorine displaces bromine from bromides. It causes serious burns if allowed to touch the skin.

9.28. Uses of Bromine

The use of bromine in manufacturing ethylene dibromide, $C_2H_4Br_2$ (also called dibromoethane), overshadows all other uses, accounting for about 70 per cent of the total. $C_2H_4Br_2$ is prepared by brominating ethylene (see Section 9.23); it is one of the components of Ethyl antiknock fluid, in which it serves as a gasoline-soluble source of Br^-. The actual antiknock component is tetraethyllead, $Pb(C_2H_5)_4$. Without the $C_2H_4Br_2$ it would burn to PbO, which would gradually clog the valves; but with the $C_2H_4Br_2$ the combustion product is $PbBr_2$, which is a gas at the temperatures achieved in the combustion chamber of a gasoline engine. (The $PbBr_2$ boils at 619° C.) Metal halides are characteristically more volatile than their oxides.

Br_2 is used in the production of innumerable organic compounds, just as Cl_2 is, but in far smaller quantities. The compounds include dyes (e.g., lipstick), drugs, tear gas, and intermediates used in the preparation of other substances. The following are some of the simpler organic bromides. Methyl bromide, CH_3Br, is a soil and grain fumigant. Freon-12B, or CBr_2Cl_2, is used in the fire-protection systems of aircraft. Stored in a steel sphere as a liquid under 600 p.s.i. nitrogen pressure, as little as 19 lb. of it is relied upon to smother a fire in any reciprocating engine. The vapor is a better fire extinguisher than CCl_4 vapor which is used in the common Pyrene extinguisher, is very low in toxicity (CCl_4 vapor is very poisonous), and has a negligible effect on metals (CCl_4 corrodes metals). CH_2BrCl is much better than CCl_4 in pump-type extinguishers.

Organic compounds account for over 90 per cent of all the Br_2 used. All inorganic compounds of bromine are also prepared from the element. These include a number of metal bromides (KBr is the largest single item) that are mostly used in the production of photographic materials, and potassium bromate.

9.29. Sources of Iodine

Iodine is much rarer than bromine. In only a few places do natural brines contain enough I^- ion to make it practicable to extract it. One of these places, fortunately for us, is in California. This brine does not come from wells driven for the purpose, but is a by-product of oil wells. Living organisms have a remarkable ability to extract I^- ion from even excessively dilute solutions and concentrate it in themselves in the form of complex iodine compounds. In mammals the compound is thyroxine, $C_{15}H_{11}O_4NI_4$, produced by the thyroid gland. Certain species of seaweed contain enough iodine for I^- ion to be recovered commercially from their ashes. It is estimated that 3 million tons a year could be obtained if the kelp along our Pacific coast were harvested. During World War I, before the presence of I^- ion in the oil well brines was discovered, a shortage of iodine in this country was met by harvesting kelp, but this method is not profitable now.

I^- ion is not the only source of iodine. In this respect iodine differs from the other halogens, which are found in nature only as the respective halide ions. The world's main source of iodine is iodate ion, IO_3^-, a minor constituent of Chilean nitrate deposits.

9.30. Preparation of Iodine

In the United States, iodine is produced by the chlorination of the above-mentioned oil well brines. The reaction is like that by which bromine is obtained (Section 9.26); as a matter of fact, some bromine is produced simultaneously. Since iodine is not volatile enough to permit its being blown out of the solution, it is removed by adsorption on charcoal, most of the bromine remaining in the solution. The iodine is then removed from the charcoal by NaOH solution.

$$3I_2 + 6Na^+ + 6OH^- \rightarrow 6Na^+ + IO_3^- + 5I^- + 3H_2O$$

It is regenerated by the addition of acid, which reverses the reaction by removing the OH^- ion. The 250 tons of iodine produced in this country are supplemented by the importation of some 400 tons from Chile, but our production is more important than comparison of these figures indicates. When Chile had a monopoly on iodine, the crude element sold for $5 per pound; it now costs us $2.

Chilean iodine is produced by reduction of IO_3^- ion with hydrogen sulfite ion, HSO_3^-.

$$2IO_3^- + 5HSO_3^- \rightarrow 3HSO_4^- + 2SO_4^{--} + H_2O + I_2$$

9.31. Properties of Iodine

With an electronegativity of only 2.5, iodine is a much weaker oxidizing agent than chlorine. It combines only weakly with hydrogen. The reaction

$$\overline{H_2} + \overline{I_2} \rightleftharpoons \overline{2HI}$$

is reversible; at 360° C., HI is 20 per cent dissociated, the dissociation increasing with the temperature.

The relative weakness of iodine as an oxidizing agent may be an advantage at times. For example, it oxidizes thiosulfate ion, $S_2O_3^{--}$, exclusively to tetrathionate ion, $S_4O_6^{--}$, instead of to an indeterminate mixture of $S_4O_6^{--}$ and SO_4^{--} ion as stronger oxidizing agents do.

$$I_2 + 2S_2O_3^{--} \rightarrow 2I^- + S_4O_6^{--}$$

It can therefore be determined quantitatively by titrating it with a standardized solution of $Na_2S_2O_3$. Oxidizing agents which cannot be titrated directly with $S_2O_3^{--}$ ion can be determined by first adding them to a solution of KI. In the presence of excess I^- ion, only I_2 is produced, and this can then be titrated accurately with $S_2O_3^{--}$ ion.

9.32. Sublimation of Iodine

Solid iodine has an appreciable vapor pressure even at room temperature; this gives it its strong smell. On a warm day it is possible to see faintly, in a partially filled bottle of iodine, the violet color of the gas from which the element gets its name. Long before the temperature reaches the melting point the vapor pressure is so high that if the gas is allowed to escape freely and heat is not supplied too rapidly, I_2 crystals will evaporate completely without ever having melted. The very considerable amount of heat which is absorbed on vaporization produces such a cooling effect that it is impossible to melt iodine in an open porcelain dish, just as it is impossible to heat water above its boiling point under the same conditions, for the same reason. When evaporation takes place directly from a solid, the process is called **sublimation.** (The word also commonly implies the reverse process on a nearby cold surface.) Crude iodine can be purified of non-volatile impurities by sublimation. If it is first mixed with NaI, the ICl and IBr which are volatile impurities commonly present in crude I_2 will be removed before sublimation begins by reactions of the type:

$$IX + I^- \rightarrow I_2 + X^-$$

9.33. Expanding the Octet

Iodine is characterized by numerous reactions in which the valence shell is expanded to hold 10 or 12 electrons, instead of the usual 8, because one or two d orbitals are used in addition to the s and p orbitals of the octet. Fluorine, of course, has no d orbitals in its valence shell, because atoms below at. no. 10 have only two layers of electrons. The use of d orbitals was mentioned in connection with the hydrolysis of Cl_2 and covalent chlorides (Section 9.20), but the d orbitals of third-period atoms are so much higher in energy than the octet (s and p) orbitals that they are used only in reactions in which a good deal of energy is evolved—and then usually to form short-lived reaction intermediates. The larger the atom the smaller the energy difference between the octet orbitals and the d orbitals in the same layer. Thus iodine's acceptance of a fifth or sixth electron pair under mild conditions exemplifies an *important general trend.* (Heavy elements with high kernel charge frequently use six valence shell orbitals.) Oxyiodine compounds of this type will be mentioned with other oxyhalogen compounds in Chapter 10. Here, however, we shall discuss interhalogen compounds which illustrate expansion of the octet.

9.34. Interhalogen Compounds

The mixed halogen molecules, ClF, BrF, BrCl, ICl, and IBr, are what we would expect to find, for each atom commonly forms single covalent bonds, and the properties of these molecules are intermediate between those of the pure halogens of which they are composed. They are polar compounds to some extent; the first element in each formula is considered to have an oxidation number of $+1$ because it is the less electronegative. IF does not exist because the difference in electronegativity is so great that the iodine would be very nearly a positive ion, $: \ddot{\overset{..}{I}}{}^{+}$ with an incomplete octet.

In addition to the above, there is a whole series of interhalogen compounds in which one atom has an expanded octet. They are: ClF_3, BrF_3, BrF_5, ICl_3, IF_5, and IF_7, all uncharged molecules; and the ions Br_3^-, Br_2Cl^-, $BrCl_2^-$, I_3^-, I_2Br^-, IBr_2^-, $IBrCl^-$, ICl_2^-, $IBrF^-$ (in each of which the larger atom, or one of them, has 10 electrons), BrF_4^-, I_5^-, ICl_4^-, ICl_3F^- (in which, as in IF_5, the atom has 12), and IF_6^- (in which, as in IF_7, it has 14). All the other atoms in each of these compounds are covalently bonded to the one with the expanded valence shell. The central atom is considered to have a positive oxidation number; and the **ligands** (the atoms bonded to this central atom) an oxidation number of -1.

9.35. Colors of Iodine Solutions

When iodine dissolves in a completely non-basic solvent such as CS_2 or CCl_4, it separates into I_2 molecules, and the solution has the beautiful violet color of I_2 molecules in the gaseous state. But if the solvent is mildly basic—i.e., has an atom with an unshared electron pair which it is capable of sharing with a highly electronegative atom—one atom in an I_2 molecule can accept a share in the offered electron pair, its octet expanding to 10 electrons. Thus I_2 in H_2O forms $H : \overset{..}{\underset{\underset{H}{}}{O}} : \overset{..}{\underset{..}{I}} : \overset{..}{\underset{..}{I}} :$, in which

one iodine atom has 10 electrons analogous to $: \overset{..}{\underset{..}{I}} : \overset{..}{\underset{..}{I}} : \overset{..}{\underset{..}{I}} :^-$ ion and has the same brown color. As a matter of fact, all the compounds in which an iodine atom has 10 electrons are yellow to brown in color. In general, liquid organic compounds which contain oxygen (e.g., alcohols and ethers) are basic enough to form addition compounds with iodine as water does and produce brown solutions. Note that the addition compound between H_2O and I_2 is of the same type as that postulated on page 221 as an unstable intermediate in the hydrolysis of Cl_2. The analogy is complete; the two compounds behave in the same way except for differences in degree due to the lower electronegativity of iodine and its greater tendency toward an expanded octet.

9.36. The Starch Test

When a little starch solution is added to even a very dilute solution of I_2 in water, the color changes from pale yellow to an intense blue. This is due to a peculiarity of the starch molecule. Starch has a giant molecule of indefinite length which is coiled helically into a tube, like the spring on a screen door. The outer surface of the tube is composed largely of —OH groups and is responsible for the solubility of the starch molecule in water. The inner surface is entirely hydrocarbon in type, repelling water and attracting non-polar molecules such as I_2. Furthermore, the diameter of the tube is of just the right size to allow I_2 molecules to enter end-on. As the I_2 molecules are pulled in, the attached H_2O molecules are broken off; to all intents and purposes, the result is a solution of I_2 in a non-basic hydrocarbon solvent. The end-to-end lining up of the I_2 molecules in the starch tube somehow produces an extraordinarily intense color; consequently the iodine-starch color is a very useful test for traces of either starch or I_2.

9.37. Extraction of I_2 from H_2O

Whenever two solvents compete for a given solute, as in the above case, the solute is distributed between them in proportion to its solubility in each. (This competition implies that the solvents do not dissolve in each other—that is, they are *immiscible*—for otherwise there would be not two solvents but one.) Thus if a dilute aqueous solution of I_2 is shaken with a small amount of CCl_4, the latter will extract I_2 from the water until the concentration of I_2 in the CCl_4 is eighty times as great as it is in the H_2O. The yellow color will largely disappear from the water, and the violet color in the CCl_4 will become very noticeable. Note, however, that although I_2 is only slightly soluble in water, it is very soluble (as I_3^- ion) in a solution containing I^- ion; hence if much I^- ion is present in the water, the **partition coefficient** may be 1 or less than 1, instead of 80. Br_2 can be extracted from water by means of CCl_4 just as I_2 can; however, the partition coefficient is smaller, and the CCl_4 solution has the same amber color as the aqueous solution.

9.38. Uses of Iodine

Tincture of iodine—that is, a solution of I_2 in alcohol—is an excellent antiseptic. The present standard concentration is 2 per cent I_2. The 7 per cent concentration formerly prescribed was a strong enough oxidizing agent to produce severe burns unless used with care.

All iodine compounds are prepared from the element. KI has by far the largest production, requiring nearly 400 tons of iodine annually in this country. Other inorganic iodine compounds, mostly NaI, require less than 50 tons, but something like 125 tons are used each year in producing organic compounds. Several hundred of these are pharmaceuticals. Because of the ability of the thyroid gland to concentrate iodine, radioactive iodine prepared in an atomic pile can be used to treat thyroid cancer without injuring other tissues.

9.39. Astatine

Astatine is the heaviest halogen. Its name means "unstable," and it is so named because all its isotopes are unstable. It occurs in nature in infinitesimal amounts. A few atoms of it have been prepared by bombarding bismuth with alpha particles. Although this was not enough to be seen, it was possible to determine that its properties are halogen-like, but with some metallic character. This was to be expected, for astatine must be less electronegative than iodine, and iodine shows some traces of incipient metallic character. The semimetallic luster of I_2 crystals is considered to be such a character. Another is the existence of iodine with an oxidation number of $+1$ in a *cation,* $Py : \overset{\cdot\cdot}{\underset{\cdot\cdot}{I}} : Py^+$, where $: Py$ represents the organic base pyridine.

9.40. Hydrogen Halides

The hydrogen halides are colorless gases notable for their extremely sharp odor and their extreme solubility in water. They fume strongly in moist air, forming a cloud of droplets of acid solution. Only hydrogen fluoride is polar enough to show hydrogen bonding, but it does this to a truly remarkable extent. On the basis of the boiling points of HI, HBr, and HCl listed in Table 9.3, we would expect that of HF to be about $-150°$ C. It is actually nearly $20°$ C. The liquid is composed of zigzag chain molecules of all lengths up to about $(HF)_5$. The association persists appreciably even into the gaseous state, which has a density corresponding to an average molecule weight of about 40.

The great solubility of the hydrogen halides in water is due to the fact that they react with water. One hundred milliliters of water will dissolve only a few milliliters of a non-reacting gas like oxygen or hydrogen, but will dissolve 33 l. of HF, 50 l. of HCl, 30 l. of HBr, or 28 l. of HI. The three heavier gases react almost completely.

$$HX + H_2O \rightarrow H_3O^+ + X^-$$

TABLE 9.3. **Some Properties of the Hydrogen Halides**

	$(HF)_x$	HCl	HBr	HI
Melting point, °C.	−92	−112	−89	−50.8
Boiling point, °C.	19.4	−84	−67	−35.5 at 4 atm.
Solubility in grams per 100 g. H_2O	∞ at 0°	82.3 at 0°	221 at 0°	244 at 10° C.
Concentration in % of constant-boiling mixture	35	20	47	57
Boiling point of constant-boiling solution	120	110	126	127
Chemicals used for preparation of the halide	$CaF_2 + H_2SO_4$	$NaCl + H_2SO_4$	$H_3PO_4 + NaBr$ or $PBr_3 + H_2O$	$P + I_2 + H_2O$
Acid strength of water solution	Weak acid	Strong acid	Strong acid	Strong acid
Heat of formation, in calories	38,000	22,000	8600	−6400

In the case of HF this reaction is much less likely to take place than the reverse reaction. The resulting equilibrium mixture:

$$HF + H_2O \rightleftharpoons H_3O^+ + F^-$$

would contain only a small concentration of H_3O^+ ions were it not for the fact that the concentration of F^- ion is reduced to a very low value by strong hydrogen bonding with HF molecules. A 0.1 M solution of HF, then, is actually 0.01 M in H_3O^+ ion, and only slightly less than this in FHF^- ion, but contains very little F^- ion. Thus:

$$2HF + H_2O \rightleftharpoons H_3O^+ + FHF^-(HF_2{}^-)$$

The rest of the solubility of HF is accounted for by its strong hydrogen bonding with the solvent. Although dissolved HF can properly be written as $HF \cdot nH_2O$, it is customary to omit H_2O from the formulas of dissolved substances, particularly when the number of H_2O molecules is not known.

When a dilute solution of a hydrogen halide is boiled, almost pure H_2O vapor is given off. As the increasing concentration begins to reverse the ionization reaction with water, HX starts to escape also. Eventually the composition of the vapor is the same as that of the solution, so the latter no longer changes. The boiling point, which has risen steadily, becomes constant. For a given halide, the composition of this

constant-boiling mixture depends only on the barometric pressure. The relationship is stated in reference tables for use in preparing standardized solutions for chemical analysis.

9.41. Ionization

It is evident that in the reaction:

$$HCl + H_2O \rightarrow H_3O^+ + Cl^-$$

a water molecule has caused a covalent chloride to split. In line with the discussion on page 220 it would be logical to call this reaction a hydrolysis, but for historical reasons this is not done. HCl was known to produce ions in solution long before it was discovered that water had anything to do with the reaction. The equation was written simply:

$$HCl \rightarrow H^+ + Cl^-$$

and the reaction was called **ionization.** We know now that the proton is far too small to be able to exist as an independent ion; the charge density is so high that it *always* attaches itself to an electron pair. But we still habitually call the reaction ionization, and we customarily write H^+ and call it hydrogen ion, even though we know perfectly well that we are talking about H_3O^+, hydronium ion. Ionization differs from other hydrolyses in one important respect. Ionization equilibrium is attained practically instantaneously, whereas other hydrolysis reactions require from seconds to days. This is so because the proton merely shifts from one electron pair to another in the complex formed between the water (base) and acid molecule.

$$H\!:\!\overset{\cdot\cdot}{\underset{H}{O}}\!: \;+\; H\!:\!\overset{\cdot\cdot}{\underset{\cdot\cdot}{Cl}}\!: \;\rightarrow\; H\!:\!\overset{\cdot\cdot}{\underset{H}{O}}\!:\!H\!:\!\overset{\cdot\cdot}{\underset{\cdot\cdot}{Cl}}\!: \;\rightarrow\; H\!:\!\overset{\cdot\cdot}{\underset{H}{O}}\!:\!H^+ \;+\; :\!\overset{\cdot\cdot}{\underset{\cdot\cdot}{Cl}}\!:^-$$

A reaction of this sort is fundamentally simple; no octets of electrons are changed or disturbed.

9.42. Acids

A substance which can transfer a proton to a base is called an **acid.** If this reaction goes practically to completion with such a weak base as H_2O, the acid is said to be a **strong acid.** (Do not confuse this use of "strong" with the words "concentrated" and "corrosive"; in chemistry these words are not synonymous.) There are few strong acids. Of these, only three are commonly encountered—sulfuric, H_2SO_4; nitric, HNO_3; and hydrochloric, HCl. Perchloric acid, $HClO_4$, is the strongest acid known; it is used much less frequently. (HBr and HI are also strong, but are used only in very special cases.) Acids may be named as hydrogen compounds—e.g., hydrogen perchlorate, hydrogen iodide—or as acids—perchloric acid, hydriodic acid. The latter is common in the case of solid or liquid acids. This holds also for a solution of a gas, but the anhydrous gas is usually called a hydrogen compound. Thus HCl gas is called hydrogen chloride; the water solution, hydrochloric acid.

9.43. Conjugate Relationships

By definition an acid is a proton donor and a base is a proton acceptor. Consequently, a proton transfer reaction *always* creates new acids and bases. After an acid transfers a proton, the residual molecule that is left can accept a proton; in other words, it is a base.* An acid always becomes a base after proton transfer. This base is called the **conjugate base** of the acid. By the same logic, when a base accepts a proton in a proton transfer reaction, it becomes an acid. This acid is the **conjugate acid** of the base. Because new acids and bases are created, the proton transfer reaction can reverse itself in order to continue proton transfer, although it may go largely to completion in one direction or the other. A few examples will clarify the terminologies.

$$HCl + H_2O \rightleftharpoons H_3O^+ + Cl^-$$

| Acid_1 | Base_2 | Acid_2 | Base_1 |
| Very strong | Weak | Strong | Very weak |

Here one conjugate acid-base pair is designated by the subscript 1; the other, by the subscript 2.

The equation from left to right reads as follows: The acid HCl, through proton transfer generates its conjugate base, Cl^-. The base, H_2O, generates its conjugate acid, H_3O^+. From right to left it reads: The acid, H_3O^+, generates its conjugate base, H_2O, through proton transfer; the base, Cl^-, generates its conjugate acid, HCl. That the reversible reaction goes virtually to completion to the right is indicated by the longer arrow. All strong acids behave this way, the preferred

---

* J. N. Brønsted, who stressed the amphoteric role that water plays in ionization and hydrolysis, popularized the idea that all proton acceptors are bases. Thus all anions (instead of just OH^- ion) are bases; so bases other than OH^- ion are sometimes called Brønsted bases.

proton transfer reaction involving the formation of the weaker conjugate pairs.

The weak acid, HF, when dissolved in water reacts only slightly:

$$HF + H_2O \rightleftharpoons H_3O^+ + F^-$$

Acid$_1$	Base$_2$	Acid$_2$	Base$_1$
Weak	Weak	Strong	Strong

Here again, note the length of the arrows in relation to the strength of the conjugate pairs.

The following generalizations are useful; test them with the above examples.

1. Strong acids generate weak conjugate bases.
2. Strong bases generate weak conjugate acids.

When we speak of a water solution of an acid, the term is understood to include the type of equilibrium mixture shown in the examples above. Thus a dilute solution that contains H_2O, H_3O^+, Cl^-, and an immeasurably small amount of HCl is called hydrochloric acid, as is also the concentrated solution which, as its head-splitting odor indicates, contains a large amount of HCl.

9.44. Hydrogen Fluoride

The commercial 40 per cent HF solution is prepared by collecting in water the HF gas that distills when fluorspar is heated with concentrated sulfuric acid.

$$\underline{CaF_2} + H_2SO_4 \xrightarrow{\Delta} \underline{CaSO_4} + \overline{2HF}$$

Large quantities of HF are also produced in manufacturing phosphate fertilizer from apatite (Section 9.3).

Hydrofluoric acid has the unique property of attacking silicon dioxide, SiO_2. It also attacks any substance containing SiO_2, such as glass. This, plus the fact that it produces dangerous, easily infected burns if spilled on the skin, has given rise to the false impression that HF is a strong acid. However, as already stated, this is not the case; actually, HF is only slightly stronger than acetic acid, the acid in vinegar. Its attack on SiO_2 is due not to the strength of the acid but to the fact that silicon tetrafluoride, SiF_4, is a gas.

$$4HF + \underline{SiO_2} \rightarrow \overline{SiF_4} + 2H_2O$$

The escape of SiF_4 as a gas prevents the hydrolysis which would otherwise reverse this reaction. HF solution dissolves SiO_2 completely; but when it attacks glass the insoluble CaF_2 remains.

The markings on thermometers, graduated cylinders, etc., and the inside frosting of incandescent light bulbs are etched by means of HF; the parts that are not to be etched are protected with wax. Polyethylene bottles are used to transport hydrofluoric acid. Anhydrous HF is used on a large scale as a catalyst in the rearrangement of hydrocarbon molecules which converts ordinary gasoline into high-octane gasoline. It is shipped to the refineries in steel tank cars. Aqueous HF (0.5 per cent) is used to remove surface discolorations from aluminum and its alloys.

9.45. Hydrogen Chloride

The method described for preparing HF—heating a salt of the desired acid with a non-volatile acid—is a general method for preparing **volatile acids.** It is the standard method for preparing HCl. In its preparation in the laboratory the reaction is:

$$\underline{NaCl} + H_2SO_4 \overset{\Delta}{\rightarrow} Na^+ + HSO_4^- + \overline{HCl}$$

Ions are shown on the right because the salt, sodium hydrogen sulfate, melts at the temperature of the reaction. The hydrogen sulfate ion is also a non-volatile acid and can be used with another mole of NaCl to produce a second mole of HCl.

$$\underline{NaCl} + Na^+ + HSO_4^- \overset{\Delta}{\rightarrow} \underline{Na_2SO_4} + \overline{HCl}$$

H_2SO_4 is, however, a far weaker acid than HCl; hence the amount of HCl in the equilibrium mixture is very small indeed. In order to drive off HCl and send the reaction to completion the temperature must be raised to low red heat. This cannot be done with glass apparatus, but with iron apparatus it is standard commercial practice. This heat was not necessary in the case of HF because HF is a weaker acid than HSO_4^-.

HCl is produced in important quantities as a by-product in a number of commercial chemical manufacturing processes. For example, vinyl chloride (page 226) is produced by heating dichloroethane (ethylene dichloride).

$$\overline{CH_2Cl:CH_2Cl} \overset{\Delta}{\rightarrow} \overline{CH_2::CHCl} + \overline{HCl}$$

(Each pair of dots represents an electron pair that is shared by two carbon atoms.) The HCl thus produced can be combined with acetylene to make more vinyl chloride.

$$\overline{CH:::CH} + \overline{HCl} \rightarrow \overline{CH_2::CHCl}$$

It can also be used in other ways. Our total production of HCl in 1960 was over 1,000,000 tons.

HCl can also be made by burning chlorine and hydrogen together.

$$\overline{H_2} + \overline{Cl_2} \rightarrow \overline{2HCl}$$

Occasionally this is practicable economically, when supplies of by-product hydrogen and chlorine are available in quantities sufficient for the purpose but in too small amounts to make a more remunerative use of them practicable, and when the HCl is used in the same plant.

The commercial 32 per cent HCl solution sells for $1\frac{1}{2}$ cents a pound in tank-car lots, which makes it next to the cheapest acid there is. It is not fair to compare acids on a pound-for-pound basis; instead, costs per equivalent must be used. Thus 1 lb.-equivalent of HCl costs $1.70; 1 lb.-equivalent of H_2SO_4, 46 cents. Naturally H_2SO_4 is the acid of choice whenever it is possible to use it, but there are times when it cannot be used. For example, it cannot be used with Ca^{++}, Sr^{++}, Ba^{++}, or Pb^{++} because the sulfates of these ions are insoluble; similarly, in strongly acid solution, particularly if hot, SO_4^{--} ion can oxidize many substances.

When H_2SO_4 can produce such undesirable side reactions, HCl is the next most economical and desirable choice. When a strong acid is needed, HCl is used for the cation H_3O^+, which all strong acids furnish with equal ease. In choosing a strong acid, it is always necessary to consider possible interference from the anion. Cl^- ion cannot possibly cause trouble by oxidizing reducing agents, because -1 is the lowest oxidation state of a halogen. There are very few insoluble chlorides, and the moderate ability of Cl^- ion to form covalent bonds may be either a help or a nuisance, depending on circumstances. Cl^- ion is a reducing agent, although a poor one; so HCl cannot be used in the presence of strong oxidizing agents such as NO_3^-, MnO_4^-, or any of the oxyhalogen ions except ClO_4^-, BrO^-, and IO_3^-.

HCl was known before the element chlorine was discovered. Because he prepared it from sea salt, Lavoisier called it muriatic acid, from the Greek word for sea. This old name is still in common commercial use. Similarly, the important fertilizer KCl is still called muriate of potash.

9.46. Hydrogen Bromide

If HBr is prepared by heating NaBr with H_2SO_4, the product will be considerably contaminated with bromine and SO_2 because HBr is a good enough reducing agent—stronger than HCl—to attack the oxidizing acid, H_2SO_4.

$$2HBr + H_2SO_4 \xrightarrow{\Delta} \overline{Br_2} + 2H_2O + \overline{SO_2}$$

Instead, phosphoric acid, H_3PO_4, which is non-oxidizing, may be used. Hydrogen and bromine combine directly at 200° C. in the presence of a platinum catalyst to form HBr. A convenient means of preparing HBr in the laboratory consists of dropping Br_2 slowly into a mixture of red phosphorus with twice its weight of water. Presumably PBr_3 is formed first and hydrolyzed at once.

$$2P + 3Br_2 \rightarrow 2PBr_3$$
$$PBr_3 + 3H_2O \rightarrow H_3PO_3 + \overline{3HBr}$$

The amount of water required is so small that most of the HBr is given off as a gas without any need of heating. HBr is a by-product when hydrocarbons are brominated by substitution, as in the production of dibromobenzene from benzene.

$$C_6H_6 + 2Br_2 \rightarrow C_6H_4Br_2 + \overline{2HBr}$$

A 48 per cent solution of HBr is sold commercially in glass containers, but the 62 per cent solution, which is also available, requires polyethylene liners. Hydrobromic acid is much more expensive than hydrochloric acid and has no advantage over it as an acid—i.e., as a source of H_3O^+ ion—hence it is used only when Br^- ion or the molecule HBr is required. Anhydrous liquefied HBr is obtainable in 10- to 40-ton tank trucks at around 35 cents per pound. HBr is used in the manufacture of dyes, perfumes, bromides, and photographic chemicals.

9.47. Hydrogen Iodide

HI is a good enough reducing agent to be used commercially for this purpose in special cases. If NaI is heated with concentrated H_2SO_4, only a small proportion of the resulting HI will escape oxidation.

$$H_2SO_4 + 8HI \xrightarrow{\Delta} H_2S + \overline{4I_2} + 4H_2O$$

HI cannot be made by combining the two elements; in fact, it decomposes into them below 200° C. The usual method of preparing it involves the action of water on a mixture of red phosphorus and I_2.

$$2P + 5I_2 + 8H_2O \rightarrow \overline{10HI} + 2H_3PO_4$$

It is interesting that the phosphorus is oxidized to the pentavalent state in this reaction, whereas in an analogous reaction with Br_2, a stronger oxidizing agent, most of it is oxidized only to $+3$.

A 50 per cent solution of hydriodic acid can be prepared by passing H_2S into a suspension of iodine in water at room temperature.

$$H_2S + I_2 \rightarrow 2H^+ + 2I^- + \underline{S}$$

This is not inconsistent with the fact that H_2S and iodine did *not* react in the first equation in this section. The redox properties of substances shift markedly with temperature, and in different directions. For example, the higher the temperature, the more strongly sulfur tends to its lowest valence, -2.

A 45 per cent solution of hydriodic acid is of some use industrially, although it costs nearly $3 per pound. It is ordinarily not kept in stock in laboratories because it is subject to atmospheric oxidation.

$$4H^+ + 4I^- + \overline{O}_2 \rightarrow 2I_2 + 2H_2O$$

QUESTIONS AND PROBLEMS

1. Indicate the variation of such properties as electronegativity, boiling and melting points, and reactivity of the halogens with their atomic number.
2. What compounds are the *main* sources of the halogens?
3. Show by means of balanced equations an industrial and a laboratory method for producing each halogen.
4. Describe the role of polarity, electronegativity, and hydrogen bonding in the formation of HF_2^- ion. Why do similar ions of the other halogens not exist?
5. In what chemical respects is fluorine unique compared to all other elements?
6. List some of the main uses of the halogens.
7. Define or describe electrolysis; electrolytic reduction; electrolytic oxidation; electrolytic conduction; electrolyte; anode; cathode.
8. How can sodium be produced electrolytically from a water solution of NaCl? Why is this possible?
9. Complete and balance the following reactions by the ion-electron redox method. Show the half-reactions and label each as to type. (Refer to Table 9.2.)
   a. $(2Na^+ + Cr_2O_7^{--}) + (H^+ + Cl^-) \rightarrow \overline{Cl}_2$
   b. $H_2O_2 + (H^+ + Br^-) \rightarrow Br_2$
   c. $Cl_2 + I_2 + H_2O \rightarrow Cl^- + IO_3^- + H^+$
   d. $MnO_4^- + Br_2 \xrightarrow{\text{alkaline}} MnO_2 + BrO_3^-$

10. Why does chlorine oxidize substances more readily than oxygen although oxygen is the more powerful oxidizing agent?

11. a. Using equations, compare the bubbling of chlorine gas into water and into sodium hydroxide solution.

  b. In what respects is the reaction of a base with chlorine similar to and dissimilar from the reaction of a reducing agent with chlorine?

12. Use equations to show what happens when the following chlorides are dissolved in water; and defend your answers.

$$BaCl_2 \qquad FeCl_3 \qquad PCl_3$$

13. Show, by equations, a substitution, an addition, and a displacement reaction involving chlorine and suitable compounds.

14. Compare the oxidizing ability of the halogens and the reducing ability of the halide ions on the basis of atomic number.

15. Using suitable equations, show all possible redox reactions of uncombined halogens with halide ions.

16. In what respects is hydrogen similar to the halogens?

17. Write the formulas and names of several interhalogen compounds, including some in which one of the halogen atoms has an expanded octet. What are the oxidation numbers of the halogens in each compound?

18. Why is a solution of iodine in CCl_4 violet and a solution of it in alcohol (tincture of iodine) brown?

19. Why is the ionization reaction of an acid in water actually a hydrolysis reaction? What chemical classification can water be given in these reactions? Show these reactions for the hydrogen halides.

20. What is a strong acid? How is this indicated symbolically in the equation of hydrolysis? Compare the equations for HCl and HF. What is a proton transfer reaction?

21. Write the hydrolysis reaction of HBr. Explain or define the following relative to this reaction: reversible reaction; equilibrium mixture; conjugate acids and bases.

22. Write complete balanced equations for laboratory methods for the preparation of each hydrogen halide. Why cannot HBr be produced, with H_2SO_4 used as a reagent? Illustrate your answer with a chemical equation.

23. List some of the most important uses of the hydrogen halides.

24. How many grams of HF, HCl, HBr, and HI are needed for 1 l. of a 1 N solution of each? How many milliliters of 2 M NaOH will each of these solutions neutralize? On the basis of these data, discuss the reasons for preferring HCl acid over the other hydrohalogens for such reactions as far as industrial economies are concerned.

10

Ions of the halogen family

10.1. Classes of Halogen-Containing Ions

Members of the halogen family form monatomic ions that are known collectively as the **halide ions.** Halogen atoms also take part in the formation of many polyatomic ions. One class of these contains only halogen atoms (Section 9.34); these are called **polyhalide ions.** In a second and more important class a halogen atom, other than fluorine, is attached to one or more oxygen atoms. These are the **oxyhalogen ions.** In a third class, one or more halogen atoms are attached to a different kind of atom that has a positive oxidation number. These ions have names of the type *halo- . . . -ate,* the part of the name represented by the dots referring to the atom with a positive oxidation number; thus BF_4^- is called fluoborate, SO_3Cl^- is chlorosulfonate.

The halide ions are among the most important inorganic non-metallic molecules. They are almost the only monatomic anions which can be obtained in water solution. Several sections of the present chapter will be devoted to their properties and uses, and to the properties of salts which can be described most easily when the component ions are simple.

10.2. Physical Properties of Halide Ions

All the halide ions have the inert gas type of structure, with a completed octet of electrons in the valence shell. The single electron which is gained to complete this shell is responsible for the characteristic electrovalence of -1. This is also their oxidation number, because these are identical in monatomic molecules. Although all the halide ions are colorless, covalent bonding in a crystal of giant molecules tends to the development of color in these ions even when the cation also is colorless. The greater the willingness of the anion to form covalent bonds the greater its tendency to have color (Table 10.1). Thus, AgCl is white, but AgBr is cream-colored, and AgI and HgI_2 are yellow and scarlet respectively.

TABLE 10.1. **Halide Ions**

Name	Fluoride	Chloride	Bromide	Iodide
Formula	F^-	Cl^-	Br^-	I^-
Radius, A.	1.33	1.81	1.96	2.19
Standard electromotive force				
$2X^- \rightarrow X_2 + 2e^-$	-2.87 v.	-1.36 v.	-1.07 v.	-0.53 v.
Polarizability	0.4	2.3	3.3	5.1
Heat of hydration	122	89	81	72

The size of an ion and its nuclear charge are determining factors in regard to its polarizability as well as its electronegativity. In order to appreciate the difference in the attractive forces by which the valence electrons of the halide ions are held by their nuclei, imagine the F^- and I^- ions stripped of those electrons. What is left would be the hypothetical positive ions F^{+7} and I^{+7}, conveniently called the **atomic kernels.** It might seem that both of these kernels would attract electrons equally. However, the I^{+7} kernel is seven times as large as the F^{+7} kernel; so the valence electrons in an I^- ion cannot get nearly as close to the nucleus of the iodine atom as can those in the F^- ion to the nucleus of the fluorine atom. For this reason the electrons in the valence shell of the F^- ions are held much more tightly than those in the I^- ion.

F^- *is the smallest of all anions.* The size of the other halide ions is not proportionate to the number of their electron shells because the size of any given shell decreases as the nuclear charge increases. Therefore the density of these ions increases with the atomic number. Cl^- ion is 33 per cent larger than F^- ion, Br^- ion is 8 per cent larger than Cl^- ion, and I^-

ion is 10 per cent larger than Br^- ion. Accordingly, Cl^-, Br^-, and I^- ions are comparable more closely to each other than to F^- ion.

The **standard electromotive force** (e.m.f.) measures in volts the difficulty of removing an electron in solutions. The negative sign means that it is harder to remove an electron from a halide ion than from a hydrogen molecule; the latter is the standard of reference and has the arbitrarily assigned e.m.f. value of zero. The electromotive force is related to the electronegativity of the elements, but depends also on the attraction of the ion for water molecules, since it is assumed that the ion is in 1 *m* aqueous solution. *The standard electromotive force of* F^- *ion is the most negative known.*

The **polarizability** of an ion measures the extent to which electrons in the valence shell can be pulled into covalent bonding by the positive charge on an adjacent cation. The polarizability of F^- ion is negligible; that is, this ion has practically no tendency to form covalent bonds. The tendency to form covalent bonds increases with the polarizability and is important in I^- ion.

Depending on its charge, an ion that is put into a polar liquid attracts one or the other end of the polar solvent molecules. F^- ion, for example, strongly attracts the $+$ ends of water molecules. This general process is called **solvation,** or **hydration** if the solvent is water; it always results in the *liberation of energy.*

10.3. Halide Ions as Reducing Agents

Only I^- ion, of all the halide ions, is good enough as a reducing agent ever to be called one. Even I^- is only moderate. A number of cations are good enough oxidizing agents to oxidize I^- ion, but obviously the iodide of such a cation cannot exist. Thus no such compound as CuI_2 or FeI_3 can be formed because of the reactions:

$$2Cu^{++} + 4I^- \rightarrow \underline{2CuI} + I_2$$
$$2Fe^{+3} + 6I^- \rightarrow 2Fe^{++} + 4I^- + I_2$$

Br^-, Cl^-, and F^- ion rank successively poorer as reducing agents. F^- is the weakest reducing agent known. (It is practically impossible to oxidize this ion chemically; electrolysis is required.) This means that F^- ion can be used in the presence of any oxidizing agent without danger of being attacked, and that Cl^- ion can be used in the presence of all except the strongest oxidizing agents.

10.4. Halide Ions as Bases

The halide ions are the *conjugate bases* of the hydrogen halides. HCl, HBr, and HI are strong acids. Hence the corresponding halide anions are weaker bases than water; they are not ordinarily called bases. This near-absence of basic properties makes it possible for Cl^-, Br^-, and I^- ions to exist as such even in strongly acid solutions—an important property. Since HF is a moderately weak acid, it follows that F^- ion is a moderate base. It reacts slightly with even as weak an acid as water, displacing a few OH^- ions.

$$2F^- + H_2O \rightleftharpoons HF_2^- + OH^-$$

This is a **hydrolysis,** the opposite of a neutralization. At equilibrium the concentrations of the two bases, F^- and OH^- ions, which are competing for protons, are inversely proportional to the strength of these ions as bases.

10.5. Cl^-, Br^-, and I^- Ions as Complex Ion Formers

The formation of a covalent bond between a base and a proton is called **neutralization.** The formation of a covalent bond between a base and any cation other than H^+ is a fundamentally similar process; but because this was not recognized to be neutralization until rather recently it was given the special name coordination. The bond thus formed, a coordinate bond, was thought to be different from a normal bond because both electrons came from the same atom instead of one coming from each. A coordinate bond does not differ from a normal bond, because the nature of a bond depends upon the difference in electronegativity of the atoms it joins, not upon the way it is formed. Thus the HCl formed "normally" by the combination of the two elements is exactly the same as that formed by the action of H_2SO_4 on salt, with both electrons originally held by the Cl^- ion.

Any base which can be coordinated by a given cation is called a **ligand** of that cation. The number of electron pairs which a cation can coordinate is called its **coordination number.** The coordination number of H^+ ion is 1; the coordination numbers of other cations range from 2 to 8. When a univalent base coordinates with H^+ ion (is neutralized), an uncharged molecule is formed, but this is not ordinarily true of other cations. For example, HCl is an uncharged molecule, but $AgCl_2^-$, $CuCl_3^{--}$, $CuCl_4^{--}$, and $SnCl_6^{--}$ are anions. An anion formed by coordination is called a **complex ion.**

The ability of an anion to form covalent bonds with cations depends upon its own polarizability, and increases from Cl⁻ through Br⁻ to I⁻ ion. It also depends upon the intensity of the charge which is effective at the surface of the cation. This is called the **charge density**; it is high for *small* ions with a *large* positive charge. The coordination number of a cation depends not only upon the charge density at its surface, but also upon the number of orbitals available for the formation of coordinate bonds and upon the size of the ligands in comparison with the size of the cation. H^+ ion has a very high charge density because of its small size, but it can coordinate only one Cl⁻ ion because there is only one orbital in its valence shell. B^{+3}, which has a high charge density and four empty valence orbitals, forms only the uncharged molecule BCl_3 because it is too small for any more Cl⁻ ions to crowd around it. But with the smaller F⁻ ion it forms both BF_3 and BF_4^-. Al^{+3}, which is the next larger ion in this family, can form the fairly stable $AlCl_4^-$ and the stable $AlCl_6^{-3}$ ion. Ions that are not of the inert gas type have higher charge densities than would be expected from their size and charge; this is due to the *d* electrons on their surfaces. These *d* electrons do not shield the positive nuclear charge from electrons in the valence shell as effectively as the *s* and *p* electrons do. Only because their surface has 10 *d* electrons can Cu^+ and Ag^+ ions form complex ions. Univalent cations of the inert gas type, such as Na^+ and K^+, have only slight ability to form complex ions, whereas cations with *d* electrons in their surface and a charge of $+2$ or more do so readily, regardless of their size.

10.6.   F⁻ Ion as a Complex Ion Former

F⁻ ion has negligible ability to form covalent bonds. This was indicated by its low polarizability in Table 10.1. The reason for this is the smallness of its kernel, which consists of only the nucleus and the 2 electrons in the K shell, and its high charge, $+7$. It is difficult for electrons to move even partly away from F⁻ ion to be shared with another atom. F⁻ ion does not bond covalently with any monovalent cation except the proton itself, which has a high charge density because of its minute size. Even in HF the hydrogen atom has little more than a quarter-share of the bonding electron pair, instead of the half-share held by each atom in a covalent bond between atoms of equal electronegativity. Only with elements in the upper half of the electronegativity scale does fluorine form bonds that are as covalent even as the bond it forms with hydrogen. Examples are BF_3, CF_4, and SF_6.

F⁻ ion is nevertheless noteworthy as a complex ion former. Fluoro-complexes are held together by the attraction between the F^- ions and a polyvalent cation at the center. This attraction obeys Coulomb's law—it varies inversely with the square of the distance—and is therefore particularly effective when the negative ion is F^-, the smallest anion. These ion clusters have no attraction for each other because the cation in each cluster is covered up by its own shell of F^- ions, and the negative surfaces repel each other. An ion cluster is, in fact, just as truly a molecule—i.e., an independent particle—as any molecule which is held together by covalent bonds. This holds true not only for complex anions but for neutral complexes. The bonds in CF_4 are 57 per cent covalent, those in SiF_4 only 30 per cent covalent, but both are perfectly typical gas molecules. The model in Fig. 10.1 shows how impossible it is for an F^- ion of one SiF_4 molecule to touch the Si^{+4} of another molecule.

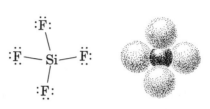

Fig. 10.1. The tetrahedral SiF_4 molecule.

Since fluoro- complexes are held together by electrical attraction, they do not form around monovalent or divalent cations. This is true of even the low-valence cations that are not of the inert gas type, which can form complexes with the other halogens by virtue of their ability to form covalent bonds because they have d electrons. Thus there are no fluoro-complexes corresponding to $ZnCl_4^{--}$ and HgI_4^{--}. In a number of cases a given oxidation number of a transition element is stable only when the element is covalently bonded to ligands. In these cases a complex can be formed with any of the other halide ions but not with fluoride, which cannot be covalently bonded. This is why there are no fluoro- complexes corresponding to $CuCl_2^-$, $AuCl_4^-$, and $PtCl_6^{--}$, to cite a few examples. On the other hand, Fe^{+3} has a large positive oxidation number which does not require covalent bonding to stabilize it; hence the ion FeF_6^{-3} exists.

Many atoms have a larger coordination number for F^-, because of its smaller size, than for the other halide ions. Thus there are the complex anions BF_4^- and SiF_6^{--}, whereas no charged chlorides such as BCl_4^- and $SiCl_6^{--}$ exist. Or there may be other fluoro- and chloro- complexes, but the former may contain a greater number of the halogen atoms—e.g., ZrF_7^{-3}—in contrast to $ZrCl_6^{--}$.

10.7. Salts

Ions cannot be studied by themselves as uncharged molecules can. It is impossible for anions to exist unless they are surrounded by enough cations to produce over-all electrical neutrality. A substance composed of ions is called a **salt,** from the name of the most familiar of them all, NaCl, common salt. A salt, then, is a substance which, instead of all its molecules being alike, has at least two kinds of molecules. This does not mean that a salt is a mixture instead of a compound, for the requirement of electrical neutrality makes it necessary that the two kinds of molecules be present in *definite proportions.*

When a salt is melted or in solution, so that the ions can move independently, they are written separately and the charge is indicated—$Na^+ + Cl^-$. But this is not necessary when a salt is in the solid state, its ions merely vibrating about fixed positions; in this case we write NaCl. Note that this is not a molecular formula but an empirical formula. It states the composition of the material but says nothing about the size of the molecules. Actually there is no such thing as a molecule of sodium chloride; the Na^+ and Cl^- ions are independent molecules. Consideration of their structure shows why this must be true. Na^+ ion is formed by the loss of one electron from sodium and has the inert neon structure. Cl^- ion is formed when the chlorine atom accepts one electron and has the argon type of structure. Each structure is satisfactory by itself; there is no need for any sharing of electrons as in Cl_2.

Experimental proof of the nonexistence of NaCl molecules either in solution or in the crystals is easily obtained. An aqueous solution of salt has only two sets of properties other than those of plain water, namely, the properties of Na^+ ion and those of Cl^- ion. If there were NaCl molecules there would have to be a third set of properties, those of NaCl molecules, which is not the case. For the crystal itself the proof is obtained from x-ray diffraction photographs which make it possible to compute the position of each constituent of the crystal. The scale model in Fig.

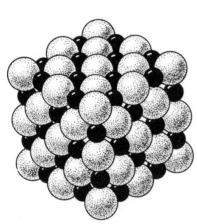

Fig. 10.2. Cubic ionic crystal lattice of NaCl. Small spheres represent Na^+, the larger spheres Cl^-.

10.2 shows clearly that it is impossible to pick out any one of the six Na^+ ions which are equidistant from a given Cl^- ion and say that the Na^+ ion is the one that "goes with the Cl^- ion."

10.8. Solubility of Halide Salts

In order to study the properties of the halide ions we make solutions of their salts, so that the ions can move independently. To separate these ions from other anions and from each other they are frequently removed from the solution in the form of insoluble salts. Accordingly, knowledge of the relative solubilities of the halide salts is important for the study of the ions.

In simple ionic crystals, lattice energies, which work against solubility, depend upon the product of the charges on two adjacent ions, and inversely upon the square of the distance between their centers; this is determined by the ionic radii. (See the equation for Coulomb's law in Section 8.4.) Other things being equal, univalent ions form the most soluble salts. From this it follows that *most halide salts are soluble*. On the other hand, an increase in radius does not have a simple effect. It decreases lattice energy because the ions are farther apart, but it also decreases hydration energy by limiting the closeness with which water molecules can approach; this hydration energy favors solubility. Thus the fact that the solubilities of the sodium halides increase on the order of $NaF \rightarrow NaI$ is due to the fact that in this particular case the decrease in the lattice energy exceeds the decrease in the hydration energy.

10.9. Insoluble Halide Salts

The radius of F^- ion is so small that most salts that have *polyvalent* cations are insoluble because of the high lattice energy. There is one monovalent cation, Li^+, that is so small that the lattice energy of LiF is high enough to limit its solubility to a great extent.

A crystal may also have high lattice energy, and therefore low solubility, because of the existence either of covalent bonds, or of bonds that are highly covalent in character, between its cations and anions. In other words, a crystal has high lattice energy if its anions are strongly polarized by its cations. A glance at Table 10.1 shows why Cl^-, Br^-, and I^- may be included here, but not F^-.

All the chlorides, bromides, or iodides whose cations are of the inert gas type are ionic and soluble; but those whose cations are not of the inert gas type and which have a low charge are insoluble. In AgCl, each ion is held to its neighbors on every side by bonds which are 24 per cent covalent. The crystal is, in effect, a single molecule with relatively high bonding energy. The high lattice energy which results from a structure such as this, is not overcome by the energy of hydration on solution; so AgCl is only very slightly soluble. The more highly polarizable I⁻ ion forms bonds with neighboring Ag⁺ ions which are 46 per cent covalent; hence AgI is even less soluble than AgCl.

The chlorides, bromides, and iodides of all Ag⁺-type ions are very slightly soluble. These ions are Cu^+, Ag^+, Au^+, Hg_2^{++}, and Tl^+. The first three of these constitute Group IB, a subfamily of Group I. Each has lost the single electron it had in its valence shell and each has 10 d electrons in the shell which thereupon becomes the surface of the ion. Thus Cu^+ has the following structure:

Shell	s Electrons	p Electrons	d Electrons
1	2		
2	2	6	
3	2	6	10

This structure may also be written: $1s^2$, $2s^2 2p^6$, $3s^2 3p^6 3d^{10}$. Similarly, Ag^+ has $1s^2$, $2s^2 2p^6$, $3s^2 3p^6 3d^{10}$, $4s^2 4p^6 4d^{10}$. Au^+ has $1s^2$, $2s^2 2p^6$, $3s^2 3p^6 3d^{10}$, $4s^2 4p^6 4d^{10} 4f^{14}$, $5s^2 5p^6 5d^{10}$.

The other two ions are peculiar. Mercury is the next element after gold, hence 2 electrons must be accounted for in the mercurous ion, Hg_2^{++}. They form a covalent bond between the two atoms, the only case of this kind. Thallium is the second element after gold; its valence layer is $6s^2 6p$. In Tl^+ the single p electron has been lost. The pair of s electrons, spread out evenly over a large surface, counterbalance two units of nuclear charge, but seem to have little influence on the covalent bond-forming ability that characterizes ions with d electrons in their surface. Pb^{++} ion is another ion with an "inert pair" of s electrons; $PbCl_2$, $PbBr_2$, and PbI_2 are only slightly soluble.

Smaller, more highly charged cations that are not of the inert gas type and have greater polarizing power form bonds that are even more covalent in character; but this is more than counterbalanced by their having much greater hydration energy. Thus in $CuCl_2$ crystals each Cu^{++} ion is bonded to four Cl⁻ ions, and each Cl⁻ ion is bonded to two Cu^{++} ions, forming a giant molecule.

$$\begin{array}{ccccccc}
 & | & & | & & | & \\
 & Cl & & Cl & & Cl & \\
 & | & & | & & | & \\
-Cu & -Cl- & Cu & -Cl- & Cu & - \\
 & | & & | & & | & \\
 & Cl & & Cl & & Cl & \\
 & | & & | & & | & \\
-Cu & -Cl- & Cu & -Cl- & Cu & - \\
 & | & & | & & | &
\end{array}$$

This does not remain insoluble; it reacts with water to form

$$\begin{array}{c}
Cl \\
| \\
H_2O-Cu-OH_2 \\
| \\
Cl
\end{array}$$

molecules which are small enough to dissolve readily.

On further dilution, first one and then both Cl^- ions are displaced by water, and the green color of $Cu(H_2O)_2Cl_2$ is replaced by the blue of $Cu(H_2O)_4^{++}$ ions. Other halides of this type behave similarly except for those with the two largest divalent cations of the non-inert gas type, Hg^{++} and Pb^{++}; their hydration energy is low. These two range from slightly to very slightly soluble in the same order as the silver halides. $HgCl_2$ is soluble enough so that adding a moderate amount of Cl^- to Hg^{++} ion does not precipitate it. $PbCl_2$ precipitates but can be dissolved in hot water.

0.10. Analytical Determination of Halide Ions

F^- ion can be precipitated from an unknown solution as CaF_2 by the addition of Ca^{++} ion. The CaF_2 is separated and HF is produced from it by adding H_2SO_4. It is identified by the fact that it will etch a piece of glass. The presence in the solution of other ions which ʋrm insoluble calcium salts does not interfere with this qualitative identification. F^- ion can be determined quantitatively by titration with a standardized Fe^{+3} solution in the presence of excess Na^+ ion, a little thiocyanate ion, CNS^-, being used as indicator. The F^- ion that is present forms the complex ion FeF_6^{-3} as fast as the Fe^{+3} ion is added, and insoluble sodium fluoferrate, Na_3FeF_6, is precipitated.

$$6Na^+ + 6F^- + Fe^{+3} + 3Cl^- \rightarrow \underline{Na_3FeF_6} + 3Na^+ + 3Cl^-$$

When no more F^- ion is present, the solution turns deep red because of the formation of the thiocyanato- complex ion $FeCNS^{++}$.

Cl⁻, Br⁻, and I⁻ ions can be separated from the solution by adding silver nitrate solution; this precipitates their insoluble silver salts.

$$X^- + \underline{Ag^+} + NO_3^- \rightarrow AgX + NO_3^-$$

The solution must be acidic to prevent interference from the anions that are the conjugate bases of weak acids. If the precipitate is white, it consists only of AgCl since AgBr is cream-colored and AgI is yellow. If it is not white, it is washed with dilute ammonia solution to dissolve any AgCl that may be present in a mixture with the other halides.

$$\underline{AgCl} + 2NH_3 \rightarrow Ag(NH_3)_2^+ + Cl^-$$

After it has been separated from the remaining precipitate, the clear solution is acidified to remove the NH_3.

$$NH_3 + H^+ + NO_3^- \rightarrow NH_4^+ + NO_3^-$$

If any AgCl was present in the original precipitate, the removal of the NH_3 will reverse the reaction forming the silver-ammonia ion, $Ag(NH_3)_2^+$, and AgCl will be reprecipitated. NH_3 dissolves AgCl because the bonds it forms with Ag^+ ions are more covalent in character than those formed by Cl^- ion. Concentrated NH_3 solution dissolves AgBr in similar fashion, thus permitting its separation from AgI. The bond between Ag^+ and I^- is too strong to be broken by even a concentrated solution of NH_3, although AgI is readily soluble in anhydrous liquefied NH_3.

When pure, the silver halides can be distinguished from one another by their color. However, a mixture of AgCl and AgI is cream-colored like AgBr; a small amount of AgBr can be present in either AgCl or AgI without greatly changing their color; and AgI turns white on contact with concentrated NH_3 solution. From this it is evident that color cannot be relied upon for analytical purposes. But there is a useful confirmatory test for AgCl; this is based on the fact that its surface turns violet on exposure to sunlight for a few minutes or to the light from burning magnesium for a few seconds.

Another means of identifying Br⁻ and I⁻ ions is the shake-out test, which involves their oxidation to the respective elements by the addition of chlorine water (Cl_2 solution), and their extraction in a non-aqueous solvent, as described in Section 9.37. If only a drop or two of chlorine water is added at first to a mixture of Br⁻ and I⁻ ions, only iodine will be set free. The CCl_4 will be amber if only Br^- ion was present. It will have the violet color of I_2 if I^- ion was present, regardless of whether there was any Br^- ion. If this violet color appears, chlorine water is added in excess, and both bromine and iodine will be displaced.

$$2X^- + Cl_2 \rightarrow 2Cl^- + X_2$$

The iodine, but not the bromine, is then further oxidized and removed from the CCl_4, going back into the water solution as iodate ion, IO_3^-.

$$I_2 + 5Cl_2 + 6H_2O \rightarrow 2IO_3^- + 10Cl^- + 12H^+$$

If Br^- ion was present in the original solution, the CCl_4 will have the yellow-to-brown color characteristic of bromine; if no Br^- ion was present, the CCl_4 will be colorless. If the CCl_4 shake-out procedure indicates the presence of Br^- or I^- ions, they should be removed before testing for Cl^- ion, for otherwise the test results will depend upon the concentration of NH_4OH used.

Br$^-$ and I$^-$ ions can be eliminated from the unknown solution by selective oxidation to the free halogen element, since both these ions are better reducing agents than Cl^- ion. Of the several oxidizing agents that can be used, 5 M HNO_3 is both convenient and effective. Equal volumes of the acid and the solution are mixed and boiled until any brownish color due to free Br_2 or I_2 disappears.

$$6X^- + 8H^+ + 2NO_3^- \xrightarrow{\Delta} \overline{3X_2} + \overline{2NO} + 4H_2O$$

The water must be replenished during the boiling to prevent concentration of the solution and consequent attack on the Cl^- ion. A portion of the solution is tested by the shake-out test, and if Br^- or I^- is still present the boiling with HNO_3 is repeated until the test is negative. The solution is then tested with $AgNO_3$. A white precipitate soluble in dilute NH_4OH is proof of the presence of Cl^- ion.

10.11. Uses of Halide Ions

All the halide ions are used in the preparation of the respective elements. Although very small amounts of F^- ion are used for this purpose, an important fraction of all Cl^- ion goes into the manufacture of chlorine (Fig. 10.3). All Br^- and I^- ions obtained from natural sources are processed into the respective elements during recovery. The relatively small amount needed in the ionic state is then obtained by reduction of the element.

F⁻ ion is the starting point for the manufacture both of HF and, either directly from HF or from the element, of all fluorine compounds not mined as such. (To supplement the natural supply, it is even used to manufacture artificial cryolite, Na_3AlF_6, used in aluminum production.) F⁻ ion is used directly, usually in the form of fluorspar, CaF_2, to opacify non-transparent glass and to lower the melting point of slags, enamels,

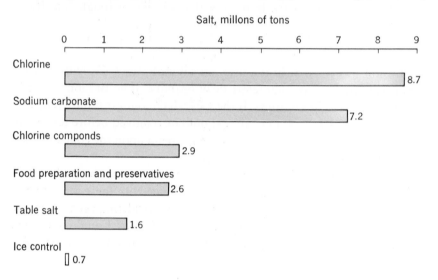

Fig. 10.3. Uses of salt in the United States, 1957.

and fused salts for electrolyses. This use as a **flux** is responsible for the name of the element (L., *fluere,* to flow). Addition of F⁻ ion to a solution containing yellow Fe^{+3} ion decolorizes it because of the formation of the colorless complex ion FeF_6^{-3}, thereby making possible certain analytical processes which the color of Fe^{+3} ion would interfere with.

Cl⁻ ion is the starting point for the preparation not only of chlorine but of all chlorine compounds. All this Cl⁻ ion comes from common salt, NaCl. No single compound of chlorine requires as much as a million tons of salt annually in its preparation, but together they accounted for the respectable amount of 2.9 million tons in 1957 (Fig. 10.3). This also includes compounds in which the Cl⁻ ion has not been chemically altered but has been paired with a different cation. Cl⁻ ion is used as a non-reacting partner with all sorts of cations (except, of course, the few listed in Section 10.9 as forming insoluble chlorides). For example, the American fertilizer industry uses about a million tons of KCl a year for its K^+ ion content; the Cl^- ion is cheap, harmless, and extremely abundant.

Cl^- ion is used in analytical chemistry for the identification and quantitative determination of Ag^+ and Hg_2^{++} ions. It also serves to *sequester* polyvalent subgroup cations by engulfing them in complex ions. For example, although nitric acid alone cannot dissolve gold, a mixture of nitric and hydrochloric acid called aqua regia can do so, because as fast as the nitric acid oxidizes gold to Au^{+3} ion, the Cl^- ions in the mixture remove it as chloraurate ion, $AuCl_4^-$, preventing the reverse reaction.

$$Au + 3H^+ + 3NO_3^- + 4H^+ + 4Cl^- \rightarrow$$
$$H^+ + AuCl_4^- + 3H_2O + \overline{3NO_2}$$

The uses of salt as such are too familiar to require discussion. Its use as a source of sodium and its compounds, briefly mentioned in Chapter 9, will be discussed in more detail in a later chapter.

Br^- ion is the starting point for the preparation of bromine and all bromine compounds. Many bromine compounds differ in properties sufficiently from the corresponding chlorine compounds to justify the higher price necessitated by the relative scarcity of Br^- ion. AgBr, for example, is the principal light-sensitive substance used in photographic materials, small amounts of AgCl or AgI sometimes being added to modify its properties. KBr is used as a sedative.

The main use of I^- ion is in the preparation of iodine and its compounds. The most important iodide is AgI, used in photography. I^- ion is used analytically in the determination of Ag^+ because of the great insolubility of AgI. It is also used in determining Cu^{++} ion and other oxidizing agents. The amount of iodine set free by such oxidizing agents can be determined more easily and more accurately than is possible with most analytical procedures in which the oxidizing agent is used directly. Iodine is reduced with a carefully standardized solution of thiosulfate ion, $S_2O_3^{--}$, according to the equation:

$$I_2 + 2S_2O_3^{--} \rightarrow 2I^- + S_4O_6^{--}$$

When the iodine that remains colors the solution only a pale yellow, starch solution is added, whereupon the inky-blue starch-iodine color appears. This grows lighter when more $S_2O_3^{--}$ ion is added, but is still easily visible when there is as little as 0.1 mg. of iodine in the solution. With the addition of the last fraction of a drop of $S_2O_3^{--}$ solution the color vanishes. The oxidation product of $S_2O_3^{--}$ ion, $S_4O_6^{--}$, is called tetrathionate ion. The amount of iodine set free can be related to the amount of oxidizing agent which liberated it by simple stoichiometry.

AgCl can readily be transformed into AgBr by contact with Br⁻ ion because, as insoluble as AgCl is, it is still two thousand times as soluble as AgBr. When solid AgCl comes in contact with a solution containing Br⁻ ions, the reaction is:

$$\text{Br}^- + \underline{\text{AgCl}} \rightarrow \underline{\text{AgBr}} + \text{Cl}^-$$

Since the Br⁻ : Cl⁻ ratio in sea water is 1 : 600, and even more favorable in certain Michigan brines, a process has been devised and patented to recover Br⁻ from these sources by filtering the water through AgCl. The process would certainly work; whether or not it would pay is another question.

10.12. Halide Ions as Food and Poison

Halide ions are necessary to life. The concentration of Cl⁻ ion in our blood is about that in a 1 per cent NaCl solution. This is believed to have been the concentration of salt in the sea when life first appeared in it. The body apparently demands a fairly definite concentration of each element that bodily processes require. If it gets much less, deficiency symptoms result; a little more than the normal amount is toxic. Thus if too much salt is lost from the body in perspiration, heat prostration follows. The salt content of the oceans at present is 3 per cent or more; the drinking of a quart of sea water is followed by death in a short time. Food is preserved against the action of microorganisms by being salted. In the concentration used for this purpose, salt is an effective poison; but when part is washed away, the rest is a useful food.

Since all soils contain polyvalent ions (Ca^{++}, Mg^{++}, Fe^{++}, etc.) which form insoluble fluorides, the concentration of F⁻ ion in natural waters is always low. Correspondingly the optimum amount of F⁻ ion required by the system is much lower than in the case of Cl⁻ ion. But if the body fails to get that small amount of F⁻ ion, tooth decay results because hydroxyapatite, $Ca_5(PO_4)_3OH$, is substituted for the harder, less soluble fluorapatite, $Ca_5(PO_4)_3F$, that is normally present in the enamel. A ten-year experiment involved fluoridation of the water supply in a city in New York State; the water supply of a similar neighboring city was not fluoridized and served as a check. The results proved that tooth decay in children was halved by the addition of 1 p.p.m. of F⁻ ion. Fifteen times that concentration of the ion, present in some southwestern water supplies, still further reduces tooth decay without injuring health. Unfortunately, however, it also produces a mottling of the enamel with brown spots. Accordingly, 1 p.p.m. (about $\frac{1}{4}$ teaspoonful per ton) has been adopted as standard in the rapidly spreading practice of fluoridizing water supplies. As in the case of Cl^- ion, high concentrations of F^- ion are poisonous. For example, NaF is used as a fungicide in wood preservation and as an insecticide for roaches.

The body seems to have no difficulty in getting the small amount of Br^- ion that it needs. Small doses of additional Br^- ion act as a sedative; this is why a dull, trite remark is called a "bromide."

Deficiency of I^- ion causes goiter, or hypertrophy of the thyroid gland. KI (0.01 per cent) is added to table salt to prevent this. The use of iodized salt is unnecessary when the diet includes sea food, and in regions where even a trace of sea spray is blown inland, but even in these cases it does no harm in the quantities that are used.

0.13. Oxyhalogen Ions

Any oxyhalogen ion may be thought of as consisting of a halide ion which has largely lost one or more electron pairs to oxygen atoms with which it is covalently bonded. Fluorine does not form oxyanions because it is the most electronegative element; it cannot lose electrons even to oxygen. But the other halogens can, and they acquire positive oxidation numbers in doing so. Each pair of electrons lost increases the oxidation number by 2. Since the oxidation number of the original halide ion is -1, the oxidation numbers of the halogen atoms in oxyhalogen ions are $+1$, $+3$, $+5$, and $+7$.

Ions of the type XO^- include hypochlorite, ClO^-, hypobromite, BrO^-, and hypoiodite, IO^-. These ions are fairly basic; i.e., hypochlorous, hypobromous, and hypoiodous acids are weak acids, weaker than carbonic acid (carbonated water). Like most weak oxyacids they are also unstable. An attempt to concentrate HClO, for example, results in its complete decomposition.

$$2HClO \rightarrow \overline{Cl_2O} + H_2O$$

This reaction is reversible; so Cl_2O may be called hypochlorous anhydride as well as chlorine monoxide. This gas is liberated by atmospheric carbon dioxide from hypochlorite solutions.

$$\overline{CO_2} + H_2O \rightarrow H_2CO_3$$
$$2H_2CO_3 + 2ClO^- \rightarrow 2HCO_3^- + \overline{Cl_2O}$$

It is Cl_2O, not chlorine, that is responsible for the odor of household bleach solutions; and $HClO$, not Cl_2 or ClO^- ion, that irritates the eyes in chlorinated swimming pools; hence the latter should be kept faintly alkaline.

Oxyhalogen ions are weaker bases the higher the electronegativity of the halogen atom, and the more oxygen atoms that are attached to it. Correspondingly, the conjugate acids are stronger. Thus chlorous acid, $HClO_2$, and iodic acid, HIO_3, are on the border line between weak and strong acids; chloric acid, $HClO_3$, bromic acid, $HBrO_3$, and periodic acid, HIO_4, are strong acids; perchloric acid, $HClO_4$, is the strongest of all acids. (A trustworthy rule says that the strength of any acid, H_xAO_y where A is any acid-forming element, increases 10,000-fold for each unit by which y exceeds x.) The stability of these acids increases with their strength, but only iodic, perchloric, and periodic acids can be obtained commercially.

All the oxyhalogen ions are excellent oxidizing agents, since they have covalent bonds between elements high in electronegativity. In general, they are better oxidizing agents than the corresponding free halogens. It is impossible to make simple statements about their relative oxidizing strength because the factors that govern this are not yet well enough understood. For the same reason no explanation can be given for the non-existence of BrO_2^-, IO_2^-, and BrO_4^- ions and their conjugate acids.

Salts of these ions are mostly moderately to highly soluble. The solubility of the chlorates, perchlorates, and periodates decreases with increasing cation size, dropping to around 1 per cent for the largest cations. Bromates are markedly less soluble than chlorates; many iodates, particularly those of the heavy metals, are insoluble.

Special features of some of the more important oxyhalogen compounds are described in the following sections.

10.14. Hypochlorite Ion

The most important of the oxyhalogen ions is hypochlorite ion, ClO^-. It is made by the reaction between Cl_2 and OH^- ion (page 222). Since these two are produced by electrolyzing a salt solution, it is only necessary to omit the diaphragm in the electrolysis and allow the cathode and anode products to mix, in order to obtain a solution of $NaClO$. Household bleach is a 5.25 per cent solution of this salt. $NaClO$ solution is also used in the refining of gasoline to remove, by oxidation, sulfur compounds which cause engine corrosion.

When an attempt is made to prepare solid $NaClO$, the extremely concentrated solution decomposes because of the loss of Cl_2O from the $HClO$ formed by hydrolysis.

$$2Na^+ + 2ClO^- + H_2O \rightarrow 2Na^+ + 2OH^- + \overline{Cl_2O}$$

The only pure hypochlorite that is available as a solid is calcium hypochlorite, known commercially as H.T.H., or high-test hypochlorite. It is made by passing chlorine into milk of lime (a suspension of calcium hydroxide in its saturated solution).

$$Ca^{++} + 2OH^- + \overline{Cl_2} \rightarrow Ca^{++} + ClO^- + Cl^- + H_2O$$

From this solution calcium hypochlorite crystallizes out as the tetrahydrate, $Ca(ClO)_2 \cdot 4H_2O$. It is quite stable and fairly soluble. The designation "high test" was given to it by way of contrast to the older and less satisfactory but still much used substance known as bleaching powder or, erroneously, chloride of lime.

Bleaching powder is prepared by allowing chlorine to be absorbed by slaked lime, $Ca(OH)_2$, which is nearly dry. The reaction of the chlorine is the production of Cl^- and ClO^- ions, as before, but it stops when only two-thirds of the hydroxide ions have been used up. The product was formerly thought to be a mixture of calcium chloride hypochlorite,

$Ca^{++} \Big\langle {\overset{\displaystyle Cl^-}{\underset{\displaystyle ClO^-}{}}}$, and unchanged calcium hydroxide. The latter being disre-

garded as an inert impurity, the formula was given as $Ca^{++} \Big\langle {\overset{\displaystyle Cl^-}{\underset{\displaystyle ClO^-}{}}}$,

$CaCl_2O$, $CaOCl_2$, or $CaCl (ClO)$. All these formulas were intended to indicate that the substance was one whose cations were all Ca^{++} and whose anions were alternately Cl^- and ClO . In 1935 x-ray photographs showed that little unchanged $Ca(OH)_2$ remained and that the

new crystals were of two kinds, $Ca(ClO)_2 \cdot 4H_2O$ and $\Big[Ca^{++} \Big\langle {\overset{\displaystyle Cl^-}{\underset{\displaystyle OH^-}{}}} \Big] \cdot H_2O$.

Salts in which OH^- or O^{--} is one of two anions present are called **basic salts.** They are all relatively insoluble. Bleaching powder is much less stable than H.T.H. because of the presence of Cl^- ion. As soon as the hygroscopic bleaching powder picks up a little moisture and CO_2 (i.e., carbonic acid) from the air, Cl^- and ClO^- ions react, forming chlorine. The reaction is the reverse of that in the hydrolysis of chlorine.

As the names bleach and bleaching powder indicate, the most important use of ClO^- ion is in the oxidative destruction of colored impurities. The most important example is the bleaching of wood pulp for paper. Pulp mills buy chlorine in quantity (in 55-ton tank cars) and make their own hypochlorite in the solution in which the pulp is suspended. Chlorine is passed in first. After it has acted on the more reactive impurities, NaOH is added, and the remaining chlorine becomes ClO^-. This is a stronger oxidizing agent and bleaches the more resistant colored impurities. Unfortunately it is also strong enough to act to some extent on the cellulose in the wood pulp itself. In order to keep the ClO^- concentration low and minimize the action on the cellulose, the amount of chlorine added first is not enough to complete the bleaching. Hence small further additions of NaClO solution, made by passing Cl_2 into NaOH solution, complete the bleaching process. In modern plants greater "brightness" of the pulp, with less weakening of the cellulose fibers, is obtained by substituting a less violent reagent for ClO^- ion in the final bleaching step. H_2O_2 and some Na_2O_2 are used for this purpose in ground-wood pulp, from which newsprint and the paper for "pulp magazines" are made, and until recently seemed likely to take over the high-grade pulp field as well. But the peroxides are now being displaced by the newest compound to be developed in chlorine chemistry, chlorine dioxide (see Section 10.16). A similar contest between bleaching agents is taking place in the cotton textile field. ClO^- ion is entirely too violent for use on silk, wool, and some of the synthetics.

10.15. Chlorate Ion

If the electrolysis of NaCl solution is carried out at 90° C., ClO^- ion dismutes into Cl^- and ClO_3^- ions as fast as it is formed. The term **dismutation** is applied to a reaction in which atoms of a given kind are both oxidized and reduced. It is sometimes easier to balance an equation of this sort merely by balancing the valence changes than by using the ion-electron method. Write the formula of the substance twice, as if the oxidizing and reducing agents were separate substances. Write the pertinent oxidation numbers, indicate the electron changes, and use each change as the coefficient for the *other* formula.

$$\underset{+1}{2ClO^-} + \underset{+1}{4ClO^-} \rightarrow \underset{-1}{4Cl^-} + \underset{+5}{2ClO_3^-}$$

gains $2e^-$

loses $4e^-$

The simplified equation is:

$$3ClO^- \rightarrow 2Cl^- + ClO_3^-$$

A reaction of this type is also called **disproportionation**. This term also includes reactions which do not involve oxidation and reduction, such as:

$$3BCl_2(OCH_3) \rightarrow B(OCH_3)_3 + 2BCl_3$$

ClO_3^- ion is a powerful oxidizing agent, particularly in acid solution, where it readily oxidizes Cl^- ion to Cl_2. The reduction product depends on the strength of the reducing agent. With a good reducing agent, the reduction half-reaction is:

$$ClO_3^- + 6e^- + 6H^+ \rightarrow Cl^- + 3H_2O$$

The large number of H^+ ions in this equation explains why the oxidizing power of ClO_3^- ion increases so rapidly with acidity. A 40 per cent solution of $HClO_3$ ignites paper. $HClO_3$ cannot be concentrated beyond 40 per cent because of dismutation.

$$7HClO_3 \rightarrow 5HClO_4 + \overline{Cl_2} + H_2O$$

Solid chlorates readily oxidize combustible materials even in the absence of acid. $KClO_3$ is used in match heads, and both it and $Ba(ClO_3)_2$ in pyrotechnics. Mixtures of a chlorate and a combustible material such as sulfur are violent explosives, dangerously sensitive to shock and even friction.

Chlorates readily decompose on heating, yielding oxygen and a chloride. $NaClO_3$ has largely replaced the older $KClO_3$ in the familiar laboratory preparation of oxygen. It costs three-quarters as much and, because of its lower formula weight, yields $11\frac{1}{4}$ per cent more O_2. $NaClO_3$ is deliquescent, a characteristic which once made it difficult to prepare and still prevents its use in matches and flares. An $NaClO_3$ solution is an effective weed killer but is likely to start fires if it dries on the dead weeds before rain washes it away. The most important use of $NaClO_3$, only recently developed, is in the manufacture of ClO_2.

10.16. Chlorine Dioxide

Several halogen oxides can be prepared by various indirect methods. Of these, only I_2O_5 and ClO_2 are ever seen in the laboratory, and only the latter, chlorine dioxide, is of commercial importance. Chlorine dioxide belongs to the very small class of *odd molecules* (molecules with an odd number of electrons), whose existence violates all the familiar rules of valence. It is a strongly yellow gas which—startlingly perhaps, but not surprisingly, considering the odd electron—explodes violently upon the slightest provocation. However, it is not spontaneously explosive if its partial pressure is kept below 70 mm. At partial pressures up to 25 mm., it is safe against light, moderate heat, and even electric sparks. It is prepared commercially on a large scale by reducing $NaClO_3$ with any of several agents. The following equations all represent processes in actual use:

$$\overline{SO_2} + 2ClO_3^- \rightarrow 2\overline{ClO_2} + SO_4^{--}$$

$$6NaClO_3 + CH_3OH + 3H_2SO_4 \rightarrow 6\overline{ClO_2} + \overline{CO_2} + 3Na_2SO_4 + 5H_2O$$
$$\text{Methanol}$$

$$2NaClO_3 + 4HCl \rightarrow 2NaCl + 2\overline{ClO_2} + \overline{Cl_2} + 2H_2O$$

When ClO_2 is prepared by the third method, water is used to scrub it out of the air stream which carries the mixed gases from the reactors. The chlorine-air mixture which remains supplements the purchased chlorine used in the first stages of bleaching. Since the effluent from the reactors contains a Cl^- ion for every ClO_3^- ion which went in, the effluent is passed through electrolytic cells in which it is reoxidized to ClO_3^- ion. Thus HCl is the only chemical that is used up. ClO_2 is produced at the lowest cost by this process, and its production is still cheaper if by-product HCl is available, as it often is.

In 46 mills that manufacture high-grade pulp for paper, ClO_2 has displaced the final hypochlorite or peroxide bleach, and its use is rapidly increasing. The particular advantage of ClO_2 is that it enables a high degree of brightness to be attained without weakening the cellulose fibers. This is true of wood, hemp, straw, nylon, and rayon. ClO_2 is now used also to bleach shellac, beeswax, fats, and oils.

Another process in which ClO_2 teams up advantageously with chlorine is the sterilization of water. After the easy part has been done by cheap chlorine, 0.5 p.p.m. of ClO_2 is added; this promptly destroys certain organic compounds which are oxidized only slowly by chlorine. Another class of organic compounds is not oxidized at all by chlorine, but on the contrary becomes an actual annoyance. These compounds, called **phenols,** are related to carbolic acid. They are present in many algae, and in some industrial wastes which sometimes contaminate municipal water supplies. Chlorination converts them to chlorophenols, which have a strong, somewhat tarry taste; indignant but chemically ignorant citizens mistakenly believe this taste to be due to excess chlorine. ClO_2 destroys chlorophenols immediately. Complete oxidation of all organic matter in a city water supply is the only way to make certain that it is sterile.

The discovery of the highly selective bleaching power of ClO_2 and of safe ways of preparing and handling it came at a particularly opportune time for millers. The Department of Agriculture had just announced that it had extracted a substance from flour bleached with nitrogen trichloride, NCl_3, a substance which, in sufficient amounts, was toxic to dogs. Flour bleached with NCl_3 had been in universal use for many years with no ill effects, but to avoid controversy the millers immediately switched to ClO_2. The relatively small amounts required are prepared conveniently and with complete safety by passing moist air that contains a little chlorine over solid $NaClO_2$.

$$\overline{Cl_2} + 2NaClO_2 \rightarrow 2NaCl + \overline{2ClO_2}$$

As recently as fifteen years ago, $NaClO_2$ was a chemical curiosity because it can be prepared only from the dangerous ClO_2. ClO_2 is not the anhydride of any acid, dissolving unaltered in water; it dismutes in the presence of a base.

$$2OH^- + 2ClO_2 \rightarrow ClO_2^- + ClO_3^- + H_2O$$

A pure chlorite is prepared by reducing ClO_2 with a peroxide.

$$Na_2O_2 + \overline{2ClO_2} \rightarrow 2NaClO_2 + \overline{O_2}$$

$NaClO_2$ is rapidly winning favor as a textile bleach, both commercial and household. It can be stored without decomposing, and like ClO_2 it bleaches without weakening the cellulose fibers themselves. It can be used in moderately acid solution, which is sometimes a practical convenience.

10.17. Perchlorate Ion and Perchloric Acid

In the absence of a catalyst (MnO_2, Fe_2O_3), $NaClO_3$ and $KClO_3$ can, with caution, be melted without decomposing. If held just above the melting point for some time, the melt dismutes and solidifies.

$$4NaClO_3 \xrightarrow{\Delta} NaCl + 3NaClO_4$$

ClO_4^- ion is prepared commercially by the electrolytic oxidation of a solution containing ClO_3^- ion.

Anhydrous perchloric acid can be prepared by vacuum distillation of an acidified perchlorate solution, and is stable up to 90° C. It detonates violently on contact with organic matter. A 70 per cent solution is used when a more powerful oxidizing agent is required, and is safe if proper precautions are taken. In Los Angeles in 1947, a little plant that employed no regular chemist was using an electro-polishing bath consisting of 150 gal. of $HClO_4$ and a quantity of acetic anhydride, an oxidizable organic substance. Through ignorance, the bath was allowed to evaporate, becoming concentrated up to the danger point. The resulting explosion damaged 116 buildings, hurled steel girders a distance as much as half a mile, and killed 17 persons. A 1 M $HClO_4$ solution is not as strong an oxidizing agent as 1 M solutions of $HClO_3$, $HClO_2$, or $HClO$ are, but the possibility of using more concentrated solutions and working at much higher temperatures more than makes up for this.

As was said earlier, perchloric acid is the strongest acid that has been measured so far. One proof of this is the fact that its monohydrate, $HClO_4 \cdot H_2O$, is stable at and above room temperature. This "hydrate" is actually the salt, hydronium perchlorate, H_3OClO_4. It is isomorphous with ammonium perchlorate, NH_4ClO_4. Other strong acids form hydronium salts which can be crystallized from solution at low temperatures, but they decompose on being heated even a few degrees. In this decomposition, the anion, acting as a base, takes a proton from the H_3O^+ ion. Evidently ClO_4^- ion is the weakest anion base, which means that $HClO_4$ is the strongest acid.

The perchlorates are the most stable of the oxyhalogen salts, but react vigorously at elevated temperatures. They are used in the manufacture of detonators and explosives, in signal flares, and as an oxidizing agent in solid-fuel rockets. Anhydrous $Mg(ClO_4)_2$ and $Ba(ClO_4)_2$ are excellent desiccants, or drying agents. Inasmuch as ClO_4^- ion has no measurable tendency to form complex ions, even with metal ions of high charge, it is commonly used where absence of complex ions is desired.

10.18. Periodic Acids and Periodates

In Sections 9.33 and 9.34 we explained the ability of iodine to accept a fifth or sixth electron pair, and illustrated it with the polyhalide ions. Further illustration is offered in a series of periodate ions that have four, five, and six oxygens around the iodine atom, and various acids conjugate to them. In the $IO_4{}^-$ ion, called metaperiodate, the oxygens are in the same tetrahedral arrangement as that in $ClO_4{}^-$. In $IO_5{}^{-3}$, mesoperiodate, the iodine atom is in the center of a triangular bipyramid of oxygens. In dimesoperiodate, $I_2O_9{}^{-4}$, one oxygen atom serves as a common vertex for two mesoperiodate groups. The oxygens in $IO_6{}^{-5}$ are arranged in an octahedron (square bipyramid), with the iodine atom in the center. The uncharged acids conjugate to these ions are more or less interconvertible by gain or loss of water, as are also the acid anions. As a result, some of the conceivable ones are unknown. Those actually obtainable are HIO_4, $H_4I_2O_9$, $H_2IO_6{}^{-3}$, $H_3IO_6{}^{--}$, and H_5IO_6. They are powerful oxidizing agents and are useful in many analytical procedures; for example, Mn^{++} ion can be identified by its periodate oxidation to the brilliant purple permanganate ion, $MnO_4{}^-$. The first step in the ionization of these acids is virtually complete in each case; thus HIO_4, $H_4I_2O_9$, and H_5IO_6 are all very strong acids. The negative ions, $H_3IO_6{}^{-2}$ and $H_2IO_6{}^{-3}$, still acids because of the presence of replaceable hydrogens, are successively weaker acids as a result of the increasing negative charges on the molecules which hinder the release of additional protons from the molecules. $H_3IO_6{}^{--}$ ion is as weak an acid as water is. Acids which have more than one replaceable hydrogen are called **polybasic** or **polyprotic acids.** Successive acids resulting from polyprotic acids are *always* weaker than those in the series whose formulas have more hydrogens. Thus $HSO_4{}^-$ is weaker than H_2SO_4, as is $HCO_3{}^-$ compared to H_2CO_3.

QUESTIONS AND PROBLEMS

1. What is the characteristic electronic structure of the halide ions? What is the oxidation number of these ions?

2. Correlate with increasing atomic number the general trend of halide ions as regards size, reducing ability, polarizability, ability to form complex ions.

3. In what properties is fluorine (fluoride ion) unique in comparison to other nonmetals or their -ide ions?

4. What is a complex ion? A ligand? Give some formula examples. What factors aid in the formation of complex ions?

5. How do you account for the fact that SiF_4 and $SiF_6{}^{--}$ both exist, whereas only $SiCl_4$ exists?

6. What is the role of lattice energy relative to the solubility of salts? How and why do fluorides differ from the other halide salts?

7. From the limited tests given, determine whether Cl^-, Br^-, and/or I^- are present, absent, or uncertain in the following unknowns. Write all equations involved and defend your conclusions.

a. Unknown No. 1 when acidified with HNO_3 gave a whitish precipitate when $AgNO_3$ was added. This precipitate completely dissolved in dilute NH_4OH.

b. One portion of Unknown No. 2 gave a yellow-brown color in the CCl_4 layer on the addition of several milliliters of chlorine water.

c. Addition of HNO_3 to another portion of Unknown No. 2, followed by boiling, gave a negative shake-out test and then a negative $AgNO_3$ test.

8. What volume of H_2 (S.T.P.) and weight of Cl_2 can be obtained from the electrolysis of 1 ton of $NaCl$ dissolved in water?

9. a. List the oxyhalogen ions according to the oxidation number of the halogen.

b. How do stability and strength of oxychlorine acids vary with the oxidation number of chlorine?

10. What oxyhalogen ions are used in bleaching? Using dot formulas, show the ions present in H.T.H. and in bleaching powder.

11. Balance the following dismutation reactions (in acid condition) by the ion-electron method and valence change methods. Show both solutions in each case.

a. $ClO^- \rightarrow Cl^- + ClO_3^-$

b. $ClO_3^- \rightarrow ClO_4^- + \overline{Cl}_2 + H_2O$

12. Balance the following redox reactions by the ion-electron method; show all half-reactions.

a. $(Na^+ + ClO_3^-) + (H^+ + Cl^-) \rightarrow \overline{ClO}_2 + \overline{Cl}_2 + Na^+ + Cl^- + H_2O$

b. $\overline{Cl}_2 + ClO_2^- \rightarrow Cl^- + \overline{ClO}_2$

c. $\overline{ClO}_2 + OH^- \rightarrow ClO_2^- + ClO_3^- + H_2O$

d. $ClO_3^- \rightarrow Cl^- + ClO_4^-$

13. List some important uses of oxyhalogen ions or compounds.

11

Sulfur and its relatives

11.1. The Oxygen Family

The family headed by oxygen consists of the elements whose valence shell has 6 electrons. They constitute Group VIA of the periodic table. Each member of this family precedes a halogen. Their characteristic kernel charge of $+6$ gives them electronegativities which are also next to those of the halogens. Note that there is the same striking gap between the electronegativities of the first two elements in the family as there is in the halogen family. The electronegativity of sulfur, the second element in the oxygen family, is down to that of the fourth halogen, iodine. Since traces of metallic properties were observable in iodine, they should be—and are—very appreciable in tellurium.

Like the halogens, elements in the oxygen family show non-metallic behavior, gaining electrons to complete the octet. There are, however, systematic differences, and the reasons for them should be carefully noted. First, each element is a weaker oxidizing agent than the corresponding halogen, because of its lower electronegativity. (This statement is equivalent to saying that their anions are better reducing

TABLE 11.1. Properties of Elements in Group VIA

	Oxygen	Sulfur	Selenium	Tellurium	Polonium
Atomic weight	16.000	32.066	78.96	127.61	210.0
Molecular formulas					
Colored crystals	O_4	S_8	Se_8	?	None
Chain molecules	O_3	S_n	Se_n	Te_n	?
Metallic form	None	None	Se	Te	Po
Gas	O_2	$S_8 - S_2$	$Se_8 - Se_2$	Te_2	?
Melting point, °C.	−218	119	220	452	
Boiling point, °C.	−183	445	688	1390	
Density, g./ml.	1.14 (s)	2.07	4.80	6.24	
Electronegativity	3.5	2.5	2.4	2.1	2.0
Percentage of earth's crust	50	0.05	10^{-5}	10^{-5}	10^{-12}

agents than the halide ions.) Second, the characteristic charge on ions of this family is -2 instead of -1. This results in striking differences in the structure of their compounds, both ionic and covalent, and in their having even instead of odd oxidation numbers. Third, as the result of a combination of higher negative charge and lower electronegativity, these ions share electron pairs more willingly than do ions of the halogens. That is, they are far stronger bases and they form two covalent bonds much more readily than the halogen-containing ions form one. Finally, they assume positive oxidation states more readily than the corresponding halogens do, and in such states they are weaker oxidizing agents. Compounds in which sulfur has oxidation numbers below its maximum of $+6$ are actually good reducing agents at room temperature.

Because of its fundamental importance, oxygen was the first element to be discussed (Chapter 6). Sulfur is comparable to chlorine in importance and will be discussed in detail in the following pages. The other elements in this family are far less important and will be mentioned only briefly.

11.2. Early History of Sulfur

Records of sulfur go back to the beginning of history. Sulfur is the Bible's famous brimstone (brinn-ston meant "burn-stone"). Linen was bleached by the fumes of burning sulfur 2000 years ago, and Homer referred to these fumes as a disinfectant. Egyptian paintings of 1600 B.C. contain colors made from sulfur. The Romans used it for incendiary materials of war and in casting bronze statues; Pliny mentioned several different kinds of it (probably based on differences in purity).

Because it burned without residue, the alchemists considered sulfur to be the principle of combustibility and thought that everything that could burn must contain at least some sulfur. It was proved to be an element by Gay-Lussac and Thenard almost as soon as the modern idea of elements was conceived.

11.3. Occurrence of Sulfur

Although sulfur is not an extremely abundant element, small amounts of sulfate ion, SO_4^{--}, are found everywhere, with the result that sulfur compounds are essential to life. More important to industry is the fact that numerous deposits of sulfur, sulfides, and sulfates exist as minerals. From a geologic point of view, most metal sulfides are primary minerals, because sulfate minerals and sulfur were formed from them after they were exposed by erosion.

Most sulfide minerals are more valuable for the other elements they contain than for the sulfur. In many cases the sulfides are the most important ores of the various metals. This is true, for example, of zinc sulfide, ZnS, lead sulfide, PbS, and the sulfides of copper, Cu_2S and CuS. One sulfide, FeS_2, commonly known as pyrites, or fool's gold, is considered an ore of sulfur rather than of iron because of the small amount of iron and the high percentage of sulfur present. Important quantities of hydrogen sulfide, H_2S, are found in natural gas. Sulfide minerals are converted to sulfates by weathering. Lead sulfate is insoluble; other metal ions are soon precipitated as carbonates, for ground water also contains carbon dioxide, CO_2. A typical equation is

$$Zn^{++} + SO_4^{--} + \overline{CO_2} + H_2O \rightarrow \underline{ZnCO_3} + 2H^+ + SO_4^{--}$$

The dilute sulfuric acid which drains continuously from coal mines, where pyrites is a common impurity, presents a serious stream pollution problem in Pennsylvania. Most of the SO_4^{--} ions are eventually precipitated as gypsum, $CaSO_4 \cdot 2H_2O$; its solubility is only about 0.25 g. per liter of water. Enormous beds of gypsum are common. Other sulfate minerals present in smaller quantities include anhydrite, $CaSO_4$, celestite, $SrSO_4$, barite, $BaSO_4$, and anglesite, $PbSO_4$.

The action of superheated water on sulfides may produce H_2S. Sulfur springs are so called because H_2S is present in the water. The H_2S is oxidized when it comes in contact with air, and elemental sulfur encrusts the fumaroles from which the springs escape. H_2S may be present in volcanic gases, as may also SO_2. If these two meet, the one is oxidized, the other reduced, to elemental sulfur.

$$\overline{2H_2S} + \overline{SO_2} \rightarrow \underline{3S} + 2H_2O$$

Places where this happens are known as solfataras and are worked for sulfur in Japan and Chile.

Much more important deposits of free sulfur are found in connection with some but not all of the curious salt domes of the Gulf coast region, both in the United States and in Mexico. These salt domes are the main source of the world's sulfur supply.

11.4. Sulfur Mining

Ordinary mining is impossible in the case of the sulfur deposits in this country, because so much of the deep overburden is unconsolidated (quicksand, swamp, or even ocean). The problem was solved in 1890 by the **Frasch process.** Vast quantities of superheated water are forced into a drilled well and melt the sulfur which runs into the bottom of the well. Air forced through the center pipe (Fig. 11.1) lifts sulfur with it as the air bubbles rise between the two inner pipes. The sulfur is run into storage bins 100 yd. square, where it solidifies. These bins have wooden sides that are raised as needed and are finally removed after a height of some 50 ft. has been reached. Sulfur is blasted down from these gigantic blocks as needed for shipment. More recently, much liquid sulfur has been shipped in tank cars and trucks, barges and ocean-going tankers, without ever having been alowed to solidify. Probably one-third of American sulfur was so shipped during 1961. Purchasers store it in heated, insulated tanks until it is used. In carload lots it sells for about $1\frac{1}{4}$ cents per pound. In 1960 we produced over 7 million tons of sulfur, 74 per cent of it by the Frasch process. This

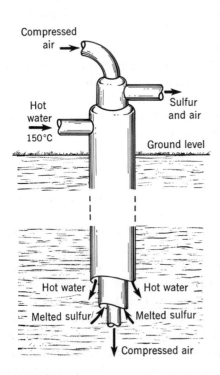

Fig. 11.1. Frasch process for mining sulfur.

was more than double the peak production during World War II.

The rapid expansion of industry at the end of that war caused a severe shortage of sulfur. Only twelve of the salt domes known in 1951 were capable of yielding sulfur in commercial quantities, and five of these had already been exhausted. Intensive (and expensive) exploration since has more than doubled the number of sulfur-producing salt domes in Texas and Louisiana. Others have been found in Mexico and by early 1957 were producing sulfur at the rate of 1 million tons a year. Some of the new sulfur wells have been drilled and are being worked from platforms in the Gulf of Mexico. One such installation, completed in 1960 at a a cost of $30 million, produces from 1000 to 2000 tons of sulfur per day.

11.5. Sulfur Recovery from Compounds

Sulfur can be recovered as such from the SO_2 in smelter gases, but this is more commonly used directly as SO_2. Natural gas containing H_2S is known as "sour" (since H_2S is a weak acid) and must be purified, because H_2S corrodes metals badly, and burns to SO_2, which is equally objectionable. The H_2S is removed by absorbing it in an alkaline liquid. When the product is heated, H_2S is given off and the absorbent is regenerated. The H_2S is then mixed with a limited amount of air and passed over a hot catalyst, partial combustion producing elemental sulfur.

$$\overline{2H_2S} + \overline{O_2} \rightarrow \overline{2H_2O} + \underline{2S}$$

Sulfur compounds are also present in petroleum, and are converted in the refinery into H_2S which is removed in the same way. It was estimated that in 1960 recovered sulfur amounted to 25 per cent of the amount produced by the Frasch process, but the recovery of sulfur from compounds is increasing so rapidly that statistics are outdated as soon as released. A newly discovered field of very sour gas in France (some of it 15 per cent H_2S) is yielding sulfur at an annual rate of over 1,000,000 tons. This field and another in western Canada (in it the gas is 34 per cent sulfur) rate as the major new sources of the world's sulfur supply.

11.6. Forms of Sulfur

Since fluorine and chlorine are so similar physically, it is surprising to find that sulfur is so different from oxygen. The fact that sulfur is a

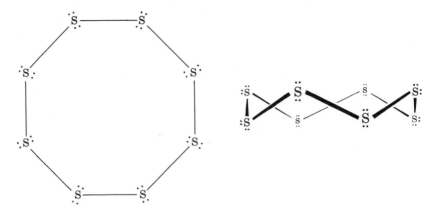

Fig. 11.2. Two views of the puckered eight-membered ring molecule of sulfur.

practically odorless solid at room temperature, instead of a gas, immediately suggests that its molecules must contain more than two atoms, for the difference in atomic weight is not enough to explain the difference in boiling points (Table 11.1). This proves to be the case; the molecules in sulfur crystals consist of eight-membered rings. Atoms with 6 valence electrons can form stable diatomic molecules only by multiple bonding. This is possible between small atoms like carbon, nitrogen, and oxygen, but not between atoms of elements beyond the second period. When two sulfur atoms combine, one of them still has an incomplete octet, $:\ddot{S}:\ddot{S}:$ if more atoms are added, the last one always remains incomplete,

$$:\ddot{S}:\ddot{S}: \quad , :\ddot{S}:\ddot{S}: \quad :\ddot{S} \quad , \text{etc.,}$$
$$:\ddot{S}:\underset{..}{S} \quad :\ddot{S}:\ddot{S}:\ddot{S}:$$

until the chain is long enough to bend around and form a bond with the first atom in it. The valence bonds of sulfur make an angle of 105° with each other; therefore the chain has to be eight atoms long. Alternate atoms lie in two different planes. This is shown in Fig. 11.2, the unshared electron pairs being represented by dots as usual, and the bonding pairs by lines. Rings of this sort are called puckered rings.

Sulfur is insoluble in water, but dissolves readily in various organic liquids, notably carbon disulfide, CS_2, and carbon tetrachloride, CCl_4. On slow evaporation, transparent yellow crystals are formed (Fig. 11.3*A*). They belong to the rhombic system; i.e., they have three axes of symmetry of unequal length, and all are at right angles to each other. If heated rapidly, rhombic sulfur melts at 113° C. to a mobile, pale yellow liquid; but if held for some time at just above 96° C., the crystals become opaque because cracks form all through them. The particles are microcrystals of monoclinic sulfur, which has a different crystalline form and melts only when heated to 119° C. Good-sized crystals of this type can be obtained by partly freezing melted sulfur, breaking the crust, and pouring off the remaining liquid. The transparent, pale yellow needles or laths (Fig. 11.3*B*) are slightly elastic and belong to the monoclinic system (two axes at an oblique angle, the third perpendicular to their plane, all axes unequal). These crystals are stable above 96° C., but at a lower temperature they become opaque because of cracks and when touched crumble into a powder of rhombic microcrystals.

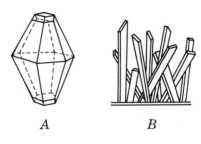

A   *B*

Fig. 11.3. Crystals of rhombic (**A**) and monoclinic (**B**) sulfur.

Both rhombic and monoclinic sulfur crystals contain S_8 molecules, merely arranged differently in the two forms. Both crystals, when melted, produce the same liquid, which is also composed of S_8 molecules. As the temperature of the liquid is raised, more and more frequently its ring molecules are broken into chains by their thermal collisions. When this happpens, the incomplete end of a chain is more likely to attach itself to a complete octet at the end of another chain than to the other end of its own chain. The color darkens and the liquid becomes more viscous. At 230° C. it is a dark reddish-brown (black except in thin layers) and cannot be poured from an inverted test tube. The chain may be several thousand atoms long. As the temperature increases, the long chains break faster than they are formed; and at 445° C., the boiling point of sulfur, the nearly black liquid pours readily.

If sulfur is cooled slowly from the boiling point, the changes just described take place in reverse order. But if boiling sulfur is poured into cold water, it solidifies into transparent yellow *elastic* threads. The molecules still form long kinky chains, and at room temperature they break up and form eight-membered rings only very slowly. In a day or so, the transformation into a brittle, opaque mass of microscopic rhombic crystals is complete. The plastic threads are rubbery for exactly the same reason that rubber is—the kinkiness of the long-chain molecules. Not surprisingly, these giant molecules are insoluble in ordinary sulfur solvents.

The gas which evaporates from boiling sulfur consists of small fragments that are broken off from the long chains; their average molecular weight is 250. If this gas is suddenly condensed on a cold surface a fine powder known as flowers of sulfur forms. About 70 per cent of it is composed of S_8 molecules in rhombic crystals, but the rest is amorphous (non-crystalline) and insoluble in CS_2 because it consists of long-chain molecules. The sudden cooling leaves no time for all the small-chain molecules to sort themselves out into neat eight-membered rings; they have to combine any way they can. At higher temperatures the average size of sulfur molecules decreases; at 1000° C. the average formula is S_2; at 2000 °C., 45 per cent of the sulfur is monatomic.

The various forms of sulfur described above—and others less easily obtained—are called **allotropic modifications** of the element.

11.7. Chemical Properties of Sulfur

Since its electronegativity is the same as that of iodine, sulfur is an oxidizing agent of only moderate strength. The solid is almost completely inactive at ordinary temperatures. Gaseous sulfur, however, oxidizes most metals and the non-metals that are of moderate electronegativity, such as hydrogen and carbon. Copper foil burns spontaneously in sulfur vapor at the boiling point of sulfur.

$$2\underline{Cu} + \overline{S} \rightarrow \underline{Cu_2S}$$

A temperature of 600° C. and a catalyst are necessary for rapid reaction with hydrogen.

$$\overline{H_2} + \overline{S} \rightleftharpoons \overline{H_2S}$$

The reverse reaction is slight at 600° C., but increases rapidly with temperature. The reaction with carbon takes place at white heat.

$$\underline{C} + \overline{2S} \rightarrow \overline{CS_2}$$

The empirical formula is used for gaseous sulfur because the gas contains several molecular species. Note that the above equations resemble the corresponding ones for oxygen. The resulting products, sulfides, have formulas like those of the oxides of the same elements. This is because sulfur, like oxygen, has 6 valence electrons.

Because of its lower electronegativity, sulfur shares electron pairs with the more extreme non-metals (oxygen, nitrogen, and the halogens) much more readily than oxygen does, and also much more readily than iodine, which has the same electronegativity as sulfur. In general, the more electrons an atom gains in completing its octet, the more readily it forms covalent bonds. Accordingly, sulfur ignites spontaneously in fluorine, burns with a brilliant blue flame in oxygen, and unites readily with chlorine. The equations follow.

$$\overline{S} + \overline{3F_2} \rightarrow \overline{SF_6} + \Delta$$

$$\overline{S} + \overline{O_2} \rightarrow \overline{SO_2} + \Delta$$

$$\overline{2S} + \overline{Cl_2} \rightarrow \overline{S_2Cl_2} + \Delta$$

In these reactions sulfur acts as a reducing agent, because in each case it partially loses electrons to the element higher in electronegativity. All these reactions are of industrial importance, particularly the second one. The reason for this will be discussed presently.

When sulfur *gains* electrons from an active metal it acquires an electrovalence (oxidation number) of -2. When it *shares* an electron pair with an element moderate in electronegativity (an inactive metal or non-metal), it acquires an oxidation number (but not an electrovalence) of -2. Each covalent bond formed with an active non-metal raises the oxidation number two units; hence sulfur is characterized by *even* oxidation numbers from -2 to $+6$. Since oxygen practically always has a negative oxidation number, sulfur can resemble oxygen only when it too has a negative oxidation number. (This situation is the same as that in the halogen family; fluorine has only a valence of -1, and the other halogens resemble it only when they also are in the -1 state.) Sulfur in the -2 state is enough like oxygen in the -2 state so that they are more or less interchangeable. The partial or complete substitution of sulfur for oxygen in this state may be designated by attaching the prefix *thio-* (from the Greek word for sulfur) to the name of the compound, thus: SO_4^{--}, sulfate, and $S_2O_3^{--}$, thiosulfate; CO_3^{--}, carbonate, and CS_3^{--}, thiocarbonate.

11.8. Uses of Sulfur

The first step in the preparation of practically all oxycompounds of sulfur, e.g., H_2SO_4, is to burn the sulfur to sulfur dioxide; more sulfur is used for this purpose than for all others put together. Other uses of the element, although small compared with this, are nevertheless of great practical importance. As we saw in the preceding section, carbon disulfide and several sulfur halides are made by direct combination of the elements. Sulfur is used in large quantities in vulcanizing rubber. Alone or mixed with lime it is an important agricultural fungicide. Sulfur is still used in making black gunpowder; larger quantities go into related products used in fireworks and blasting. Its low melting point, resistance to acid, and electrical insulating properties combine to make sulfur a useful cement for some purposes. Altogether, approximately 6 million tons of sulfur are used annually in the United States.

11.9. Hydrogen Sulfide

H_2S, the sulfur analogue of water, differs strikingly from water in its physical properties because its molecules are relatively non-polar. Consequently there is no hydrogen bonding; and H_2S has the melting and boiling points ($-86°$ C. and $-61°$ C.) normal for a molecular weight of 34. The gas has a characteristic strong odor, faintly perceptible in hard-boiled eggs, but tends to paralyze the sense of smell. For this reason the warning odor should be heeded immediately, because continued exposure to as little as 1 part in 1000 parts of air is fatal.

The preparation of H_2S from the elements has been mentioned. It is commonly prepared by the action of dilute HCl on ferrous sulfide, FeS.

$$FeS + 2H^+ + 2Cl^- \rightarrow \overline{H_2S} + Fe^{++} + 2Cl^-$$

This is a neutralization reaction; S^{--} ion is a strong base. (The cheaper pyrites, FeS_2, cannot be substituted for FeS because it contains persulfide ion, S_2^{--}, instead of S^{--}, and is too insoluble to react with dilute acids.) H_2S is conveniently produced in the laboratory by heating a mixture of paraffin (empirical formula CH_2) and sulfur.

$$CH_2 + \underline{S} \xrightarrow{\Delta} \underline{C} + \overline{H_2S}$$

Asbestos is used in the mixture so that there will be sufficient porosity to permit the gas to escape easily from the charge. The reaction stops when the source of heat is removed. H_2S is generated even more conveniently in the solution in which it is to be used, by the hydrolysis of thioacetamide.

$$CH_3CSNH_2 + 2H_2O \rightarrow CH_3CO_2^- + NH_4^+ + \overline{H_2S}$$

This reaction does not occur with appreciable speed at room temperature, but is quite rapid at $80°$ C. or above. Both of these excellent laboratory methods are too expensive for commercial use.

1.10. Chemical Properties of H_2S

Like all low-valence sulfur compounds, H_2S is a strong reducing agent. If exposed to the air, a solution of it becomes milky because of sulfur particles.

$$2H_2S + \overline{O_2} \rightarrow 2H_2O + \underline{2S}$$

The gas burns with a blue flame which is hot enough to dissociate the H_2S in the interior of the flame into hydrogen and sulfur.

$$\overline{2H_2S} + \overline{3O_2} \rightarrow \overline{2H_2O} + \overline{2SO_2} + \Delta$$

If a cold surface is put into the inner cone of the flame, sulfur will be deposited upon it. The equation is the same as that given above for the oxidation of H_2S at room temperature.

Many other oxidizing agents oxidize H_2S to sulfur. Examples include:

$$\overline{2H_2S} + \overline{SO_2} \rightarrow \underline{3S} + 2H_2O$$

$$H_2S + I_2 \rightarrow 2H^+ + 2I^- + \underline{S}$$

$$H_2S + 2Fe^{+3} \rightarrow 2Fe^{++} + 2H^+ + \underline{S}$$

Stronger oxidizing agents, such as peroxides and nitric acid, may further oxidize the resulting sulfur to SO_2 or SO_4^{--}.

$$3H_2S + 8(H^+ + NO_3^-) \rightarrow \overline{8NO} + 3(H^+ + HSO_4^-) + 4H_2O$$

Although a stronger acid than water, H_2S is still a very weak acid. The reaction with water (ionization):

$$H_2S + H_2O \rightleftharpoons H_3O^+ + HS^-$$

reaches equilibrium when only about 0.1 per cent of the H_2S has *dissociated* and therefore has only a moderate effect on the solubility of the gas. The saturated solution is about 0.1 M and is comparable in strength to the more familiar weak acids, boric, H_3BO_3, and carbonic, H_2CO_3. The slight sour taste of the latter, due to the H^+ ions in it, is evident in plain club soda; the slight sweet taste of HS^- ion is also perceptible in H_2S solution. One who has been exposed to H_2S in the air may have this same sweet taste in his mouth if he smokes a cigarette, even after half an hour.

11.11. Polybasic Acids

An acid which is able to lose more than one proton is called polyprotic (see section 10.18). It is also often called **polybasic.** This adjective was originally applied because a mole of a polyprotic acid can neutralize two or more moles of a *mono-acid base* like OH$^-$ ion. It can also be thought of as referring to the fact that such an acid has several conjugate bases. Thus H$_2$S, a diprotic acid, can lose one proton to form HS$^-$ ion (conjugate base 1), which in turn can lose the remaining proton to form S^{--} ion (conjugate base 2).

You are already familiar with the important diprotic acid, hydronium ion, H$_3$O$^+$. It is a strong acid only as far as the first proton loss is concerned. Its conjugate base 1 is H$_2$O, a very weak acid. In fact, H$_3$O$^+$ ion is frequently considered a monoprotic acid because water is such a weak acid. H$_2$S is regularly called a diprotic acid because HS$^-$, unlike OH$^-$, has appreciable acid strength. The contrast in strength between H$_3$O$^+$ and H$_2$O is typical. The second dissociation of any polyprotic acid is always much weaker than the first. In writing the equilibria involved in the dissociation of H$_2$S we emphasize this fact by using different sizes of letters. The large letters in the formula indicate 0.1 M

$$\textbf{H}_2\textbf{S} \rightleftharpoons \text{H}^+ + \text{HS}^-$$

$$\text{HS}^- \rightleftharpoons \text{H}^+ + \text{S}^-$$

concentration, the intermediate size 10^{-5} M, and the smallest size 10^{-15} M. Thus only one ten-billionth of the H$^+$ ion concentration in the solution is due to the second dissociation.

HS$^-$ ion is almost as weak an acid as water, which means that its conjugate base, S^{--} ion, is almost as strong a base as OH$^-$ ion, the conjugate base of H$_2$O. It is natural for very few molecules of a good base like S^{--} ion to remain free in an even slightly acid solution like that of H$_2$S. If S^{--} ions are put into a much weaker acid solution, say plain water, more of them will remain free. A 0.12 M Na$_2$S solution is 50 per cent hydrolyzed, in accordance with the equation:

$$2\text{Na}^+ + \text{S}^{--} + \text{H}_2\text{O} \rightleftharpoons 2\text{Na}^+ + \text{HS}^- + \text{OH}^-$$

In other words, even in this basic solution half the S^{--} ions have succeeded in taking a proton from a water molecule. Thus the concentration of S⁻⁻ ion in a solution can be regulated by the addition of acid or base to the solution. In general, the conjugate base of any weak acid is a moderate to strong base; its concentration will be very low in an acidic solution, and high in a basic solution.

1.12. Sulfide Ion

In accordance with the lower electronegativity of sulfur, S^{--} ion is much more polarizable than O^{--} ion. Accordingly, the sulfides of most metal ions are largely bonded covalently into giant sulfide molecules and are correspondingly insoluble. The only soluble sulfides are those of the metals with the lowest electronegativity (Groups IA and IIA, and the lower part of IIIA), which are preponderantly ionic in character. As was true of I^- ion, polarization of the normally colorless S^{--} ion imparts intense color. With the exception of ZnS (white), the insoluble sulfides are yellow, orange, red, brown, or—most commonly—black.

In solubility, the "insoluble" metal sulfides show a wide range of variation. This fact is put to practical use in separating metal ions into groups in **qualitative analysis.** Table 11.2 shows part of one of the most popular schemes of separation, which is based on the insolubility of certain chlorides and the varying solubilities of sulfides.

Analytical Group II, the copper-arsenic group, consists of the cations whose sulfides are so insoluble that they can be precipitated by even the minute concentration of S^{--} ion that is in equilibrium with 0.3 M H^+ ion. A typical equation is:

$$Cd^{++} + H_2S \rightarrow \underline{CdS} + 2H^+$$

The Cd^{++} ion is precipitated almost but not quite completely from the solution. Actually there is a saturated solution of CdS, the solid being in equilibrium with tiny quantities of its ions.

$$\underline{CdS} \rightleftharpoons Cd^{++} + S^-$$

If the concentration of the S^{--} ion is reduced to a negligible value by the addition of enough strong acid, the CdS will dissolve. Boiling the mixture aids this dissolution by removing H_2S.

$$2H^+ + 2HSO_4^- + \underline{CdS} \rightarrow \overline{H_2S} + Cd^{++} + 2HSO_4^-$$

To dissolve the more insoluble sulfides it may be necessary to reduce the concentration of S^{--} ion still further by oxidizing it to sulfur, or

TABLE 11.2. **Separation of Several Common Cations into Analytical Groups**

(All the cations are assumed to be in solution.)

Make 0.3 *M* with HCl

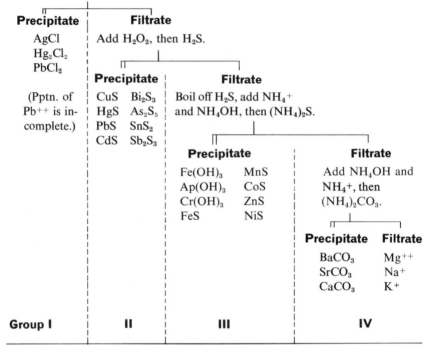

Precipitate	II	III	IV
Precipitate AgCl Hg$_2$Cl$_2$ PbCl$_2$ (Pptn. of Pb^{++} is incomplete.)			

Precipitate
AgCl
Hg$_2$Cl$_2$
PbCl$_2$

(Pptn. of
Pb^{++} is in-
complete.)

Filtrate
Add H$_2$O$_2$, then H$_2$S.

Precipitate
CuS Bi$_2$S$_3$
HgS As$_2$S$_5$
PbS SnS$_2$
CdS Sb$_2$S$_3$

Filtrate
Boil off H$_2$S, add NH$_4$$^+$
and NH$_4$OH, then (NH$_4$)$_2$S.

Precipitate
Fe(OH)$_3$ MnS
Ap(OH)$_3$ CoS
Cr(OH)$_3$ ZnS
FeS   NiS

Filtrate
Add NH$_4$OH and
NH$_4$$^+$, then
(NH$_4$)$_2$CO$_3$.

Precipitate
BaCO$_3$
SrCO$_3$
CaCO$_3$

Filtrate
Mg^{++}
Na$^+$
K$^+$

Group I   **II**   **III**   **IV**

even, in addition, removing the metal ion as fast as it is freed from the sulfide, by sequestering it in a complex ion.

$$8H^+ + 2NO_3^- + 3\underline{CuS} \rightarrow 3Cu^{++} + \overline{2NO} + 3\underline{S} + 4H_2O$$

$$8H^+ + 2NO_3^- + 12Cl^- + 3\underline{HgS} \rightarrow 3HgCl_4^{--} + \overline{2NO} + 3\underline{S} + 4H_2O$$

Before the members of the copper subgroup are separated from each other by means of their differing solubility in acid, the sulfides of the arsenic subgroup are removed by treatment with (NH$_4$)$_2$S, which dissolves them and forms complex thio- anions.

$$\underline{Sb_2S_3} + 3S^{--} \rightarrow 2SbS_3^{-3}$$

The members of this subgroup are called **amphoteric sulfides** (Gr., both) because they can be dissolved not only by strong acids as can CdS, but by strong bases such as HS^- and S^- ions. SbS_3^{-3} is called thioantimonite ion. After the solution of thio- anions has been separated from the insoluble sulfides of the copper subgroup, they can be reprecipitated as sulfides by the addition of acid, which removes the S^{--} ion with which they are in equilibrium.

$$2SbS_3^{-3} + 6H^+ \rightarrow \overline{Sb_2S_3} + \overline{3H_2S}$$

A further separation within the subgroup can be made by taking advantage of the fact that SnS_2 and Sb_2S_3 dissolve in 6 M HCl, which has no effect on the extremely insoluble As_2S_5.

In the precipitation of analytical Group II in Table 11.2, the H_2O_2 was added for the purpose of oxidizing Sn^{++} and As^{+3} ions to their highest oxidation state, because in this state they are readily soluble in bases.

The sulfides of Ni^{++}, Co^{++}, Mn^{++}, and Zn^{++} are much more soluble than those in analytical Group II. In order to get a high enough S^{--} ion concentration to precipitate them, the solution must be made basic enough so that the much more insoluble hydroxides of the trivalent cations in analytical Group III precipitate. This is done by adding a properly proportioned mixture of NH_4OH and NH_4^+ ion. Treating the mixed sulfides and hydroxides with NaOH and Na_2O_2 again removes a base-soluble subgroup.

The cations in analytical Group IV have already been mentioned as forming soluble ionic sulfides.

11.13. Non-Metal Sulfides

Sulfur forms compounds with non-metals that are analogous to the non-metal oxides. They are covalently bonded non-polar substances. Unless the other element is higher in electronegativity than sulfur, the compounds are called sulfides. Hydrogen sulfide has already been discussed in detail. Although the preparation of carbon disulfide was mentioned in Section 11.7, both this compound and an interesting sulfide of phosphorus will be described in connection with carbon and phosphorus respectively.

11.14. Polysulfides

The ability of sulfur to combine with itself and form chains extends even to its anions. A whole series of chain anions of the type S_x^{--} exists, up to S_9^{--}. By analogy with peroxide ion, the sulfur in persulfide ion, S_2^{--}, may be considered to have the oxidation number -1. In trisulfide ion, S_3^{--}, and the other polysulfide ions, the oxidation number of the two terminal sulfur atoms is -1; that of the others zero. The color of these ions ranges from yellow to deep red as the length of the chain increases. The simple action of a solution of an ionic sulfide, such as $(NH_4)_2S$, on solid sulfur readily forms a mixture of the lower members of this series, known either as yellow ammonium sulfide or as ammonium polysulfide. Like peroxide ion, the polysulfide ions are oxidizing agents, but much milder. The following is a typical reaction useful in qualitative analysis:

$$SnS + 2NH_4^+ + S_2^{--} \rightarrow SnS_2 + 2NH_4^+ + S^{--}$$

Tin (II) sulfide is not soluble in colorless $(NH_4)_2S$ because the charge on the Sn^{++} ion is too low to enable it to form a complex thio- anion; but tin (IV) in SnS_2 readily forms covalent bonds with the S^{--} ions that result from the reduction of the S_2^{--} ions, producing thiostannate ion, SnS_3^{--}, in solution.

$$SnS_2 + 2NH_4^+ + S^{--} \rightarrow 2NH_4^+ + SnS_3^{--}$$

In some procedures SnS is oxidized with H_2O_2.

$$SnS + 5H_2O_2 \rightarrow SnO_2 + 2H^+ + SO_4^{--} + 4H_2O$$

The tin (IV) oxide dissolves easily in plain $(NH_4)_2S$.

$$SnO_2 + 6NH_4^+ + 3S^{--} \rightarrow 2NH_4^+ + SnS_3^{--} + 4NH_3 + 2H_2O$$

Under carefully controlled conditions the addition of acid to a polysulfide yields a yellow oil that is a mixture of hydrogen polysulfides, H_2S_x. Hydrogen persulfide is an excellent solvent for a number of covalent compounds, and particularly for sulfur. The acidification of a polysulfide solution regularly results in the formation of sulfur and H_2S.

$$2NH_4^+ + S_x^{--} + 2H^+ + 2Cl^- \rightarrow 2NH_4^+ + 2Cl^- + \overline{H_2S} + (x-1)S$$

11.15. Sulfur Halides

In the compounds it forms with the halogens sulfur has positive oxidation numbers; accordingly these compounds are called sulfur halides, not halogen sulfides. Sulfur ignites spontaneously in fluorine and burns to the hexafluoride. The peculiar inertness of SF_6 was explained at the end of Section 9.20. Up to red heat it is not affected by any familiar strong acid, base, oxidizing or reducing agent except H_2S. This reaction is:

$$\overline{SF_6} + \overline{3H_2S} \rightarrow \overline{6HF} + \underline{4S}$$

Boiling sodium (b.p. 883° C.) converts SF_6 to sodium sulfide and fluoride. SF_6 has remarkable high-voltage insulating properties; its use in a transformer permits doubling the voltage.

Two sulfur chlorides are important in rubber technology—the monochloride, S_2Cl_2 (named from the empirical formula, SCl), and the dichloride, SCl_2. The monochloride has the structural formula : $\ddot{C}l : \ddot{S} : \ddot{S} : \ddot{C}l :$, in which the oxidation number of the sulfur is $+ 1$. (Oxidation numbers for sulfur are odd only in molecules containing two sulfur atoms.) SCl_2 is : $\ddot{C}l : \ddot{S} : \ddot{C}l :$, with $+2$ as the oxidation number of the sulfur. S_2Cl_2 is an excellent solvent for sulfur, iodine, certain metal halides, and many organic compounds. The sulfur chlorides are red liquids which fume in moist air. The fuming is due to the HCl which is liberated by hydrolysis (Section 9.20).

11.16. Sulfur Dioxide

Only two of the oxides of sulfur—SO_2 and SO_3—need to be discussed in an elementary text, but both of these are so important that they are discussed separately.

When sulfur or any sulfide is burned in air the sulfur is converted to SO_2, with only traces of SO_3. Most of the SO_2 produced in this country comes from elemental sulfur. Melted sulfur is burned like fuel oil under steam boilers which utilize the heat given off.

$$S + \overline{O_2} \rightarrow \overline{SO_2} + \triangle$$

When freight rates make it advantageous, pyrites, FeS_2, is burned like coal under the boilers. The amount of pyrites burned in the United States in 1959 produced as much SO_2 as could have been produced by burning half a million tons of sulfur, but in Europe more SO_2 was produced by burning pyrites than by all other processes combined.

$$\underline{4FeS_2} + \overline{11O_2} \rightarrow \underline{2Fe_2O_3} + \overline{8SO_2} + \triangle$$

The "ashes" are briquetted and sold to iron smelters.

Copper, lead, and zinc smelters are an auxiliary source of SO_2 that is about equal in importance to pyrites. The first step in smelting a sulfide ore involves roasting it to the oxide.

$$2CuS + \overline{3O_2} \xrightarrow{\Delta} 2CuO + \overline{2SO_2}$$

(This process is called roasting rather than burning because external heat has to be applied, as a result of the low percentage of sulfur that is present.)

If the world supply of elemental sulfur is ever exhausted, SO_2 can be obtained in unlimited quantities, though at higher cost, by reducing $CaSO_4$ (anhydrite, or dehydrated gypsum) with carbon.

$$2CaSO_4 + \underline{C} \xrightarrow{\Delta} 2CaO + \overline{CO_2} + \overline{2SO_2}$$

The amount of SO_2 produced annually in Europe by this process would require 400,000 tons of sulfur for an equivalent amount produced by burning the sulfur.

A convenient process for the laboratory preparation of SO_2 takes advantage of the fact that sulfurous acid loses water readily.

$$Na^+ + HSO_3^- + H^+ + HSO_4^- \rightarrow Na^+ + \underline{HSO_4^-} + H_2SO_3$$
$$H_2SO_3 \rightarrow H_2O + \overline{SO_2}$$

SO_2 is a gas that boils at $-10°$ C.; a pressure of only 2 to 3 atm. is necessary to keep it in the liquid state at room temperature. Its strong odor is perceptible at a dilution of 1 : 60,000; it is suffocating at 1 : 5000. Vegetation is destroyed by concentrations which human beings can endure. The first electric refrigerators used SO_2 as the refrigerant. The evaporation of 1 g. of SO_2 absorbs 95 cal. of heat, more than is absorbed by the more costly chlorinated and fluorinated hydrocarbons that have replaced SO_2 in this use. However, the hydrocarbons have the advantage of being odorless and non-toxic. An important current use of liquid SO_2 is as a preferential solvent for certain objectionable substances that are naturally present in lubricating oil.

SO_2 is a good reducing agent, though not as powerful as H_2S. In fact, H_2S forces it to act as an oxidizing agent.

$$\overline{2H_2S} + \overline{SO_2} \rightarrow 2H_2O + \underline{3S}$$

The sulfur appears as a cloud of yellow smoke when the two gases are mixed. Typical of the reducing action of SO_2 is its reduction of bromine to Br⁻ ion, the equation for which was given in Section 9.26 in connection with the commercial preparation of bromine.

11.17. Sulfurous Acid and Its Anions

SO_2 dissolves freely in water (45 ml. in 1 ml. at 15° C.), forming sulfurous acid, H_2SO_3. Thus SO_2 is the *anhydride* of H_2SO_3. The following equilibria exist in the solution:

$$\overline{SO_2} + H_2O \rightleftharpoons H_2SO_3 \rightleftharpoons H^+ + HSO_3^- \rightleftharpoons 2H^+ + SO_3^{--}$$

H_2SO_3 is a moderately weak diprotic acid. Its conjugate base, HSO_3^- ion, is a weak base and also a weak monoprotic acid. Its correct name is hydrogen sulfite ion, but it is usually called bisulfite ion. Sulfite ion, SO_3^{--}, is a good base. The above equilibria may be shifted to the right by the addition of a strong base, or to the left either by heat, which drives off SO_2, or by the addition of a strong acid, which increases the concentration of H^+ ions.

H_2SO_3 has no particular use as an acid, but it is a good reducing agent. In fact, when SO_2 is used as a reducing agent water is usually present and the SO_2 therefore is in the form of H_2SO_3. A typical example is the use of SO_2 as an antichlor after water purification. When SO_2 is in equilibrium with its water solution, there is some seven times as great a concentration of it in the water as above the water. Such solutions are used to bleach substances that are too delicate to withstand the harsh action of chlorine, such as wool, hat straw, white wines, and dried fruits. (In the latter case, as a fortunate side effect, vitamin C is saved from being destroyed by atmospheric oxygen.) When chlorine bleaches a colored molecule by taking electrons from it, the colored molecule is usually completely destroyed. But when H_2SO_3 bleaches such a molecule by *adding* electrons, the molecule may retain its structure. Eventually atmospheric oxygen may take these added electrons away again, whereupon the bleached straw or silk reverts to its original yellowish color.

A solution of HSO_3^- ion can dissolve lignin, the bonding material which holds the cellulose fibers together in wood. High-grade sulfite pulp used in making paper is produced when wood chips are digested in sulfite liquor. This liquor is made by passing SO_2 into a suspension of a cheap base in water. The cheapest base is slaked lime, as calcium hydroxide, $Ca(OH)_2$, is called. The reaction is:

$$Ca(OH)_2 + \overline{2SO_2} \rightarrow Ca^{++} + 2HSO_3^-$$

The production of 1 ton of sulfite pulp requires 500 lb. of SO_2.

Disposing of the waste sulfite liquor that is saturated with lignin has been a tremendous problem for the paper industry. Some of it has been processed to salvage useful material from the lignin. (This is the source of vanillin, one of the components of vanilla that is used in making imitation vanilla flavor.) Most of the liquor, however, has been burned after some preliminary evaporation; this converts the Ca^{++} and HSO_3^- into $CaSO_4$, for which unfortunately there is no use. Recently a more economical process has been discovered; it involves the substitution of $Mg(OH)_2$ for $Ca(OH)_2$. The following reaction takes place as the waste sulfite liquor is being evaporated:

$$Mg^{++} + 2HSO_3^- \rightarrow MgO + \overline{H_2O} + \overline{SO_2}$$

When the magnesium oxide is removed by filtration and suspended in cold water, it again forms $Mg(OH)_2$; this absorbs the SO_2 that is recovered and regenerates sulfite liquor. However, this process does not pay if plants produce less than 200 tons of pulp a day.

Although SO_2 is no longer a popular disinfectant and fumigant, it does have the advantage of being non-toxic in food products in the quantities used, and of preventing the growth of bacteria and molds. In manufacturing cornstarch, for example, a little H_2SO_3 is essential in the water in which the kernels are soaked, to prevent spoilage. It is used similarly in the beet sugar, brewing, and wine-making industries.

SO_3^{--} is important in photography. Photographic developers are reducing agents which reduce silver ions in AgCl or AgBr crystals in exposed portions of the sensitive material to the black metallic silver of which the image is composed. In doing so they are themselves oxidized to products which have two objectionable qualities. They are colored and hence stain the film or print, and they catalyze the oxidation of the unused developer by the atmosphere. The SO_3^{--} ion combines with these oxidation products, reducing them to colorless compounds without catalytic activity.

11.18. Oxidation of SO_2 by Oxygen

All the uses of SO_2 mentioned thus far require a total of half a million tons annually, a small quantity compared with the 10 million tons used in the manufacture of sulfuric acid, H_2SO_4. Of the H_2SO_4 produced in the United States, 85 per cent is prepared from SO_3 which in turn is prepared by the oxidation of SO_2. The reaction:

$$\overline{2SO_2} + \overline{O_2} \rightleftharpoons \overline{2SO_3} + 45 \text{ kcal.}$$

looks simple enough, but there are difficulties in bringing it about. Like many inorganic chemical reactions, this is a reversible reaction and eventually attains a state of equilibrium. Chemical equilibrium will be treated in detail in a later chapter, but for the present it is enough to say that a state of equilibrium is reached when the speed of a reaction to the right is equal to the speed of the reaction to the left. If equilibrium could be attained at room temperature in this particular case, the equilibrium mixture would be composed almost entirely of SO_3, the desired product. Unfortunately, the rate of reaction at this temperature is so slow that no appreciable amount of SO_3 is produced in a reasonable length of time. It is well known that chemical reactions speed up at higher temperatures; so if the mixture is heated to, say, $1000°$ C., equilibrium will be rapidly established, but only a little of the product is SO_3.

This fact creates a dilemma; at low temperature the reaction rate is too slow, at high temperature the desired equilibrium product is not obtained in quantity. At first glance it may seem impossible to solve the problem, but fortunately this is not the case. The solution to the problem illustrates a fundamental principle applicable to reversible reactions. We must see why an increase in temperature speeds up any chemical reaction, but has a greater effect on a reversible reaction that is going in the endothermic direction.

11.19. Effect of Temperature on Reaction Velocity

In order to react, two molecules must collide with a certain minimum force. They must break each other's shells, so to speak and form a **collision complex** in which the component atoms can be arranged in accordance with the products of the reaction or return to their original positions. The energy which must be present in a collision for this result to be achieved is called the **energy of activation.** The name is based on the fact that it is possible to "activate" a molecule by increasing its *internal*—as opposed to its kinetic—energy to such a point that the slightest collision will bring about a reaction. This can be done by raising an electron to an orbital of higher than normal energy by means of irradiation or electron bombardment. Sometimes one or more of these activated molecules are the immediate resultants of a step in a chemical reaction.

Activation energy can also be regarded as resistance to chemical reaction. In other words, a reaction which has high activation energy needs lots of energy to make it proceed. Reactions in which O_2 enters tend to have high energies of activation because of the multiple bonding in this molecule. If a reaction proceeds slowly at a given temperature, it is because most of the collisions are weak because the molecules lack kinetic energy. If all molecules had exactly the same kinetic energy at a given temperature, no reaction would take place at a temperature such that the kinetic energy per molecule was less than the energy of activation; but when the temperature rose to the point at which the kinetic energy equaled the activation energy, every collision would bring about a reaction. The speed of reaction would be too fast to measure. Obviously this is not the case.

There is no contradiction here with the kinetic theory. Only over an average time is there equal distribution of energy. In any single collision one molecule may bounce away with much more than its share of the energy, or it may be greatly slowed down. Mathematical investigation shows that most of the molecules have average energy or a little more or less than this, but that a few have a great deal more or less than average energy. A precise equation can be obtained; from it the curves in Fig. 11.4 were plotted. The average energy, b, corresponding to the higher temperature, T_2, is only a little greater than the average energy, a, corresponding to the lower temperature, T_1. If the energy of activation for a reaction is c, the shaded region under the curve and to the right of c will represent the number of molecules with sufficient energy to react on collision. The total area under the curve represents the total number of molecules. It is evident that the speed of reaction is much higher at T_2 than at T_1. A reaction having a considerably higher activation energy, d, will proceed extremely slowly at T_1 but many times as rapidly at T_2. In general, a temperature increase of 10° C. will double or treble the speed of a reaction that is already proceeding at a moderate rate. *The higher the energy of activation, the greater the effect of raising the temperature.*

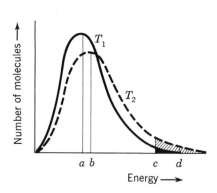

Fig. 11.4. Distribution of energy among molecules at two temperatures. Energy is plotted to the right, number of molecules upward.

In a reversible reaction the collision complex is *identical* for the forward and reverse reactions. In fact, this identity is a condition that is necessary for reversibility. This being true, the heat of reaction must be the difference in the energy of activation in the two directions.

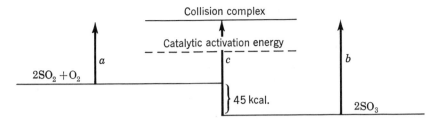

Fig. 11.5. Activation energy and reaction energy. Energy is plotted upward.

The reaction between SO_2 and O_2 is exothermic, so in Fig. 11.5 the $2SO_3$ is on a lower line than the $2SO_2 + O_2$. Since heat was given off in forming the SO_3, the latter must have less internal energy than the mixture which formed it. (The activation energies are indicated by the two arrows, *a* and *b*.) The activation energy of SO_3 is greater for the reverse reaction than the activation energy of the mixture for the direct reaction because the SO_3 had less internal energy to start with. When SO_2 and O_2 react, the amount of energy, *a*, is absorbed in forming the collision complex, and the amount of energy, *b*, is given off in forming SO_3. The difference between the energy absorbed and that given off is the **net heat of reaction.** Here *b* is 45 kcal. *greater* than *a*; hence the heat of reaction is $+45$ kcal. When SO_3 decomposes to form SO_2 and O_2, the reverse changes take place and the heat of reaction is -45 kcal.

Thus it is plain that the energy of activation must always be greater for the endothermic part of a reversible reaction, and that an increase in temperature must speed up the endothermic part more than it does the exothermic part. This leads directly to **van't Hoff's law**, which states that *if heat is applied to a system which is in equilibrium, the equilibrium is shifted in the direction of the reaction which absorbs heat.*

11.20. The Effect of a Catalyst

A **catalyst** is a substance which increases the speed of a chemical reaction without itself being permanently used up. It does this by providing a new reaction path calling for lower activation energies. A catalyst that is dissolved homogeneously in the reaction mixture may react rapidly with one component and form a compound; the latter in turn reacts rapidly with the other component to form the final product and release the catalyst molecule to start a new reaction cycle. This is called **homogeneous catalysis.** The increase in speed is always due to lower activation energies. The opposite of homogeneous catalysis is **hetero-**

geneous catalysis, more commonly called **contact catalysis.** If the catalyst does not dissolve in the reaction mixture, the intermediate compound can form only on the surface of the catalyst; at most, only a layer one molecule thick, a monomolecular layer, can be formed. The principles here are the same as those involved in homogeneous catalysis.

In effect, then, what a catalyst does is to lower the energy of activation for a reaction. Thus by means of a catalyst the activation energy is lowered by the amount c (Fig. 11.5), in comparison to the energy required to form the collision complex in the absence of a catalyst. The catalyst cannot initiate a reaction which would not occur at a lower speed in the absence of the catalyst. Most important, in a reversible reaction the catalyst lowers both activation energies the same amount. Therefore the direct and the reverse reactions are speeded up in the same proportion. *A catalyst cannot shift an equilibrium.* It can only enable a reacting mixture to reach more quickly the equilibrium corresponding to the existing temperature.

Although the term negative catalyst is occasionally seen, accurately speaking there is no such thing. To offer a reaction path with higher activation energy would not slow down a reaction. The reaction would continue in the original path at the original speed. The only way a reaction can be slowed, the temperature remaining constant, is to *remove* the catalyst. The catalysts for many reactions are numerous and may be effective out of all proportion to the amount present. For example, if tomato juice is run through copper tubing to the kettles, the almost immeasurably small amount of Cu^{++} ion it picks up will catalyze the practically complete destruction, by oxidation, of the vitamin C in the juice. A substance which would isolate the Cu^{++} ion into a stable complex would suppress its catalytic action and hence might be called a negative catalyst.

11.21. The Contact Process for the Production of SO_3

As we saw in Section 11.18, when a mixture of SO_2 and O_2 is heated enough to attain a reasonable speed of reaction, the percentage conversion to SO_3 is too low. In order to obtain sufficient reaction speed at a temperature low enough for nearly complete conversion to SO_3, a catalyst must be used. If the gas mixture is passed over finely divided platinum that is dispersed upon an inert supporting material, the reaction is rapid enough at 445° C. for 96 per cent of the SO_2 to be converted to SO_3 without any additional external heat. This is **contact catalysis,** which gives the process its name.

Platinum is not the only contact catalyst available for the oxidation of SO_2. The most important of the others is vanadium pentoxide, V_2O_5, which competes successfully with platinum. Besides being much cheaper, it is not as easily "poisoned" by the arsenic compounds that are likely to be present in the SO_2. (A catalyst is "poisoned" when material that is foreign to the desired reaction interferes with the surface activity of the catalyst and inhibits or destroys its efficiency for the reaction.) On the other hand, eventually V_2O_5 must be thrown away, whereas used platinum catalysts have a high salvage value. There are also operating differences which must be considered in individual cases.

11.22. Forms of SO_3

The SO_3 molecule (Fig. 11.6) consists of three oxygen atoms which form an equilateral triangle, with a sulfur atom in the center. Each of the oxygen atoms has completed its valence octet by attaching itself to 2 of the 6 electrons that originally belonged to the sulfur atom. This would leave the sulfur atom with one vacant p orbital were it not for the fact that this orbital, whose axis is perpendicular to the plane of the molecule, overlaps, both above and below the plane, p orbitals of the three oxygen atoms which are similarly oriented. Each of the oxygen orbitals contains a pair of electrons, and the overlapping permits the sulfur atom to draw a fraction of each pair into its fourth orbital. This amounts to saying that the sulfur atom has $1\frac{1}{3}$ covalent bonds with each oxygen atom. The dot formula, $:\overset{..}{O}:S::\overset{..}{O}:$, represents this state of affairs. Since no way has $:\overset{..}{O}:$ been devised to show the sharing of a fraction of an electron pair, we have adopted the convention that a double bond shown with only one of three identical atoms means that each of the three is contributing equally toward filling the fourth orbital of the central atom.

Sulfur is too large an atom to form a stable double bond (Section 4.13). SO_3 thus reacts vigorously with H_2O:

$$:\overset{..}{\underset{..}{O}}: \quad \overset{..}{O}:S \quad + \quad :\overset{..}{O}:H \rightarrow :\overset{..}{O}:\overset{\overset{H}{\overset{..}{O}}:}{\underset{\underset{..}{O}}{S}}:\overset{..}{O}:H$$

In the resulting molecule of sulfuric acid the oxygens are arranged tetrahedrally around the sulfur atom; i.e., the oxygen atoms form a triangular

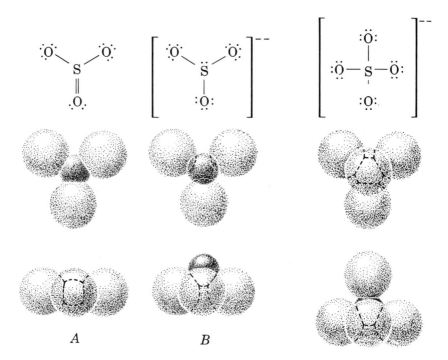

Fig. 11.6. **A,** The SO_3 molecule (a plane triangle) compared with **B,** the SO_3^- ion (a low triangular pyramid).

Fig. 11.7. The tetrahedral sulfate ion, SO_4^-.

pyramid, with the sulfur atom in the center. The models in Figs. 11.6 and 11.7 should make this clear.

SO_3 may also assume the more stable single-bond arrangement within the molecule by adding onto a molecule of H_2SO_4, in which there are no multiple bonds. The dot formula:

$$\begin{array}{ccc} & :\!\ddot{O}\!: & :\!\ddot{O}\!: \\ :\!\ddot{O}\!:\!S\!:\!\ddot{O}\!:\!S\!:\!\ddot{O}\!:\!H \\ & :\!\ddot{O}\!: & :\!\ddot{O}\!: \\ & & H \end{array}$$

shows that the new molecule, disulfuric acid, also has no multiple bonds. A glance will show that there is nothing to prevent molecule after molecule of SO_3 from adding on, forming trisulfuric acid, tetrasulfuric acid, and so on, until there is an almost infinitely long chain molecule. Practically speaking, this is a high polymer of SO_3, $(SO_3)_x$. Because of the shape of its molecules this substance forms fibrous, asbestos-like crystals, whereas SO_3 is a liquid at room temperature if all trace of water is absent.

11.23. Sulfuric Acid from SO_3

If the gas stream (excess air and residual nitrogen) containing the SO_3 is bubbled through water, a large part of the SO_3 will not be absorbed but will emerge as a fine mist of H_2SO_4. This is due to the rapid evaporation of water molecules into the bubbles. Since the molecular weight of SO_3 is more than four times that of H_2O, the H_2O molecules move more than twice as fast as the SO_3 molecules and collide with most of them before they reach the wall of the bubble. Further collisions of H_2O and SO_3 molecules produce droplets that are visible, though microscopic in size. At the same time, in some unexplained manner the droplets acquire an electrical charge that repels them from each other and from the wall of the bubble.

This difficulty is avoided by absorbing the SO_3 in concentrated H_2SO_4. Since no H_2O molecules evaporate into the bubble, the SO_3 molecules quickly strike the walls and are absorbed. As we saw in Section 11.22, they react with the H_2SO_4 to form disulfuric acid, $H_2S_2O_7$.

$$\overline{SO_3} + H_2SO_4 \rightleftharpoons H_2S_2O_7$$

Disulfuric acid is also known as pyrosulfuric acid because its salts were first obtained by heating acid sulfates over a hot fire.

$$2NaHSO_4 \xrightarrow{\Delta} Na_2S_2O_7 + \overline{H_2O}$$

A solution of $H_2S_2O_7$ in H_2SO_4 is known commercially as oleum, because of its oily consistency, or as fuming sulfuric acid, because the SO_3 which evaporates from it fumes in moist air.

For some chemical purposes oleum containing 15 or 30 per cent SO_3 is used as such, but most of it is reduced to a strength of about 95 per cent H_2SO_4. This is done by adding dilute H_2SO_4 to it. The water in the dilute acid reacts.

$$H_2O + H_2S_2O_7 \rightarrow 2H_2SO_4 + \Delta$$

The old name, oil of vitriol, is still frequently used commercially for this concentrated H_2SO_4. The addition of dilute H_2SO_4 solution instead of plain water to oleum has a twofold advantage. In the first place, it moderates the extremely exothermic reaction, which is so violent as to be explosive with pure water. In the second place, the dilute H_2SO_4 is converted into concentrated acid by the reaction between the water it contains and the oleum to form more H_2SO_4, thus making unnecessary the expense of concentrating it by evaporation. A number of chemical industries use concentrated H_2SO_4 to absorb the water produced in a reaction; this diluted H_2SO_4 ("spent acid") becomes a by-product. Moderately dilute H_2SO_4 (78 per cent) is also manufactured by the lead chamber process.

11.24. The Lead Chamber Process for the Production of H_2SO_4

About one-seventh of our total production of H_2SO_4 is made by the **lead chamber process,** one of the oldest chemical manufacturing processes. Its beginnings date back nearly 300 years, and no fundamental change has been made in it for a century. The basis of this process is a series of homogeneous gas reactions which may be summarized by the equation:

$$\overline{SO_2} + \overline{NO_2} + H_2O \rightarrow H_2SO_4 + \overline{NO}$$

The nitric oxide, NO, then reacts with oxygen to regenerate nitrogen dioxide, NO_2, which thus acts as a catalyst.

$$\overline{2NO} + \overline{O_2} \rightarrow \overline{2NO_2}$$

Because this latter reaction is relatively slow, a large volume of reaction space is required. Hence lead-lined chambers with volumes on the order of 25,000 cu. ft. are used. H_2SO_4 is produced in the form of a fog of droplets which settle to the floor as chamber acid (63 per cent H_2SO_4). When H_2SO_4 comes in contact with lead it promptly forms an impervious coating of insoluble $PbSO_4$, which protects the metal from further attack. A diagram of a lead chamber plant is shown in Fig. 11.8.

The SO_2 (from sulfur burners, pyrites burners, or smelter gases) is carried into the process in a tenfold excess of air to provide the desired concentration of oxygen. In order to prevent a loss of NO and NO_2, which would render the process uneconomical, the waste gases are passed upward through a recovery unit 70 ft. tall called a Gay-Lussac tower, countercurrent to 78 per cent H_2SO_4 which is trickling downward over the tower's acid-proof packing. The oxides of nitrogen dissolve in the acid and react as follows:

$$\overline{NO} + \overline{NO_2} + 2H_2SO_4 \rightleftharpoons 2H(NO)SO_4 + H_2O$$

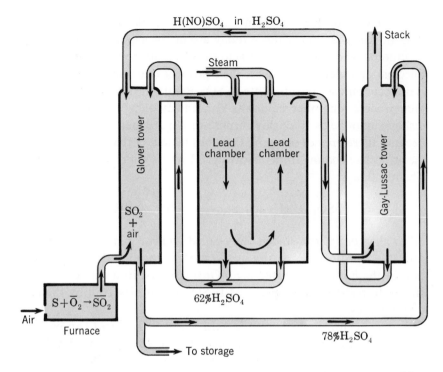

Fig. 11.8. Diagram of the lead chamber process for manufacturing H_2SO_4.

The unfamiliar formula is that of nitrosylsulfuric acid; the dot formula

is: $H : \ddot{O} : \overset{\displaystyle : \ddot{O} :}{\underset{\displaystyle : \ddot{O} :}{\ddot{S}}} : \ddot{O} : \ddot{N} :: \ddot{O} :$. This reaction is reversible; addition of water

sends it to the left. To reintroduce the recovered oxides of nitrogen into the lead chambers the H_2SO_4 solution of $H(NO)SO_4$ is pumped from the bottom of the Gay-Lussac tower to the top of a similar tower called the Glover tower. There the necessary water is mixed with it in the form of the dilute chamber acid. The hot gases from the sulfur burner pass upward through the Glover tower. At the top they pick up the oxides of nitrogen from the dilute acid and pass on into the lead chamber. As the dilute acid, now free of $H(NO)SO_4$, trickles downward over the packing, it meets continually hotter gases from the burner and much of its water content is boiled off. When it emerges from the bottom of the Glover tower, the H_2SO_4 is 78 per cent. The necessary amount of this returns to the top of the Gay-Lussac tower; most of the rest is used in the manufacture of superphosphate fertilizer.

No new lead chamber plants have been built since before World War II. All those in existence today are the property of fertilizer manufacturers, who can use dilute acid or have built contact plants to produce enough oleum to convert their product into concentrated acid; it is not economical to ship dilute H_2SO_4. Before the invention of the contact process, chamber acid was concentrated by evaporation. Lead dishes cannot be used for this purpose with more than 78 per cent H_2SO_4 because there are not enough SO_4^{--} ions in acid of that strength to keep the protective coating from dissolving. (HSO_4^- is not really a strong acid.) The reaction is:

$$\underline{PbSO_4} + H^+ + HSO_4^- \rightarrow Pb^{++} + 2HSO_4^-$$

Silica glass or an iron-silicon alloy called Duriron can be used. Duriron acquires a protective coating of silica, SiO_2, through the oxidizing action of the hot concentrated acid. Ordinary cast iron contains enough silicon to resist 95 to 98 per cent H_2SO_4, but is dissolved by the more dilute grades.

Any concentration of sulfuric acid below 96 per cent can be easily determined by means of a hydrometer. (At 96 per cent the density ceases to change much with increasing concentration.) The hydrometer most widely used has an arbitrary scale invented by Baumé, and specific gravities are usually expressed commercially in degrees Baumé (°Bé.). Thus chamber acid (62 per cent) is 50° Bé.; 77 per cent acid is 60° Bé.; and the concentrated acid is 66° Bé.

11.25. Properties of H_2SO_4

H_2SO_4 is a colorless, oily-looking liquid with a density of about 1.84. Its liquid range is from about 10° C. to 338° C., but it has no true boiling point. When a water solution of H_2SO_4 is boiled, only water is given off until the concentration reaches 98.3 per cent and the temperature 338° C. At that temperature the acid decomposes, and H_2O and SO_3 are given off in equimolar proportions; the composition of the boiling liquid remains constant. When the gases cool they recombine, forming dense white clouds of droplets of H_2SO_4 that are usually called fumes of SO_3.

H_2SO_4 *is one of the strongest acids known.* This is its most important chemical property. Anhydrous H_2SO_4 transfers protons with the greatest readiness not only to H_2O, but to much weaker bases, such as Cl^- ion, and to molecules which are not ordinarily considered bases at all, such as benzene, C_6H_6, and acetic acid, $HC_2H_3O_2$. Even a minute amount of water reacts completely with H_2SO_4.

$$H_2SO_4 + H_2O \rightarrow H_3O^+ + HSO_4^-$$

The hydronium and hydrogen sulfate ions remain dissolved as free ions in the remaining H_2SO_4, which is an excellent ionizing solvent, or in water if an excess is added. If equimolar quantities of water and H_2SO_4 are mixed, the compound, hydronium hydrogen sulfate, H_3OHSO_4, forms. Since it has a melting point of only 8° C., it cannot crystallize out as an ordinary salt. It is called sulfuric acid monohydrate, or simply $83\frac{1}{2}$ per cent sulfuric acid solution. The reaction which produces it, particularly when it takes place in the presence of excess water, is generally called the ionization of sulfuric acid; the usual equation is:

$$H_2SO_4 \rightarrow H^+ + HSO_4^-$$

Never pour water into concentrated H_2SO_4. Being of lower density, the water will float on top. When the first of it reacts with the H_2SO_4 the large amount of heat produced will flash the rest of the water explosively into steam, splattering the concentrated acid in all directions. *Always pour the acid carefully into the water.*

The extreme vigor with which H_2SO_4 reacts with water makes it a powerful dehydrating agent. H_2SO_4 can force many substances which contain oxygen and hydrogen atoms to rearrange these atoms into water molecules with which it then combines. Pouring concentrated H_2SO_4 onto sugar provides a striking example of this. The acid causes the sugar, $C_{12}H_{22}O_{11}$, to break down into black carbon and water. The water combines with H_2SO_4 and the temperature rises to the point at which some of the carbon is oxidized.

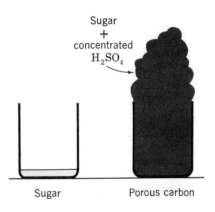

Fig. 11.9. Dehydration of sugar by sulfuric acid.

$$\underline{C} + 2H_2SO_4 \rightarrow \overline{CO_2} + \overline{2SO_2} + \overline{2H_2O} + \Delta$$

A voluminous foam of melted sugar and carbon, and bubbles of mixed carbon dioxide, sulfur dioxide, and steam, rises out of the beaker, solidifying as it cools (Fig. 11.9). Cotton and wood, chemically related to sugar, are also charred by H_2SO_4. Even dilute H_2SO_4, if spilled, should be carefully neutralized, for it becomes dangerous as the water evaporates.

When hot and concentrated, H_2SO_4 is a strong oxidizing agent. The preceding equation is typical of its action on moderately electronegative non-metals, including phosphorus and sulfur. Its ability to oxidize HBr and HI was mentioned in Sections 9.46 and 9.47. Moderate or poor reducing agents reduce H_2SO_4 to SO_2.

$$\underline{Cu} + 2(H^+ + HSO_4^-) \rightarrow Cu^{++} + SO_4^{--} + \overline{SO_2} + H_2O$$

Good ones, however, such as HI or zinc, may reduce it clear down to H_2S.

$$\underline{4Zn} + 5(H^+ + HSO_4^-) \rightarrow 4(Zn^{++} + SO_4^{--}) + \overline{H_2S} + 4H_2O$$

11.26. Uses of H_2SO_4

The United States alone used more than 17 million tons of H_2SO_4 in 1961. No other pure inorganic compound is manufactured in such quantity; only some nine others reach the million-ton use mark. H_2SO_4 is used somewhere along the line in the production of practically every substance and object required in a modern industrial civilization. These multifarious uses all stem from the properties described in the preceding section and from the fact that sulfate ion, SO_4^-, forms insoluble salts with Ca^{++}, Ba^{++}, and Pb^{++} ions, but is not an oxidizing agent at moderate temperatures. A further reason is the fact that the acid is extremely cheap, selling at about 1 cent a pound. A few of the more important and typical of these uses will be described.

Nearly 5 million tons of H_2SO_4 are used annually by the fertilizer industry in the United States as a cheap source of the H^+ ions that are needed to make soluble the phosphate ions of phosphate rock, $Ca_3(PO_4)_2$. The reaction for the manufacture of fertilizer is:

$$2H^+ + 2HSO_4^- + \underline{Ca_3(PO_4)_2} \rightarrow \underline{Ca(H_2PO_4)_2} + 2CaSO_4 + \triangle$$

The heat of the reaction drives off the water in the dilute H_2SO_4. The dry mixture of solids is known in the trade as superphosphate.

In phosphoric acid production, advantage is taken of the insolubility of $CaSO_4$, which is filtered out of the solution produced by the following reaction:

$$3H^+ + 3HSO_4^- + \underline{Ca_3(PO_4)_2} \rightarrow \underline{2H_3PO_4} + 3CaSO_4$$

Dilute "spent acid" can be used in this process.

A million and a half tons of H_2SO_4 are used in the production of another important fertilizer, $(NH_4)_2SO_4$. This soluble salt is crystallized from the solution resulting from the neutralization of ammonia.

$$H^+ + HSO_4^- + 2NH_3 \rightarrow 2NH_4^+ + SO_4^{--}$$

Another 1.5 million tons are used for inorganic pigments, mainly for paints. The most important of these pigments is titanium dioxide. The principal titanium ore is ilmenite, $FeTiO_3$. When it is treated with H_2SO_4 the strong base O^{--} ion is neutralized.

$$3H^+ + 3HSO_4^- + \underline{FeTiO_3} \rightarrow Fe^{++} + Ti^{+4} + 3SO_4^{--} + 3H_2O$$

The pigment is then precipitated from this solution by dilution.

$$Ti^{+4} + 2SO_4^{--} + 2H_2O \rightarrow \underline{TiO_2} + 4H^+ + 2SO_4^{--}$$

Over 1 million tons of H_2SO_4 are used in the pickling of iron and steel. Before the metal can be coated with tin (for tin cans, etc.) or galvanized (coated with zinc—for buckets, corrugated roofing, wire, etc.), the surface must be freed of the scale of iron oxide which forms while the white-hot billets are being rolled. Sulfuric acid does this cheaply, although unfortunately 2 or 3 per cent of the iron itself is also dissolved.

$$\underline{Fe} + \underline{Fe_3O_4} + 4H^+ + 4HSO_4^- \rightarrow 4Fe^{++} + 4SO_4^{--} + 4H_2O$$

The rayon and cellulose film industry (cellophane) accounts for over 600,000 tons of H_2SO_4. The acid is used in the regenerating bath to neutralize bases used in dissolving the cellulose.

H_2SO_4 is used in storage batteries not merely to supply the H^+ ions for the redox reaction which is the source of energy, but also to hold the Pb^{++} ion, which is produced, as insoluble $PbSO_4$.

Because it is a cheap, non-volatile strong acid, H_2SO_4 is used in the production of volatile acids from their salts. Over 25,000 tons of HCl are annually produced in this way from common salt.

$$NaCl + H_2SO_4 \rightarrow NaHSO_4 + \overline{HCl} \quad \text{(in glass apparatus)}$$

$$NaCl + NaHSO_4 \rightarrow Na_2SO_4 + \overline{HCl} \quad \text{(in cast iron at red heat)}$$

Nitric acid, HNO_3, was formerly produced in this way before the discovery of the ammonia oxidation process to be described in the next chapter.

Sulfuric acid is used in the synthesis of ethyl alcohol from the hydrocarbon ethylene. When H_2SO_4 is added to ethylene, ethylsulfuric acid is formed.

The very weak base HSO_4^- is readily displaced from ethylsulfuric acid by

the strong base OH^-, yielding ethyl alcohol, $H:\overset{\overset{\displaystyle H}{\cdot\cdot}}{\underset{\underset{\displaystyle H}{\cdot\cdot}}{C}}:\overset{\overset{\displaystyle H}{\cdot\cdot}}{\underset{\underset{\displaystyle H}{\cdot\cdot}}{C}}:\overset{\cdot\cdot}{\underset{\cdot\cdot}{O}}:$. More than

half of our ethyl or grain alcohol is now made from ethylene obtained from oil refinery gases. Hydrocarbons which, like ethylene, contain a double bond—i.e., two electron pairs shared between the same two carbon atoms—are called *unsaturated* because of their ability to add acidic reagents like H_2SO_4. Some unsaturated hydrocarbons of higher molecular weight boil in the gasoline range; they must be removed from gasoline because their gradual reaction with atmospheric oxygen forms gummy matter that clogs carburetors. Half a million tons of H_2SO_4 are used annually for this purpose.

Alcohol reacts with acids to form covalent compounds called **esters.** These have a variety of uses, depending upon their composition. For example, some are explosives and plastics, others are soap substitutes. H_2SO_4 is used in the synthesis of esters for two reasons; first, to furnish the sulfate (or hydrogen sulfate) groups for the synthesis of various sulfate esters, and second to help the reaction go toward completion by combining with the water produced in the reaction.

$$C_2H_5OH + HOSO_2OH \rightleftharpoons C_2H_5OSO_2OH + H_2O$$

The esterification reaction is reversible, and the removal of water by means of H_2SO_4 forces the reaction to completion toward the right. This is accomplished by having excess H_2SO_4 in the reaction mixture because some of the H_2SO_4 is used up to form the monoester ethyl hydrogen sulfate, $C_2H_5OSO_2OH$. Since all monoesters of H_2SO_4 contain an —OH group and therefore are strongly acidic, they can react with additional alcohol to form diesters.

$$C_2H_5OSO_2OH + C_2H_5OH \rightleftharpoons (C_2H_5)_2SO_4 + H_2O$$

The diester diethyl sulfate, $(C_2H_5)_2SO_4$, is a typical example of this type of ester. Other monoesters and diesters can be made by using other alcohols. The monoesters of H_2SO_4 are unlike H_2SO_4 in that they do not form insoluble salts. The sodium salt of the ester lauryl hydrogen sulfate, $C_{12}H_{25}SO_4Na$, has soaplike properties but is not precipitated by the Ca^{++} ions in hard water the way soap is. Materials of this type are sold under such trade names as Dreft.

When other acids are used to synthesize esters—for example, HNO_3 for nitrate esters—H_2SO_4 is still present in the reaction to remove water and force the reaction to completion.

$$C_2H_5OH + HONO_2 \rightleftharpoons C_2H_5ONO_2 + H_2O$$

The ester ethyl nitrate, $C_2H_5ONO_2$, is representative of a class of nitrate esters made successfully from various alcohols when H_2SO_4 is present as a dehydrating agent. Two important nitrate esters of more complicated alcohols are cellulose nitrate and glyceryl trinitrate, commercially miscalled nitrocellulose and nitroglycerin respectively. The first, also known as guncotton, is the basis of celluloid (the original synthetic plastic), smokeless powder, and some rayon; the second, of dynamite.

The dehydrating power of H_2SO_4 is responsible for its enormous use in the organic chemical industry. In one of the most important of these reactions H_2SO_4 takes OH^- from HNO_3, supplying the H^+ ions itself to produce first H_2O, then H_3O^+.

$$2H_2SO_4 + HNO_3 \rightarrow H_3O^+ + NO_2^+ + 2HSO_4^-$$

The nitronium ion, NO_2^+, is the active agent in a type of reaction called **nitration,** which is fundamental in the production of many dyes, drugs, and explosives. A similar reaction called **sulfonation,** in which one of the H_2SO_4 molecules furnishes the OH^-, is used in solubilizing drugs and dyes and in the production of another class of synthetic detergents. Nitro compounds and sulfonates differ from nitrate and sulfate esters in that the nitrogen or sulfur is attached to carbon directly instead of through oxygen—for example, trinitrotoluene (TNT), $C_7H_5(NO_2)_3$, and benzenesulfonic acid, $C_6H_5SO_3H$. In these compounds a carbon atom has been oxidized.

After H_2SO_4 has been used as a dehydrating agent, the spent acid may be fortified with oleum and used again. This fortification produces an additional mole of H_2SO_4 for every mole of water which was present in the spent acid. Over 700,000 tons of H_2SO_4 are produced in this way annually and sold to other users.

Another use of H_2SO_4 depends on its ability as an oxidizing agent in the preparation of copper sulfate from scrap copper.

$$\underline{Cu} + 2H_2SO_4 \rightarrow Cu^{++} + SO_4^{--} + \overline{SO_2} + 2H_2O$$

11.27. HSO_4^- and SO_4^- Ions

Since HSO_4^- ion is the conjugate base of a very strong acid, it is a much weaker base than water.

$$H_2SO_4 + H_2O \rightarrow H_3O^+ + HSO_4^-$$

It is also, of course, an acid since it contains a replaceable hydrogen.

$$HSO_4^- + H_2O \rightleftharpoons H_3O^+ + SO_4^{--}$$

As was mentioned previously, the second step in the dissociation of a polyprotic acid is always less extensive than the first; but even so, HSO_4^- is almost a strong acid. In a 0.1 M solution of $NaHSO_4$ the concentration of the H^+ and SO_4^{--} ions is 0.036 M. In a 0.1 M solution of H_2SO_4 the H^+ produced by the complete first step in the dissociation depresses the extent of ionization in the second step because there are more H^+ ions to react with SO_4^{--} in the reverse reaction; hence the SO_4^{--} ion concentration in such a solution is only 0.015 M. This corresponds to an H^+ ion concentration of 0.115 M and an HSO_4^- concentration of 0.085 M. These figures show why dilute H_2SO_4 is regularly written as $H^+ + HSO_4^-$ in ionic equations. Always remember, however, that the SO_4^{--} ion concentration remains appreciable until the acid is fairly well concentrated.

The HSO_4^- ion, although properly called hydrogen sulfate ion, is more often called bisulfate ion; its salts are occasionally called acid sulfates. All of them are soluble. $NaHSO_4$ is used to some extent when a moderately strong *solid* acid is needed.

Sulfate ion, SO_4^{--}, has relatively few chemical properties. It is a stronger base than water, but not sufficiently stronger to impart noticeably basic properties to a solution. It has no appreciable oxidizing ability at room temperature. It never acts as an acid or a reducing agent. Nearly all sulfates are soluble, the exceptions being those of Pb^{++}, Ra^{++}, Ba^{++}, Sr^{++}, and Ca^{++}. The stability of the SO_4^{--} ion, together with its inability to precipitate most cations, makes it a convenient "handle" for a large number of cations. Metal sulfates can usually be relied on to form solutions in which the properties of the cations will be evident without any interference from the $SO_4{}^{--}$ ion.

Several of the sulfates are common enough to be known by old, nonsystematic names. Among them are the following:

Alum, $KAl(SO_4)_2 \cdot 12H_2O$ Copperas ⎱ $FeSO_4 \cdot 7H_2O$
Barytes ⎫   Green vitriol ⎰
Blanc-fixe ⎬ $BaSO_4$ Epsom salt, $MgSO_4 \cdot 7H_2O$
Fixed white ⎭   Glauber's salt, $Na_2SO_4 \cdot 10H_2O$
Blue vitriol, $CuSO_4 \cdot 5H_2O$ Gypsum, $CaSO_4 \cdot 2H_2O$
White vitriol, $ZnSO_4 \cdot 7H_2O$ Plaster of Paris, $(CaSO_4)_2 \cdot H_2O$

Some sulfates, particularly the most insoluble ones such as $BaSO_4$, $SrSO_4$, and $PbSO_4$, are always **anhydrous.** Most sulfates, however, crystallize either in the anhydrous state or with **water of crystallization.** Often the same salt may be obtained with different amounts of water of crystallization, depending on the conditions that are present. Thus sodium sulfate can be prepared not only as the decahydrate, $Na_2SO_4 \cdot 10H_2O$ (Glauber's salt), but also as the heptahydrate, $Na_2SO_4 \cdot 7H_2O$, and as anhydrous Na_2SO_4 (known commercially as salt cake). So also with the two hydrates of calcium sulfate in the above list; anhydrous $CaSO_4$, which can also be prepared, occurs in nature as the mineral anhydrite. When several crystalline forms of a compound are known, each has its own individual crystal habit, density, and solubility.

The water of crystallization seems in some cases to consist simply of water molecules which fill up small spaces in the crystals between the ions. In other cases some or all of the water molecules are coordinated with the cations or, less frequently, with the anions. In blue vitriol, $CuSO_4 \cdot 5H_2O$, four of the water molecules are attached to the Cu^{++} ions by bonds largely covalent in character; the fifth water molecule is hydrogen-bonded to the $SO_4{}^{--}$ ion. In the following diagram of a portion of a crystal of $CuSO_4 \cdot 5H_2O$, the covalent bonds are shown by solid lines, the hydrogen bonds by dotted lines:

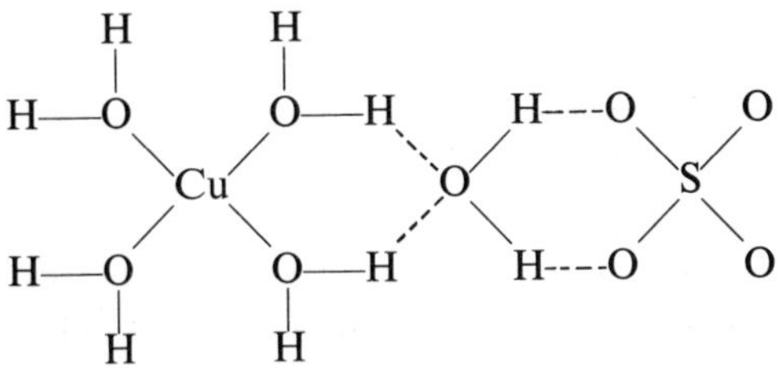

Note that the fifth water molecule is also hydrogen-bonded to two of the water molecules which are coordinated with the Cu^{++} ion. The name vitriol was given long ago to $FeSO_4 \cdot 7H_2O$ because of its glassy appearance, and was later extended to $CuSO_4 \cdot 5H_2O$. The modern extension of the term has been limited to salts of the type $M^{II}SO_4 \cdot 7H_2O$, where M^{II} represents a divalent metallic ion, all of these salts being **isomorphous** (of the same crystalline form); it has excluded the pentahydrates, which are not isomorphous with the true vitriols. In the true vitriols the cations are coordinated with six instead of four water molecules. In writing salt formulas, no attempt is ordinarily made to differentiate between the various possible modes of combination of the water of crystallization. When a dot is used to connect two parts of a formula it conveys absolutely no information as to how the parts are related.

11.28. Lower Valence Oxyanions of Sulfur

There are many anions in which a sulfur atom may be thought of as having taken the place of an oxygen atom that would normally be present. In such cases the sulfur atom is assumed to have the same valence as the oxygen atom it replaces, -2, and its presence is indicated by adding the prefix *thio-* to the name of the ion (see Section 11.7). The most important of these ions is thiosulfate ion, $S_2O_3^{--}$, the dot formula of which is

$$\begin{array}{c} :\overset{\cdot\cdot}{\underset{}{O}}: \\ :\overset{\cdot\cdot}{\underset{\cdot\cdot}{O}}:\overset{\cdot\cdot}{\underset{\cdot\cdot}{S}}:\overset{\cdot\cdot}{\underset{}{S}}:^{--} \\ :\overset{}{\underset{\cdot\cdot}{O}}: \end{array}$$ (Because of an error in analysis it was first called hy-

posulfite; it is still known by this name or "hypo," by photographers.) This ion is made by boiling Na_2SO_3 solution with sulfur. The SO_3^{--} ion is oxidized by sulfur in exactly the same way that it is by oxygen.

$$SO_3^{--} + \underline{S} \rightarrow SO_3S^{--} \text{ or } S_2O_3^{--}$$

$S_2O_3^{--}$ ion is a good reducing agent and is used commercially as an antichlor after bleaching, to remove excess chlorine quickly and thus prevent damage to fabric.

$$S_2O_3^{--} + \overline{4Cl_2} + 5H_2O \rightarrow 8H^+ + 2HSO_4^- + 8Cl^-$$

In this reaction the chlorine removes 8 electrons from the thio- sulfur atom. The weak oxidizing agent iodine removes only 1, leaving the ion otherwise intact. Two of these $:\overset{\displaystyle :\ddot{O}:}{\underset{:\ddot{O}:}{\ddot{O}:\ddot{S}:\dot{S}\cdot}}$ radicals then unite to form a

tetrathionate ion, $:\overset{\displaystyle :\ddot{O}:\quad:\ddot{O}:}{\underset{:\ddot{O}:\quad:\ddot{O}:}{\ddot{O}:\ddot{S}:\ddot{S}:\ddot{S}:\ddot{S}:\ddot{O}:}}{}^{--}$

$$2S_2O_3^{--} + I_2 \rightarrow 2I^- + S_4O_6^{--}$$

As a matter of fact, the general formula $O_3S(S)_nSO_3^{--}$ describes a series of five thionate ions, running from dithionate ($n = 0$) to hexathionate ($n = 4$). $S_2O_6^{--}$ ion is as unreactive as SO_4^{--} ion; the other polythionates are more reactive because of the exposed sulfur atoms. All are very weak bases.

If one oxygen atom is removed from a dithionate ion, $S_2O_5^{--}$ ion remains. The actual method of formation, however, is by evaporating a solution of $NaHSO_3$ with excess SO_2. For this reason $S_2O_5^{--}$ was erroneously supposed to have the structure $O_2SOSO_2^{--}$ and was called pyrosulfite ion (also disulfite and metabisulfite). Because the reaction

$$2HSO_3^- \rightleftharpoons S_2O_5^{--} + H_2O$$

is easily reversible, this ion is a convenient source of hydrogen sulfite ion (bisulfite ion) for photography and the preservation of light wines.

If an atom of oxygen is removed from each of the sulfur atoms in the dithionate formula, the result is $:\overset{\displaystyle :\ddot{O}:}{\underset{:\ddot{O}:}{\ddot{O}:\ddot{S}:\ddot{S}:\ddot{O}:}}{}^{--}$. This is the formula of dithionite ion. (This ion is known, incorrectly, as hyposulfite and as hydrosulfite.) $Na_2S_2O_4$ is such an active reducing agent that it ignites spontaneously in air if allowed to become moist.

No oxyacid of sulfur in which the sulfur has an oxidation number below $+6$ is stable. For example, if a water solution of $Na_2S_2O_3$ is exposed to the air it soon becomes milky because the carbon dioxide in the air dissolves in the solution and produces carbonic acid.

$$2Na^+ + S_2O_3^{--} + H_2CO_3 \rightleftharpoons 2Na^+ + HCO_3^- + HS_2O_3^-$$
$$\uparrow \quad \hookrightarrow HSO_3^- + \underline{S}$$

The sulfur is so finely divided that it looks white. Early chemists called the suspension "lac sulphuris," milk of sulfur.

There is some doubt as to the existence of SO_2^{--} ion, although the preparation of the sodium, zinc, and cobalt(II) salts has been claimed. Curiously enough, from its formula SO_2^{--} can legitimately be called hyposulfite, but actually it is called sulfoxylate.

11.29. Derivatives of SO_4^{--}

Ions in which +6 sulfur is attached to three oxygen atoms and to one other atom or group may properly be considered to be derivatives of SO_4^{--} ion, because of similar structure and because the chemical properties of both ions are related. Although several of these have already been discussed, they will be mentioned again to bring all of them together in one section.

Two ions which are derivatives of both SO_4^{--} and H_2O_2 were mentioned in Section 6.16. These are peroxymonosulfate, O_3SOO^{--}, and peroxydisulfate, $O_3SOOSO_3^{--}$, both extremely strong oxidizing agents because of the presence of the peroxide group. $Na_2S_2O_8$, for example, can oxidize manganous ion, Mn^{++}, to permanganate ion, MnO_4^{-}. $S_2O_3^{--}$ ion, described in the preceding section, is a derivative of both SO_4^{--} and S^{--}. The covalent bond-forming ability characteristic of the latter gives $S_2O_3^{--}$ noteworthy ability to form complex ions with subgroup metal cations. This is responsible for its use in photography.

If the fourth oxygen of a sulfate ion is replaced by a monovalent instead of a divalent anion, the resulting anion will itself be monovalent instead of divalent. Important examples include cases in which the replacing ion is F^-, Cl^-, NH_2^- (amide ion), or ions of various hydrocarbon groups. All of these are called sulfonates; thus O_3SF^- is fluosulfonate, O_3SCl^- is chlorosulfonate, $O_3SNH_2^-$ is aminesulfonate, etc. In these formulas the oxygen is written first to emphasize that it is the sulfur, not one of the oxygen atoms, to which the remaining group is attached. The conventional way of writing these formulas is SO_3F^-, etc. $SO_3NH_2^-$, useful in weed killing, flameproofing, and electroplating is usually called sulfamate ion.

The acids corresponding to these ions are all strong and, except for thiosulfuric acid, stable. They are all more or less readily hydrolyzed to H_2SO_4. HSO_3Cl is particularly easy to hydrolyze; its use in producing smoke screens is based upon this reaction.

$$H_2O + HSO_3Cl \rightarrow H_2SO_4 + \overline{HCl}$$

Both products fume strongly in moist air.

1.30. Analytical Tests

Elementary students are often asked to identify some of the sulfur anions as a laboratory exercise. To identify S^{--} ion, add HCl to some of the unknown in a test tube. Across the mouth of the test tube lay a strip of filter paper that has been moistened with lead acetate solution. If the unknown contains a not too insoluble sulfide, H_2S will be produced.

$$S^{--} + 2H^+ + 2Cl^- \rightarrow \overline{H_2S} + 2Cl^-$$

When the gas reaches the mouth of the test tube it will precipitate lead sulfide.

$$\overline{H_2S} + Pb^{++} + 2C_2H_3O_2^- \rightarrow \underline{PbS} + 2HC_2H_3O_2$$

PbS may be brown or black depending on circumstances; frequently it has a semimetallic luster.

If no test for H_2S is obtained, add a drop of iodine solution to the liquid in the test tube. If it is decolorized, H_2SO_3 is present.

$$H_2SO_3 + I_2 + H_2O \rightarrow 3H^+ + HSO_4^- + 2I^-$$

This H_2SO_3 may have come either from a sulfite

$$SO_3^{--} + 2H^+ + 2Cl^- \rightarrow H_2SO_3 + 2Cl^-$$

or from a thiosulfate.

$$S_2O_3^{--} + 2H^+ + 2Cl^- \rightarrow H_2SO_3 + \underline{S} + 2Cl^-$$

The nearly white precipitate of finely divided sulfur is a means of distinguishing $S_2O_3^{--}$ ion from SO_3^{--} ion. The reduction of iodine is not a specific test for H_2SO_3; but H_2S, the only other reducing agent likely to be present, has been distinguished by the first test.

To test for SO_4^{--} ion, add barium nitrate or chloride to an acidified solution of the unknown. If SO_4^{--} is present, a white precipitate of $BaSO_4$ will be formed.

$$SO_4^{--} + Ba^{++} + 2NO_3^- \rightarrow \underline{BaSO_4} + 2NO_3^-$$

A false test may be obtained here if the solution is not strongly acid. *All* polyvalent anions precipitate insoluble barium salts, but SO_4^{--} ion is the only one that is a weak enough base to remain free to any extent in an acid solution. The others are conjugate bases of weak acids and are therefore fairly strong bases; hence they readily take up protons to form the weak acid. This was illustrated above in the case of SO_3^{--} ion.

11.31. Selenium and Tellurium

The remaining elements of the sulfur family are selenium, tellurium, and polonium. Polonium, which was discovered by Pierre and Marie Curie and named for her native land, is so rare that it is of interest only because it was the first strongly radioactive element to be discovered. The other two will be discussed briefly to illustrate the effect of increasing atomic radius on chemical properties.

Since the electronegativity of selenium is slightly below that of iodine, it is not surprising that one of its allotropic modifications is slightly more metallic in appearance than iodine and has some ability to conduct electricity. Tellurium is definitely metallic in appearance and conductivity. The electrical conductivity of selenium is very low in the dark, but increases 100,000-fold with illumination. A selenium photocell thus amounts to a light-operated switch. If a thin wafer of selenium is pressed against a metal surface and heat is applied until the two are cemented together by a film of metal selenide, another peculiarity appears. Electrons will cross the selenide film only in the direction of the metal. This is the basis of the selenium rectifier. The oldest use of selenium is to color glass red. When selenium is colloidally dispersed through glass it produces stop-light red by scattering the short wave lengths in the light; the long wave lengths of red pass by unchanged. Atmospheric dust gives sunsets their red color by the same physical process. At the present relatively low prices for the element, selenium red may be used for coloring ceramics as well. As a selenide, the element has a promising new outlet in the phosphors for TV screens.

The formulas of selenium compounds are what would be expected from its relationship to sulfur, but there are systematic differences in the properties. The increase in acid strength and the decrease in thermal stability which occur with increasing atomic weight in the hydrogen halides is observed in the hydrogen compounds of the oxygen family as well. SeO_2 is a solid instead of a gas like SO_2 because it is a long-chain polymer: $\ddot{S}e : \ddot{O} : \ddot{S}e : \ddot{O} : \ddot{S}e : \ddot{O} :$ $: \ddot{O} : \quad : \ddot{O} : \quad : \ddot{O} :$ This is another example of the fact that the larger an atom, the greater its difficulty in sharing multiple electron pairs. Along with its somewhat metallic properties, in its compounds selenium does not easily acquire the high positive oxidation numbers characteristic of non-metals. Thus H_2SeO_3 is an oxidizing agent instead of a reducing agent; H_2SeO_4 is strong enough as an oxidizing agent to attack gold, whereas silver is the limit for H_2SO_4.

The chemical properties mentioned in connection with selenium apply also to tellurium. In addition it tends to enlarge the valence shell as iodine does; but although $+7$ iodine may exist either as IO_4^- or as IO_6^{-5}, $+6$ tellurium holds six oxygens to itself. There is no TeO_4^{--} ion, only TeO_6^{-6}; so tellurates are not isomorphous with sulfates and selenates. The substance Na_2TeO_4 exists, but the anion is actually a high polymer:

$$\cdots \quad \overset{\overset{\displaystyle O \quad\; O}{|\qquad|}}{\underset{\underset{\displaystyle O \quad\; O}{|\qquad|}}{>Te<}} \quad \overset{\overset{\displaystyle O \quad\; O}{|\qquad|}}{\underset{\underset{\displaystyle O \quad\; O}{|\qquad|}}{>Te<}} \quad > \quad \cdots$$

in which each tellurium atom is in the center of an octahedron of oxygen atoms. Each octahedron has two oxygen atoms in common with the octahedron on its left, and two in common with the octahedron on its right. In the formula above, the oxygen atoms should be thought of as being in three dimensions; those which are directly above and below each tellurium atom should actually be placed one in front of it and one in back of it.

Selenium compounds are widely distributed, but there are never enough in one place to make mining selenium feasible. There is enough selenium in some 50,000 acres of semiarid soil in Wyoming and South Dakota to make some of the vegetation fatal to livestock, but the only commercial source of the element is as a by-product of copper refining. A shortage of selenium in 1956 drove the price to $35 per pound, but the use of improved recovery techniques by a single company the following year boosted our output 35 per cent and reduced the price to $12 per pound. Practically all sulfide ores contain some selenide and a trace of telluride. The town of Telluride, Colorado, was named for the gold telluride which was mined there. (Gold sulfide does not exist because S^{--} ion reduces gold ions to the metal.) Bi_2Te_3 and $PbTe$ are promising new thermoelectric materials. They can be used in the direct conversion of heat into electricity. Conversely, by forcing a current into one of these tellurides refrigeration can be produced without moving parts. A temperature of $-85°$ C. has been produced in this manner in a volume of one cubic inch.

QUESTIONS AND PROBLEMS

1. Compare the oxygen and halogen families as far as similarities and dissimilarities are concerned. How do you explain these?

2. Account for the occurrence of sulfur, sulfides, sulfates, and sulfur springs from a geochemical viewpoint.

3. Describe the Frasch process for mining sulfur deposits in the United States. What other important sources of sulfur are utilized in this country?

4. Describe and explain the allotropism and the peculiarities in the changes of state shown by sulfur when heated.

5. Use balanced equations to compare the direct union of oxygen and sulfur with other elements. How do sulfur and oxygen compare in electronegativity? In oxidizing ability?

6. Illustrate the reducing ability of elemental sulfur by means of balanced equations. Is it peculiar for an element to behave as either an oxidizing or a reducing agent? Explain.

7. What does the prefix thio- indicate as far as composition and valence are concerned? Give examples.

8. Write the balanced chemical equations for three laboratory methods of preparing H_2S.

9. Illustrate the following properties of H_2S by means of balanced chemical equations: reducing ability; precipitating ability; weak acid characteristics.

10. Balance the redox reaction of H_2S and $(H^+ + NO_3^-)$, with NO_2 and SO_4^{--} as products of the reaction.

11. How does the low electronegativity of S and the resultant high polarizability of S^- produce the insolubility and color characteristic of *most* metallic sulfides?

12. Use four appropriate insoluble sulfides to illustrate the dissolving of sulfides by:
    a. Neutralization of S^{--} ion.
    b. Oxidation of S^{--} ion.
    c. Complexing into thio- ions.
    d. A combination of the oxidation of S^{--} ion and the complexing of the metal ion.

13. What is a polysulfide ion? Compare it with peroxide ion chemically and electronically.

14. Show, by balanced equations, four different methods of preparing sulfur dioxide.

15. Indicate all the molecular species present in a water solution of SO_2 by using reversible (equilibrium) reactions.

16. a. Is HSO_3^- ion an acid or a base, or both? Explain.
    b. What is meant by the statement that H_2S and H_2SO_3 are diprotic acids?
    c. Write the formulas of three other diprotic and five monoprotic acids.

17. What are the important chemical properties of H_2SO_3 (or SO_2)? Illustrate with appropriate balanced chemical equations.

18. Both Cl_2 and SO_2 may be used for bleaching and sterilization. What are the advantages and disadvantages of each?

19. What is meant by a reversible reaction? A chemical equilibrium?

20. What is activation energy? How does a catalyst effect it? What is the main purpose of a catalyst in a chemical equilibrium?

21. Compare the two commercial processes used in the manufacture of H_2SO_4 relative to reactions and conditions for each, and the quality of the H_2SO_4 produced by each.

22. Give the many names used for the concentrated contact process acid.

23. List the more important properties of H_2SO_4 and its uses that are based on them.

24. What volume of H_2SO_4, sp. gr. 1.8, 80 per cent H_2SO_4 by weight, is needed to dissolve 100 g. of copper?

25. Write the formulas for anhydrous nickel sulfate and nickel sulfate heptahydrate. How many grams of each are necessary to make up 1 l. of 2 M solution?

26. Draw dot formulas for the following: H_2SO_3; H_2SO_4; thiosulfate ion; tetrathionate ion; peroxydisulfate ion; sulfamate ion.

27. Compare family trends of the elements in Groups VIA and VIIA. Consider such factors as properties of the elements and their ions, electronegativities, bonding characteristics, etc.

12

Nitrogen and phosphorus

12.1. The Nitrogen Family

Group VA of the periodic system contains only one strongly electronegative element, nitrogen, the first member of the family. The electronegativity of nitrogen, 3.0, is equal to that of chlorine; only oxygen and fluorine exceed it. But the characteristically large drop in electronegativity between the first and second members of a group brings phosphorus and arsenic down to the middle of the electronegativity scale, and antimony definitely below the middle. Group VA, then, starts out with a strong nonmetal, includes some intermediate elements, and ends with bismuth, almost a true metal. Earlier chapters mentioned the trace of metallic properties in the elements at the bottom of the halogen family, and the more than trace in the heavier elements in the oxygen family. In the nitrogen family, however, the first traces of metallic properties appear in phosphorus; they are pronounced in arsenic and predominant in antimony and bismuth. The chemical behavior of these last three elements is relatively complicated because they act like non-metals in some ways and like metals in others.

Because the chemistry of the typical metals in Groups IA and IIA is much simpler and far better suited for an introduction to the properties of metals, only nitrogen and phosphorus will be treated in the present chapter. The other three elements will be studied in a later chapter.

12.2. Preparation of Nitrogen

All commercial nitrogen is obtained from air. When liquid air is distilled, nitrogen (78 per cent) is given off first, accompanied by argon (1 per cent). The argon does not interfere with subsequent use of the nitrogen, but can, if desired, be separated for use when a completely inert gas is needed. A trace of oxygen is always present in commercial nitrogen. This can be removed, if necessary, by passing the gas over hot copper. For some purposes a mixture of nitrogen and hydrogen serves as well as pure nitrogen. If the demand for nitrogen is too small to justify building a liquid-air plant, the nitrogen-hydrogen mixture can be obtained by the catalytic decomposition of ammonia at a moderately high temperature.

$$2NH_3 \xrightarrow{\Delta} 3H_2 + N_2$$

Even though the ammonia is itself made from nitrogen, it is cheaper to prepare nitrogen in this way than to buy it, because of the cost of shipping the heavy steel cylinders needed for a gas under high pressure. Ammonia is easily liquefied; hence an ammonia cylinder has light walls and holds several times as much nitrogen per liter volume.

Really pure nitrogen, free from traces of the inert gases, is practically never required. However, it can be prepared by warming a solution containing ammonium ions and nitrite ions.

$$Na^+ + NO_2^- + NH_4^+ + Cl^- \xrightarrow{\Delta} Na^+ + Cl^- + N_2 + 2H_2O$$

The gas which comes off must of course be dried.

12.3. Properties of Nitrogen

Most of the physical properties of nitrogen are familiar to us because we are in constant contact with the nitrogen in the atmosphere. Others are listed in Table 12.1. One liter of water at 0° C. dissolves only 23.5 ml. of nitrogen. This amount is negligible at 1 atm. pressure, but under high pressures enough nitrogen dissolves in the blood to produce nitrogen narcosis, a form of anesthesia. It is this fact that limits the depth to which a swimmer can safely submerge with an aqualung.

TABLE 12.1. **Physical Properties of N₂, P₄, NH₃, and PH₃**

Name	Nitrogen	Phosphorus	Ammonia	Phosphine
Symbol	N_2	P_4	NH_3	PH_3
Melting point, °C.	−210	44	−78	−133
Boiling point, °C.	−196	280	−33	− 88
Critical temperature, °C.	−147	695	132	51
Molecular weight	28	124	17	34
Electronegativity	3.0	2.1		

There are only 10 valence electrons in a diatomic molecule of nitrogen. Each atom completes its octet by sharing three pairs of electrons with its neighbor, : N : : : N : . One of these electron pairs forms a cloud whose maximum density is on the line joining the nuclei. The molecular orbital is formed from the overlapping of a p orbital from each atom, end-on, as in the formation of any ordinary single bond (Section 4.8). Each of the other two molecular orbitals is formed by the overlapping of a pair of p orbitals, one from each atom, with axes at right angles to the axis of the molecule. These approach each other with their axes parallel, and overlap in two regions, one on either side of the molecular axis, forming a

Fig. 12.1. Model of the nitrogen molecule, N_2. The distance between nuclei is abnormally short because of the triple bond.

bond of the π type (Section 4.13). This triple bond is more than three times as strong as a single bond. The nuclei are drawn closer together; the distance between them is only three-quarters of what it would be if there was only a single bond (Fig. 12.1). Therefore each bonding electron cloud attracts each nucleus much more strongly. *The result is the strongest bond known to exist between any two atoms.*

The strong bonding in the nitrogen molecule is not disturbed by any collision that takes place at ordinary temperatures. Only at high temperatures is there enough energy in a collision to break the triple bond and enable the individual nitrogen atoms to display the high chemical activity that corresponds to their high electronegativity. This fact is expressed by the statement that N_2 has a remarkably high activation energy and is therefore inert at ordinary temperatures. The only reaction that nitrogen is capable of under mild temperatures is the one in which it is converted into organic derivatives of ammonia by the action of certain algae, fungi, mosses, and bacteria. Some of these bacteria live in nodules on the roots of leguminous plants and of alders and are of immense importance in agriculture and forestry because they *fix* much more nitrogen than the plants use. The nature of the reaction is not known.

At high temperatures nitrogen is as reactive as its high electronegativity would lead us to expect. It oxidizes active metals, completing its own octet to form nitride ion, N^{-3}. N^{-3} ion resembles O^{--} ion but, in accordance with its higher charge, is an even stronger base. Nitrides which are at all soluble react with water, taking protons from it.

$$Mg_3N_2 + 6H_2O \rightarrow 3Mg(OH)_2 + \overline{2NH_3}$$

The high charge of N^{-3} ion makes most of its compounds insoluble and very hard. Steel is casehardened by heating it in nitrogen until a surface layer of nitride has formed. One crystalline form of boron nitride, BN, is practically as hard as diamond.

Nitrogen can be made to combine with non-metals as well as with metals; but unless the difference in electronegativity is greater than 0.5 unit, these compounds are unstable. Many of them—NCl_3, for example—are actually explosive.

$$2NCl_3 \rightarrow \overline{N_2} + \overline{3Cl_2} + \triangle$$

TABLE 12.2. **Oxides of Nitrogen**

Name	Formula	Color	Oxidation Number of N
Nitrous oxide	N_2O	None	+1
Nitric oxide	NO	None	+2
Nitrous anhydride	N_2O_3	Blue	+3
Nitrogen dioxide	NO_2	Brown	+4
Dinitrogen tetroxide	N_2O_4	None	+4
Nitric anhydride (Nitrogen pentoxide)	N_2O_5	None	+5

This is due to the large amount of energy given out in the formation of the remarkably stable N_2 molecule. Only in NF_3, among the nitrogen halides, is the difference in electronegativity, 1.0 unit, great enough to stabilize the molecule.

The oxides of nitrogen (Table 12.2), border-line in stability, are remarkable for their number. Of these, NO and NO_2 are commercially important, as will be seen later in this chapter. The structures of these two molecules are exceptional in that they involve an *odd number* of electrons; they will not be discussed in this text.

12.4. Fixation of Nitrogen

Any process which causes elemental nitrogen to combine chemically is said to result in the **fixation** of nitrogen. In addition to the biological process mentioned earlier, there is one other natural process—the combining of nitrogen and oxygen, in the path of a lightning flash, to form nitric oxide.

$$\overline{N_2} + \overline{O_2} \rightarrow \overline{2NO}$$

This oxide eventually becomes nitric acid by a series of reactions which are discussed in Section 12.11, and is washed to the earth by rain. Nitrogen compounds are essential to plant growth. The amount produced by these natural processes falls far short of supplying the food needs of the present world population; fortunately, however, other processes have been invented.

The **arc process** produced NO by blowing air through an electric arc, in imitation of the process with natural lightning. At the 3000° C. temperature of the arc, the equilibrium mixture contained only 5 per cent NO, but commercial yields never exceeded 1 per cent. This method became obsolete because it was so wasteful of power.

The synthesis of NH_3 by the **cyanamide process** involves passing nitrogen over calcium carbide in an electric furnace at 1100° C.

$$\underline{CaC_2} + \overline{N_2} \rightarrow \underline{CaCN_2} + \underline{C}$$

The product, calcium cyanamide, is used directly as fertilizer or is processed further to produce other nitrogen compounds. It was once the only source of synthetic ammonia; the reaction is:

$$\underline{CaCN_2} + 3H_2O \rightarrow \underline{CaCO_3} + \overline{2NH_3}$$

It is no longer important as a source of ammonia. Cyanamide ion, CN_2^{--}, has the structure: $\overset{..}{N} :: C :: \overset{..}{N} :^-$, the same electronic structure as in carbon dioxide, CO_2. Molecules with identical electronic structures are referred to as **isoelectronic molecules.**

In the **Haber process,** ammonia is directly synthesized from the elements.

$$\overline{N_2} + \overline{3H_2} \rightleftharpoons \overline{2NH_3} + 24{,}400 \text{ cal.}$$

This reaction, together with the contact process for the production of sulfur trioxide, is among the most important inorganic syntheses in industrial chemistry. Both reactions are reversible and challenged the ingenuity of chemists and engineers in efforts to obtain the maximum amount of product. The importance of catalysts and temperature was considered in Sections 11.19 and 11.20 in connection with the contact process. The statements made there are of course general, and hence are applicable here as well as in many other reactions. We now consider, for the Haber process, some other factors of general application, which involve changing the proportions in equilibrium mixtures for more favorable results. Le Chatelier's principle shows clearly how this can be accomplished when it states: *If any change is made in the conditions affecting an equilibrium, the equilibrium will shift in the direction which tends to counteract the change.* This applies to both physical and chemical equilibria.

Obviously an equilibrium must first be established before it can be shifted in one direction or the other. Thus in the reaction

$$\overline{N_2} + \overline{3H_2} \rightleftharpoons \overline{2NH_3} + \triangle$$

a catalyst is necessary, as it is in the contact process, to obtain a reasonable reaction speed at a moderate temperature so that equilibrium can be established rapidly. An increase in temperature shifts the equilibrium in the direction which absorbs heat; this favors the reaction to the left, but this is not desired. The highest practicable temperature is found to be 475° C. Equilibrium is achieved rapidly at this temperature if a catalytic mixture of iron oxide and potassium aluminate is used. Other catalysts require higher equilibrium temperatures, and as a consequence the mixture has a lower concentration of ammonia. Once equilibrium is established, the reaction can be shifted toward the right—that is, toward the production of more ammonia—by an increase in pressure. In the direct reaction, four molecules of the initial materials are converted into two molecules of the product; this tends to counteract the increase in pressure.

Haber began with a pressure of 200 atm., but pressures of 1000 atm. are now used. Not only new engineering methods but new alloys of steel had to be developed to make this possible, for hydrogen diffuses very rapidly through ordinary steel at such pressures. Although more recent technological developments make possible the use of even higher pressures, the higher costs involved in attaining these pressures argue against their use. True, more ammonia would be produced, but the added return from it would be less than the cost of producing it.

The equilibrium mixture under present methods of production is less than 50 per cent NH_3; accordingly, the gases from the reaction chamber are cooled until the NH_3 liquefies. The uncondensed nitrogen and hydrogen are added to the entering mixture of nitrogen and hydrogen. From time to time some must be vented to prevent the accumulation of argon. In 1957, the 52 Haber process plants in the United States had a capacity which was 25 per cent greater than our demand for NH_3 that year, but even more plants were planned and built because the use of NH_3 had increased so rapidly that it appeared certain that the overcapacity would be only temporary, as proved to be the case.

12.5. Uses of Nitrogen

Nearly all the nitrogen which is separated from the atmosphere is made into ammonia. The ammonia industry is widespread, enormous, and growing rapidly. In the United States alone, over 6 million tons of nitrogen were made into ammonia in 1961—more than was fixed by all processes in the entire world ten years previously. (It is about the amount contained in the air over a surface of 35 sq. mi.) Compared with this use, all the other uses of nitrogen are small, totaling about one-half of a million tons in 1961. Of this, about 150,000 tons were made into cyanamide; the rest was used as elemental nitrogen.

Liquid nitrogen is used to maintain extremely low temperatures and to obtain extra fast cooling; it is also the most convenient form for shipping the gas. The gas is used to strip dissolved oxygen from liquids; to blanket oxidizable oils, paints, drugs, metals, and vitamins; to transfer flammable liquids; to dry materials sensitive to oxidation; and to dilute flammable gas mixtures. In these uses the value of the nitrogen is small compared with that of the material for whose transportation or protection it is used. An example of great interest to chemists in this connection is liquid fluorine, which could be shipped in tank trucks for the first time at the end of 1956. The tank is actually a tank within a tank, the liquid fluorine being in the inner one. It is kept below its boiling point by liquid nitrogen in the surrounding outer tank. The outer tank—or jacket, as it is called—is in turn surrounded by thick insulation. Any heat that leaks in through this insulation is used up in boiling off some of the nitrogen, which is vented to the air.

Nitrogen has some 40 applications in food processing. The gas in pressure-packed coffee is nitrogen. Other foods that are processed and shipped fresh with the aid of nitrogen include edible oils, wine, nuts, potato chips, and various dehydrated fruits and vegetables.

Nitrogen pressure is used to force spontaneously flammable fuels and their oxidizers, such as fuming nitric acid, into rocket motors. Military applications have been responsible for a large increase in the use of free nitrogen in recent years.

12.6. Ammonia

The oxidation number of nitrogen in NH_3 is -3. This is also its oxidation number in ammonium ion, NH_4^+, and in a multitude of substances which living organisms produce from NH_3 and NH_4^+ by replacing one or more protons with complex carbon-containing groups of atoms. These organic compounds which contain -3 nitrogen include proteins, amino acids, alkaloids, and urea. All compounds of -3 nitrogen are readily interconverted. For example, urea, the form in which animals excrete nitrogenous waste, is slowly hydrolyzed to ammonia in the soil. The following equation adopts the practice of organic chemists in showing a covalent bond by a line and omitting unshared electron pairs:

$$
\begin{array}{cc}
& \text{H} \qquad\quad \text{H} \\
& |\qquad\quad\ \ | \\
\text{H} & \text{N---H} \quad \text{H---N---H} \\
| & |\qquad\quad\ \ \text{- - - - - - - -} \\
\text{O} + & \text{C}{=}\text{O} \rightarrow \text{O}{=}\text{C}{=}\text{O} \qquad \text{or} \qquad \overline{2NH_3} + \overline{CO_2} \\
| & |\qquad\quad\ \ \text{- - - - - - - -} \\
\text{H} & \text{N---H} \quad \text{H---N---H} \\
& |\qquad\quad\ \ | \\
& \text{H} \qquad\quad \text{H}
\end{array}
$$

Conversely, when NH_3 and CO_2 are heated at $135°$ C. under pressure, urea is formed. Large amounts of urea are manufactured in this way for use as a slow-acting fertilizer and as a supplement to stock food, and for many chemical processes.

On account of this easy convertibility, all these compounds are considered *forms of ammonia* in the statement, "Ammonia is widely distributed in nature." It is contained not only in manure and other animal and vegetable wastes, but in fossilized plant material, namely, coal. Some NH_4^+ ion is present in nearly all water supplies, but mineral deposits of ammonium salts are negligible because *nearly all ammonium salts are soluble.*

12.7. Physical Properties of Ammonia

As would be expected from its low molecular weight, NH_3 is a gas under ordinary conditions. It is, however, easily liquefied; only about 10 atm. pressure is required at room temperature. Its boiling point at 1 atm. pressure is $-33°$ C. When this is compared to the boiling points of the non-polar molecules N_2, O_2, and F_2, with molecular weights of 28 to 38, compared with 17 for NH_3, it is evident that NH_3 is another polar molecule, like H_2O and HF. The covalent bond between hydrogen and nitrogen is just as polar as that between hydrogen and chlorine, since the differences in electronegativity are the same. But if the NH_3 molecule

Fig. 12.2. The NH_3 molecule. The vacant tetrahedral position is occupied by an unshared electron pair.

were a plane triangle, with the nitrogen atom in the center, it would be non-polar because of its symmetry. Actually, the molecule is a low triangular pyramid, with the negative nitrogen atom at its vertex and the three positive hydrogen atoms at the corners of the base (Fig. 12.2). It is even more polar than this description implies because the unshared electron pair is concentrated in the region directly below the nitrogen atom. The NH_3 molecule is practically identical in shape and size with the H_3O^+ ion, with which it is isoelectronic.

The dielectric constant of liquid NH_3 is only one-quarter as great as that of H_2O (18 : 80), but is still many times that of non-polar liquids. It is therefore a solvent for salts, though not as good as H_2O is. On the other hand, it is a better solvent for slightly polar substances; for some purposes this more than makes up for its relatively poor ability to dissolve salts. The chemical properties of a solvent are also important; those of NH_3 and H_2O are compared in the next section.

Like fluorine and oxygen, nitrogen when negative is capable of forming hydrogen bonds as a result of its high electronegativity and small size. It is hydrogen bonding that is responsible for the abnormally high boiling point of NH_3, just as it is in the case of H_2O and HF. The high boiling point is of course accompanied by an abnormally high heat of vaporization, for all the hydrogen bonds are broken as the liquid becomes a gas. No other liquid with a conveniently low boiling point absorbs as much heat when it boils as NH_3 does; hence its use as the working fluid in ice plants and other large commercial refrigeration installations. Basically, a refrigerator consists of an evaporator, a pump, and a condenser. The evaporator is in the space to be cooled, and as the working liquid boils under reduced pressure it absorbs its heat of vaporization from its surroundings. The pump removes the gas from the evaporator and compresses it into the condenser, where the heat of vaporization is given out as the gas liquefies, and is carried away by an air blast or a spray of cooling water (Fig. 12.3).

In household refrigerators and air conditioners the amount of heat to be transferred is so small that the quantity of working fluid is a minor consideration. In these machines less efficient liquids with higher boiling points are preferred to NH_3 because the lower pressures involved

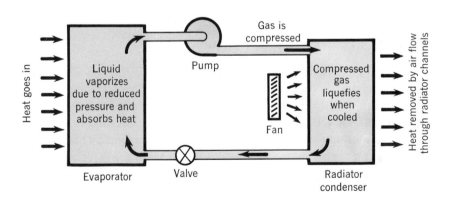

Fig. 12.3. Diagram of a mechanical refrigerator. The heat of vaporization of the refrigerant is absorbed in the evaporator and pumped into the condenser, where it is given off at considerably higher temperature. A proper valve system makes it possible to interchange the functions of evaporator and condenser so that the same machine which pumps heat out of a house in summer will pump heat in in winter.

require smaller motors and compressors. **Absorption (non-electric) refrigerators,** however, are an exception. In this type of machine the NH_3 gas is allowed to dissolve in water in the evaporator; it is then boiled off and forced into the condenser by means of a small flame. The cold water in the condenser (called an absorber in this type of refrigerator) serves as the suction side of a pump, the flame as the pressure side. An absorption refrigerator has no moving parts except the thermally operated valves.

The solubility of a gas in water is usually included as one of its physical properties, and this is proper enough in dealing with gases whose solubilities are on the order of a few percentage points by volume, such as O_2, H_2, and N_2. But gases like NH_3 and HCl, of which 1000 to 1200 l. are dissolved in 1 l. of water, do this by chemical reaction. In the case of NH_3, the reaction is:

$$\overline{NH_3} + H_2O \rightleftharpoons NH_4OH + \triangle$$

This is easily reversed by heat; a few moments of boiling drives off all the NH_3 from a water solution. The ease with which the original NH_3 is recovered is responsible for its dissolving being thought of as though it were a physical phenomenon only. When any chemical reaction uses up NH_3, it of course also reverses the reaction for the formation of ammonium hydroxide. We may therefore speak of a solution of ammonia in water and write NH_3, or of a solution of ammonium hydroxide and write NH_4OH, as suits our convenience.

12.8. Chemical Properties of Ammonia

The most noticeable chemical property of NH_3 is the fact that it is a base. Non-metal atoms share an electron pair with a proton, or any other cation, more readily the lower the electronegativity of the non-metal atom. (It is assumed, of course, that other important factors, such as charge and atomic radius, remain approximately constant.) Thus we find that HF has no basic properties, even though there are three unshared electron pairs on the fluorine atom; although the oxygen atom has two unshared electron pairs, H_2O is a very weak base; and NH_3 is a good base, although the nitrogen atom has only one electron pair to share. Similarly, F^- is a fair base, OH^- a strong one, and NH_2^- too strong to exist in water solution; it takes a proton from even such a weak acid as H_2O.

Its basic nature enables NH_3 to neutralize strong acids, and even moderately weak ones such as acetic acid, $HC_2H_3O_2$, the acid of vinegar.

$$NH_3 + HC_2H_3O_2 \rightarrow NH_4^+ + C_2H_3O_2^-$$

NH_3 also shares its electron pair with cations of the non-inert gas type, displacing, if necessary, molecules of the much weaker base H_2O. The following reaction with copper(II) ion is typical:

$$Cu(H_2O)_4^{++} + 4NH_3 \rightarrow Cu(NH_3)_4^{++} + 4H_2O$$

In accordance with the practice of omitting water of hydration from the formulas of ions in water solution, the water may be omitted from this equation. The systematic name of $Cu(NH_3)_4^{++}$ is tetramminecopper(II) ion, but its old name, copper-ammonia ion, is more commonly used. Its intense dark blue color makes it possible to recognize the presence of copper(II) ion in a solution so dilute that the pale blue color of the hydrated ion (tetraaquocopper(II) ion) is invisible.

As would be expected from the fact that NH_3 is a good base, its acid properties are negligible. For example, the alkali metals—sodium, etc.—dissolve in liquid NH_3 without chemical action. H_2 is liberated only slowly or in the presence of a catalyst.

$$2Na + 2NH_3 \xrightarrow{\text{catalyst}} 2Na^+ + 2NH_2^- + \overline{H_2}$$

In liquid ammonia, acting as a solvent, acids form ammonium ion, NH_4^+; this is analogous to the formation of hydronium ion, H_3O^+, in water.

$$NH_3 + HCl \rightarrow NH_4^+ + Cl^-$$
$$H_2O + HCl \rightarrow H_3O^+ + Cl^-$$

Since NH_3 is a good base, NH_4^+ ion, in contrast to H_3O^+ ion, is a weak acid. Any acid stronger than NH_4^+ ion reacts completely with NH_3, forming NH_4^+ ion; consequently NH_4^+ ion is the strongest acid which can exist as such in NH_3 solution. On the other hand, since NH_3 is not an acid, bases that are too strong to exist in water solution—for example, amide ion, NH_2^-, from $NaNH_2$, and hydride ion, H^-, from NaH or LiH—can dissolve in it unchanged. Ammonia solutions of these "superbases" can neutralize acids that are too weak to be neutralized by any base which can exist in water solution.

NH_3 is not a good reducing agent, but it can be oxidized, both biologically and by ordinary chemical means. It will not burn in air unless heated, but will burn in oxygen.

$$\overline{4NH_3} + \overline{3O_2} \rightarrow \overline{2N_2} + \overline{6H_2O} + \triangle$$

By controlled oxidation a number of more interesting products may be obtained. Hydrazine,* $H_2N—NH_2$, bears the same relation to NH_3 as H_2O_2 does to H_2O. Hydroxylamine, $H_2N—OH$, is intermediate between hydrazine and hydrogen peroxide. The most important use of the controlled oxidation of NH_3 is in the **Ostwald process** for producing nitric oxide, NO, the first step in making nitric acid, HNO_3, from NH_3. In this process a mixture of NH_3 and air is blown through platinum gauze at about 400° C.

$$\overline{4NH_3} + \overline{5O_2} \rightarrow \overline{4NO} + \overline{6H_2O} + \triangle$$

12.9. Ammonium Ion, NH_4^+

When NH_3 takes a proton from an acid, ammonium ion, NH_4^+, is formed. This ion is a symmetrical tetrahedron, like ClO_4^- and SO_4^{--}. It

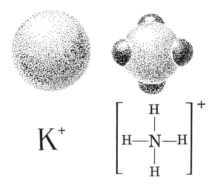

$$K^+ \qquad \left[\begin{array}{c} H \\ | \\ H—N—H \\ | \\ H \end{array} \right]^+$$

Fig. 12.4. The similar size and charge of potassium and ammonium ions is responsible for the closely related properties of their compounds.

is about the size of K^+ ion and nearly as symmetrical (Fig. 12.4). Since the charge on each is $+1$, the two ions are very similar in regard to the crystal forms and solubilities of their salts. One striking difference is the fact that NH_4^+ is an acid, K^+ is not. Although NH_4^+ is a very weak acid, it is strong enough to react readily with OH^- ion. Thus a convenient laboratory means of preparing NH_3 involves heating a mixture of any ammonium salt and a strong base, such as calcium hydroxide (lime), $Ca(OH)_2$.

$$\underline{(NH_4)_2SO_4} + \underline{Ca(OH)_2} \xrightarrow{\triangle} \underline{CaSO_4} + \overline{2NH_3} + \overline{2H_2O}$$

---

* The syllable -*az*-, used in the names of many nitrogen compounds, comes from *azote* (without life), the French name for nitrogen.

A less obvious but important difference between NH_4^+ and K^+ ions is that the former is capable of hydrogen bonding with OH^- and F^- ions. Thus NH_4OH is not an ionic compound like KOH, but a *weak electrolyte*. When OH^- ion is added to a solution containing NH_4^+ ion, all but a trace of the NH_4^+ is converted into NH_4OH. Since the equilibrium with NH_3 is established simultaneously, the strong, characteristic odor of ammonia can be perceived (if the solution is dilute, it may be necessary to warm it); this odor provides a *good analytical test for the presence of* NH_4^+ *ion*.

NH_4OH is not merely a weak electrolyte, it is also a weak base. In fact, such basic properties as are shown by a solution containing it may be due entirely to the small quantities of NH_3 and OH^- ion that are in equilibrium with it as a result of the two ways in which the molecule can break up.

$$H_2O + \overline{NH_3} \rightleftharpoons NH_4OH \rightleftharpoons NH_4^+ + OH^-$$

12.10. Uses of Ammonia and Ammonium Ion

In both NH_3 and NH_4^+ the oxidation number of nitrogen is -3, and for fertilizer, the most important of all uses of nitrogen, NH_3 and NH_4^+ are equally good. Cost, convenience, and custom determine which will be used in a particular case. Before 1913 the only available fertilizer of this type was ammonium sulfate, a by-product of the manufacture of steel, made by scrubbing coal gas and coke oven gas with dilute H_2SO_4. Our current production of ammonium sulfate from this source is around 850,000 tons annually, but we now produce at the same time about 1,000,000 tons of it from synthetic ammonia. The most important use of this is as fertilizer. It contains only 26 per cent of nitrogen and is priced accordingly. About one-fourth of the vastly expanded modern demand for nitrogenous fertilizer is supplied by ammonium nitrate, NH_4NO_3, our annual use of which is now 1,250,000 tons. The nitrogen in NH_4^+ ion is more effective in earlier stages of crop growth, and that in NO_3^- in later stages. The total nitrogen content of NH_4NO_3 is 35 per cent. The present trend is toward applying nitrogen in liquid form, as NH_4OH solution (ammonia liquor) with or without dissolved NH_4NO_3; and, most recently, as anhydrous liquid NH_3. The latter ranks first among nitrogen fertilizers in current use, accounting for at least 30 per cent of all the nitrogen man applies to the soil. It is applied on a custom basis by local dealers, with machines resembling grain drills which deposit it several inches below the surface and cover the furrows (see Fig. 12.5). The liquid NH_3 dissolves in the soil moisture as fast as it vaporizes, no

Fig. 12.5. The direct application of anhydrous ammonia into soil. The injector teeth of the applicator are being lowered into the soil. These in turn knife the fertilizer into the soil at least eight inches deep. (Courtesy, Nitrogen Division, Allied Chemical Corporation.)

more than 2 per cent, it is claimed, being lost to the atmosphere. A considerable portion of it is oxidized by soil bacteria to NO_3^- ion; so it has much the same effect as NH_4NO_3 does. However, the cost is lower; since only NH_3 (82 per cent nitrogen) is used, no costly nitric acid plant is required, and tank-car shipments involve less labor than sacking and handling a solid. The amount of anhydrous liquid ammonia applied directly to the soil rose from 5000 tons in 1947 to nearly 720,000 tons in 1960.

Other uses of ammonia include refrigeration (20,000 tons), and the manufactuer of ammonium salts (1.1 million tons) and of nitric acid, HNO_3 (900,000 tons). In many cases ammonium salts are of interest only for their anions, for which the NH_4^+ ion serves only as a convenient positive ion to pair off with the negative ion in order to complete the compound. In this sense NH_4^+ ion can be considered as being a convenient "handle" for negative ions which are under study. As a handle, NH_4^+ ion has the advantage that practically all its salts are soluble. (In a similar vein, and for the same reason, NO_3^- ion is a good handle for positive ions.) Sometimes, however, as was mentioned in connection with fertilizer, an ammonium salt is used specifically for the NH_4^+ ion. Ammonium chloride (sal ammoniac), NH_4Cl, is used as a weak acid in dry cells and to dissolve zinc oxide from galvanized iron before soldering. In ammonium bicarbonate, NH_4HCO_3, the weakly acid cation reacts with the weakly basic anion at baking temperatures, producing the gases which leaven crackers.

$$NH_4HCO_3 \xrightarrow{\Delta} \overline{NH_3} + \overline{H_2O} + \overline{CO_2}$$

In addition to its use in fertilizer, NH_4NO_3 is used extensively as a high explosive. It can be handled without any precautions, and can be detonated by means of a booster charge of a more sensitive explosive. The reaction is:

$$2NH_4NO_3 \rightarrow \overline{2N_2} + \overline{4H_2O} + \overline{O_2}$$

Since it contains an excess of oxygen, NH_4NO_3 is sometimes mixed with another high explosive like TNT (trinitrotoluene), which is deficient in oxygen. When decomposed by heat instead of shock, melted NH_4NO_3 produces nitrous oxide, N_2O, the light anesthetic that dentists ordinarily call "gas."

$$NH_4NO_3 \xrightarrow{\Delta} \overline{N_2O} + \overline{2H_2O}$$

If, however, combustible material is present, detonation may occur. Fig. 12.6 shows the disastrous effects in nearby chemical plants of the explosion caused by a fire in a ship loaded with NH_4NO_3 packed in *paper sacks*.

12.11. Nitric Acid

Animal wastes, such as manure, contain compounds of ammonia. Under certain conditions these may be oxidized largely to NO_3^- ion and leached out, together with K^+ ion, by rain water. This solution may evaporate elsewhere and deposit crusts of KNO_3 on the ground. This material was known in ancient times as saltpeter (rock salt) to distinguish it from sea salt, $NaCl$, and the old name is still more common commercially than the chemical name, potassium nitrate.

Fig. 12.6. Fires set at Texas City by the explosion of ammonium nitrate fertilizer on a burning freighter. The fire at the extreme left was at the dock where the ship was berthed; the others were set when flying pieces of steel pierced oil tanks, stills, and gas lines. The Monsanto plant in the foreground produced one-eighth of the styrene (page 663) used in the production of synthetic rubber during World War II. (United Press International photo.)

Nitric acid, HNO_3, was originally made by distilling saltpeter with concentrated sulfuric acid.

$$KNO_3 + H_2SO_4 \xrightarrow{\Delta} \overline{HNO_3} + KHSO_4$$

In more modern times $NaNO_3$ was substituted for KNO_3 when certain portions of the last residues of a dried-up sea in Chile were found to contain important quantities of $NaNO_3$ along with the $NaCl$ and dirt. $NaNO_3$ is commonly called Chile saltpeter. It is still important as a fertilizer but is no longer used in making HNO_3; the latter is now made almost entirely from NH_3.

The manufacture of HNO_3 from NH_3 begins with the oxidation of NH_3 to NO by the Ostwald process mentioned in Section 12.8. (In one new plant, designed to produce 250 tons of HNO_3 per day, this oxidation generates enough heat to supply all the power the Ostwald process requires.) When the colorless NO, together with excess air, has been cooled somewhat, it unites with more oxygen to form the brown gas, nitrogen dioxide, NO_2; this in turn reacts with water to form HNO_3.

$$\overline{2NO} + \overline{O_2} \rightarrow \overline{2NO_2}$$
$$\overline{3NO_2} + H_2O \rightleftharpoons 2HNO_3 + \overline{NO}$$

The NO thus produced reacts with more oxygen and is eventually used up. Furthermore, the HNO_3, a strong acid, is completely ionized as long as a reasonable amount of water is present; so we may write the overall reaction as

$$\overline{4NO_2} + 6H_2O + \overline{O_2} \rightarrow 4H_3O^+ + 4NO_3^-$$

A solution containing 68 per cent HNO_3 is sold as concentrated nitric acid. More concentrated solutions contain appreciable amounts of un-ionized HNO_3 molecules. Accordingly they have increasing vapor pressures of HNO_3 and fume in moist air like concentrated solutions of hydrochloric acid. The fuming nitric acid of commerce is pure HNO_3; it boils at 86° C. and has a vapor pressure of 48 mm. at 20° C. Unless freshly distilled or cleansed by a current of air bubbled through it, this acid is yellow, owing to the presence of a little NO_2 produced by the slow decomposition of HNO_3 molecules (*not* H_3O^+ and NO_3^- ions). The equation is:

$$6HNO_3 \rightarrow \overline{O_2} + 2H_3O^+ + 2NO_3^- + \overline{4NO_2}$$

At high temperatures this decomposition is rapid. A glowing ember completely submerged in hot fuming HNO_3 burns brilliantly. HNO_3 is itself a good solvent for NO_2. The solution, which is known as red fuming nitric acid, is a more active oxidizing agent than pure HNO_3.

12.12. Properties and Uses of HNO_3

HNO_3 is a very strong acid, probably intermediate in strength between HCl and H_2SO_4. However, the fact that it is a powerful and active oxidizing agent is of far greater importance. Because of its higher price it is never used merely as an acid unless for some reason the Cl- and SO_4^{--} ions of the other two cheaper acids are not desirable. Such a reason might be the presence of cations which would form insoluble chlorides or sulfates; all nitrates are soluble. HNO_3 is a strong enough oxidizing agent to oxidize Cl- to nitrosyl chloride, NOCl, or to Cl_2, sulfur to H_2SO_4, copper to Cu^{++}, and silver to Ag^+. Thousands of tons of silver are dissolved in HNO_3 annually to make photographic film and paper. It is easy to see why the alchemists called HNO_3 *aqua fortis* or strong water. Gold is not affected by pure HNO_3; this, as well as its costliness, is why it was called "king of the metals." It dissolves readily, however, in a mixture of HNO_3 and HCl, which is therefore called *aqua regia,* or royal water (Section 10.11).

When concentrated HNO_3 acts as an oxidizing agent, the reduction product is always NO_2. Even if the reducing agent is powerful enough to carry the reduction further (*Danger!*) any product in which the nitrogen has a lower oxidation number than $+4$ would be oxidized back to NO_2 before it could escape from the HNO_3. When dilute HNO_3 acts on an ordinary oxidizing agent the product must be NO; for even if NO_2 is the initial product it will react with the water that is present and be converted into NO and HNO_3 (Section 12.11).

$$3\underline{Cu} + 8(H^+ + NO_3^-) \rightarrow 3Cu^{++} + 6NO_3^- + 2\overline{NO} + 4H_2O$$
$$\text{dil.}$$

$$\underline{Ag} + 2(H^+ + NO_3^-) \rightarrow Ag^+ + NO_3^- + \overline{NO_2} + H_2O$$
$$\text{conc.}$$

Since HNO_3 is a strong acid we might expect that active metals would liberate hydrogen from it. This doubtless occurs; but unless the metal is at least as active as magnesium and the acid is very dilute, the hydrogen will not be produced fast enough to escape being reoxidized by the HNO_3. The more active metals reduce to still lower valences not only HNO_3 but the NO produced by the oxidation of hydrogen. Thus when zinc is dissolved in sufficiently dilute HNO_3, no gas is produced.

$$4\underline{Zn} + 10H^+ + 10NO_3^- \rightarrow 4Zn^{++} + NH_4^+ + 9NO_3^- + 3H_2O$$

Large quantities of HNO_3 are used in making fertilizer. The most important of these, NH_4NO_3, has been discussed, but two others are worth mentioning. One large plant in this country manufactures $NaNO_3$ at a price which enables it to compete with natural Chile saltpeter. The raw materials are $NaCl$ and HNO_3; chlorine is an important by-product. The reaction is:

$$4HNO_3 + 3\underline{NaCl} \rightarrow 3NaNO_3 + \overline{NOCl} + \overline{Cl_2} + 2\overline{H_2O}$$

The NOCl and some of the H_2O are then converted by atmospheric oxygen into chlorine and HNO_3. The HNO_3 is returned to the production process, so the final result is:

$$4HNO_3 + \overline{4NaCl} + \overline{O_2} \rightarrow 4NaNO_3 + \overline{2Cl_2} + 2H_2O$$

The HNO_3 may be said to catalyze the oxidation of Cl^- ion by oxygen, since no NO_3^- ion is lost. HNO_3 is also used to a considerable extent in place of H_2SO_4 in solubilizing phosphate rock. The result is a mixed fertilizer containing NO_3^- ion instead of the useless SO_4^{--} ion that is present in superphosphate.

12.13. Nitration

HNO_3 reacts with concentrated H_2SO_4 thus:

$$H^+ + NO_3^- + 2(H^+ + HSO_4^-) \rightarrow NO_2^+ + H_3O^+ + 2HSO_4^-$$

NO_2^+ is known as nitronium (or sometimes nitryl) ion. Its structure can be represented by the dot formula: $\overset{..}{O} :: N :: \overset{..}{O} :^+$, but it has an extremely strong tendency to acquire a share in an additional electron pair; its structure then becomes $R : N :: \overset{..}{O} :$, where R stands for an atom, which
$$: \overset{..}{\underset{..}{O}} :$$
may be part of a large molecule, that has donated a share in one of its electron pairs. R need not be a free base, with an unshared electron pair; the NO_2^+ ion is quite capable of displacing a proton from the electron pair it shares with a base.

$$NO_2^+ + 2H_2O \rightarrow HNO_3 + H_3O^+$$

G.N. Lewis pointed out that when a base shares an electron pair with a molecule such as NO_2^+ it is neutralized just as it would be by sharing the electron pair with a proton; hence molecules of this sort show definitely acidic behavior. Non-protonic acids are now known as **Lewis acids**. NO_2^+ ion is a very strong Lewis acid, and an extremely useful one. The reaction in which an NO_2^+ ion displaces a proton from a compound containing carbon (an *organic* compound) is called **nitration**. Nitrations are involved in the synthesis of most dyes, drugs, and high explosives. If the displaced proton was attached to a carbon atom, the product is a nitro compound, since the covalently bonded $-NO_2$ is called the nitro group. A fairly familiar nitro compound is trinitrotoluene (TNT), largely used as the bursting charge in artillery shells and conventional airplane bombs. It is made by nitrating toluene.

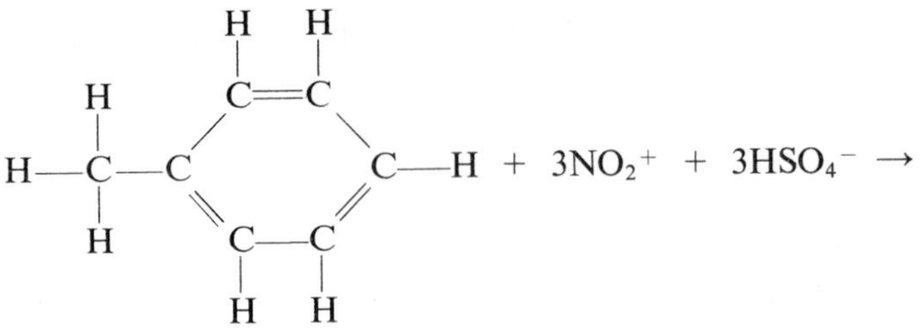

Toluene

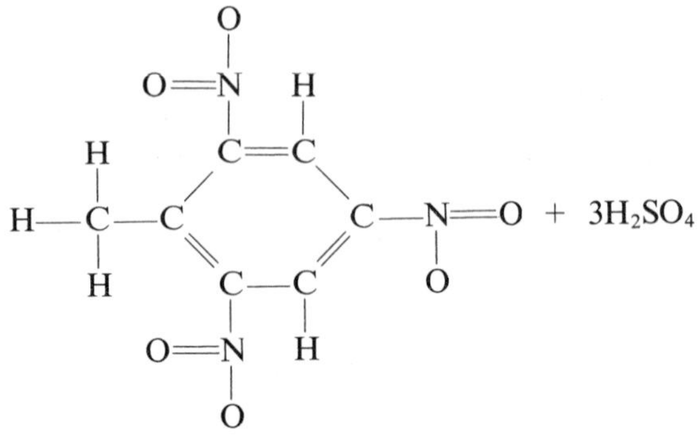

Trinitrotoluene

If the displaced proton was attached to an oxygen atom the product is a covalently bonded nitrate. Thus nitration of glycerol (commonly called glycerin) yields glyceryl trinitrate.

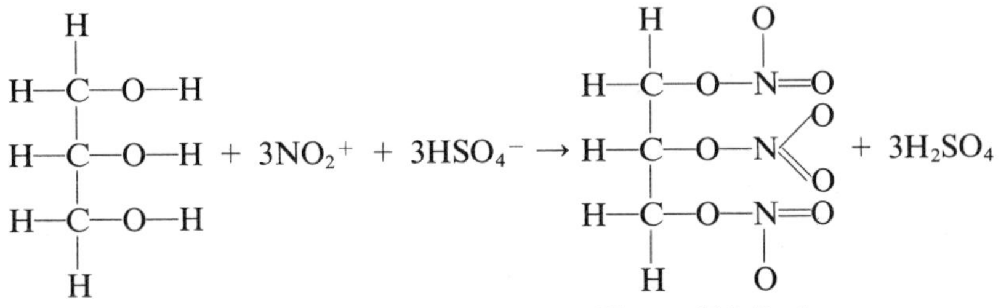

Glycerol   **Glycerol trinitrate**

Glyceryl trinitrate is known commercially as nitroglycerin. It is a high explosive that is too sensitive to shock for ordinary use—it is used for "shooting" oil wells—but can be handled safely if it is soaked up into an absorbent material. This discovery was made by Alfred Nobel, and was the basis of the fortune with which he established the famous Nobel prizes. He used diatomaceous earth as the absorbent and named the product dynamite. When cellulose nitrate (nitrocellulose, or guncotton) is used as the absorbent, it gelatinizes. The product, gelatin dynamite, is not as sensitive to shock as either of its components; but when properly detonated by a high-explosive primer, it is a more powerful explosive than pure nitroglycerin.

Nitro compounds owe their use in the dye and drug industries to the fact that they can be reduced to amines; these are derivatives of NH_3 in which one or more protons have been replaced by organic groups.

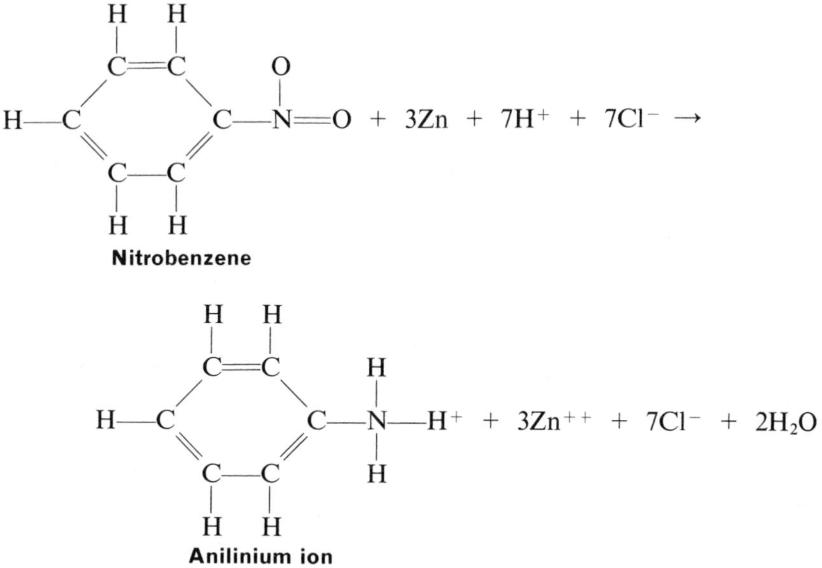

Nitrobenzene

$$\text{Nitrobenzene} + 3Zn + 7H^+ + 7Cl^- \rightarrow$$

Anilinium ion

$$\text{Anilinium ion} + 3Zn^{++} + 7Cl^- + 2H_2O$$

Anilinium chloride is known commercially by its older name, aniline hydrochloride. Anilinium ion, like ammonium ion, is an acid, but a somewhat stronger one; the free base, aniline, can be prepared from it exactly as the free base ammonia is prepared from ammonium ion. Aniline was the starting point for mauve, the first synthetic dye. Other amines are the basis of other dyes and of most of the natural and synthetic drugs.

12.14. Nitrate Ion

The NO_3^- ion is a plane triangle with the nitrogen atom in the center (Fig. 12.7). It is isoelectronic with the identically shaped SO_3 molecule (Section 11.22), but has a charge of -1 because the central atom is N(V) instead of S(VI). In NO_3^- as in SO_3, each oxygen forms $1\frac{1}{3}$ bonds with the central atom. The dot formula, $: \overset{..}{O} : N :: O :^-$, symbolizes this $: \overset{..}{O} :$

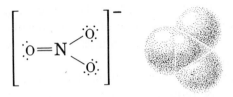

Fig. 12.7. The planar-triangle nitrate ion, NO_3^-. The ion is of the same geometric shape as the SO_3 molecule with which it is isoelectronic.

state of identical bonds between nitrogen and oxygen for the same reasons as those given for the identical situation in the SO_3 molecule (Section 11.22).

The NO_3^- ion is a weaker base than water and has little tendency to form complex ions. Its oxidizing power is only moderate except in the presence of high H^+ ion concentrations or at high temperatures. All metal nitrates are soluble. These properties make NO_3^- ion the most desirable anion to have present during qualitative analysis for cations. Accordingly, nitrates are the most common metallic salts on laboratory stock shelves.

Sodium and potassium nitrates are stable at temperatures a little above their melting points; but when sufficiently heated, they lose some of their oxygen, forming nitrites.

$$2NaNO_3 \xrightarrow{\Delta} 2NaNO_2 + \overline{O_2}$$

The nitrite ion formed in these melts is highly reactive as an oxidizing agent, forming free nitrogen. This accounts for the use of KNO_3, together with sulfur and carbon, in old-fashioned black gunpowder. Considered stepwise, the reactions would occur as follows:

$$2KNO_3 + C \rightarrow 2KNO_2 + \overline{CO_2}$$

$$4KNO_2 + 3C \rightarrow 2K_2O + \overline{3CO_2} + \overline{2N_2}$$

Sulfur would behave similarly to carbon, forming SO_2. This is also the reason for the use of $NaNO_3$ in brown blasting powder (giant powder).

Nitrates of the less active metals decompose into the metal oxides, nitrogen dioxide, and oxygen.

$$2Pb(NO_3)_2 \rightarrow 2PbO + \overline{4NO_2} + \overline{O_2}$$

The presence of even a trace of NO_3^- ion in solution can be recognized by means of the **brown ring test**. A little iron(II) sulfate solution is added to some of the solution to be tested and then floated on some concentrated H_2SO_4 in a test tube. The H^+ ion concentration is high at the surface of contact, so the NO_3^- ion oxidizes *some* of the Fe^{++} ion.

$$4H^+ + NO_3^- + 3Fe^{++} \rightarrow 3Fe^{+3} + \overline{NO} + 2H_2O$$

The NO molecules which are produced attach to the Fe^{++} ions that are present in excess. The resulting ferrous nitrosyl complex ion, $FeNO^{++}$, has an intense dark brown color that is easily visible as a ring or disk at the interface.

12.15. Nitrite Ion

If one oxygen atom is removed from an NO_3^- ion, leaving an unshared electron pair on the nitrogen, the result is an angular molecule, the NO_2^- ion (Fig. 12.8). The dot formula, which for convenience is usually written

$: \overset{..}{\underset{..}{O}} : \overset{..}{N} :: \overset{..}{O} :^-$ rather than $N :: \overset{..}{\underset{..}{O}}^-$, shows that each oxygen atom forms $: \overset{..}{\underset{..}{O}} :$

$1\frac{1}{2}$ bonds with the nitrogen atom. NO_2^- is a weaker oxidizing agent than NO_3^- ion; it can reduce strong oxidizing agents, such as MnO_4^- ion, be-

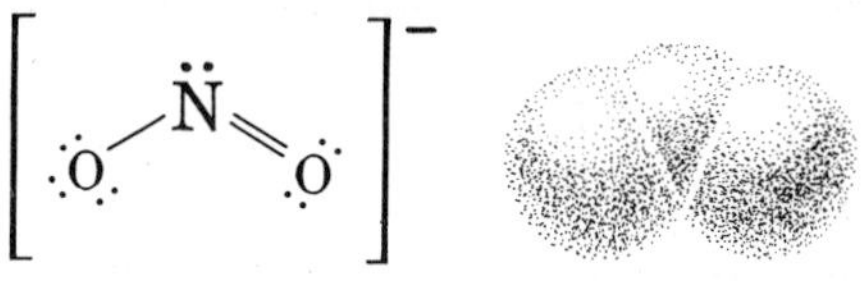

Fig. 12.8. The non-linear nitrite ion, NO_2^-.

ing itself oxidized to NO_3^- ion. It is a moderate base, so nitrous acid, HNO_2, is a moderately weak acid. Nitrite ion forms covalent bonds much more readily than NO_3^- ion; it forms many complex ions. One of them, hexanitritocobaltate(III) ion, $Co(NO_2)_6^{-3}$, forms a potassium salt that is sufficiently insoluble to be used for the analytical detection of K^+ ion in not too dilute solutions.

The most frequent use of NO_2^- ion, though one of the least known, is to give meat a red color. An oxidizing agent as well as the trace of NO_2^- ion is necessary for this purpose. For ham, the oxidizing agent is NO_3^- ion. For hamburger it is oxygen; this is why a pile of hamburger in a butcher shop is grayish (its natural color) below the appetizing red of the surface layer. A much more important use of NO_2^- ion is in organic chemistry, particularly in dye manufacturing.

HNO_2 is not only weak, it is unstable. It cannot exist in the pure state, and even in solution it is always in equilibrium with its anhydride, N_2O_3. (In this respect it is like $HClO$.) In the pure state, nitrogen trioxide, N_2O_3, is a liquid that is intensely dark blue in color. If an ice-cold solution of a nitrite is slightly acidified, a pale tint of this color becomes visible. On evaporation from either the solution or the pure liquid, N_2O_3 dissociates into NO and NO_2; the reaction is reversible. The color contrast between the blue of the liquid and the brown of the gas is startling.

$$N_2O_3 \rightleftharpoons \overline{NO} + \overline{NO_2}$$

Because of this equilibrium, the ring test can be used with NO_2^- ion even without a high enough H^+ ion concentration to enable it to oxidize Fe^{++} ion. Even acetic acid produces HNO_2 and then NO. After the N_2O_3 is boiled off, the ring test for NO_3^- ion can be made.

Like NO_3^- ion, NO_2^- ion can be covalently bonded to organic groups. If the bonding involves one of the oxygen atoms, the compound is a nitrite; thus

$$H : \overset{\overset{\displaystyle H}{..}}{\underset{\overset{..}{\displaystyle H}}{C}} : \overset{\overset{\displaystyle H}{..}}{\underset{\overset{..}{\displaystyle H}}{C}} : \overset{..}{\underset{..}{O}} : \overset{..}{N} :: \overset{..}{\underset{..}{O}}$$

is ethyl nitrite, a volatile liquid whose vapor is inhaled to relieve the pain of angina pectoris. If the bonding involves the nitrogen atom, a nitro compound is formed, as was mentioned above. Thus

$$H : \overset{\overset{\displaystyle H}{..}}{\underset{\overset{..}{\displaystyle H}}{C}} : \overset{\overset{\displaystyle H}{..}}{\underset{\overset{..}{\displaystyle H}}{C}} : \overset{..}{N} :: \overset{..}{\underset{\underset{\displaystyle :\overset{..}{O}:}{}}{O}} :$$

is nitroethane, a gas that has very different properties. Two compounds whose molecules are composed of the same atoms, but differently arranged, are called **isomers**. Their properties vary just as much as the meaning of the words *steak* and *stake,* which likewise differ only in the arrangement of the identical component parts.

12.16. Preparation of Phosphorus

Phosphorus occurs in nature only in the form of phosphate ion, PO_4^{-3}. Of the several phosphate minerals, those that are important as sources of phosphorus are the calcium phosphates, which are grouped under the general name phosphate rock. The most abundant of these is apatite, $Ca_5(PO_4)_3X$; X may be OH^- or F^- ion. Some phosphorite, $Ca_3(PO_4)_2$, is also mined. Phosphorus may be prepared from any of these minerals by reduction with carbon in an electric furnace. Silica, SiO_2, is added as a flux so that the residue will be the fusible salt, calcium silicate, $CaSiO_3$, rather than the extremely refractory oxide, CaO. The latter, a basic anhydride, reacts readily with the acid anhydride, SiO_2. The equation may be written:

$$2Ca_3(PO_4)_2 + \underline{10C} + 6SiO_2 \rightarrow 6CaSiO_3 + \overline{10CO} + \overline{P_4}$$

The phosphorus is condensed by cooling the stream of carbon monoxide and phosphorus vapor which emerges from the furnace. The resulting liquid phosphorus is run into molds, where it solidifies. Alternatively, the phosphorus can be burned to phosphoric anhydride, P_4O_{10}, without being separated.

The quantity of elemental phosphorus consumed in the United States in 1960 was 400,000 tons, an increase of 25 per cent over 1955. About 85 per cent of this is burned. Of the remainder, 25,000 tons go into the compounds to be described in Sections 12.19 and 12.20, and 6000 tons into such alloys as phosphor bronze.

2.17. Physical Properties of Phosphorus

Phosphorus displays as marked differences in properties compared to nitrogen as sulfur and chlorine do relative to their first-row family members. Phosphorus and sulfur do not form multiple bonds between pairs of their atoms as nitrogen and oxygen do. The fact that both are solids at room temperature indicates their existence as large polyatomic molecules, in contrast to their diatomic gaseous first-row relatives. Phosphorus, with 5 valence electrons, needs 3 more to complete its octet. Hence in forming covalent bonds it must form three such bonds, thus acquiring a share in 3 additional electrons. Since it cannot form stable multiple bonds, a phosphorus atom must be bonded to three other phosphorus atoms in order to form these three single covalent bonds. In P_4, the interesting tetraatomic molecule thus formed, *each* phosphorus is linked to the other three (Fig. 12.9). This four-membered molecule is *tetrahedral,* and bond angles of 60° are geometrically necessary in it. It was pointed out in Section 4.13 that the electron clouds of p orbitals of a given level are concentrated at the ends of three mutually perpendicular axes. Chemists have found that molecules in which p orbitals or combinations of s and p orbitals are used in forming three bonds to one atom have bond angles of approximately 90° and 120° respectively. A bond angle of 60° indicates that d orbitals are involved. Therefore, in phosphorus some d orbitals of the third layer must be involved in forming the P_4 molecules. This explains the difference of elemental phosphorus

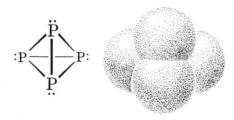

Fig. 12.9. The tetrahedral molecule, P_4. Each phosphorus atom forms single covalent bonds with each of its three equidistant neighbors.

and nitrogen in chemical behavior. Since d electrons have higher energy than either s or p electrons, the bonds they form are weaker than s and p bonds. Accordingly the stronger s and p multiple bonds of nitrogen are responsible for its higher activation energy compared to phosphorus; that is, it is more difficult to break the nitrogen bonds. This accounts for the greater ease with which phosphorus reacts compared to nitrogen, *even though nitrogen is more electronegative.* Because of its greater electronegativity, the nitrogen *atom* is more reactive than the phosphorus atom, but the tightly bonded diatomic *molecule,* N_2, is less reactive than the more loosely bonded P_4 molecule.

Atomic vibrations in the P_4 molecule that are due to light radiation or thermal energy occasionally rupture the weak bonds. When this happens in solid phosphorus the bonds may form again between atoms of different P_4 molecules, and join them. This process eventually produces a giant molecule, P_x, covalently bonded in a disordered fashion. The regularity of the crystal state no longer exists. Such a solid is **amorphous.** P_4, crystalline phosphorus, is commonly known as white or yellow phosphorus, whereas P_x is known as red or violet phosphorus. In addition to these two forms, a third allotropic form can be made by putting phosphorus under high pressure. This forms a crystalline giant molecule P_y, which extends indefinitely in two-dimensional sheets. Extremely rare, it is called black phosphorus.

Yellow phosphorus melts at 44° C. and boils at 280° C. The giant-molecular varieties do not melt, but sublime at high temperatures when a few surface atoms break off at a time. These unite into P_4 molecules as fast as they collide in the resulting phosphorus vapor. There is no way to form solid P_4 directly from either red or black phosphorus, because their bonds are more stable than those in the yellow variety. Yellow phosphorus is soluble in a number of non-polar solvents, e.g., CCl_4, but the

giant-molecular varieties are insoluble. As in the case of iodine and selenium, the black of phosphorus may be taken as a sign of the first traces
of metallic properties in the family. Note that this occurs one element
earlier in each family; it actually begins with carbon, the first element
in Group IV. Iodine is a non-conductor of electricity, gray selenium a
fair conductor when illuminated, and black phosphorus a fair conductor in the absence of light. (Graphite, the black form of carbon, is a good
conductor.)

2.18. Chemical Properties of Phosphorus

The electronegativity of phosphorus is only 2.1. This is responsible for
striking differences in chemical behavior between phosphorus and nitrogen. The strength of a covalent bond depends upon the difference in electronegativity in the atoms it connects. Phosphorus therefore forms much
stronger bonds with highly electronegative elements than nitrogen does,
and much weaker bonds with elements of moderate electronegativity.
For example, phosphorus burns brilliantly in oxygen—the yellow variety
ignites spontaneously—forming stable oxides, whereas all the oxides of
nitrogen decompose on heating. Phosphine, PH_3, and NH_3 differ in the
opposite direction because the difference in electronegativity between
phosphorus and hydrogen is zero. PH_3 cannot be made by direct combination of the elements because no energy would be given out. It burns
readily in air to the highest oxide. Diphosphine, P_2H_4, the phosphorus
analogue of hydrazine, is spontaneously flammable. Although the PH_3
molecule has the same shape as the NH_3 molecule, it is completely non-
polar because in each bond the phosphorus atom shares the electron pair
equally with the hydrogen atom. Accordingly, liquid PH_3 is not associated by hydrogen bonding to form molecular polymers as ammonia is;
it boils at a temperature consistent with its molecular weight, well below
the boiling point of NH_3. Since the phosphorus in PH_3 has no excess
negative charge, it does not share its fourth electron pair anywhere near
as easily. PH_3 is therefore a weaker base than water, whereas NH_3 is
stronger; and phosphonium ion, PH_4^+, is a strong acid. This discussion
about the properties of PH_3 should be carefully compared with the corresponding discussion about NH_3; remember that these differences are
all due to the difference between the two elements in electronegativity.
Another group of differences between the two elements is due to the
larger size of the phosphorus atom, with which is associated the presence of empty d orbitals in the valence layer. The trend sulfur and iodine
display because of their larger size and their available d orbitals continues

with phosphorus. Thus complex polyatomic attachments to phosphorus can occur because it is large enough to accommodate up to six atoms. Hence H_3PO_4, PF_5, and even PF_6^- exist, whereas nitrogen can achieve a $+5$ oxidation state only if there are multiple bonds to a few ligands, e.g., NO_3^-.

The last important difference between nitrogen and phosphorus is the absence of any principal phosphate ion that corresponds to NO_3^-. This is due to the fact that as we saw in Section 12.17, phosphorus does not form multiple bonds easily.

12.19. Compounds Containing the P_4 Group

The reaction of phosphorus with a limited supply of oxygen is shown by the equation:

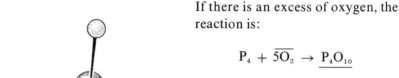

$$P_4 + \overline{3O_2} \rightarrow \underline{P_4O_6}$$

If there is an excess of oxygen, the reaction is:

$$P_4 + \overline{5O_2} \rightarrow \underline{P_4O_{10}}$$

The two oxides are known respectively as phosphorus trioxide and phosphorus pentoxide. In both oxides each phosphorus atom is linked to the other three through oxygen. This is shown in Fig. 12.10 for the pentoxide. The pentoxide has four additional oxygen atoms, one on each phosphorus atom. Thus instead of the bond angle of $60°$ in the P_4 molecule, each phosphorus has three strong bonds at the tetrahedral angle ($109°$) in the P—O—P bonds which more closely approaches the $90°$ angle of p orbitals.

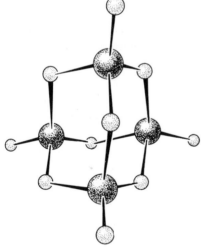

Fig. 12.10. A model of the P_4O_{10} molecule. It consists of interlinked PO_4 tetrahedra, and the four phosphorus atoms are also arranged tetrahedrally with respect to each other. Removal of the four oxygens which form single covalent bonds with phosphorus leaves the P_4O_6 molecule.

The trioxide and pentoxide are so called because the empirical formulas, P_2O_3 and P_2O_5, were known long before the molecular structure was determined. The empirical formulas are still generally used in writing equations, as is that of phosphorus itself, P, because the substances are used in the solid state. P_2O_3 is of little interest, but P_2O_5 is of immense practical importance because it is the anhydride of H_3PO_4. The reaction of P_2O_5 with water:

$$\underline{P_2O_5} + 3H_2O \rightarrow 2H_3PO_4 + \triangle$$

is so vigorous and so complete that phosphorus pentoxide ranks high as a drying agent; it is used for removing the last traces of moisture from non-basic gases and liquids.

Phosphorus forms a pentasulfide, P_4S_{10}, which is like the pentoxide in structure, but it does not form a trisulfide, P_4S_6. Instead, a peculiar molecule, phosphorus sesquisulfide, P_4S_3, forms when phosphorus is burned in a limited supply of sulfur. One sulfur attaches itself to the unshared electron pair on each of *three* phosphorus atoms without disturbing the tetrahedron; why this occurs is not known.

White phosphorus was used for matches before 1913, but it caused many deaths from poisoning among workers in match factories as well as children who sucked the match heads. However, neither P_4S_3 nor red phosphorus is poisonous, and therefore both are now used for matches. P_4S_3 is the easily flammable substance that is in the light-colored "bird's-eye" on the heads of strike-anywhere matches. Red phosphorus is used on safety match boxes. When a safety match is struck, the heat of friction converts a little of the red phosphorus into the white; this ignites and in turn ignites the match head. The patent controlling the use of P_4S_3 was formerly owned by the Diamond Match Company. When the objection was raised that a law forbidding the use of white phosphorus would give the company a monopoly, the Diamond Match people promised to release P_4S_3 for free public use if the law was passed. The company kept its promise.

2.20. Phosphorus Halides

Phosphorus burns in the more active halogens and forms the trihalides, PX_3. It readily combines at room temperature with bromine to form PBr_3. In striking contrast to the nitrogen compounds, even the phosphorus halides which differ little in electronegativity are stable. As we saw earlier, the explosiveness of the corresponding nitrogen compounds is due primarily to the extraordinary stability of the N_2 molecule; the P_4 molecule, on the contrary, is far less stable.

The pentahalides form readily under proper conditions. In order for there to be five covalent bonds, a d orbital must be included. As was mentioned in Section 12.17, the use of d orbitals in the valence layer produces weaker bonds. Accordingly, at only moderately high temperatures the pentachloride, for example, is in equilibrium with the substances which form it.

$$\overline{PCl_3} + \overline{Cl_2} \rightleftharpoons \overline{PCl_5}$$

A non-polar substance like PCl_5 might be expected to be a liquid like PCl_3, or at least a low-melting solid. In reality, it is a saltlike material which sublimes when sufficiently heated. This is so because in the solid state it actually becomes the salt, chlorophosphonium chlorophosphate, $PCl_4^+ + PCl_6^-$. The first of these ions is tetrahedral, the second octahedral. Because of this curious *disproportionation,* the use of any d orbitals by half the phosphorus atoms is avoided and the molecules are packed more closely than would be possible with PCl_5 molecules. For some reason, the coordination number 5—this indicates the formation of five covalent bonds by one central atom—is very rare in solids. Although there is not room enough around a phosphorus atom for six bromine atoms, nevertheless, on solidifying, PBr_5 forms a salt, bromophosphonium bromide, $PBr_4^+ + Br^-$. PI_5 does not exist, even in saltlike forms such as the chlorides and bromides. Probably the combination of the large size of iodine and the small electronegativity difference between the elements defeats the formation of the pentaiodide.

Like non-metallic halides in general, the phosphorus halides are readily hydrolyzed, yielding the hydrogen halide and the oxyacid corresponding to the valence of the non-metal. The fluorides are an exception because fluorine, being more electronegative even than oxygen, forms covalent bonds with phosphorus which are more stable than the phosphorus-oxygen bonds. Hydrolysis of PBr_3 is the most convenient way to prepare HBr. HI is prepared by dropping water on a mixture of red phosphorus and iodine.

$$PBr_3 + 3H_2O \rightarrow H_3PO_3 + \overline{3HBr}$$
$$\underline{2P + 3I_2} + 3H_2O \rightarrow 2H_3PO_3 + \overline{6HI}$$

PI_3 is believed to be formed as an intermediate and then hydrolyzed. Because of the looseness with which the last two chlorine atoms are held, PCl_5 can be used as a chlorinating agent in cases when the action of free chlorine would be too violent.

2.21. The Oxyacids of Phosphorus

Pure phosphoric acid, H_3PO_4, is prepared by the hydration of its anhydride, P_2O_5; some 300,000 tons are produced each year. A million tons annually of a less pure product, green phosphoric acid, are prepared "in the wet way," by the action of dilute H_2SO_4 on phosphate rock.

$$Ca_3(PO_4)_2 + 3H^+ + 3HSO_4^- \rightarrow 3CaSO_4 + 2H_3PO_4$$

The $CaSO_4$ is filtered out and discarded. H_3PO_4 is a triprotic (or tribasic) acid that ionizes as follows:

$$H_3PO_4 \rightleftharpoons H^+ + H_2PO_4^-$$
$$\rightleftharpoons H^+ + HPO_4^{--}$$
$$\rightleftharpoons H^+ + PO_4^{-3}$$

The first ionization is almost strong. A 1 M solution of H_3PO_4 is a little more than 0.1 M with respect to H^+ ion and the dihydrogen phosphate ion, $H_2PO_4^-$. $H_2PO_4^-$ ion is a weak acid. As a solution of $Ca(H_2PO_4)_2$ it gives a pleasant sour taste to a "phosphate" fountain drink, and causes the evolution of CO_2 from HCO_3^- ion when liquid is added to baking powder. But HPO_4^{--} ion is a fairly good base, and in the presence of the large amount of H^+ produced by the first dissociation it can remain free only to the extent of 10^{-7} M; hence the second dissociation contributes only that much to the total concentration of H^+ ion. HPO_4^{--} ion is a very weak acid; accordingly both the concentration of PO_4^{-3} ion and the contribution of the third dissociation to the H^+ ion are negligible. Two-thirds of the pure H_3PO_4 which is produced goes into the manufacture of the various sodium phosphates. Twice as much Na_3PO_4 is made as of all the other kinds of sodium phosphates combined.

The structure of H_3PO_4 is shown by its dot formula:

$$\begin{array}{c} :\!\ddot{O}\!: \\ H\!:\!\ddot{O}\!:\!P\!:\!\ddot{O}\!:\!H \\ :\!\ddot{O}\!: \\ H \end{array}$$

When Na_2HPO_4 is heated sufficiently, the neighboring HPO_4^{--} ions condense, with the elimination of water.

$$\begin{array}{ccc}
\ddot{\underset{..}{O}}: & \ddot{\underset{..}{O}}: & \ddot{\underset{..}{O}}: \;\; \ddot{\underset{..}{O}}: \\
:\ddot{\underset{..}{O}}:\!\overset{..}{\underset{..}{P}}\!:\ddot{\underset{..}{O}}:H^{--} + H:\ddot{\underset{..}{O}}:\overset{..}{\underset{..}{P}}:\ddot{\underset{..}{O}}:^{--} & \xrightarrow{\Delta} & :\ddot{\underset{..}{O}}:\overset{..}{P}:\ddot{\underset{..}{O}}:\overset{..}{P}:\ddot{\underset{..}{O}}:^{-4} + \overline{H_2O} \\
:\underset{..}{\overset{..}{O}}: & :\underset{..}{\overset{..}{O}}: & :\underset{..}{\overset{..}{O}}: \;\; :\underset{..}{\overset{..}{O}}:
\end{array}$$

$P_2O_7^{-4}$ is the diphosphate ion. It is commonly called pyrophosphate ion because of its method of preparation (*pyro* means fire). If NaH_2PO_4 is heated, each ion may condense with those on either side of it, forming a chain molecule of a polyphosphate. Depending on conditions, it is possible to obtain triphosphate, tetraphosphate, and so on up to an "infinite" chain length which is called metaphosphate (*meta* means change). Its formula is $O(PO_3)_x$ with $x + 2$ negative charges. The empirical formula, obtained by dividing this by x, is indistinguishable from PO_3^-, and is so written. Easy proof that this anion is much larger than the empirical formula indicates is the fact that sodium metaphosphate does not form a clear solution in water. The anions are too small to be seen individually, but are large enough to scatter light. The phosphate ion, PO_4^{-3}, is called orthophosphate (*ortho* means regular) when it is necessary to distinguish it from the polyphosphates. Ordinarily, when a chemist uses the term phosphate ion without qualification, it is PO_4^{-3} that he means. There are moderately strong acids corresponding to all these ions.

All polyphosphate ions are readily split to orthophosphate ions by means of hydroxide ion; the reaction is the same as the one shown here for pyrophosphate ion.

$$P_2O_7^{-4} + 2OH^- \rightarrow 2PO_4^{-3} + H_2O$$

In all solutions of polyphosphates equilibrium between the various phosphate ions is established slowly (more rapidly at the boiling point). The relative amount of PO_4^{-3} and the various polyphosphate ions depends upon the concentration and acidity of the solution. Boiling for a minute or two forms enough PO_4^{-3} from any polyphosphate to produce the brilliant yellow phosphomolybdate precipitate that is the characteristic analytical test for that ion.

$$72H^+ + 72NO_3^- + 72NH_4^+ + 12Mo_7O_{24}^{-6} + 7PO_4^{-3} \rightarrow$$
$$36H_2O + 7\underline{(NH_4)_3PMo_{12}O_{40}} + 51NH_4^+ + 72NO_3^-$$

The fantastic coefficients are due to the fact that both the molybdate and the phosphomolybdate ions are polyatomic to a very high degree. There are also individual tests for the different polyphosphate ions; for example, $Ag_4P_2O_7$ is white instead of yellow like Ag_3PO_4, and PO_3^- coagulates albumen.

Since the phosphorus atom in phosphoric acid is already sharing all its valence electrons with oxygen, perphosphoric acid cannot exist, but phosphorous acid, H_3PO_3, and hypophosphorous acid, H_3PO_2, do exist. Curiously, the former is a diprotic and the latter a monoprotic acid. For that reason chemists are inclined to believe that their structures are like those in the first two of the following dot formulas:

$$
\begin{array}{ccc}
\overset{\displaystyle H}{H:\overset{..}{\underset{..}{O}}:\overset{..}{\underset{..}{P}}:\overset{..}{\underset{..}{O}}:H} &
\overset{\displaystyle H}{H:\overset{..}{\underset{..}{P}}:\overset{..}{\underset{..}{O}}:H} &
\overset{\displaystyle H}{H:\overset{..}{\underset{..}{P}}:\overset{..}{\underset{..}{O}}:} \\
:\overset{..}{\underset{..}{O}}: & :\overset{..}{\underset{..}{O}}: & H
\end{array}
$$

It is assumed that only the protons attached to oxygen can be removed by bases. This idea is supported by the fact that phosphine oxide, the substance represented by the third formula, is not an acid. All three of these compounds are good reducing agents.

12.22. Uses of Phosphates

By far the largest use of PO_4^{-3} ion is as fertilizer. Phosphate rock is too insoluble to be satisfactory for this purpose. It is therefore converted into $Ca(H_2PO_4)_2$ by acidulation with H_2SO_4, HNO_3, or H_3PO_4. The anion of the added acid remains in the prepared fertilizer together with the excess Ca^{++} ion, a useless burden in the case of H_2SO_4, a valuable addition in the case of HNO_3 and H_3PO_4. The common commercial names for these fertilizers are, respectively, superphosphate, nitrophos, and triple superphosphate. The percentages (the old-fashioned way of expressing analytical data) of P_2O_5 in each of these are 20, 29, and 47; thus the term triple superphosphate is a considerable misnomer. A fertilizer that better deserves the name is calcium metaphosphate, derived from phosphate rock and elemental phosphorus.

$$Ca_3(PO_4)_2 + P_4 + \overline{5O_2} \rightarrow 3Ca(PO_3)_2$$

This product of research, recently ready for the market, contains 62 per cent P_2O_5. By using H_3PO_4 to recover NH_3 from coke oven gas, another high-analysis fertilizer, $(NH_4)_2HPO_4$, is obtained. It contains 21 per cent nitrogen as well as 53 per cent P_2O_5. In the 1958–1959 crop year nearly 410,000 tons of triple superphosphate were used here, and more than 525,000 tons of superphosphate. The triple contained almost twice as much P_2O_5 as the superphosphate.

All the phosphate ions are of value in detergents because of three properties; they are good bases, good dispersing agents, and good sequestrants for Ca^{++} and Mg^{++} ions. However, they differ in the extent to which they display these properties. Thus PO_4^{-3} is the best dispersing agent, and some of the metaphosphates sequester undesirable cations very effectively. The basic nature of these ions is useful because nearly all detergents are most efficient in alkaline solution. The ions help to disperse particles of soil by attaching themselves to the particles; this gives them a negative charge which makes them repel each other. An anion is said to **sequester** a cation when it forms a complex with it that is sufficiently stable to remove the cation effectively from the field of action. The phosphate complexes of Ca^{++} and Mg^{++} ions cannot precipitate soap, so the water is as soft as though these ions had actually been removed from the solution. The water-softening action is also exerted independently of detergents; "Calgon" (from "calcium gone") is the trade name of a $NaPO_3$ sold in grocery stores for that purpose.

Their dispersing action gives phosphates other uses. One of the most important is the suspension of solids in the drilling mud of oil wells. This liquid must be dense enough to support the proper proportion of the weight of a long "string of tools" and to bring the grindings from the drill head to the surface. Not only clay, but heavier minerals such as $BaSO_4$ (barite, or "heavy spar," density 4.5), must be suspended in the mud to accomplish this. Phosphates also produce the smooth texture characteristic of "process" cheese.

QUESTIONS AND PROBLEMS

1. List the members of the nitrogen family in order of decreasing electronegativity. Which are metals? Which are non-metals? Which are both?

2. How would you prepare *pure* nitrogen for laboratory use? For industrial use?

3. Write equations for the cyanamide and Haber processes and discuss conditions pertinent for the success of each. Compare these processes as to their importance in ammonia production.

4. What kinds of compounds can be considered "derivatives" of ammonia?

5. Draw the dot formulas for ammonia and NH_4^+. Compare these molecules with others which they resemble physically and electronically. Also compare their properties and origin, from the structural standpoint.

6. Illustrate by chemical equations:
   a. The equilibria in a solution of NH_3 in water.
   b. The acid property of NH_4^+.
   c. The basic property of NH_3.
   d. The oxidation of NH_3 to form NO.

7. Starting with N_2, H_2, O_2, and H_2O, show how nitric acid is made.

8. Complete and balance the following redox reactions by the ion-electron method.

    a. $\underline{Cu}$ + (conc.) $HNO_3 \rightarrow Cu^{++}$

    b. $\underline{S}$ + (conc.) $HNO_3 \rightarrow SO_4^{--}$

    c. $\underline{Mg}$ + (dil.) $HNO_3 \rightarrow Mg^{++} + NH_4^+$

    d. $\underline{Pb}$ + (dil.) $HNO_3 \rightarrow Pb^{++} + \overline{NO}$

9. Show by equation the formation of nitronium ion. What type of acid is it? Give reasons for your answer.

10. How do salts that contain ammonium or nitrate ion compare generally in solubility with salts that lack these ions?

11. Illustrate all the oxidation numbers of nitrogen with suitable formulas. Designate the oxidation number in each case. Which are the most common?

12. a. Suppose you had a salt which was a nitrate or a nitrite; how would you prove which it was?

    b. You have a mixture of $NaNO_3$ and $NaNO_2$. Outline a method to prove the presence of both.

13. The electronegativity of F_2 is greater than that of Cl_2, and F_2 reacts more vigorously than Cl_2. The electronegativity of N_2 is greater than that of P_4, but P_4 burns directly in oxygen upon ignition, whereas N_2 does not. Explain.

14. Why does phosphorus pentoxide have the formula P_4O_{10}? Give the name and formula of another oxide of phosphorus. Of what acid is each the anhydride?

15. Which oxidation state of phosphorus is most common? Which oxyanion? Is this anion a strong or weak base?

16. Write the ionization reactions of orthophosphoric acid and compare the strengths of all acids and conjugate bases in the reactions.

17. Defend the statement: PCl_5 is a saltlike substance.

18. How could you distinguish among three solutions if each contained one of the following ions: PO_3^-, $P_2O_7^{-4}$, PO_4^{-3}?

19. How do you explain the fact that hypophosphorous acid, H_3PO_2, is monobasic, phosphorous acid, H_3PO_3, is dibasic, and phosphoric acid, H_3PO_4, is tribasic?

20. How are the sequestering and dispersing properties of phosphate ions put to use?

13

Chemical equilibrium and the equilibrium law

13.1. Reversible Reactions

Reversible reactions are the rule rather than the exception in chemistry. Most important industrial syntheses—e.g., the contact and Haber processes, along with many others—involve such reactions. And similar reactions occur in the test tubes and beakers at your laboratory bench. The ionization (hydrolysis) of acids, bases, and salts, the forming and dissolving of precipitates, and the stability of complex ions in solution are intimately concerned with the reversibility of reactions. In all cases, several species of molecules are present in the reaction mixture simultaneously. The reactant molecules and the product molecules coexist at all times. The only difference from case to case is in the proportion of each that may be present. In a reaction such as:

$$A + B \rightleftharpoons C + D$$

a state of equilibrium is eventually reached. Experience has shown that when this occurs, the concentrations of A, B, C, and D no longer change with time provided such conditions as pressure, temperature, etc., do not change (van't Hoff's law; Le Chatelier's principle). However, it can be proved that in a reversible reaction the reaction never stops but goes on continuously. Since this is the case, it is absolutely essential that the speed of both reactions be identical when a state of equilibrium is reached. When the speed of either reaction is altered, the equilibrium shifts. This means that the products of the faster of the two reactions accumulate, and therefore the concentrations change. Eventually, however, a new state of equilibrium is reached; in it the concentrations are different from those which existed previously, but again they no longer change with time. The shifting of equilibrium is very important in industrial and laboratory practice because it is by this means that a reversible reaction is made to yield a greater amount of the desired product.

Thus it is obvious that the crux of the equilibrium problem involves the speed of chemical reactions. Before we can treat the problem quantitatively we must consider the factors which affect speed of reactions and how they can be controlled.

13.2. Reaction Velocity

Several factors which affect reaction velocities have been mentioned in earlier chapters. The most important of these from the standpoint of the quantitative treatment of equilibrium is molecular concentration. However, we briefly review the other factors in order to bring them all together in one place.

Temperature. If molecules are to react when they collide, they must have sufficient energy for reaction. This, the activation energy, was treated extensively in Section 11.19. At *any* temperature *some* molecules of a reaction mixture have enough energy to react. The number of these increases with increasing temperature, and there is a resultant increase in reaction speed. A reasonable temperature for a reaction is one at which enough molecules have sufficient energy to react so the reaction proceeds at a reasonable rate. In general chemistry, most reactions are studied at or near room temperature, and equilibria are concerned mainly with reactions occurring in solution at room temperature. The principles developed, though, hold for any temperature.

An important fact to remember is that a rise in temperature does *not* increase the velocities of all reactions equally. In a reversible reaction, one of the two reactions regularly speeds up more than the other. The higher the energy of activation, the greater the effect of heating. The equilibrium concentrations will therefore be different at various temperatures. *In discussing the relationship between concentration and reaction velocities we shall assume that the temperature remains constant.* The effect of temperature on speed of reaction and equilibrium concentration can be treated quantitatively provided certain data are available. However, this is too involved for a beginning course and hence will be omitted.

Catalysts. It was pointed out in Section 11.20 that catalysts, which speed up chemical reactions, increase the speed of both parts of a reversible reaction equally. For this reason a catalyst allows equilibrium to be attained more rapidly *but it has no effect on the substances coexisting at equilibrium.* Because of its equal effect on the velocity of both reactions and its lack of effect on equilibrium concentrations, we need not be concerned with catalysis in the quantitative treatment of chemical equilibrium.

Concentration. The concentration of the reacting molecules in a container has a profound effect on the speed of the reaction, and it is this effect that we shall treat quantitatively. It is obvious that no reaction can occur until the appropriate molecules collide with one another. Thus anything that changes the number of collisions will change the velocity of a reaction. For example, an increase in temperature will increase the velocity of the molecules and they will collide more frequently provided the volume of their container remains constant. This will contribute to increased reaction velocity in addition to the effect produced when more molecules have the proper activation energy. This is why the effect of temperature on reaction velocity is very complex.

All other factors remaining constant, an increase in molecular concentration increases the number of collisions per second and hence the reaction velocity. The concentration may be increased by adding more of some reactant to a solution or by increasing the pressure of a gas reactant. The pressure of gases is a measure of their concentration.

The effect of molecular concentration on reaction rates and on the ultimate establishment of equilibrium in a reversible reaction is illustrated in Fig. 13.1 for a hypothetical reaction:

$$A + B \rightleftharpoons AB$$

Consider the reaction occurring at the higher temperature T_2. At zero time with A and B in the reaction vessel (there is no AB yet because it

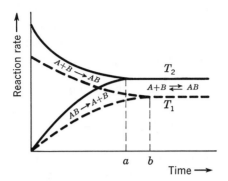

Fig. 13.1. Effect of temperature on reaction rate and time in the establishment of an equilibrium.

will be formed by the reaction), the concentration of AB is zero and so therefore is the velocity for the reaction:

$$AB \rightarrow A + B$$

At this instant the concentration of A and B is at a maximum because they have not started to use each other up. Hence the number of possible collisions between their molecules is also at a maximum. As a consequence the instant they start to react, the reaction will have maximum velocity for the experiment and some A and B will be used up. The next instant the remaining A and B molecules will collide less frequently because there are fewer of them, and the reaction will go more slowly. At the first instant that AB is formed, there will be a slow reaction because there are few AB molecules.

$$AB \rightarrow A + B$$

The slowness of this reaction does not compensate for the rate at which AB is synthesized. In other words, with the passage of time, AB accumulates faster than it disappears, and A and B are used up faster than they are produced. As a consequence, the velocity of the reaction:

$$A + B \rightarrow AB$$

diminishes with time, whereas the velocity of the reaction:

$$AB \rightarrow A + B$$

increases with time. The two velocities approach each other and meet at time *a*. When this happens, *AB* is being produced and used up at the same speed. Obviously its concentration *can no longer change and therefore the speed at which it is used up must remain constant from this moment on*. A state of equilibrium now exists, and in the reaction:

$$A + B \rightleftharpoons AB$$

concentrations no longer change and the velocities of *both* reactions are equal.

The same arguments hold true for a lower temperature, T_1. The difference lies in the fact that the curves are flatter because of the slower reaction rates associated with lower temperatures. As a consequence, the curves coincide and equilibrium is established after a longer time, *b*. The speed of reaction in the equilibrium state is also slower at temperature T_1.

13.3. Quantitative Aspects of Concentration

Consider the reaction:

$$A + B \rightarrow AB$$

What effect is produced upon the rate of formation of AB by increasing either *A* or *B* or both? Let us suppose that there are varying numbers of molecules of *A* and *B* in equal-sized containers, as shown in the accompanying diagram. The lines indicate the collisions which are pos-

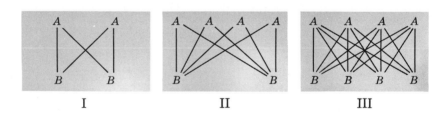

I II III

sible and which could therefore lead to the formation of *AB*. In container I there are 4 possible collisions, whereas if the number of *A* molecules is doubled (container II) the number of possible collisions is doubled, i.e., 8. *AB* will be produced twice as fast in container II as in container I. In container III the *B* molecules have also been doubled. There are 16 collisions possible; that is, the speed of reaction is double

TABLE 13.1. **Reaction Speed Compared with Molecular Concentration**

	I	II	III	Ratio
Relative speed	S	$2S$	$4S$	$1:2:4$
Molecular concentration product, $A \times B$	$2 \times 2 = 4$	$4 \times 2 = 8$	$4 \times 4 = 16$	$4:8:16$ or $1:2:4$

that in container II. Thus, if the speed in container I is S, then in II it is $2S$ and in III it is $4S$. In other words, each time the number of *any* of the molecules is doubled, the speed of the reaction doubles. Table 13.1 shows that the ratio of speeds is comparable to the ratio of the *product* of the number of reacting molecules. If the number of molecules in each container were increased several millionfold these ratios would still hold. In reality, multitudes of molecules are present; even 1 ml. of a 0.16 M solution contains 10^{20} molecules. Thus the effect of concentration on reaction speed is expressed more conveniently with *mole* concentrations instead of in terms of individual molecular collisions. By analogy, then, containers I, II, and III could represent concentrations of 2 M A and 2 M B, 4 M A and 2 M B, and 4 M A and 4 M B respectively. Thus the *molar* concentration products from each container bear the same relative relationship to each other as do the speed ratios; e.g., $4:8:16 = 1:2:4$.

Let us suppose that our simple hypothetical reaction:

$$A + B \rightleftharpoons AB$$

is an intermediate step in forming an ultimate product AB_2. In other words, two reactions occur.

1. $A + B \rightleftharpoons AB$
2. $AB + B \rightleftharpoons AB_2$

Often a chemist does not know the intermediate steps of a reaction. In such cases the reaction is written as though it occurred in one simple step.

3. $A + 2B \rightleftharpoons AB_2$

This equation is correct in stating the initial reactants and final product realized. But it is incorrect in implying that the product, AB_2, can be formed by a three-bodied collision between one molecule of A and two molecules of B. Such collisions are highly improbable; indeed they would result in a very slow reaction because of the infrequency with which they would occur. However, we shall see that the rate at which AB_2 molecules form, relative to the concentration of A and B molecules, is the same whether we consider AB_2 to form by reactions 1 and 2 or by the simplified single-step reaction in 3.

We have already considered the effect of increasing the concentrations of A and B on the rate at which AB forms in reaction 1. Doubling either reactant results in doubling the rate of formation of AB. But what effect does this have on the rate at which AB_2 forms? If the concentration of A is doubled, then AB_2 will be formed twice as fast. This is so because the speed of 1 is doubled, and therefore the amount of AB produced and available for reaction 2 is doubled. But if the concentration of B is doubled, the rate at which AB_2 forms will be *quadrupled*. The reason for this is that the concentrations of both AB and B are doubled for reaction 2; and since either would double the rate, both together must quadruple it. In summary, the rate of formation of AB_2 is proportional to the concentration of A and to the square of the concentration of B. The combined effect of both A and B on the rate of formation of AB_2 is expressed mathematically as follows:

$$\text{Rate} \propto [A][B]^2$$

In this and following relationships, formulas in brackets represent molar concentrations of the substances within the brackets, and $\propto$ means "proportional to." The coefficient 2 preceding B in the balanced equation in reaction 3 is the power used in the rate relationship stated above, and when used with the concentration of B will indicate the same rate as do the calculations from intermediate reactions.

In general, *the speed of a chemical reaction is proportional to the product of the molar concentrations of the reactants raised to the appropriate powers.*

The simple speed relationships developed here follow a consistent simple pattern and provide a convenient and direct means of arriving at a final conclusion regarding equilibrium. Although the pattern of the reaction and the assumptions pertaining to it may be incorrect, the final equilibrium expression is correct. This practice is not unusual in science.

13.4. The Equilibrium Constant

The relationships between speed of reaction and concentration discussed in the preceding section are of value in determining equilibrium constants. As will be shown, an equilibrium constant is related to the concentrations of reactants and products at equilibrium. In the reaction at equilibrium:

$$A + 2B \rightleftharpoons AB_2$$

the speed of the reaction to the right is equal to the speed of the reaction to the left. The speeds are:

$$S_R \propto [A][B]^2 \text{ and } S_L \propto [AB_2]$$

A mathematical proportionality can be converted to an equality by multiplying one side of the proportionality by a constant, called the **proportionality constant** thus:

$$S_R = k_R[A][B]^2 \text{ and } S_L = k_L[AB_2]$$

The proportionality constants k_R and k_L do not equal each other. They will assume other constant values if the temperature changes, but otherwise they remain specific constants for the particular reactions. Since, at equilibrium, $S_R = S_L$, we can equate factors equal to the speeds.

$$k_R[A][B]^2 = k_L[AB_2]$$

Algebraic rearrangement gives

$$\frac{k_R}{k_L} = \frac{[AB_2]}{[A][B]^2} = K_E$$

since a constant divided by a constant (k_R/k_L) is a constant. K_E is known as the **equilibrium constant.** The expression could just as well have been written as follows:

$$\frac{k_L}{k_R} = \frac{[A][B]^2}{[AB_2]} = K'_E$$

This is the reciprocal of the preceding expression. Chemists have adopted the convention that products appear in the numerator and reactants in the denominator in expressions of equilibrium constants.

The mass law (a poor name for it) or preferably the law of equilibrium constants states that *at equilibrium the product of the molar concentrations of the resultants divided by the product of the molar concentrations of the reactants, each raised to the proper power, is a constant.*

This is the final correct expression, mentioned at the end of the preceding section, which is obtained whether we adopt erroneous assumptions regarding reaction mechanisms or use the actual, experimentally determined relationships.

The magnitude of the equilibrium constant tells at a glance the relative nature of the concentrations at equilibrium. For example, a large figure for the constant indicates a larger proportion of product to reactant in the equilibrium mixture; a small figure, the reverse of this.

Since the concentrations of reactants and products vary with temperature (Section 13.2), the value of K_E varies accordingly. For this reason lists of equilibrium constants in reference tables specify the temperature at which they apply. For constants applicable to solutions, the temperatures are usually 20° or 25° C.

The numerical value of the equilibrium constant cannot be obtained experimentally unless the substances in the system can be subjected to quantitative analysis. However, one analysis may determine several quantities. Thus if a known amount of acetic acid, say 0.1 mole, is dissolved in 1 l. of water and part of it ionizes, determining only the hydrogen ion concentration will yield all the quantities needed for computing the equilibrium constant. This is due to the fact that they are all related by the chemical equation:

$$HC_2H_3O_2 + H_2O \rightleftharpoons H_3O^+ + C_2H_3O_2^-$$

It is evident that if the solution now contains X moles of H_3O^+ ion, it must contain X moles of $C_2H_3O_2^-$ ions also, and $0.1 - X$ moles of $HC_2H_3O_2$. This of course is based on the assurance that no other substance was added to the solution to produce either H_3O^+ or $C_2H_3O_2^-$ ions.

13.5. The Ionization Constant

Weak acids, such as acetic acid, undergo partial dissociation or ionization in solution. Strong acids react with water either completely or so nearly completely that they can be considered 100 per cent dissociated. Ionization equilibrium constants can be calculated for weak acids but not for strong ones. For the acetic acid reaction:

$$HC_2H_3O_2 + H_2O \rightleftharpoons H_3O^+ + C_2H_3O_2^-$$

the ionization equilibrium constant is:

$$K_E = \frac{[H_3O^+][C_2H_3O_2^-]}{[HC_2H_3O_2][H_2O]}$$

The reaction in a solution of weak acid is sufficiently slight so that the amount of water used up is negligible compared to the original amount (1000 g. or 55.5 moles). For this reason the $[H_2O]$ in the denominator of these expressions always has a constant value, 55.5, within the limits of analytical accuracy. Hence this value can be eliminated by treating it as a constant.

$$K_E \times 55.5 = \frac{[H_3O^+][C_2H_3O_2^-]}{[HC_2H_3O_2]} = K_{ion}$$

K_{ion} (also frequently written K_I) is called the **ionization constant** of the acid. Before protons were known to be hydrated in solution, the equation for the ionization was written:

$$HC_2H_3O_2 \rightleftharpoons H^+ + C_2H_3O_2^-$$

This gives the same K_{ion} expression except that $[H^+]$ instead of $[H_3O^+]$ appears in the numerator. The values for these are molar concentrations, and numerically a mole of H^+ is no different from a mole of H_3O^+. In other words, either expression gives the same numerical result.

We now consider calculating the equilibrium constant from analytical data. If a 0.10 m acetic acid solution is found to have a hydrogen ion concentration of 0.0013 m, what is the K_{ion}?

$$K_{ion} = \frac{[H_3O^+][C_2H_3O_2^-]}{[HC_2H_3O_2]} = \frac{[0.0013][0.0013]}{[0.10 - 0.0013]}$$

$$= \frac{0.0000017}{0.0987} = \frac{1.7 \times 10^{-6}}{9.9 \times 10^{-2}} = 1.7 \times 10^{-5}$$

The constant is obviously a small number. This is the case with all *weak* acids because the number of ions produced is necessarily small. Many ionization constants are considerably smaller even than this. They are generally given to two (as in this example) or three significant figures. Constants for various equilibria are given in the appendix.

13.6. The Common Ion Effect

The case just discussed in which the ion concentrations of the acetic acid solution are alike is unique, in that it holds true only for a bottle of acetic acid on a shelf. When, as is more usual, the acid is used in a reaction, other chemicals and their corresponding ions mingle with it. The ion concentrations are no longer the same, although the value of the equilibrium constant does remain the same. If acetic or any other acid is mixed with another acidic or basic substance the H_3O^+ concentration will change. It will increase in the case of the acidic substance, and decrease in the case of the basic. The addition of HCl adds H_3O^+ ion to the solution, an ion that is *common* to both the HCl and the $HC_2H_3O_2$ solution. This increases the rate at which the H_3O^+ ions react with the $C_2H_3O_2^-$ ions and thus decreases the amount of $HC_2H_3O_2$ that is ionized, thereby changing the concentration of all the molecules involved in the equilibrium. Similarly, the dissociation of acetic acid can also be repressed by adding $NaC_2H_3O_2$, which has $C_2H_3O_2^-$ ion in *common* with the acetic acid. These are known as **common ion effects** and are utilized to control ion concentrations. This control involves the following principles: (1) The anion concentration of a weak acid can be decreased by adding a strong acid. The common ion is H_3O^+. (2) The hydrogen ion can be decreased by adding a salt that contains the anion of the weak acid.

For example, if 0.050 mole of HCl is added to 1 l. of 0.10 M* acetic acid, what is the $C_2H_3O_2^-$ ion concentration?

It can safely be assumed that the strong acid HCl is 100 per cent ionized; therefore:

$$HCl + H_2O \rightarrow H_3O^+ + Cl^-$$
$$ 0.050 \quad 0.050$$

The concentration of the acetic acid to which the HCl is added is (see preceding section):

$$HC_2H_3O_2 + H_2O \rightleftharpoons H_3O^+ + C_2H_3O^-$$
$$0.099 0.0013 \quad 0.0013$$

The HCl that is added gives the solution an additional 0.050 mole of H_3O^+ ions; hence the acetic acid equilibrium shifts to the left (Le Chate-

---

* Solution concentrations used in equilibrium calculations are normally expressed as molalities (in advanced treatments a corrected concentration called "activity" is used). When *dilute* solutions are involved and calculations are carried out only to two significant figures, molarity (M) and molality (m) are numerically equivalent.

lier's principle). In this shift the acetic acid cannot take up more than 0.0013 mole of H_3O^+ ion because there is only 0.0013 mole of $C_2H_3O_2^-$ ion to couple up with it. Therefore at *least* 0.05 mole of H_3O^+ from the HCl still remains in solution. In fact, there is slightly more than this because all the $C_2H_3O_2^-$ cannot be de-ionized. If it were, the $[C_2H_3O_2^-]$ ion concentration in the expression for K_{ion} would be zero and therefore K_{ion} would become zero, a contradiction of the equilibrium law. Thus when a strong acid is added to a weak acid the $[H_3O^+]$ is automatically the value from the strong acid plus a little more that can be neglected in most cases because it is so little. The amount of un-ionized weak acid is the total amount originally present, less the very little that ionizes; the latter is small enough to be neglected. Thus the adjusted equilibrium amounts of molecules in the above solution would be:

$$HC_2H_3O_2 + H_2O \rightleftharpoons$$
$$0.1$$

$$H_3O^+ + C_2H_3O_2^-$$
$$0.05 \qquad X$$

The only unknown is $C_2H_3O_2^-$ ion, which we at least know is small. It can be calculated as follows:

$$K_{ion} = 1.7 \times 10^{-5} = \frac{[H_3O^+][C_2H_3O_2^-]}{[HC_2H_3O_2]} = \frac{[0.050][x]}{[0.10]}$$

$$x = \frac{0.10 \times 1.7 \times 10^{-5}}{0.050} = 3.4 \times 10^{-5} \ M$$

13.7. Polyprotic Acids

Polyprotic weak acids follow the same principles regarding ionization constants that were formulated in the preceding sections, except that more than one equilibrium is involved. The most important acid in this respect is the dibasic acid H_2S because of its extensive use in analytical chemistry as a precipitant. Control of its ionic equilibria by means of the common ion effect is a decisive factor in separating metallic ions into subgroups of sulfide precipitates (Section 11.12 and Table 11.2). The ionic equilibria of H_2S and the value of the constants are as follows:

1. $H_2S \rightleftharpoons H^+ + HS^-$ $K_1 = \dfrac{[H^+][HS^-]}{[H_2S]} = 9.1 \times 10^{-8}$

2. $HS^- \rightleftharpoons H^+ + S^{--}$ $K_2 = \dfrac{[H^+][S^{--}]}{[HS^-]} = 1.2 \times 10^{-15}$

3. $H_2S \rightleftharpoons 2H^+ + S^{--}$ $K_{12} = \dfrac{[H^+]^2[S^{--}]}{[H_2S]} = 1.1 \times 10^{-22}$

As expected, the second ionization is less extensive (the constant, K_2, is smaller) than the first. The third reaction, the over-all ionization constant, is obtained in the usual manner by adding stepwise reactions and canceling formulas common to both sides of the arrow. This constant is always the product of the constants of the individual stepwise reactions.

$$K_1 \times K_2 = \frac{[H^+][\cancel{HS^-}]}{[H_2S]} \times \frac{[H^+][S^{--}]}{[\cancel{HS^-}]} = \frac{[H^+]^2[S^{--}]}{[H_2S]} = K_{12}$$

K_{12} is read K one-two, not K twelve. Remember that the expressions for K_1 and K_2 are for coexisting equilibria in one and the same solution. For this reason the numerical values of $[H^+]$ and $[HS^-]$ are the same in both expressions because these ions are available for *any* equilibria that involve them in the same solution.

In a *pure* solution of H_2S or at least one to which no extraneous acidic or basic constituent has been added, a unique situation exists regarding the H^+ and HS^- ion concentrations. If only reaction 1 occurred, these would be identical in value. However, in reaction 2 a very slight amount of HS^- ion dissociates, diminishing its value very slightly and increasing the total H^+ ion by the same amount. Thus the total H^+ ion concentration is very slightly larger than the HS^- ion concentration. In terms of the number of significant figures used for the constants this is negligible; hence from the practical standpoint $[H^+] = [HS^-]$. This being the case:

$$K_2 = \frac{[\cancel{H^+}][S^{--}]}{[\cancel{HS^-}]} = 1.2 \times 10^{-15}$$

In other words, in a "pure" solution of H_2S the S^{--} ion concentration is 1.2×10^{-15} M. To generalize: In a pure solution of a weak polyprotic acid the concentration of the negative ion produced by the second ionization reaction is equal to K_2. However, when an acid or base is added, the S^{--} ion concentration is less than 1.2×10^{-15} M in acidic solutions and more than this in basic solutions. In such cases it must be calculated from the K_{12} expression.

The solutions of H_2S used for analytical purposes are saturated with the gas; at room temperature they contain 0.1 mole per liter. Since the amount of H_2S which ionizes is very small, the denominator of K_{12} is virtually a constant, i.e., 0.1. For this reason, the expression is often used for calculation with the 0.1 incorporated in the value of the ionization constant.

$$K_{12}[H_2S] = [H^+]^2[S^{--}] = 1.1 \times 10^{-23}$$

Consider the following problem: How many moles of HCl must be added to 1 l. of saturated H_2S solution in order to adjust the S^{--} ion concentration to 1×10^{-25} M? In solving this problem, the K_{12} expression must be used because an extraneous acid is present. Substitute the desired S^{--} ion concentration and solve for the H^+ ion concentration that is needed to maintain this value. This will be the HCl concentration in moles/liter (molarity) since the H^+ from the H_2S will be negligible in comparison.

$$[H^+]^2[S^{--}] = 1.1 \times 10^{-23}$$
$$[H^+]^2[1 \times 10^{-25}] = 1.1 \times 10^{-23}$$
$$[H^+]^2 = 1.1 \times 10^{2}$$
$$[H^+] = 1.0 \times 10^{1} = 1.0\ M$$

Thus 1.0 M HCl solution saturated with H_2S will contain a sulfide ion concentration of 1×10^{-25} M.

13.8. Ionization of NH$_4$OH

NH$_4$OH ranks second to H_2S as an important analytical reagent. It is a weak base and accordingly it fits the ionic equilibria theory nicely. The ionization equilibrium:

$$NH_4OH \rightleftharpoons NH_4^+ + OH^-$$

can be expressed mathematically as follows:

$$K_B = \frac{[NH_4^+][OH^-]}{[NH_4OH]} = 1.8 \times 10^{-5}$$

Problems involving NH_4OH are treated similarly to those involving acid equilibria.

In order to control OH^- ion concentrations in solution for values lower than that obtained from pure NH_4OH solutions, the common ion effect is employed by adding solid ammonium salts to NH_4OH. These salts, being ionic, suppress the ionization of NH_4OH and therefore diminish the concentration of OH^- ion.

$$NH_4OH \rightleftharpoons NH_4^+ + OH^-$$

Procedures described above enable us to calculate the quantity of NH_4^+ ion, and therefore ammonium salt, that is needed to maintain the desired OH^- concentration in a given NH_4OH solution. NH_4Cl or NH_4NO_3 is usually the salt added as the source of NH_4^+ ion.

13.9. Ionization of Water, K_w

Most ionic equilibria exist in water solutions. At least this is true in work done in beginning chemistry. Water undergoes a slight amount of ionization because it is a weak acid and base. In a mixture such as a solution, all equilibria are maintained and the equilibrium law is obeyed. Thus in water solutions not only must the equilibria of the weak electrolyte solutes satisfy their constants, but the ions associated with the ionic equilibrium of water must also adjust to these constants if required.

The reaction for water is as follows:

$$H_2O + H_2O \rightleftharpoons H_3O^+ + OH^-$$

The equilibrium expression is:

$$K_E = \frac{[H_3O^+][OH^-]}{[H_2O]^2}$$

The reaction is very slight. In 1 l. (1000 g.) of pure water only 1×10^{-7} moles dissociates. If either an acid or a base is added to water, the equilibrium shifts to the left. Thus the maximum amount of water which dissociates is 1×10^{-7} moles per liter. This is negligible compared to the 55.5 moles there were to start with. Consequently the denominator in the expression is always $[55.5]^2$, a constant. Incorporating it in K_E gives:

$$K_E \times [55.5]^2 = [H_3O^+][OH^-] = K_w = 1 \times 10^{-14}$$

This constant holds for *all* water solutions at room temperature. Neither $[H_3O^+]$ nor $[OH^-]$ can ever be zero, for this would require the other to become infinite. This means that some OH^- ion must still be present even in the strongest acid solutions with a tremendous quantity of H_3O^+ ion.

Table 13.2 lists some data for typical acidic and basic solutions. Note the conformity of the ionic concentrations to the demands of K_W. The pH in the last column is a measure of acidity. Neutrality, pH $= 7$, exists when a water solution is neither pronouncedly acidic nor basic in character, e.g., $[H^+] = [OH^-]$. As pH values diverge from 7, the acid or basic strength increases, depending upon whether the pH value grows smaller or larger.

TABLE 13.2. **Relationships Between [H+], [OH-], and pH**

	$[H^+]$	$[OH^-]$	$[H^+][OH^-]$	pH $(-\log [H^+])$
Strong	1×10^{-1}	1×10^{-13}	1×10^{-14}	1
↑ (Acidic)	1×10^{-3}	1×10^{-11}	1×10^{-14}	3
Weak	1×10^{-6}	1×10^{-8}	1×10^{-14}	6
Neutral	1×10^{-7}	1×10^{-7}	1×10^{-14}	7
Weak	1×10^{-8}	1×10^{-6}	1×10^{-14}	8
↓ (Basic)	1×10^{-10}	1×10^{-4}	1×10^{-14}	10
Strong	1×10^{-13}	1×10^{-1}	1×10^{-14}	13

3.10. Degree of Acidity of a Solution; pH

The amount of acid in a solution and the acidity of the solution are two different things. A 1 M solution of HCl or HNO_3 is much more strongly acidic than a 1 M solution of $HC_2H_3O_2$. In the first two solutions the H^+ concentration is 1 M, because the reaction of a strong acid with water is virtually complete.

$$HCl + H_2O \rightarrow H_3O^+ + Cl^-$$

0 mole   1 mole   1 mole

In the third solution there is nearly a mole of $HC_2H_3O_2$ and only a small fraction of a mole of H^+ and $C_2H_3O_2^-$ ion.

$$HC_2H_3O_2 + H_2O \rightleftharpoons H_3O^+ + C_2H_3O_2^-$$
$$0.996 0.0043 0.0043$$

It would take just 1 mole of sodium hydroxide to neutralize *either* solution, but the properties of acids are hundreds of times more intense in the HCl solution than in the $HC_2H_3O_2$ solution.

The H^+ ion concentration of a solution is a perfect measure of its degree of acidity in distinction to the concentration (molarity) of the weak or strong acid that may be present. In its lower ranges, it also measures the alkalinity of a solution, for any base that is dissolved in water removes H^+ ion from the solution to an extent proportional to the concentration and strength of the base.

This measure of the degree of acidity or alkalinity is the pH mentioned in Section 13.9. The pH is a direct measure of the H^+ ion concentration of a solution. Mathematically the pH is defined as the negative logarithm of the hydrogen ion concentration:

$$pH = -\log [H^+]$$

If $[H^+]$ is 1×10^{-x}, the pH is X. Note the value of pH and of $[H^+]$ in Table 13.2. When $[H^+]$ is $Y \times 10^{-x}$, the pH is $X - \log Y$. For example, if $[H^+] = 1.8 \times 10^{-9}$, the pH is $9 - \log 1.8$; in other words, it is between 8 and 9.

The pH values of solutions of several substances are listed in Tables 13.3 and 13.4. These values can be determined experimentally for all kinds of solutions and can also be calculated from equilibria data. The pH can be approximately determined by means of indicators (Section 13.11). However, in industries where pH control is important, the pH can be read from the dial of a pH meter which measures the voltage

TABLE 13.3. **pH Values of Various Acids and Bases (0.1 N)**

Acids	pH Value	Bases	pH Value
Hydrochloric acid	1.0	Sodium bicarbonate	8.4
Sulfuric acid	1.2	Borax	9.2
Phosphoric acid	1.5	Ammonia	11.1
Sulfurous acid	1.5	Sodium carbonate	11.6
Acetic acid	2.9	Trisodium phosphate	12.0
Alum	3.2	Sodium silicate	12.2
Carbonic acid	3.8	Lime (saturated)	12.3
Boric acid	5.2	Sodium hydroxide	13.0

TABLE 13.4. **Approximate pH of Some Common Substances**

Apples	3	Milk of magnesia	10.5
Asparagus	5.5	Sauerkraut	3.5
Beer	4–5	Salmon	6.2
Cabbage	5.3	Shrimp	7
Carrots	5	Tomatoes	4.2
Ginger ale	2–4	Sea water	8.2
Lemons	2.3	Human spinal fluid	7.4
Cows' milk	6.6	Human urine	4.8–8.4

generated from electrodes immersed in the solution in question. This voltage is dependent upon the H^+ ion concentration, and the pH values thus obtained are accurate to 0.02 of a unit.

Calculating the pH of a solution from equilibrium data is shown in the following example. What is the pH of 1 l. of 1 M NH_4OH solution to which has been added 0.5 mole of NH_4Cl?

K_B of $NH_4OH = 1.8 \times 10^{-5}$

$$NH_4OH \rightleftharpoons NH_4^+ + OH^-$$
$$1 - X \qquad X \qquad X$$

The ionization of the very small quantity, X moles, of NH_4OH in the presence of NH_4Cl produces X moles each of NH_4^+ and OH^- ions. There is also 0.5 mole of NH_4^+ ion in solution from the ionic compound NH_4Cl; so the total NH_4^+ ion concentration is $X + 0.5$. Hence:

$$K_B = \frac{[NH_4^+][OH^-]}{[NH_4OH]} = \frac{[X + 0.5][X]}{[1 - X]} = 1.8 \times 10^{-5}$$

But X is very small compared to 0.5 and 1, and therefore it can be disregarded when it is *added to* or *subtracted from* such numbers.

$$1.8 \times 10^{-5} = \frac{0.5X}{1}$$
$$X = 3.6 \times 10^{-5} \text{ moles/1.}$$

This verifies the assumption that X was small. If this value were larger —e.g., about 10^{-2}—the calculation would be the same except that the X terms would be kept. Solve the quadratic equation to verify the fact

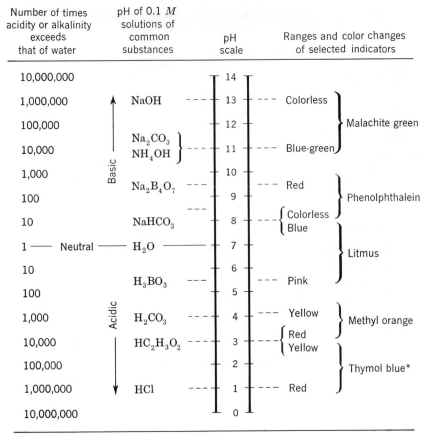

Number of times acidity or alkalinity exceeds that of water	pH of 0.1 M solutions of common substances	pH scale	Ranges and color changes of selected indicators
10,000,000		14	
1,000,000	NaOH	13	Colorless
100,000		12	Malachite green
10,000	Na_2CO_3 NH_4OH	11	Blue-green
1,000		10	
100	$Na_2B_4O_7$	9	Red Phenolphthalein
10	$NaHCO_3$	8	Colorless Blue
1 — Neutral —	H_2O	7	Litmus
10		6	
100	H_3BO_3	5	Pink
1,000	H_2CO_3	4	Yellow Methyl orange
10,000	$HC_2H_3O_2$	3	Red Yellow
100,000		2	Thymol blue*
1,000,000	HCl	1	Red
10,000,000		0	

Basic (above neutral), Acidic (below neutral)

* Thymol blue also changes color from yellow (pH 8.0) to blue (pH 9.5)

Fig. 13.2. pH scale. pH $= -\log$ H$^+$.

that the answer is the same (to two significant figures) as was obtained when the X terms were dropped. Since

$$[OH^-] = 3.6 \times 10^{-5} \ M$$

the pH can be determined with the K_w of water.

$$K_w = [H^+][OH^-] = [H^+][3.6 \times 10^{-5}] = 1 \times 10^{-14}$$
$$[H^+] = 2.8 \times 10^{-8} \ M$$

Therefore
$$pH = 8 - \log 2.8$$
$$= 7.6$$

13.11. Indicators

When precise pH control is not essential, the pH can be determined to within about 0.2 unit by means of indicators, thus avoiding the need for the expensive pH meter. An **indicator** is usually a colored organic acid in which the bonding electrons are arranged one way when the loose proton is removed, and another way when it is restored. As a result, the acid has one color; and the anion, its conjugate base, another (Fig. 13.2). If the acidity of the solution is such that the acid is half ionized, a mixture of the two colors appears. In general, a change of 0.2 unit in pH causes the proportions to shift, with an accompanying change in color that is clearly visible when comparison tubes are used. After the equilibrium has been shifted well to one side or the other, an indicator is no longer useful, for there is nowhere nearly as much difference in color between a 99 : 1 and a 9 : 1 mixture (which corresponds to a whole unit of difference in pH) as there is between a 55 : 45 and a 45 : 55 mixture (which corresponds to a pH difference of 0.2 unit). However, there are some exceptions to this, for a few indicators—e.g., phenolphthalein and paranitrophenol—have one colorless form. These are most sensitive in the region in which there is just enough of the colored form to be faintly visible. Any one indicator is useful at most only over a range of about 1 pH unit. Fortunately, indicators are available for practically any desired pH. Carefully chosen mixtures of indicators provide a succession of color changes over a range of several pH units. These are called **universal indicators.**

3.12. Hydrolysis; the Hydrolysis Constant, K_H

When any base is put into water it takes protons from the water until an equilibrium is reached. The reaction is of the type:

$$NH_3 + H_2O \rightleftharpoons NH_4^+ + OH^-$$
$$S^{--} + H_2O \rightleftharpoons HS^- + OH^-$$
$$C_2H_3O_2^- + H_2O \rightleftharpoons HC_2H_3O_2 + OH^-$$
$$\text{Base 1} + \text{Acid 2} \rightleftharpoons \text{Acid 1} + \text{Base 2}$$

The amount of OH^- produced and the resultant basicity of the solution are a measure of the amount and strength of the base which was introduced. Note that essentially these reactions are no different from acid hydrolysis reactions.

$$HC_2H_3O_2 + H_2O \rightleftharpoons H_3O^+ + C_2H_3O_2^-$$
$$\text{Acid 1} + \text{Base 2} \rightleftharpoons \text{Acid 2} + \text{Base 1}$$

Both types involve water and in both types a constant product is obtained—OH^- in the case of base hydrolysis and H_3O^+ in the case of acid hydrolysis. In base hydrolysis H_2O acts as acid 2, and in acid hydrolysis H_2O acts as base 2. In both cases, as is to be expected, the pH is the measure of basicity and acidity. The extent to which the basic substance is hydrolyzed depends upon K_W and the K_{ion} of any acid generated. This is so because there are *three* equilibria in the one solution and their constants must be maintained. This necessarily involves an adjustment of all concentrations. For simplification in the following reactions and equilibrium expressions H^+ is used for H_3O^+. In addition, H_2O is omitted from the equilibrium expression by incorporating it in the constant for the reasons mentioned earlier in connection with the expressions for K_{ion} and K_W.

1. $C_2H_3O_2^- + H_2O \rightleftharpoons HC_2H_3O_2 + OH^- \qquad K_H = \dfrac{[HC_2H_3O_2][OH^-]}{[C_2H_3O_2^-]}$

2. $\qquad HC_2H_3O_2 \rightleftharpoons H^+ + C_2H_3O_2^- \qquad K_{ion} = \dfrac{[H^+][C_2H_3O_2^-]}{[HC_2H_3O_2]}$

3. $\qquad H_2O \rightleftharpoons H^+ + OH^- \qquad K_W = [H^+][OH^-]$

The interdependence of the equilibria is obvious from a diagram of the reactions such as the following:

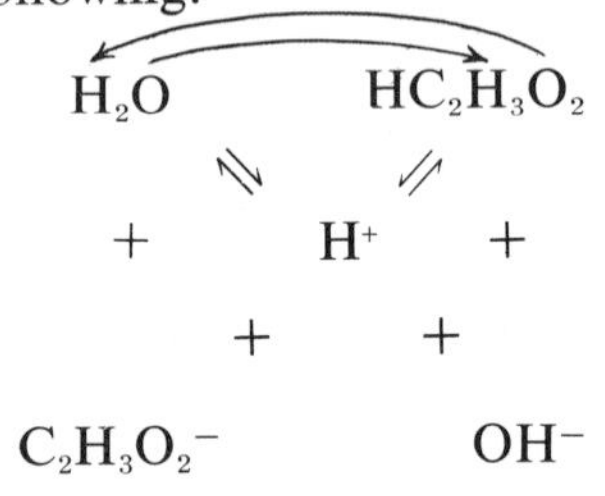

$$H_2O \qquad HC_2H_3O_2$$
$$+ \qquad H^+ \qquad +$$
$$+ \qquad +$$
$$C_2H_3O_2^- \qquad OH^-$$

Adding reactions 1 and 2 algebraically gives reaction 3 because common terms on both sides of the arrows cancel out. Thus reaction 3 is the over-all reaction for these hydrolysis reactions. Furthermore, as we saw in Section 13.7, the over-all ionization constant of a series of reactions is the *product* of the ionization constants of the individual reactions. Therefore:

$$\underbrace{\dfrac{[HC_2H_3O_2][OH^-]}{[C_2H_3O_2^-]}}_{K_H} \times \underbrace{\dfrac{[H^+][C_2H_3O_2^-]}{[HC_2H_3O_2]}}_{K_{ion}} = [H^+][OH^-]$$
$$ = K_W$$

Hence the hydrolysis constant is readily obtained from known constants.

$$K_H = \frac{K_W}{K_{ion}}$$

A typical problem involving the hydrolysis constant follows. If 0.10 mole of sodium acetate is dissolved in 1 l. of water, is the solution acidic or basic? What is the pH of the solution?

K_{ion} of $HC_2H_3O_2 = 1.8 \times 10^{-5}$

$$C_2H_3O_2^- + H_2O \rightleftharpoons HC_2H_3O_2 + OH^-$$
$$0.10 - X \qquad\qquad X \qquad X$$

$$K_H = \frac{K_W}{K_{ion}} = \frac{[HC_2H_3O_2][OH^-]}{[C_2H_3O_2^-]} = \frac{1 \times 10^{-14}}{1.8 \times 10^{-5}} = 5.6 \times 10^{-10}$$

It is obvious from the magnitude of K_H that the numerator, the product of the concentration of acetic acid and hydroxide ion, is small compared to the denominator, the concentration of acetate ion. Thus it is safe to assume, as it usually is, that X is very small compared to 0.10. Therefore, for practical reasons, $0.10 - X \cong 0.1$. By substitution:

$$\frac{X \cdot X}{0.1} = 5.6 \times 10^{-10}$$
$$X^2 = 5.6 \times 10^{-11}$$
$$X = 7.5 \times 10^{-6} M = [OH^-]$$

$$K_W = 1 \times 10^{-14} = [H^+][7.5 \times 10^{-6}]$$
$$\frac{1 \times 10^{-14}}{7.5 \times 10^{-6}} = [H^+] = 1.3 \times 10^{-9} M$$
$$pH = -\log 1.3 \times 10^{-9}$$
$$= 9 - \log 1.3 = 8.9$$

The solution is basic.

13.13. Buffer Mixtures

It is frequently important not merely to establish a certain pH, but to maintain it with little variation even though a considerable amount of acid or base is added to or produced in the solution. Such a solution is said to be **buffered** and the constituents added to maintain the pH constitute a **buffer mixture.** In order to maintain the pH, the solution must contain more acid than is needed to neutralize the expected additional base, and also a corresponding amount of base. It may seem impossible at first for both acid and base to be present in quantity at the same time; however, this can be accomplished in two ways. The most widely employed method is to use an acid and its own conjugate base. These will of course react with each other continuously, just as any other acid and base will. But consider the equation:

$$HB + B^- \rightleftharpoons B^- + HB$$

This is really no reaction at all. The other method involves using a substance that is both an acid and a base. The most important substance in this class is bicarbonate ion, HCO_3^-.

To compute the $[H^+]$ in a buffer mixture consisting of an acid and its conjugate base, we solve the ionization constant expression for $[H^+]$.

$$[H^+] = \frac{[HB]}{[B^-]} \times K_{ion}$$

The most efficient buffer mixture is one that contains an equimolar mixture of the acid and its conjugate base, for the addition of a given amount of acid or base will produce the smallest percentage change in their ratio. If the solution is to be buffered at a pH that does not exactly correspond to the K_{ion} of any available acid, a swing of half a pH unit in either direction can be accomplished by using a $3:1$ or a $1:3$ instead of a $1:1$ mixture, without sacrificing too much of the buffering ability. The same change of half a pH unit would be produced in a $1:1$ buffer mixture by adding enough acid or base to use up half of one component.

A single-ion buffer like HCO_3^- is much less efficient. The addition of half enough NaOH to neutralize the HCO_3^- would convert it into a $1:1$ $HCO_3^- + CO_3^{--}$ buffer mixture of the acid-conjugate base type. The $[H^+]$ would equal the second ionization constant of carbonic acid, $K_2 = 6 \times 10^{-11}$. Addition of a similar amount of HCl would produce a $1:1$ $H_2CO_3 + HCO_3^-$ mixture. The pH then would correspond to K_1 of H_2CO_3, which is 3×10^{-7}. Hence there would be a total swing of 3.8 pH units, as compared with the single unit in the case of the NaOH.

13.14. Ion and Solubility Products

The equilibrium in a saturated solution of a salt can also be described in terms of mass action. So-called insoluble compounds are never completely insoluble. Only an extremely small amount of such a compound may be dissolved to form a saturated solution of it, but this amount may be very important in industrial and analytical processes. Chemists are not always concerned with how much material they can dissolve in solution; often their concern involves how much they can remove by precipitation or crystallization. Under the latter circumstances the amount of solute remaining in solution may be controlled by applying equilibrium concepts, for these state the conditions that are necessary to remove ions from solution or to obtain ions in solution from an otherwise insoluble substance.

When a salt such as PbI_2 is added to water it dissolves steadily until the solution reaches saturation. In the process, the concentrations of both ions, Pb^{++} and I^-, continually increase. When saturation is reached, the concentrations of the ions are at a maximum and no longer change. However, it can be shown by appropriate experimental techniques that solid PbI_2 is still dissolving. How can the concentrations of ions remain constant if more compound is dissolving? This can occur only if the ions leave the solution as rapidly as they reenter it. In other words, an equilibrium has been established.

$$PbI_2 \rightleftharpoons Pb^{++} + 2I^-$$

As was said earlier, once a solution becomes saturated, no more solid can dissolve as long as the *temperature remains constant.* Therefore if 10 grams more of solid PbI_2 is added to our solution, there will be no more Pb^{++} or I^- ions in the solution than before. *Once saturation is reached, the amount of solute ions in the solution is independent of the quantity of excess solute, provided the temperature remains constant.*

The equilibrium expression for the PbI_2 reaction is written in accordance with the usual principles.

$$K_E = \frac{[Pb^{++}][I^-]^2}{[PbI_2 \text{ (solid)}]}$$

Since $[Pb^{++}]$ and $[I^-]$ are independent of excess solid PbI_2 and it is impossible to write "concentration" for an undissolved solid, the final expression has the following form:

$$\text{Ion product} = K_{sp} = [Pb^{++}][I^-]^2$$

The significance of the term *ion product* is obvious because the mathematical expression is exclusively a product of ionic concentrations. Since the situation at saturation is unique, the ion product is called K_{sp} or

solubility product constant. There are a multitude of ion products for each insoluble substance, but there is only *one solubility product for each substance at a given temperature and this is the ion product at saturation.*

Whenever an insoluble substance like PbI_2 is added to water, the ratio of the molarity of the ions in the resulting solution is the same as it is in the formula, in this case $1 : 2$. This coincidence of the two ratios holds true *only if the ions come from the same compound.* However, this is usually not the case. For example, a chemist may wish to precipitate the lead from a solution containing, say, $Pb(NO_3)_2$. So he adds a reagent containing I^- ion, perhaps NaI solution. Suppose that when he adds the first drop of the I^- ion reagent, nothing happens. Obviously the ion product does not yet equal the solubility product. After the next drop of reagent a faint cloudiness develops—precipitate of PbI_2. Now the ion product equals the solubility product. Also the Pb^{++} ion concentration remaining

TABLE 13.5. | **Results of Successive Additions of I^- Ion Reagent to a Solution Originally 0.05 M in Pb^{++} Ion**

$$K_{sp} \text{ of } PbI_2 = 1.5 \times 10^{-8}$$

Addition	$[Pb^{++}]$	$\times$	$[I^-]^2$	= Ion Product	Result
1	5×10^{-2}	$\times$	1×10^{-8}	$= 5 \times 10^{-10} \neq K_{sp}$	(No precipitation)
2	5×10^{-2}	$\times$	3×10^{-7}	$= 1.5 \times 10^{-8} = K_{sp}$	(Precipitation begins)
3	1×10^{-2}	$\times$	1.5×10^{-6}	$= 1.5 \times 10^{-8} = K_{sp}$	(Precipitation continues)
4	1×10^{-4}	$\times$	1.5×10^{-4}	$= 1.5 \times 10^{-8} = K_{sp}$	(Precipitation continues
5	1×10^{-6}	$\times$	1.5×10^{-2}	$= 1.5 \times 10^{-8} = K_{sp}$	(Precipitation continues)
6	1×10^{-8}	$\times$	1.5	$= 1.5 \times 10^{-8} = K_{sp}$	(Precipitation continues)

in solution is slightly less than it was because some lead ion has been removed as insoluble PbI_2. The I^- ion concentration is greater than before in order to compensate for the Pb^{++} ion which was removed and to maintain the equality of ion product and solubility product. As more I^- ion is added, more Pb^{++} is removed as PbI_2. Thus, when more reagent is added, the lead ion concentration continually diminishes and the I^- ion concentration increases; this results in a *variety* of concentrations for both ions, *the ion product always being kept equal to the solubility product.* This is summarized in Table 13.5. Note how the lead ion concentration continually diminishes while I^- increases. By the sixth addition the Pb^{++} ion concentration has been reduced 5,000,000-fold from its original value. Also note that the Pb^{++} concentration is never reduced to zero, nor is the I^- ion concentration ever double the Pb^{++} ion concentration as it would be if *pure* PbI$_2$ solid had been the source of *both* kinds of ions. The two examples that follow illustrate this point further.

1. What is the concentration of Mg^{++} ion in a saturated solution of Mg(OH)$_2$? $K_{sp} = 1.4 \times 10^{-11}$. Since no other information is given regarding the source of the ions, all ions can be assumed to come from *solid* Mg(OH)$_2$ which is added to water. Therefore the concentration of OH$^-$ ion in this solution is double that of Mg^{++} ion.

$$\underline{Mg(OH)_2} \rightleftharpoons \underset{X}{Mg^{++}} + \underset{2X}{2OH^-}$$

$$K_{sp} = [Mg^{++}][OH^-]^2 = X \cdot (2X)^2 = 1.4 \times 10^{-11}$$

Note that the law of equilibrium requires that the [OH$^-$] be squared regardless of its value. Here it is $2X$ and therefore the $2X$ must be squared. Hence:

$$X \cdot 4X^2 = 1.4 \times 10^{-11} = 4X^3$$
$$X^3 = 0.35 \times 10^{-11} = 3.5 \times 10^{-12}$$
$$X = \sqrt[3]{3.5 \times 10^{-12}} = 1.5 \times 10^{-4}\ M = [Mg^{++}]$$
$$2X = 2 \times 1.5 \times 10^{-4} = 3.0 \times 10^{-4}\ M = [OH^-]$$

2. What is the maximum possible molarity of Mg^{++} ion in a solution 1.0 M in NH$_4$Cl and 1.0 M in NH$_4$OH?

K_B of NH$_4$OH $= 1.8 \times 10^{-5}$, and K_{sp} of Mg(OH)$_2 = 1.4 \times 10^{-11}$.

The concentration of magnesium possible in this solution is limited by the solubility of Mg(OH)$_2$. This problem involves the common ion effect, NH$_4^+$ from NH$_4$Cl modifying the OH$^-$ ion concentration from NH$_4$OH. Two equilibria must be considered: that involving the basic ionization of NH$_4$OH and that involving the solubility product of Mg(OH)$_2$.

$$1.\quad K_B = \frac{[NH_4^+][OH^-]}{[NH_4OH]}$$
$$2.\quad K_{sp} = [Mg^{++}][OH^-]^2$$

Because of the common ion effect, very little NH$_4$OH ionizes; therefore the amount of un-ionized NH$_4$OH is so nearly the original amount that it can be called 1 M without introducing any error. NH$_4^+$ is also 1 M, because NH$_4$Cl is ionic and none of this additional ion is needed to form un-ionized NH$_4$OH. Thus:

$$K_B = 1.8 \times 10^{-5} = \frac{[1][OH^-]}{[1]}$$

Substituting this value for $[OH^-]$ in the second equilibrium relationship gives

$$K_{sp} = 1.4 \times 10^{-11} = [Mg^{++}][1.8 \times 10^{-5}]^2$$
$$[Mg^{++}] = \frac{1.4 \times 10^{-11}}{3.2 \times 10^{-10}} = 4.4 \times 10^{-2} \ M$$

A very considerable concentration of Mg^{++} ion can be present in this strongly ammoniacal solution when the ionization of the NH_4OH is repressed by the common ion effect.

QUESTIONS AND PROBLEMS

1. What factors affect reaction speeds? How do they do this?
2. The reaction $A + B \rightarrow C$ occurs at temperature T_1 at a rate R. The temperature is increased to T_2, with the result that twice as many molecules have energy equal to or greater than the activation energy. Their velocity is 1.02 times as great as at T_1.
   a. What is the increase in R resulting from the change in energy?
   b. What is the increase in R resulting from frequency of collisions?
   c. What is the total increase in R?
3. Write the equilibrium constant for the reaction:
$$2\overline{SO_2} + \overline{O_2} \rightleftharpoons 2\overline{SO_3} + \triangle$$
4. How will the equilibrium concentrations change in the preceding reaction if pressure is increased? If temperature is increased? If more oxygen is added?
5. In connection with the ionization of H_2S, if HCl is added to the solution, which of the following are correct? Give reasons for your answers.
   a. The H^+ will be higher, lower, the same.
   b. The S^{--} will be higher, lower, the same.
   c. The HS^- will be higher, lower, the same.
6. Answer the preceding question if NH_4OH is added to the solution of H_2S. Which of these is the common ion effect? Give your reasons.
7. What would you add to an NH_4OH solution to repress the OH^- ion concentration it furnishes? Is this the common ion effect? Generalize regarding the common ion effect for weak acidic and basic solutions in controlling H^+ ion, negative ion of the acid, and OH^- ion of weakly basic solutions.
8. The ionization constant of an acid HA is 1×10^{-8}. What is the concentration of A^- ion in a 0.1 M solution of the acid?
9. How many moles of NaA would need to be added to 1 l. of 1 M HA in order to maintain H^+ at $1 \times 10^{-6} \ M$?

10. A 1 M HCl solution is saturated with H_2S. Calculate the $[S^{--}]$ in this solution.

11. How many moles of NH_4Cl must be added to 1 l. of 0.5 M NH_4OH for the pH of the solution to be 8?

12. The K_{ion} of HF is 7.4×10^{-4}. What is the pH of a 0.5 M NaF solution?

13. Calculate the pH's of the following buffer mixtures of $HC_2H_3O_2$ and $C_2H_3O_2$. K_{ion} of $HC_2H_3O_2$ is 1.8×10^{-5}.
    a. 0.5 mole $HC_2H_3O_2$ + 0.5 mole $NaC_2H_3O_2$ in 1 l. of solution.
    b. 0.2 mole $HC_2H_3O_2$ + 0.8 mole $NaC_2H_3O_2$ in 1 l. of solution.
    c. 0.8 mole $HC_2H_3O_2$ + 0.2 mole $NaC_2H_3O_2$ in 1 l. of solution.

14. What is the molar solubility of $Cd(OH)_2$ if its solubility product is 1×10^{-14}?

15. The solubility of a compound MX_2 is 1×10^{-10} moles per liter. Calculate the solubility product.

16. If 500 ml. of a solution containing 1 mole of Mg^{++} is added to 500 ml. of a solution containing 1 mole of OH^-, what are the concentrations of Mg^{++} and OH^- that are left in solution? K_{sp} of $Mg(OH)_2 = 1.4 \times 10^{-11}$.

17. How many moles of HCl must be present in 1 l. of 0.05 M Zn^{++} solution to prevent ZnS from precipitating when the solution is saturated with H_2S? K_{sp} of ZnS $= 1.2 \times 10^{-23}$.

14

Metals and metallurgy

14.1. Characteristics of Metals

You are already familiar with a few metals, their uses and properties. Iron, aluminum, magnesium, and copper alloys are familiar because of their use in the average home. In the chapters dealing with atomic structure, distinctions between metals and non-metals were based solely upon the electronic differences in the valence shells. It is interesting to note that of the 100-odd elements known, only 17 are strictly non-metallic. All the others are metals or have sufficient metallic characteristics to be so considered. From the chemical viewpoint, a metal is an element which forms monatomic positive ions. (Hydrogen was long thought to behave like a metal in forming H^+ ion; the formula H_3O^+ was not then known. This is why hydrogen is so frequently misclassified as a metal.) However, there are so many other differences between metals and non-metals that an all-inclusive list of these differences would be very long. In fact, since the metals include the vast majority of elements, there are differences among the metals themselves that are as distinct and important as the differences between metals and non-metals. Table

14.1 summarizes, in general, the physical properties of metals and non-metals, but there are, of course, exceptions here as in most qualitative generalizations.

TABLE 14.1. **Comparison of Some Physical Characteristics of Metals and Non-Metals**

Characteristic	Metals	Non-Metals
Melting point	Medium-high	Low[a,b]
Boiling point	Medium-high[a]	Low[a,b]-medium
Density	Medium-high[a]	Low[a]-high
Luster	High	Low or none
Hardness	Low-high	Low
Ductility	High	Low (brittle)
Conductivity	High	Low

[a] Predominant.
[b] Exceptionally high melting and boiling points are found in the few cases in which all the atoms in a crystal are connected to each other by covalent bonds, forming a giant molecule (Chapter 24).

14.2. Electronic and Periodic Table Variations

Most metals have from 1 to 3 valence electrons, 2 being the most common. All the elements in a given horizontal row of the periodic table have identical electron shell systems. The first row (the smallest atoms) contains only non-metals. The second row, with larger atoms than those in the first, contains two metals and six non-metals. The third row, with atoms larger than those in the preceding row, has one more metal and one less non-metal. This trend continues into the longer periods. Size and the associated electronegativity are important factors in classifying an element as metallic or non-metallic. Size decreases, accompanied by an increase in electronegativity, from left to right across a row. The larger the atom at the beginning of a given row, the greater the number of atoms which must be traversed for the size to decrease and the electronegativity to increase sufficiently for the first non-metal to appear. This is why there are so few non-metals and why, starting with the second row, they decrease in number in each succeeding horizontal row in the periodic table.

None of the non-metals have partially filled d electron orbitals, but in many of the metals, e.g., the transition elements, the d orbitals are partially filled. Between the transition elements and the non-metals is a group which displays some non-metallic characteristics. These elements have completely filled d and f orbitals but do not have exclusively non-metallic properties because of their size and electronegativity. Since in the transition elements d electrons are being added and 2 s electrons are being maintained in the valence shell, the metals have a preponderantly +2 oxidation state.

14.3. The Metallic Bond

The formation of polyatomic molecules of non-metallic elements and compounds—e.g., Cl_2 and HCl—was shown in earlier chapters to be due to the formation of covalent bonds. Crystals composed of small molecules of covalent substances, generally weak and low-melting, are built up by the relatively weak van der Waals' forces which hold the molecules together in a regular crystalline pattern. In contrast to this, ionic crystals such as Na^+Cl^- are strong and usually have fairly high melting points. These crystals may be thought of as giant molecules consisting of positive and negative ions held together by strong electrostatic forces of attraction. The strong and high-melting crystals of metallic elements and intermetallic compounds cannot be accounted for entirely on the basis of similar bonding conditions. Metals on the right of the periodic table that have large numbers of valence electrons conceivably could form covalent bonds. This would account for the bonding of Sb and Bi atoms to form crystals, as well as for intermetallic compounds such as AlSb. The extension of the following atomic array:

$$
\begin{array}{c}
\cdot \ddot{S}b : Al : \ddot{S}b \cdot \\
\cdot \ddot{A}l : \ddot{S}b : \ddot{A}l \cdot \\
\cdot \ddot{S}b : \ddot{A}l : \ddot{S}b \cdot
\end{array}
$$

would produce a crystal by covalent bond formation. The non-metallic amphoteric character of such metals is in accord with this type of bonding. However, the formation of crystals of highly electropositive metals —those low in electronegativity—such as Ba and Li and of compounds like $BaLi_4$ cannot be explained exclusively in this way or on purely ionic grounds. Furthermore, simple valence rules generally fail to hold true because the electrons involved in the formation of compounds of this sort are not sufficient to complete the octets.

The term **metallic bond** is utilized to explain the bonding of like and unlike metallic atoms to each other. This bond may be considered as a modification of the ionic bond. In essence, each metal atom liberates its valence electrons to the crystal of which it is a part as if they were donated to a common pool. In other words, an array of metal ions exists in a sea of loose electrons. Each metal ion is held to its nearest ion neighbors by the mobile electron field between them much as a chloride ion mutually attracts and holds diametrically opposite sodium ions in a crystal of Na^+Cl^- (Fig. 14.1). In this sense a metallic crystal can be regarded as a pseudocompound of metal cations and electrons, a **metallic electride.** Such a structure would be strong but still ductile because of the mobility

$$
\begin{array}{llll}
e^- & e^- & e^- \\
Ba^{++}\ e^-\ Ba^{++}\ e^-\ Ba^{++}\ e^- \\
e^- & e^- & e^- \\
Ba^{++}\ e^-\ Ba^{++}\ e^-\ Ba^{++}\ e^- \\
e^- & e^- & e^- \\
Ba^{++}\ e^-\ Ba^{++}\ e^-\ Ba^{++}\ e^-
\end{array}
\qquad
\begin{array}{llll}
Na^+ & Cl^- & Na^+ & Cl^- \\
Cl^- & Na^+ & Cl^- & Na^+ \\
Na^+ & Cl^- & Na^+ & Cl^-
\end{array}
$$

A   B

Fig. 14.1. A, Part of a barium crystal containing barium ions in an electron sea. **B,** Part of an ionic crystal consisting of sodium ions regularly arranged in an array of negative chloride ions.

of the flexible, free electron field which would accommodate positional distortions of the metal ions. It is possible that the lack of ductility usually observed in ionic crystals is due to the fact that *all* components—i.e., positive and negative ions—occupy essentially *fixed* positions in the crystal lattice, whereas in metals the free electrons are not restricted in this sense. The strength would be due to the electrostatic attractive force that has been proved strong in crystals of ordinary ionic compounds. The high mobility and "looseness" of the valence electron pool would also account for the high electrical conductivity of metals as well as their consistent luster, since essentially similar loose electron surfaces would be exposed in the crystals of all the metals.

According to the wave mechanics viewpoint, the common pool of electrons of a metallic crystal exist at a common energy level shared simultaneously by all the atoms in the crystal. This borders upon covalent bond formation between these atoms. Thus 10^{10} barium atoms, which constitute a typical small crystal, would supply 2×10^{10} electrons to this *crystal energy level.* Each additional atom that attaches to the crystal adds 2 more electrons to this energy level. Theoretical considerations indicate that the greater the number of electrons, the lower and more stable the energy level becomes. The transition elements, with unpaired d electrons, can accommodate such a complexity of electrons more easily, as well as contribute more to the common pool, thus giving the crystal even greater stability. As a consequence, these crystals are stronger and have higher melting points. The metals which precede and follow the transition elements have either completely paired d electrons or none at all in the energy level considered and hence are very soft and relatively low-melting.

It should be apparent now that from the electronic viewpoint the solid state of metals and alloys is complex. That the whole gamut of bonding conditions must be considered should not be surprising since the metals are present virtually throughout the entire periodic table. As far as chemical properties are concerned, the problem involves simply the formation of positive ions and the characteristics of these ions. The variation in chemical properties of the metals and their resultant ions can be attributed to electronegativity, size, and charge of ions, and also to whether they have d electrons in the outer shell.

14.4. Crystallinity and Polymorphism of Metals

In the solid state the physical and mechanical properties of a metal are profoundly affected by its crystalline nature. Remarkable changes in these properties can be brought about in a given metal by changing its crystalline habit from one form to another, or by refining its crystals or changing their growth or orientation.

Generally, metals solidify into a polycrystalline mass consisting of many microcrystals called **grains**, randomly oriented with respect to each other. If the metallic surface is appropriately ground, polished, and etched—that is, if the crystals and their boundaries are defined by means of a reagent—the microcrystals can be seen under a microscope by reflected light (Fig. 14.2). These photographs display grains each of which is a single crystal surrounded by definite boundaries. Grain sizes vary from sample to sample, depending upon preliminary treatment such as rate of solidification, nucleation, and crystal growth. A structure consisting of fine grains is usually harder and tougher than a coarse-grained structure. The grains of zinc on the surface of galvanized iron are sufficiently large to be visible to the naked eye. With proper conditions and techniques many metals may be caused to form single crystals. A polycrystalline rod of zinc is strong and stiff, whereas a single-crystal zinc

A

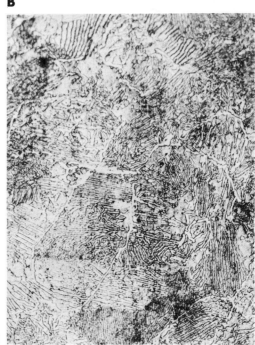

B

Fig. 14.2. A, Ingot iron grains. The small dark spots are dirt–for example, slags and oxides. **B,** Low-carbon steel (0.2 per cent C). It contains iron grains similar to those in **A,** and dark grains of pearlite, a mixture of iron and iron carbide (Fe₃C). **C,** Pearlitic steel (0.8 per cent C) at high magnification, showing the lamellar pattern of iron and iron carbide in the pearlite grains. Pearlite is responsible for the strength and hardness of annealed steels.

C

rod of similar dimensions is so pliable that it bends like rubber tubing when it is lifted up from a table top. Hence it is not surprising that diffusion, electrical conductivity, tensile strength, etc., vary in accordance with the crystalline state of a metal.

Most metallic elements form cubic or hexagonal crystals. No metals form simple cubic crystals; instead their crystals are face-centered or body-centered modifications (Fig. 14.3). The hexagonal crystal system is a modification referred to as hexagonal close-packed. These systems are consistent with the tendency of metallic atoms to form highly symmetrical crystalline patterns, as closely packed as possible, as a result of the simplicity of molecular shapes (simple spheres) and the absence of directive bonds. The positions of the atoms shown in Fig. 14.3 rep-

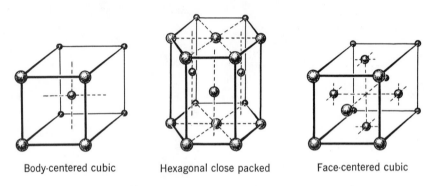

Body-centered cubic   Hexagonal close packed   Face-centered cubic

Fig. 14.3. The three most common crystal systems of metals.

resent the location of their centers. Actually the atoms are in contact with their nearest neighbors in the crystal lattice.

One of the unique features displayed by many metals is their ability to form several modifications of crystals at different temperatures. This is called **polymorphism.** For example, iron is body-centered cubic from below room temperature up to 910° C., at which temperature it becomes face-centered cubic. It retains this form up to 1400° C., but then becomes body-centered cubic again. Iron of the low-temperature body-centered cubic form can dissolve a maximum of 0.025 per cent carbon in the solid state, whereas the face-centered cubic can dissolve 1.7 per cent carbon. Polymorphism is mainly responsible for giving steels their heat-treatable characteristics; without this polymorphism of iron, steels as we know them would not exist.

14.5. Metallurgical Classifications of Metals

Metals fall into two main classes: **ferrous** and **non-ferrous.** The ferrous metals are associated with iron and its alloys. There are relatively few of them, but together with iron they constitute the most important branch of metallurgy. The non-ferrous classification includes all metals which are not used primarily in iron alloys. Since there are so many

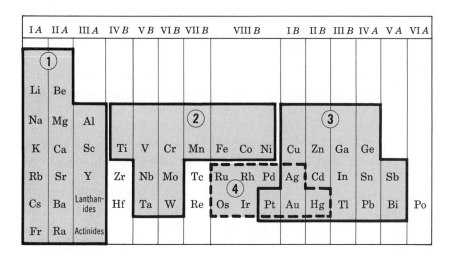

Fig. 14.4. A classification of the metals for convenience in studying their properties.

1. The very active metals. The metals in Group IA of the periodic table in this class are called the alkali metals, and those in Group IIA are called the alkaline earth metals.

2. Iron and the metals frequently used with it. These metals are often referred to as the ferrous metals.

3. The soft metals (the very active metals are excluded). The metals in Group IB of the periodic table in this class are commonly called the coinage metals.

4. The noble metals (dashed line). The Group VIIIB metals of the periodic table in this class are known as the platinum metals.

metals in this class, it is broken down into several subclasses. Fig. 14.4 shows the various classes in relation to their position in the periodic table.

At this time a few general remarks about each class will suffice to show that there is some logic for this classification from the viewpoint of either chemical nature or metallurgical characteristics and adaptation. These metals will be discussed in detail in subsequent chapters.

It is interesting to note that similarities in chemical properties which are utilized to separate ions into specific analytical groups lead to analytical groups which bear a relationship to the metallurgical classifications in Fig. 14.4. For example, the ions of *analytical* Group I (Ag^+, Hg_2^{++}, and Pb^{++}) and Group II (Cu^{++}, Cd^{++}, Hg^{++}, Sn^{++}, Pb^{++}, Sb^{+3}, and Bi^{+3}) are in class 3 in the figure. With the exception of Al^{+3} and Zn^{++}, the ions of analytical Group III (Cr^{+3}, Mn^{++}, Fe^{+3}, Co^{++}, and Ni^{++}) are in class 2. Analytical Group IV (Na^+, K^+, Mg^{++}, Ca^{++}, Sr^{++}, and Ba^{++}) consists of ions that are in class 1.

Since they are very reactive, the metals in class 1 are used chiefly as deoxidizers and getters (scavengers). Only Be, Mg, and Al in this class are used extensively as major alloying components in light-weight structural alloys.

Iron and the ferrous metals in class 2 are the most important structural metals. Besides having many similar properties and uses as individual metals, various alloys of these metals with iron make up our vast variety of steels. Although small quantities of metals from other classes—e.g., Al, Cu, and Zr—may be added to steel, their importance as alloying components of steel never approaches that of the recognized ferrous metals.

The metallurgy of each of the *common* stable soft metals in class 3 is sufficiently like that of the others so that these elements can be studied together. Many important non-ferrous alloys are made from metals in this class. Their alloys make possible an extremely wide variety of compositions, properties, and uses that is too complex for anything but general consideration. Copper, the most important *heavy* non-ferrous metal, is a particularly good example, for it forms a wide range of useful alloys, such as sterling and coin silver, 18-carat gold, brass (with zinc), and bronze (with tin). Bronzes are also made from copper alloyed with beryllium, aluminum, manganese, and nickel (Monel metal), and with the non-metals silicon and phosphorus.

The noble metals, which make up class 4, are so called because of their lack of pronounced chemical reactivity. The common uses of silver, platinum, gold, and mercury are based on this fact. The use of the other less common noble metals in industry and research depends upon their inertness. Copper would be classed with the noble metals except that it is slightly too reactive. Its resemblance to silver and gold is to be expected from the fact that these three metals constitute Group IB of the periodic table. Likewise the platinum metals in Group VIIIB have much in common with each other chemically and are frequently found together in natural deposits.

The fact that metals in a given class are closely related chemically, and electronically as well, indicates once again that similarities of electronic structure must be closely related to the physical characteristics of the metals that lead to their use in particular alloys.

14.6. Alloys

An **alloy** is a metallike substance that consists of more than a single element and has physical characteristics similar to those of the metallic elements. Most alloys contain two or more metals; for example, brass is made of copper and zinc. Certain compounds of metals and non-metals, such as borides, carbides, and nitrides, are soluble in some metals and are often excellent alloying components. Thus all steels contain carbon, which is usually present as iron carbide, Fe_3C. Iron alloyed with iron carbide forms the common plain carbon steels. Similarly the compounds which metals form with other metals can alloy with one of the metals in the compound; e.g., $BaLi_4$ forms alloys with an excess of either barium or lithium.

The properties of alloys may vary markedly with changes in the proportions of the constituents. Hence in most alloy systems the only alloys that are commercially feasible may have very narrow ranges of composition.

When a metal is melted it usually is an excellent solvent for other metals. Except for their high temperatures, these solutions resemble other solutions in regard to certain physical properties. We have seen how solutes like NaCl lower the freezing point of such solvents as water. Similarly, metal solutes lower the freezing point of metal solvents. Thus the melting points of alloys of two constituents depend upon the composition of the alloy. Study of the melting points of alloys with various compositions provides data which can be plotted to give a temperature-composition diagram, such as that in Fig. 14.5 for the lead-antimony system.

The curved lines which meet at 88 per cent Pb and 12 per cent Sb are the melting-point curves for the various alloys of this system. Above 12 per cent Sb, antimony is the solvent because its melting point (630° C.) is lowered by the addition of lead. From 0 to 12 per cent Sb, lead is the solvent because its melting point (324°) is lowered by the addition of antimony. The composition with the lowest melting point (247°) corresponding to 12 per cent Sb and 88 per cent Pb is called the **eutectic composition** (Gr., easily melted). All these alloys will be completely solid below 247° C. and at least partly melted above this temperature, except for the eutectic, which is completely melted. This is only one of several temperature-composition diagrams which can be plotted. Others are exceedingly complex, involving solid solutions (liquid melts which

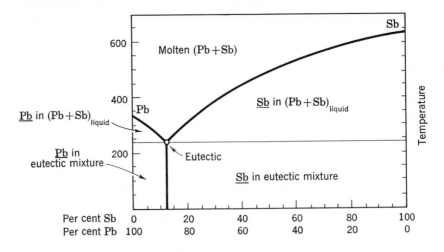

Fig. 14.5. Melting-point curves of mixtures of antimony and lead.

solidify without separation of one constituent from the other) and inter-metallic compounds. Moreover, some solids which form first may undergo changes in the solid state on further cooling. Some of these diagrams may take years of study before they are completely and accurately worked out.

Alloys of a given composition may display a variation in some property such as hardness, depending upon how they are heat-treated. Certain changes which the alloy would normally undergo in slow equilibrium cooling may be partially modified or completely suppressed by rapid cooling (quenching). Thus, seemingly limitless variations of properties may be developed by varying the components, their composition ranges, and the subsequent heat treatment.

14.7. Extractive Metallurgy ; Ore Concentration

Extractive metallurgy concerns the chemistry associated with the treatment of a suitable ore to produce the desired metal. Ores mined and processed at present range from high to low grades, the latter being more prevalent. Low-grade ores are now worked because high-grade ore fields either were never found or have petered out. Glamour metals such as gold—and now uranium—have led many a budding prospector in search of a fortune. Larger potential fortunes lie in finding worth-while ore fields of such metals as copper, iron, tungsten, and molybdenum.

Common ores of the metals are sulfides, oxides, carbonates, and hydroxides. (Other compounds that may be found in some specialized cases will be discussed in connection with the various individual metals.) Along with the metallic compound in the ore, there will be undesirable constituents or earthy siliceous material, essentially SiO_2. Such materials are dug up with the metallic constituents and obviously must be removed as completely as possible, for handling, working, and hauling costs as much for a ton of useless material as for a ton of usable ore. Usable ore is separated from undesirable constituents, called tailings, by one of several ore concentration methods.

On the basis of tons of treated material, the electrostatic separation and ore flotation methods are the most important. **Electrostatic separation** is based on the fact that substances with like electrical charges repel each other, whereas substances with unlike charges attract each other. If a pulverized mixture of good and poor conductors, such as metallic sulfides and sandstone, comes in contact with a highly charged surface, the good conductor (metallic sulfide) takes the charge from the surface and is then repelled from it. Because the ore must be dry for this process, dust presents a serious problem.

The **ore flotation process,** which is extremely important at present, is applicable to many ores and creates no dust problem because the ore must be wet. This process (Fig. 14.6) involves the addition of a chemical to finely pulverized ore; this causes a froth to form when air is blown through the wet mixture. The use of many non-soluble oils such as pine, creosote, eucalyptus, and camphor for wetting agents makes it possible to float first one metal ore and then another (Fig. 14.7). The valuable ore is carried to the surface; silica and other non-metallic constituents remain suspended in the liquid. As the froth comes to the surface a paddle wheel brushes it off into another container. Acid is added to break the froth, and the ore is then filtered on vacuum rotary filters covered with a special canvas. A scraper on one side of the filter dislodges the sticky ore concentrate.

The ore concentrate thus obtained is subjected to high-temperature treatments (**pyrometallurgy**). The various chemical changes effected by these treatments are considered separately in the following section.

14.8. Pyrometallurgy; Smelting

Smelters are generally operated at or near the mines to avoid the expense of shipping impure ore. **Smelting** is any high-temperature treatment of the ore which separates the metal or a desirable compound of it in the molten condition from the earthy material. Compounds called fluxes are added to combine with the high-melting siliceous material and form lower-melting substances called slags. Limestone is a common flux. It decomposes readily in the smelters to lime and carbon dioxide.

$$CaCO_3 \overset{\Delta}{\rightarrow} CaO + \overline{CO_2}$$

The lime in turn readily dissolves and combines with SiO_2.

$$CaO + SiO_2 \overset{\Delta}{\rightarrow} CaSiO_3$$

The resultant glassy slag floats on top of the molten metal or the molten mixture of metallic compounds. Slags are usually of value because they provide a liquid protective coating for the melt on which they float.

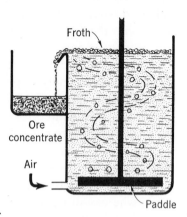

Fig. 14.6. Ore flotation. A schematic sketch showing a typical ore flotation unit.

Calcining. A few metals, generally non-ferrous, occur in nature in the form of carbonate ores. These decompose into oxides in the smelters.

$$ZnCO_3 \overset{\Delta}{\rightarrow} ZnO + \overline{CO_2}$$

The decomposition of carbonate ores is usually called **calcining**.

Dehydration. Metals that occur as hydroxide (or hydrated oxide) ores are quite common. Virtually any metallic oxide has water of hydration associated with it. Such oxides decompose and lose all this water. Chemical treatment to purify an ore can result in the formation of a hydroxide of the metal. This is the case in the Bayer process for purifying bauxite, $Al_2O_3 \cdot 2H_2O$. The purified hydroxide is then roasted.

$$2Al(OH)_3 \overset{\Delta}{\rightarrow} Al_2O_3 + \overline{3H_2O}$$

Roasting. Sulfide ores are treated by a process called **roasting**; that is, the ore is heated in a stream of air. Oxidation-reduction reactions occur, in contrast to the previously mentioned processes involving no valence changes. The valence of the end product depends upon time, tem-

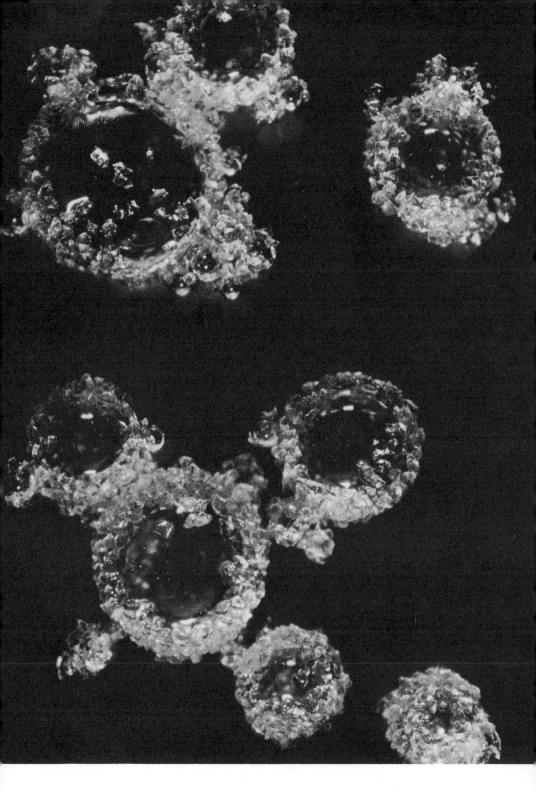

Fig. 14.7. Air bubbles adhering to sand particles because of the presence of selective wetting agents. (Photograph courtesy of General Mills, Inc.)

perature, and extent to which the heated ore is exposed to the air.

If ZnS is roasted at a moderate temperature the sulfate is formed.

$$ZnS + \overline{2O_2} \xrightarrow{\Delta} ZnSO_4$$

This can be extracted from the rocky impurities by leaching with water; the resulting solution is electrolyzed to obtain the zinc. At a higher temperature the oxide forms.

$$2ZnS + \overline{3O_2} \xrightarrow{\Delta} 2ZnO + \overline{2SO_2}$$

In the case of some ores, controlled roasting techniques produce a mixture of sulfates and oxides. These in turn react with the excess sulfide at the high temperature maintained in the smelter, producing the desired metal.

$$PbS + \overline{2O_2} \xrightarrow{\Delta} PbSO_4$$

$$PbS + PbSO_4 \xrightarrow{\Delta} 2Pb + \overline{2SO_2}$$

$$2PbS + \overline{3O_2} \xrightarrow{\Delta} 2PbO + \overline{2SO_2}$$

$$2PbO + PbS \xrightarrow{\Delta} 3Pb + \overline{SO_2}$$

Copper sulfides behave similarly.

A molten mixture of sulfates, sulfides, and oxides is called *matte*. The by-product sulfur dioxide is produced in sufficient quantities to warrant the installation of sulfuric acid plants in conjunction with the smelters. In fact, a considerable portion of our output of sulfuric acid is produced in this way. This gives the sulfide ores added importance.

Reduction.   Most oxides of the metals require a better reducing agent than the metal sulfide. Only a few are suited to reduction by roasting, considered under sulfide ores. The cheapest reducing agent is carbon.

$$ZnO + C \xrightarrow{\Delta} \overline{Zn} + \overline{CO}$$

The escaping zinc vapor is condensed as solid metal on a cold condenser over the reaction vessel. Usually CO rather than the element is responsible for the reduction.

$$CuO + C \xrightarrow{\Delta} Cu + \overline{CO}$$

$$CuO + \overline{CO} \xrightarrow{\Delta} Cu + \overline{CO_2}$$

In many cases the free metal and carbon combine to form carbides. This may or may not be desirable. In the case of iron the carbide can be tolerated; but in the case of tungsten it cannot, especially if the tungsten is to be used ultimately as fine filaments for lamps. Tungsten carbide, WC, makes the filaments brittle and also increases their electrical resistance. Hydrogen is an excellent though costlier reducing agent.

$$\underline{WO_3} + \overline{3H_2} \xrightarrow{\Delta} \underline{W} + \overline{3H_2O}$$

Many metal oxides which can be reduced by carbon are also reduced by hydrogen, especially if the powder form of the metal is desired for powder metallurgical fabrication. A finely pulverized pure oxide gives equally finely pulverized pure metal provided the reduction is carried out at temperatures below the melting or welding point of the metal particles.

Whenever the metal oxide is sufficiently stable to resist reduction with carbon or hydrogen under normal reaction conditions, more vigorous reducing agents are used, such as active metals. Aluminum is frequently utilized for this purpose. Reduction by means of aluminum is usually called the **thermite process.** Oxides of many of the more reactive metals can be successfully reduced in this way.

$$2Al + \underline{Cr_2O_3} \rightarrow 2Cr + \underline{Al_2O_3} + \triangle$$
$$2Al + 6BaO \underset{vacuum}{\rightleftarrows} 3Ba + Ba_3Al_2O_6 + \triangle$$

The latter reaction, which is reversible, is shifted to the right to virtual completion when carried out under vacuum. The barium evaporates and is condensed on a water-cooled condenser set up over the reaction mixture. This prevents the barium from entering a reduction reaction with the aluminate.

Electrolytic reduction can be used to obtain most metals from suitable compounds. It is the cheapest and most direct method for use with the highly reactive metals such as the alkali and alkaline earth metals and aluminum. Furthermore, through voltage control, selective electrolysis makes direct refining possible (see below). This is why electrochemical processes are preferable in the case of several metals—Cu, Zn, Cd, and Ag, for example—which can be obtained by means of chemical reactions. Fundamentally the process involves the reduction of the metallic ion at the cathode.

$$Cu^{++} + 2e^- \xrightarrow{\triangle} Cu$$
$$Na^+ + e^- \xrightarrow{\triangle} Na$$

The oxidation at the anode depends upon the composition of the electrolyte compound. The electrolysis may be carried out in water solutions (Cu, Zn, Cd, Ag) or in melts of the metallic compound (NaCl, $MgCl_2$, etc.), or in molten solutions of the metallic compound in a suitable molten solvent (Al_2O_3 dissolved in molten cryolite, Na_3AlF_6). In all cases, however, the fundamental electrolytic *reduction* reaction is the same.

Refining. The purpose of refining metals, of course, is to obtain a product that is as pure as is possible or necessary. Refining may take place before, during, or after extraction of the metal or in some cases at several stages of the extractive processes. Obviously, the purer the starting materials the purer the end product. This is why ores may themselves be purified initially or converted to more suitable compounds which permit chemical treatment and purification.

Various techniques are available. Although they are too numerous to consider here, a few are mentioned to illustrate the variation possible. Impure tin can be converted to liquid $SnCl_4$; this in turn can be purified by distillation and pure tin extracted by reduction. Al_2O_3 is removed from insoluble impurities by being dissolved in NaOH. Subsequent precipitation of $Al(OH)_3$ by means of pH control then removes soluble impurities. The aluminum thus produced is of a high degree of purity.

Salts, such as those of the rare earth metals, can be purified by selective ion exchange. This process involves the use of porous particles of a synthetic resin. The molecules of the resin are enormous, so the resin is insoluble. However, negatively charged groups occur at frequent intervals on these molecules, and cations adhere to these groups. These cations are in equilibrium with the solution which permeates the pores of the resin particles; they continually break loose into the solution and are replaced by other cations from the solution. No two ionic species have exactly the same equilibrium concentration in the solution. When a solution containing a mixture of cations of the rare earth metals is poured into the top of a long column packed with resin grains and slowly washed through it, the ions which remain in the solution most of the time are washed along most rapidly. If the column is long enough, the first effluent will contain only the cation species that is least strongly adsorbed, and practically all of it will be washed out before any cations of the next species appear. This process has rendered obsolete the tedious fractional recrystallization process and made pure rare earth metals commercially available for the first time. In order to handle the large quantities of solutions necessitated by commercial production of the rare earths, columns up to 60 in. in diameter are now in use.

Electrolytic refining may be realized through selective voltages used in the electrolysis. Thus a low voltage plates copper but not some of the more reactive impure metals in the electrolytic bath. Silver ion, which plates out even more easily than copper ion, is precipitated by the addition of chloride ion to the bath. Other reagents may be used to inhibit or cause the precipitation of other ions, depending on the nature of the impurities.

The metal thus produced, although as pure as the refining process permits, may be further purified by additional treatment. For example, it may be **sublimed** to remove it from impurities not completely removed by other methods. The metal may be **zone-refined.** This process is based on the principle that impurities are more soluble in the molten than in the solid metal. A narrow *melted zone* is produced in one end of a bar of the metal and is moved slowly along it to the other end. Impurities are dissolved and retained in the liquid layer as it moves along. Fantastically high degrees of purity have been achieved with this technique.

14.9. Pure Metals

You may well ask, "How pure is a pure metal and are pure metals necessary?" The answer to the first part of this question is more or less arbitrary. Generally a "pure" metal is one that is as pure as it can be made. This does not mean that it is 100 per cent pure. For example, after all the known techniques have been applied to purify calcium, it is found to be 99.93 per cent Ca. Anyone using this grade of calcium refers to it as "pure" calcium. Perhaps in the future someone will succeed in preparing 99.99 per cent Ca. This would then be called "pure" calcium. Generally speaking, a metal that has a purity of 99.99 per cent (called "four 9 purity") is regarded as having very high purity. Only a few metals have been refined to this degree of purity. Ordinary aluminum has a purity of 99.0 per cent, the impurities being chiefly iron and silicon. Malleable or wrought iron, the purest iron commercially available, is 99.5 per cent Fe.

As to whether high-purity metals are necessary, this depends upon the properties desired for their use. Very high-purity metals are costly, and the end use must warrant the cost. A metal 99.9 per cent pure may cost twice as much to make as the same metal 99.0 per cent pure. Although automobiles made of high-purity iron rust less rapidly, it is cheaper to repaint than to pay $1000 more for a car made of this iron. However, there are uses—and undoubtedly more will be discovered—for which only very high-purity metals are suitable because of their remarkable properties. For example, titanium is ideal for certain applications in missiles and aircraft, but it cannot be worked or machined if it contains a considerable fraction of 1 per cent of oxygen. It is so brittle that it is useless. Germanium, presently zone-refined to "nine 9 purity," is the critical ingredient of transistors. Copper that contains 0.1 per cent of oxygen has an electrical conductivity so much lower than 99.99 per cent copper as to make it impractical for use in making household conductor wire. On the other hand, 99.99 per cent sheet aluminum is *too* pure. It work-hardens to such a degree that it smashes steel dies and stamps that are strong enough to fabricate parts from sheet steel of the same thickness. Similar exaggerated changes in properties have been observed in other metals as the purity varies. Minute amounts of certain impurities added to a very pure metal (this is called **doping**) may be responsible for the presence of certain valuable properties or characteristics. For example, boron added in this way to germanium gives it desired semiconductor characteristics.

Thus the role of impurities may be a predominant factor in deciding properties and utilizations yet to be discovered for many metals. The intriguing and challenging question for the scientist is, "Why does the presence or absence of certain impurities cause these observed effects?" When he knows and understands the answer to this question, he can probably tailor-make metals and alloys that will have properties beyond anything presently known.

QUESTIONS AND PROBLEMS

1. On the basis of electronic considerations, defend the fact that there are many more metallic than non-metallic elements.
2. Why is a valence of +2 most prevalent among the metallic elements? Give reasons for your answer.
3. Compare metals and non-metals with respect to physical and chemical characteristics.
4. Distinguish between ionic, covalent, and metallic bonding.
5. Define ore; alloy; solid solution; intermetallic compound.
6. Define grain; grain boundary; hexagonal close-packed lattice; polymorphic modification.
7. Illustrate the following processes by means of chemical equations: calcining; roasting; reduction; electrolytic refining.

8. What is meant by a "pure" metal? What degrees of purity are common? What degrees are rare?

9. Which of the following metals are ferrous and which are non-ferrous: calcium; chromium; nickel; copper; manganese; aluminum; zinc?

15

The very active metals. Analysis of analytical group IV

15.1. Electronegativity and Metallic Behavior

In showing characteristic chemical behavior, a metal loses one or more electrons and becomes a simple cation. This is the exact opposite of the chemical behavior of a typical non-metal. When a chemist speaks of characteristic metallic or non-metallic behavior, he means behavior at either extreme, not the behavior of average or ordinary metals or non-metals. Just as the elements with the highest electronegativity, in the upper right-hand corner of the periodic table, are regarded as typical non-metals, so those with the lowest electronegativity, in the lower left-hand corner, are considered to be metals above all others. From the layman's point of view these are not typical metals as far as physical properties are concerned. True, they have a brilliant silvery luster and are good conductors of heat and electricity like the metals he is familiar with in everyday life; and they are malleable, instead of being brittle as most solid non-metals are. But they lack the hardness and tensile strength of iron, nickel, copper, and chromium. Chemically, this is logical. The uncharged atoms are held together only loosely for the same reason that they so readily lose electrons in chemical reactions, namely, their low electronegativity. An atom that cannot hold onto its own valence electrons effectively will be even less effective in holding onto those of neighboring atoms. Almost complete inability to form covalent bonds is, in fact, one of the chemical characteristics of the very active metals.

A reasonable criterion for classifying a metal as very active is the ability to decompose cold water, with the liberation of hydrogen. This property is displayed by all the elements in Group IA of the periodic table, and by all metals below magnesium in Group IIA. The electronegativities of these elements range from 0.7 to 1.0. Magnesium (electronegativity 1.2) is border line; powdered magnesium decomposes boiling water.

15.2. The Alkali Metals

The elements that come immediately after the inert gases, each with a single s electron in the valence layer, constitute the family known as the **alkali metals.** The name does not indicate that these metals are bases; rather, it means "the metals obtained from the alkalies." (The word alkali goes back to the period when the Arabs were the only students of natural science. The Arabic word for potassium carbonate, K_2CO_3, was *kali; al* means the.) The carbonates of all this family of metals are soluble enough (Li_2CO_3 is the least soluble) to produce quite basic solutions, so they all came to be known as alkalies. (CO_3^{--} ion is a slightly weaker base than NH_3.) Since their hydroxides are more soluble and OH^- ion a stronger base than CO_3^{--} ion, the hydroxides became known as the **caustic alkalies.** The metals themselves, which were unknown to the ancients, were obtained by electrolysis of the fused hydroxides. Table 15.1 lists some of the physical properties of the alkali metals.

Na^+ ion accounts for 2.83 per cent of the weight of igneous rocks in the

TABLE 15.1. **Some Physical Properties of the Alkali Metals (Excluding Francium)**

Name	Lithium	Sodium	Potassium	Rubidium	Cesium
Symbol	Li	Na	K	Rb	Cs
Density of solid, g./ml.	0.535	0.971	0.862	1.532	1.90
Melting point, °C.	179	98	63.5	39	28.5
Boiling point, °C.	1336	883	758	700	670
Electronegativity	1.0	0.9	0.8	0.8	0.7
Radius of M+ ion, A.	0.60	0.95	1.33	1.48	1.69

earth's crust, and K^+ ion for 2.59 per cent. The ions of the other alkali metals, except Fr^+, range in amount from one thousandth to a few hundredths of 1 per cent. Francium occurs only as very minute traces of a short-lived radioactive decay product of the very rare element actinium. Ions of the alkali metals are found in aluminosilicate minerals such as the feldspars and micas (both of which are constituents of granite); the weathering of these minerals releases them into solution. K^+ ions are strongly adsorbed by clay and remain in the soil which is formed; Na^+ ions are not adsorbed but are leached into rivers and carried into the sea. This explains why the sea contains so much salt, and why land plants use K^+ ion, whereas seaweed uses Na^+ ion. This is why potassium salts must be applied as fertilizer when the soil supply has been depleted, and why herbivorous animals (whose blood still has the Na^+ ion concentration of the primordial sea in which animal life originated) require salt.

The seas and salt lakes, and the salt beds, surface or buried, left behind by their evaporation, are the commercial source of Na^+ and K^+ ions from which the free metals and all their compounds are prepared. As was mentioned in connection with the halogens, NaCl is overwhelmingly the main constituent of salt deposits, as it is of the ocean. The minor constituents were concentrated in the last portions of the brine as it dried up, but much exploration has been required to locate the regions where this took place. Prior to World War I, Germany had a monopoly of the world's K^+ ion supply with her famous Stassfurt deposits of carnallite, $KCl \cdot MgCl_2 \cdot 6H_2O$. The United States became independent of Germany in this respect in 1934, as the result of a strenuous exploration, research, and development program. The brine of Searles Lake, in the Mojave Desert in California, had long been known to contain 4.75 per cent of KCl. The development of a practicable process for separating it was a triumph of research in physical chemistry. The discovery of the underground salt deposits containing K^+ ion near Carlsbad, New Mexico, was the result of geologic explorations. Deposits like those in Stassfurt and Carlsbad have been found in Tunis, Spain, France, Poland, Russia, and the Dead Sea. These are being worked by methods similar to those in use at Searles Lake. Although widely distributed, Li^+ ion occurs in quantity only in a few rare minerals. These include some complex phosphates, in addition to the aluminosilicates mentioned above. Few of these minerals contain as much as 5 per cent of Li^+.

15.3. Commercial Preparation of the Alkali Metals

The alkali metals are prepared by the electrolysis of fused salts, since they themselves are the strongest chemical reducing agents available. In the obsolete Castner process NaOH was used because it melts at only 318° C. Sodium made "the big time" with the invention of Ethyl antiknock fluid; this made it necessary to use NaCl, the cheapest raw material available, in spite of the engineering difficulties caused by its 804° C. melting point. The **Downs process** (Fig. 15.1) is now used in the production of 150,000 tons of the metal annually. Less than half of this goes into sodium-lead alloy for the production of the tetraethyllead required for

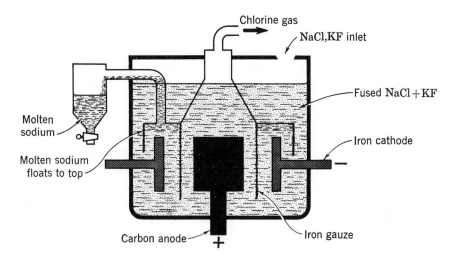

Fig. 15.1. Cross section of a circular cell for the production of metallic sodium. Cell devised by J. C. Downs.

the antiknock fluid. The story is a familiar one in chemistry—increased production made lower prices possible and lower prices resulted in the development of new uses. The current price is 17 cents per pound in tank cars with heating coils for remelting. Prices are progressively higher for the metal in solid-pack drums and in bricks ranging from 1 to 12 lb. in weight. The manufacture of a few sodium compounds—notably the hydride, NaH, the amide, $NaNH_2$, the azide, NaN_3, the peroxide, Na_2O_2, and the cyanide, NaCN—starts directly with the metal. A much greater amount of sodium is used as a reducing agent in the manufacture of indigo and other dyes, and of intermediates for detergents, resins, and plasticizers. For these uses the melted metal is frequently dispersed in an inert liquid into a slurry of micron-sized particles that offer a relatively large surface. Dispersions of sodium and lithium are used as catalysts in manufacturing synthetic rubber. Sodium has a number of metallurgical uses. Acting as an immiscible solvent, it removes arsenic and antimony from tin and lead. By its deoxidizing action it increases the low-temperature impact strength of steel, the fluidity of steel for castings, and the wetting ability of steel in hot-dip galvanizing and tinning. New uses are rapidly growing; they include the reduction of zirconium and titanium from their chlorides to the metallic state. Approximately one-sixth of the sodium produced in 1956 was used in reducing titanium. Retractions in military aircraft orders have reduced this use of sodium in recent years.

Pure metallic potassium is not an article of commerce, but a sodium-potassium alloy is available when an even more active reducing agent than sodium is needed. It ranges in price from $3 to $4 per pound. Sodium and potassium mutually lower each other's melting points; one of their alloys is actually liquid at room temperature. This alloy is used as a heat-transfer medium in some nuclear energy installations.

Our production of lithium, now about 50 tons a year, is due for a tenfold increase by 1970, according to the American Lithium Institute. Big increases are expected in its use in synthesizing new metal-organic compounds and as a catalyst in making plastics and elastomers (rubberlike materials). Its low density makes lithium a promising coolant for nuclear power aircraft plants. Current uses include the manufacture of lithium salts that are valuable selective reducing agents; these salts include the hydride, LiH, the borohydride, $LiBH_4$, and the aluminohydride, $LiAlH_4$. The price of lithium ranges from $13 to $20 per pound.

15.4. Chemical Properties and Uses of the Alkali Metals

The fact that the alkali metals are our most powerful reducing agents has already been mentioned. When they react with any oxidizing agent (they force even H_2 to act as an oxidizing agent), they lose the single, weakly bonded s electron from the valence layer. The univalent cation which remains has the electronic structure of the preceding inert gas. The farther the valence electron from the nucleus, the more weakly it is held; hence with most reagents (e.g., dry oxygen, bromine) the reactivity of the alkali metals increases regularly with size. Lithium is the most reactive with the very small non-metals such as hydrogen, carbon, and nitrogen, because the tightness with which the valence electron is held is more than counterbalanced by the extra lattice energy resulting from the close approach that is possible for two small ions. Because of its high heat of hydration, lithium is also abnormally active in reactions in which Li^+ ion goes into aqueous solution.

A characteristic test of the reducing action of metals is their reaction with acids, liberating hydrogen. In the case of the alkali metals, this reaction is explosive with all except the weakest acids. It is dangerous even with such a weak acid as water. When a piece of sodium the size of an uncooked rice grain is dropped into water it buzzes around over the surface, jet-propelled, so to speak, by the hydrogen it is liberating.

$$\underline{2Na} + 2H_2O \rightarrow 2Na^+ + 2OH^+ + \overline{H_2}$$

At the end of the reaction there is a faintly red ball of melted NaOH which glides around on a cushion of steam for a few seconds more. When this drops down into the water and dissolves, there is a sharp crack as more steam is produced; caustic NaOH solution splatters around. If the movement of the sodium on the water is impeded by a piece of filter paper, so that the sodium is not cooled as effectively, the heat ignites the hydrogen being given off, and it and the sodium burn together; the flame has a yellow color because of the sodium. A piece of potassium reacts too rapidly for water cooling to be effective; it ignites immediately. (This flame has a violet color because of the potassium.) In fact, a small piece of potassium will melt and ignite from the heat of its reaction with water vapor in moist air. For this reason it is extremely hazardous for large pieces of these metals to be near water or in moist air.

Sodium reacts safely enough with some organic compounds which are far weaker acids than water. Thus sodium ethylate is formed by the reaction of sodium with ethyl alcohol.

$$\underline{2Na} + 2C_2H_5OH \rightarrow 2C_2H_5ONa + \overline{H_2}$$

Similarly molten sodium liberates hydrogen even from ammonia, forming sodium amide.

$$2Na + \overline{2NH_3} \rightarrow \underline{2NaNH_2} + \overline{H_2}$$

Ammonia is a far weaker acid than water; the alkali metals dissolve in anhydrous liquid NH_3 without any reaction unless a catalyst is present. The beautiful deep blue solutions which are formed show metallic-type conduction, and the metals can be recovered unchanged by evaporating the ammonia. The solutions are powerful reducing agents. Sodium ethylate and sodium amide are salts. The ethylate ion and the amide ion are far stronger bases than the hydroxide ion, corresponding to the fact that alcohol and ammonia are far weaker acids than water. Both are used as bases in the chemical industry, but only in non-aqueous solutions. In the presence of water both are hydrolyzed completely. Sodium amide is also used in the manufacture of sodium azide, from which the detonator, lead azide, $Pb(N_3)_2$, is prepared.

Hydrogen reacts with the alkali metals as though it were a halogen, forming salts whose negative ion is the hydride ion, H^-.

$$2Na + \overline{H_2} \rightarrow 2NaH$$

The hydride ion is an extremely strong reducing agent. Although, of necessity, not as strong in that respect as the alkali metals are, it reacts immediately with water, liberating hydrogen.

$$\underline{NaH} + H_2O \rightarrow Na^+ + OH^- + \overline{H_2}$$

Sodium hydride can reduce mill scale, Fe_3O_4, to metallic iron.

$$\underline{Fe_3O_4} + 4Na^+ + 4H^- \rightarrow \underline{3Fe} + 4Na^+ + 4OH^-$$

For this use it is dissolved in fused sodium hydroxide.

Lithium burns in air to the oxide, Li_2O; sodium to the peroxide, Na_2O_2; and potassium to the superoxide, KO_2. Na_2O_2 is among the important oxidizing agents used in the chemical laboratory and in industry.

All the alkali metals can be stored in sealed cans or drums. After the oxygen and nitrogen in the container have been used up, no further reaction occurs. The very thin layer of oxide and nitride can be easily scraped off when the container is opened. Thereafter all these metals—except lithium, which floats on oil—can be kept safely under kerosene. *Never forget the great danger to yourself and to others when you work with these metals.*

15.5. The Alkaline Earth Metals

The second element beyond each inert gas is an **alkaline earth metal.** The term alkaline earth is very old; it dates back to the time when any insoluble, more or less claylike material was called an earth, nothing being known about its composition. Slaked lime, which we now know is calcium hydroxide, $Ca(OH)_2$, was such a material. It made a smooth, plastic paste which could be spread like moist clay, and it made even better plaster. But it had one property which sharply differentiated it from clay—it could neutralize acids; therefore it was an *alkaline* earth.

TABLE 15.2. **Some Physical Properties of the Alakline Earth Metals**

Name	Beryllium	Magnesium	Calcium	Strontium	Barium	Radium
Symbol	Be	Mg	Ca	Sr	Ba	Ra
Density of solid, g./ml.	1.86	1.75	1.55	2.6	3.59	5.0
Melting point, °C.	1280	651	842	774	725	700
Boiling point, °C.	1500	1107	1487	1366	1537	1140
Electronegativity	1.5	1.2	1.0	1.0	0.9	0.9
Radius of M^{++} ion, A.	0.31	0.65	0.99	1.13	1.35	1.40

A similar material in this family is $Mg(OH)_2$; this is also an alkaline earth. (A suspension of it in water is the familiar milk of magnesia used internally as an antacid.) Thus these two hydroxides gave the family its name, although beryllium hydroxide is not alkaline, and the hydroxides of the heavier elements are too soluble to be earthy. Some of the physical properties of this family are listed in Table 15.2.

As was true of the alkali metals, only the second and third of the alkaline earth metals—magnesium and calcium, respectively—are abundant. Magnesium constitutes 2.1 per cent and calcium 3.6 per cent of the igneous rocks of the earth. The proportions of the others are similar to those of the corresponding alkali metals, except that radium is almost as abundant as gold, since its radioactive ancestor, uranium, is far more plentiful than actinium. With the exception of various forms of silica, SiO_2—such as quartz, flint, agate, and chalcedony—nearly all rocks that have no ions of the alkali metals do contain ions of the alkaline earth metals. These ions also are released into ground waters by the weathering of the rocks. Their ultimate fate, however, is different from that of the alkali metal ions because of the insolubility of the carbonates of the alkaline earth metals and of the sulfates of the heavier of these elements. Enormous beds of limestone exist on the site of ancient seas. In many cases they shade into dolomite (equal numbers of Mg^{++} and Ca^{++} ions) or magnesite, $MgCO_3$. Not so universal but still very common are great beds of gypsum, $CaSO_4 \cdot 2H_2O$. Sr^{++} and Ba^{++} are also found as both sulfate and carbonate rocks. Magnesium sulfate is soluble, and its carbonate is less insoluble than those of the heavier ions; so the concentration of Mg^{++} in sea water is three times that of Ca^{++}. Sea-water residues such as those at Stassfurt contain Mg^{++} ion in quantities comparable to those of K^+ ion, much of it crystallized as schönite, $K_2Mg (SO_4)_2 \cdot 6H_2O$.

15.6. Commercial Preparation of the Alkaline Earth Metals

Magnesium has been very much a war baby, but by 1955 civilian use of it was exceeding its military use. Before World War II the Dow Chemical Company was producing some 3000 tons a year from the mother liquors that remained after crystallizing NaCl from the brine of their Michigan salt wells. Foreseeing the war, Dow doubled the size of this plant in 1940 and in 1941 increased it as much again. By this time, the government was having new magnesium plants built in a dozen locations. One, with a capacity equal to the total capacity of the expanded Michigan plant, was put into operation by the Dow Company at Freeport, Texas, that same year; its capacity was doubled in 1942. This plant obtained its magnesium from sea water. Sea water contains only 0.13 per cent of Mg^{++}, but a cubic mile of it would last the expanded Freeport plant for two centuries. Other plants reduced MgO with natural gas or with ferrosilicon (a 50 : 50 iron-silicon alloy) at high temperatures. A number of these plants had serious engineering difficulties, but by 1943 the successful new plants were producing at the rate of 246,000 tons a year, far more than proved to be needed. The unsuccessful plants were dismantled and the others were cut back to a 40,000-ton output. The end of the war cut this still further to 12,000 tons. Since then the production of magnesium has fluctuated sharply, following military aircraft orders. For example, it was 81,000 tons in 1957 and dropped to 30,000 tons in 1958. In 1960 the production was 40,000 tons.

In 1956 all our magnesium was being made from sea water, though only 40 per cent of the productive capacity was owned by Dow. In the sea-water process, oyster shells dredged up from a vast deposit are burned to lime with natural gas. This lime is used to bring the pH of the strained sea water to 11, whereupon $Mg(OH)_2$ precipitates and is filtered out.

$$Ca^{++} + 2OH^- + Mg^{++} + 2Cl^- \rightarrow \underline{Mg(OH)_2} + Ca^{++} + 2Cl^-$$

The $Mg(OH)_2$ cake is dissolved into a concentrated solution of $MgCl_2$ by treatment with HCl gas.

$$\underline{Mg(OH)_2} + \overline{2HCl} \rightarrow Mg^{++} + 2Cl^- + 2H_2O$$

This solution is evaporated in an atmosphere of HCl to prevent the reversal of the above reaction by hydrolysis, fed to electrolytic cells, and decomposed to magnesium and chlorine.

$$Mg^{++} + 2Cl^- \xrightarrow{\triangle} Mg + \overline{Cl_2}$$

The chlorine is burned in natural gas to supply the HCl needed for the process.

$$\overline{2CH_4} + \overline{O_2} + \overline{4Cl_2} \rightarrow \overline{2CO} + \overline{8HCl}$$

All the war plants in the United States that used chemical reducing agents for producing magnesium were shut down during or after World War II, but Dominion Magnesium, Ltd., has continued to operate its ferrosilicon plant in Canada. Two of the four government-owned ferrosilicon plants in the United States were reactivated during the Korean War, and one of them was still operating in 1957. Late that year a new 10,000-ton ferrosilicon plant with improved methods was put into operation in Alabama jointly by Dominion and a United States firm. Instead of sea water this plant uses dolomite as its source of Mg^{++}. This is calcined to a mixture of CaO and MgO which is mixed with pulverized ferrosilicon and briquetted. The briquettes are heated under vacuum in a large cylindrical retort to 1200° C. (100° above the boiling point of magnesium).

$$\underline{2CaO} + \underline{2MgO} + \underline{FeSi} \xrightarrow{\Delta} Ca_2SiO_4 + \underline{Fe} + \overline{2Mg}$$

The crystals of magnesium which condense at the cooled end of the retort must be remelted and cast into solid ingots. This magnesium contains less than a quarter as much impurity as electrolytic magnesium does, and therefore commands a premium price.

Calcium is also prepared, in relatively small amounts, by electrolysis of the fused chloride. The metal is deposited on an internally cooled central cathode which is gradually withdrawn. The hot metal must be protected by an inert atmosphere.

Strontium is not an article of commerce, but barium is, although it has a much smaller market than calcium does. The metal is prepared by the King process, which involves the reduction of BaO by aluminum in a vacuum electric furnace. At the reaction temperature of 1000° C. an equilibrium mixture results.

$$\underline{6BaO} + 2Al \underset{\Delta}{\rightleftharpoons} Ba_3Al_2O_6 + \overline{3Ba}$$

Both metals are liquid. Since barium has a higher vapor pressure than aluminum at 1000° C., it becomes a gas in the vacuum furnace and is condensed on a surface whose temperature is lower than that of the reaction mixture. Before removal from the reactor, the condensed barium is cooled in an argon atmosphere, because the active barium would react even with nitrogen.

15.7. Uses of Magnesium as a Metal

Magnesium is the lightest metal with any appreciable strength except the rare beryllium. Its density is 65 per cent as great as that of aluminum, 22 per cent of that of steel. Although aluminum and steel are stronger than magnesium, its lighter weight more than compensates for its lesser strength in many uses. A piece of magnesium twice as thick as a piece of steel is 70 per cent more rigid but only half as heavy. Magnesium has exceptional capacity to absorb shocks and vibration. These properties obviously account for the fact that nearly one-third of the magnesium we produce is used by the aircraft industry. Magnesium can be rolled, deep-drawn, or extruded with ease above 400° C., making it possible to produce a wide variety of strong, light, and durable objects (Fig. 15.2). Although magnesium competes with aluminum and zinc in die castings, magnesium castings offer a decided advantage for power hand tools and

Fig. 15.2. Extruded magnesium flooring in Lockheed RC-121 transport plane. (Courtesy, Lockheed Aircraft Corporation.)

for machine parts in which a rapid change in the direction of motion is required.

Magnesium is commonly used in the form of alloys containing from 3 to 10 per cent aluminum, a little zinc, and a trace of manganese. About one-fifth of our total output of this metal goes into the production of various high-strength aluminum alloys, some of which contain up to 10 per cent magnesium. A recently developed alloy with zirconium and thorium permits the use of relatively high temperatures, but magnesium of a high degree of purity is required. Small amounts of magnesium— 0.1 per cent or so—in many cases improve the properties of other metals to a remarkable degree. For example, if the sulfur content of nickel is not kept below 0.005 per cent, it cannot be rolled or forged; but adding a trace of magnesium changes the NiS film on the nickel crystals to small crystalline particles which permit the processing of nickel that contains as much as 0.05 per cent sulfur. Treating cast iron with magnesium increases its tensile strength from three to six times by a similar change in the distribution of the graphite particles it contains (Fig. 15.3). The uses of magnesium which depend on its chemical properties are discussed in the following section.

15.8. Chemical Properties of the Alkaline Earth Metals

Like the alkali metals, the alkaline earth metals are extremely strong reducing agents; in fact, barium is as active as sodium. The ratio $(radius)^2/charge$ is almost identical for Ba^{++} and Na^+ ions. Strontium and even calcium liberate hydrogen from cold water, forming the corresponding hydroxides.

$$\underline{Ca} + 2H_2O \rightarrow Ca^{++} + 2OH^- + \overline{H_2} + \triangle$$

Magnesium, however, must be finely subdivided and the water must be boiling. Under these conditions $Mg(OH)_2$, which is insoluble, decomposes to the oxide.

$$\underline{Mg} + \overline{H_2O} \rightarrow \underline{MgO} + \overline{H_2} + \triangle$$

All these metals burn vigorously. Burning magnesium is responsible for the brilliant white light of flash bulbs and fireworks, including military flares and star shells. This light comes from white-hot solid magnesium oxide that is dispersed as smoke particles throughout the flame. Military uses include tracers for machine-gun bullets and casings for incendiary bombs which burn right along with the contents. All these

Fig. 15.3. Flake graphite (above) as it occurs in untreated cast iron, and spheroidized graphite (right) that forms when molten cast iron is treated with magnesium. (Courtesy, The Dow Chemical Company.)

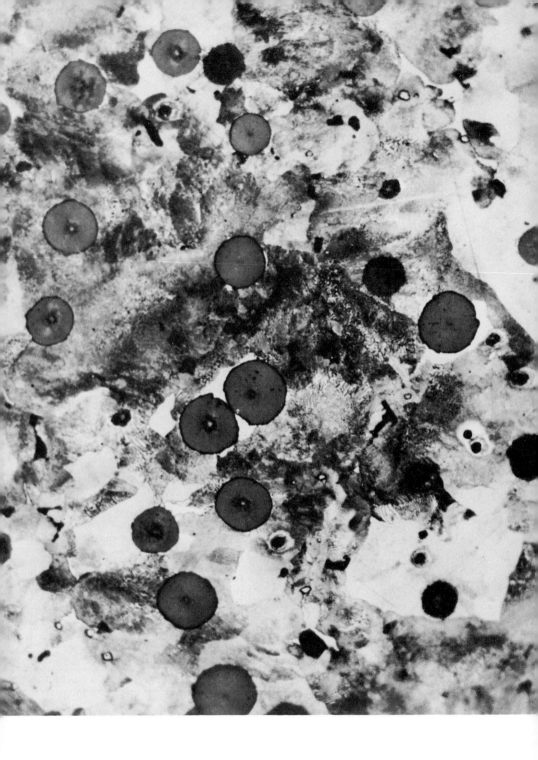

pyrotechnic uses, although spectacular, consume only 0.9 per cent of our production of magnesium.

When the alkaline earth metals burn, they combine not only with oxygen but also with nitrogen and even hydrogen. This property is responsible for the use of calcium and barium as getters in TV and other electron tubes. When the evacuated finished tube is sealed, a pellet of a getter is vaporized electrically to clean up residual traces of gases. The reactions are:

$$\overline{2Ba} + \overline{O_2} \rightarrow \underline{2BaO} + \triangle$$
$$\overline{3Ba} + \overline{N_2} \rightarrow \underline{Ba_3N_2} + \triangle$$
$$\overline{2Ba} + \overline{H_2O} \rightarrow \underline{BaO} + \underline{BaH_2} + \triangle$$
$$\overline{5Ba} + \overline{2CO_2} \rightarrow \underline{4BaO} + \underline{BaC_2} + \triangle$$

The excess metal vapor condenses as a mirror on the wall of the tube. Magnesium, and to some extent calcium, are added to metal melts just before casting, as deoxidizers; the reaction is similar to those above. The MgO is insoluble in the metal and floats to the top, whereas many other oxides are soluble in their own metal. The deoxidized castings are sounder, finer-grained, and more malleable. High-purity magnesium is used to reduce titanium, zirconium, beryllium, and uranium from their compounds. This use of magnesium may eventually reach the million-ton level.

An important amount of magnesium—6 per cent per year—is used to protect pipelines, ships, boilers, and other iron and steel structures that are exposed to corrosion by water. When dissolved oxygen takes electrons from iron atoms, Fe^{++} ions go into solution and the iron is eventually corroded. If a billet of magnesium, which loses electrons far more readily than iron, is wired to the pipeline and buried near it, the electrons will be furnished by the magnesium instead of by the iron and Mg^{++} ions instead of Fe^{++} ions will go into solution. The Mg^{++} ions form a coating of $Mg(OH)_2$ on the billet which protects it from direct attack by the water. Because the only area of the iron from which electrons can be lost is the small surface exposed by a crack or pinhole in the protective coating, the magnesium lasts a long time; furthermore, it is replaced much more easily than a ship or a pipeline. Since a pound of magnesium delivers 2.7 times as many electrons as a pound of zinc, and at a higher voltage, magnesium is preferable to zinc for use in dry cells (Section 22.10).

Magnesium is, of course, very susceptible to attack by acids, but the formation of an oxide or of an oxide and hydroxide coating protects it satisfactorily against air, water, and even salt water. If contaminated by the presence of even a few thousandths of 1 per cent of iron or nickel, the protective coating cannot be absolutely tight, and rapid corrosion takes place. Now that this fact has become known, magnesium and its alloys can be made reasonably weatherproof. The heavier alkaline earth metals, however, must be protected from air and moisture.

15.9. Ions of the Alkali and the Alkaline Earth Metals

The chemistry of the ions of both the alkali metals and the alkaline earth metals is very simple. In the first place, only one valence is possible for each of these ions—that given by the group number, acquired by losing the entire valence layer. In the second place, they have very little tendency to form polyatomic molecules by covalent bonding. This property is very important in a negative way, for it means that in water solutions of their compounds the properties of the anions appear at full strength, instead of being changed or diminished by being tied up to the cation. It also means that almost all their salts that have moderate-sized univalent anions are soluble. The exceptions are the alkaline earth metal salts of the very smallest anion, F^-, and the Ca^{++} and Mg^{++} salts of the next smallest anion, OH^-. In these cases the lattice energy is largest because of the possibility of close approach. Polyvalent anion salts of the alkali metal ions are also soluble, but this is true only of $MgSO_4$ and $MgCrO_4$ among corresponding salts of the alkaline earth metal ions. $CaSO_4$ and $CaCrO_4$ are slightly soluble. The oxides and sulfides of the alkaline earth metal ions are soluble enough to react with water, the water acting as an acid.

$$\underline{CaO} + H_2O \rightarrow Ca^{++} + 2OH^-$$

$$\underline{BaS} + H_2O \rightarrow Ba^{++} + OH^- + HS^-$$

The alkali metal oxides and sulfides behave similarly. For this reason the ions of the two metal families cannot be precipitated as sulfides and hydroxides, with the exception of $Ca(OH)_2$ and $Mg(OH)_2$, as previously noted.

The alkali and alkaline earth metal ions are all hydrated in solution, the H_2O molecules being attached very loosely to the univalent ions larger than Li^+ ion, and more strongly to the divalent ions, which are smaller. But only in the case of Mg^{++}, which has already been mentioned as a border-line case, is the attachment close enough to affect the chemical nature of the water, and even then this occurs only at boiler-water temperatures. Mg^{++} must be avoided in boiler water because of the reaction:

$$Mg^{++} + H_2O \rightleftharpoons \underline{MgO} + 2H^+$$

This causes corrosion as well as the formation of an undesirable precipitate. None of the other ions in this group affect the pH of water appreciably.

The ability to form covalent bonds with oxygen is shown in the formation of insoluble hydroxides, e.g., $Mg(OH)_2$, the hydrolysis of hot $MgCl_2$ solution, and the ease with which $MgCO_3$ decomposes into MgO and CO_2 when heated. These are all related to the fact that magnesium is the most electronegative of the metals studied in this chapter. To generalize, the thermal decomposition of any oxygen-containing salt into a metal oxide and the anhydride of the corresponding acid proceeds more readily the greater the ability of the metal ion to form covalent bonds with oxygen, i.e., the higher its electronegativity.

Note that the decomposition of a hydroxide into its oxide and H_2O is really an example of this same reaction. Thus the hydroxides of the alkali metals and barium can be melted without decomposing; $Ca(OH)_2$ has a dissociation pressure of 1 atm. (into CaO and steam) at 450° C.; boiler temperatures are enough for this pressure in the case of $Mg(OH)_2$.

Another example of the ability of Mg^{++} ions to form bonds that are considerably covalent in character is furnished by a class of magnesium compounds called the **Grignard** (pronounced "greenyard") **reagents,** which are of great importance in organic syntheses, both laboratory and commercial. These compounds are formed by allowing magnesium shavings to reduce compounds of the type R : X in ether solution. (R represents a group of atoms attached to a carbon atom which is sharing an electron pair (:) with a halogen atom X.) The magnesium adds 2 electrons so the R and X separate from each other, both as anions; but the resulting Mg^{++} ion forms considerably covalent bonds with both electron pairs. Its tendency to do this is intensified by the fact that ether is a poor ionizing solvent. The formula of a Grignard reagent is conventionally written RMgX. Actually each Mg^{++} probably forms four bonds, and the four ligands of any individual Mg^{++} may be any combination of R^-, X^-, and ether molecules.

Another chemical property which seems to be related to the low electronegativity of these elements is the ability of their oxides to react with oxygen to form peroxides or superoxides. This is not true of MgO, Li_2O, or CaO. When Na_2O or BaO is heated in air, or when SrO is heated in oxygen at 125 atm., the peroxide is formed.

$$2BaO + \overline{O_2} \rightarrow 2BaO_2$$

RbO forms the superoxide.

$$2Rb_2O + \overline{3O_2} \rightarrow 4RbO_2$$

K_2O forms a mixture of the peroxide and superoxide. Apparently even the smallest trace of covalent bonding with a metal ion enables O^{--} to resist the oxidizing action of O_2. All these higher oxides decompose at higher temperatures.

5.10. The Caustic Alkalies

Hydroxide ion, the strongest base that can exist in water solution, is an extremely valuable reagent. The number of cations which can co-exist with it is very limited; most of them are precipitated as hydroxides. A saturated solution of $Ca(OH)_2$ is 0.02 M (Section 15.12); of LiOH, 0.5 M; of $Sr(OH)_2$, 0.75 M; of $Ba(OH)_2$, 1.0 M. The only cations which can be used as handles for OH^- in preparing a solution that is stronger than 1 M are Na^+, K^+, Rb^+, and Cs^+. Of these, Na^+ is cheap and abundant, K^+ is several times as expensive, and the last two are almost unobtainable. KOH is produced in moderate quantities for a few special purposes such as the manufacture of liquid soaps and for use in alcohol solution in organic reactions (NaOH is almost insoluble in alcohol). NaOH, on the other hand, is one of the "big ten" chemicals of which more than 1 million tons are manufactured annually in the United States. Our output of NaOH runs to nearly 5 million tons a year. Most of this is made by electrolysis of NaCl solution, in which the NaOH is a co-product with chlorine (Chapter 9), but about 10 per cent is made by the **causticization of soda** by means of lime. When a slurry of $Ca(OH)_2$ is mixed with a 20 per cent solution of Na_2CO_3, the Ca^{++} ion which is in solution precipitates as $CaCO_3$, causing the solid $Ca(OH)_2$ to dissolve. When the $CaCO_3$ is filtered off, a solution of caustic soda, NaOH, remains.

$$Ca(OH)_2 + 2Na^+ + CO_3^{--} \rightarrow CaCO_3 + 2Na^+ + 2OH^-$$

Although not too pure, the NaOH is satisfactory for many purposes when the solution is used where produced. The amount of it manufactured depends upon the price of NaOH and $Ca(OH)_2$, freight costs, etc.

The common industrial name for NaOH is caustic soda; that for KOH is caustic potash. The terms soda lye and potash lye are also used. The names caustic and lye are also used alone; however, in this case NaOH rather than KOH is usually meant. These names were derived from the use of soda and potash (Section 15.11) in the causticization process just described.

NaOH is very soluble in water, KOH even more so. In fact, there is no limit to the solubility if the temperature is raised continuously. For economy in handling, NaOH is commonly shipped as 76 or 50 per cent solution in tank cars. The 76 per cent grade solidifies in the cars and is melted at the destination by running steam into heating pipes with which the cars are equipped. The unusual concentration is selected because it is the highest that can be melted by steam at atmospheric pressure. The 76 per cent grade is also shipped in drums in solid, flaked, or powdered form; it sells at about 4 cents per pound. The 50 per cent solution is the highest concentration that remains liquid at room temperature. When 50 g. of NaOH (23 cc.) is dissolved in 50 ml. of water, the volume of the resulting solution is only 65 ml.; hence it is not surprising that a great amount of heat is given off during the dissolving action.

NaOH which is prepared electrolytically in standard diaphragm cells may contain as much as 1 per cent NaCl. This is undesirable in one of its most important uses, the manufacture of rayon and of cellulose film. The salt may be extracted by means of anhydrous liquid NH_3, in which NaOH is insoluble. Rayon-grade NaOH is produced directly by means of mercury cathode cells (Section 9.13).

NaOH is also used in soap making, the refining of both petroleum and vegetable oils, the reclaiming of rubber, and the manufacture of other chemicals. Among the more important chemicals manufactured from or with the aid of NaOH are phenol (carbolic acid), glycerin, beta-naphthol (a dye intermediate), and Na_2S (used as a depilatory and in the synthesis of sulfur dyes). It is an ingredient of heavy-duty cleaners, frequently with Na_3PO_4.

The other hydroxides that have been mentioned in this section as being soluble enough to be caustic are, with the exception of lime, more expensive than NaOH, and hence are used only when their special cations are definitely needed, as in the case of KOH. Thus one company produces $Sr(OH)_2 \cdot 8H_2O$ to make the strontium soaps used in the manufacture of greases which are resistant to alternations of high and low temperature and to water and gasoline. Similarly, in spite of its cost ($LiOH \cdot H_2O$ costs 80 cents per pound) and its limited solubility, some 2000 tons of LiOH are used annually in the production of lithium soap for special purposes (cosmetics, lubricants in powder metallurgy and sheet elastomers, gelling agent in liquid insecticides, flowing and sticking agent in insecticide dusts) and in the manufacture of certain plastics.

5.11. The Alkalies

Alkalies is the common commercial term for Na_2CO_3 and K_2CO_3; it usually includes $NaHCO_3$ and the much less important $KHCO_3$ as well. Soda includes the monohydrates and decahydrates of Na_2CO_3, the anhydrous salt (commonly called soda ash), $NaHCO_3$ (baking soda or sodium bicarbonate), and various trade mixtures. Potash normally refers only to K_2CO_3; but when used in connection with fertilizers it means the hypothetical K_2O whose potassium content would be equivalent to that of the KCl or K_2SO_4 actually present. The word soda is the Italian name of a plant found on sea beaches and in salt marches from whose ashes Na_2CO_3 used to be leached; hence the name soda ash. K_2CO_3 was obtained by leaching wood ashes.

Even though its output exceeds 5 million tons, Na_2CO_3 ranks below NaOH, for its bulk price is as low as 1.6 cents per pound. Less than 700,000 tons are obtained from natural sources, such as alkali lakes. The rest is manufactured by the **Solvay ammonia-soda process.** The Solvay plant at Syracuse, New York, was the first one in the western hemisphere; it is still one of the largest. This plant pipes and purifies brine from wells some 20 miles distant. The purified saturated salt solution is first treated with ammonia gas and then saturated with carbon dioxide; this results in the formation of crystals of the less soluble $NaHCO_3$ which are filtered from the solution of NH_4Cl and unreacted salt (about one-third of the original amount) in the equilibrium mixture.

$$\overline{NH_3} + H_2O \rightleftharpoons NH_4OH$$

$$\overline{CO_2} + H_2O \rightleftharpoons H_2CO_3$$

$$NH_4OH + H_2CO_3 \rightarrow NH_4{}^+ + HCO_3{}^- + H_2O$$

$$NH_4{}^+ + HCO_3{}^- + Na^+ + Cl^- \rightleftharpoons NH_4{}^+ + Cl^- + \underline{NaHCO_3}$$

The $NaHCO_3$ crystals are washed with a little water, then dried and heated, forming sodium carbonate.

$$\underline{2NaHCO_3} \xrightarrow{\Delta} \underline{Na_2CO_3} + \overline{CO_2} + \overline{H_2O}$$

This carbon dioxide is returned to the absorption towers and used to prepare more $NaHCO_3$. The NH_3 is recovered by treating the NH_4Cl with lime and steam. (Some NH_4Cl is purified and sold.)

$$2NH_4{}^+ + 2Cl^- + Ca^{++} + 2OH^- \xrightarrow{\Delta} \overline{2NH_3} + Ca^{++} + 2Cl^- + \overline{2H_2O}$$

Carbon dioxide is prepared at the Syracuse plant by heating calcium carbonate.

$$CaCO_3 \overset{\Delta}{\to} CaO + \overline{CO_2}$$

Heat is required in the Solvay process to "burn" the limestone, convert the bicarbonate to carbonate, and generate the steam needed in the recovery of the NH_3. Tall towers called columns, which operate on the countercurrent principle, provide the necessary surface for rapid absorption. Every effort is made to prevent the loss of the relatively costly NH_3.

Calcium chloride, formerly considered a by-product, has gradually assumed the importance of a co-product, although still less than half the potential tonnage is evaporated for sale. It is used extensively as a soil binder in secondary roads, as well as to lay the dust on lesser roads, drives, tennis courts, and playgrounds. In freezing weather it thaws ice and prevents skidding on slippery highways. It is mixed with coal to hold the dust, and with coal as well as iron ore to prevent freezing in winter. It speeds up the curing of concrete, absorbs moisture in drying operations, and serves as the antifreeze in refrigeration brines.

All the other forms of soda are prepared from Na_2CO_3. Even $NaHCO_3$ is prepared in this way, for the $NaHCO_3$ that is first precipitated in the Solvay process is not of sufficient purity.

The glass industry uses more than one-quarter of the total output of Na_2CO_3; this is its largest single use. Here it serves as a source of Na_2O, the CO_2 being driven off by the non-volatile acid anhydride silica (glass sand) at the temperature of the glass furnace.

$$Na_2CO_3 + SiO_2 \overset{\Delta}{\to} Na_2SiO_3 + \overline{CO_2}$$

This use is responsible for the fact that the customary standard of purity for soda ash is 58 per cent. This refers to the Na_2O content, and means that the Na_2CO_3 is better than 99 per cent pure. Other important uses of Na_2CO_3 are in the causticization of lime and the treatment of aluminum ore. A large amount of sodium silicate is produced independently of the glass industry for use as a soap "builder" and an adhesive, in the manufacture of porous silica and alumina silica for cracking catalysts (petroleum industry), and in water softening and the absorption of water and other vapors. More than 20 per cent of our output of Na_2CO_3 is used to neutralize acids whose sodium salts are desired, notable among them being H_3PO_4, chromic acid, H_2CrO_4, and SO_2 (to make $NaHSO_3$). Na_2CO_3 is used as well as $NaOH$ in making soap and in preparing cleaning compounds. In this connection the term modified soda means that some $NaHCO_3$ has been added to the Na_2CO_3 to make it less alkaline, or some NaOH has been added to make it more alkaline. The use of soda in water softening will be described in Section 15.15.

$NaHCO_3$ is very mildly alkaline; hence it can be taken internally or used in the eyes. Nevertheless, it neutralizes acids completely because H_2CO_3 promptly decomposes to H_2O and CO_2, which escapes. For this same reason it is an excellent source of small quantities of CO_2, and is so used in baking powders and in fire extinguishers.

Fire extinguishers of the type that has to be inverted in order to be used are filled with concentrated $NaHCO_3$ solution, above which is a small open bottle of concentrated sulfuric acid. The reaction is:

$$2Na^+ + 2HCO_3^- + H_2SO_4 \rightarrow 2Na^+ + SO_4^{--} + 2H_2O + 2\overline{CO_2}$$

The CO_2 supplies pressure to eject a stream of solution through the hose. The amount of acid is not sufficient to use up more than part of the $NaHCO_3$. The remainder can decompose in the heat of the fire, liberating CO_2, which helps extinguish the flame. Some extinguisher solutions also contain a foaming agent so that a froth is ejected which can float on oil or cling to a motor.

All baking powders contain $NaHCO_3$ and some acid, which reacts with it according to the equation:

$$Na^+ + HCO_3^- + HX \rightarrow Na^+ + X^- + H_2O + \overline{CO_2}$$

The bubbles of CO_2 *leaven* (lighten) the bread or cake. The acid, represented by HX in the above equation, is commonly one of three—the bitartrate ion, $HC_4H_4O_6^-$, the dihydrogen phosphate ion, $H_2PO_4^-$, or the aluminum ion, $Al(H_2O)_6^{+3}$. The bitartrate ion is used in the form of the potassium salt, $KHC_4H_4O_6$, commonly called cream of tartar. Calcium acid phosphate, $Ca(H_2PO_4)_2$, furnishes the dihydrogen phosphate ion. The hydrated aluminum ion is not put into the baking powder as such; instead, anhydrous sodium aluminum sulfate is used, which hydrates itself as soon as the water is added. This latter substance is obtained by drying sodium alum, $NaAl(SO_4)_2 \cdot 12H_2O$. For this reason baking powders that contain it are sometimes referred to as "alum baking powders." The chemical reaction in the case of this acid is not well represented by the type of reaction given above. It is:

$$Al(H_2O)_6^{+3} + 3HCO_3^- \rightarrow \underline{Al(H_2O)_3(OH)_3} + 3H_2O + 3\overline{CO_2}$$

or, in conventional form:

$$2Al^{+3} + 3SO_4^{--} + 6Na^+ + 6HCO_3^- \longrightarrow$$
$$2Al(OH)_3 + 6Na^+ + 3SO_4^{--} + 6CO_2$$

All baking powders are diluted to a standard strength with starch. They differ from each other in the rate at which CO_2 is liberated at different temperatures. Some, called double-action baking powders, contain two different acids, one of which reacts at a lower temperature than the other. The choice of baking powder depends entirely on which one gives best results; all leave only harmless products in foods.

K_2CO_3 and Li_2CO_3 are used in small quantities; the respective costs are 8.5 and 85 cents per pound. K_2CO_3 is used in the manufacture of extra clear glass; a 21-inch TV tube contains 5.5 lb. of it. Some 2000 tons of Li_2CO_3 are used in ceramics. This relatively insoluble salt (1 per cent) can be precipitated from H_2SO_4 extracts of lithium ores by the addition of Na_2CO_3; it is the usual starting point in the production of lithium compounds. As the result of the work of the Atomic Energy Commission, the potential output of Li_2CO_3 has been expanded to 19,000 tons; perhaps the light isotope, ^6Li, is to be extracted from this for use in fusion bombs. If the approximately 92 per cent of the Li_2CO_3 that remains is made available in commercial markets, the supply will be roughly equal to double our present consumption. This should have an interesting effect on its price, and therefore on the development of new uses for this compound.

15.12. Lime

Lime is truly a chemical giant. Its annual output of 12 million tons is surpassed, among manufactured chemicals, only by the output of H_2SO_4. The term lime includes both quicklime, CaO, and slaked lime, $Ca(OH)_2$. CaO is produced by calcining limestone in a kiln.

$$CaCO_3 \xrightarrow{\Delta} CaO + \overline{CO_2}$$

CaO reacts with water so energetically that fires have been started when flood water reached freight cars filled with barrels of quicklime.

$$CaO + H_2O \rightarrow Ca(OH)_2 + \triangle$$

$Ca(OH)_2$ is a strong base, but only slightly soluble. At $0°$ C. its saturated solution is 0.025 M; at $100°$ C., only 0.01 M. Lime is the cheapest of the strong bases and more than 60 per cent of the output is thus used by the chemical industry and other industries not usually classified as chemical. The production of sodium carbonate requires some 2.5 million tons; the paper industry as much more. Steel, sugar, glass, calcium carbide, cyanamide, and water softening call for large quantities; its demand for tanning and insecticides is far from negligible. The bonding of crushed quartzite, SiO_2, into refractory linings for coke ovens, glass tanks, the roofs of open-hearth steel furnaces, etc., constitutes the largest single chemical use. Building operations, plaster, and mortar consume 1.25 million tons of lime. The agricultural demand—for "sweetening sour soil," i.e., neutralizing soil acidity—is far behind, with 0.25 million tons.

15.13. Carbonates of the Alkaline Earth Metals

The existence of unlimited deposits of limestone, $CaCO_3$, and the manufacture of lime from it, and from beds of seashells of the same composition, have already been mentioned. Enormous as this use of limestone is, far more of it is used as a reagent in metallurgy; it combines with siliceous impurities in ores to makes a fusible slag. For instance, the production of 76 million tons of iron (our annual output normally equals or exceeds this figure) requires 38 million tons of limestone. $CaCO_3$ is used in making glass in the same way, and in comparable quantity, as Na_2CO_3.

More hard water is due to limestone than to gypsum in spite of limestone's being much less soluble. This is true because there is so much more of it and also because it is dissolved by the carbonic acid formed in rain water by the carbon dioxide in the air.

$$H_2CO_3 + \underline{CaCO_3} \rightarrow Ca^{++} + 2HCO_3^-$$

This reaction accounts for the huge limestone caverns in Virginia, Kentucky, and New Mexico, among other places. If the solution evaporates as it drips from the roof of a cave, the reaction is reversed by the escaping CO_2 and the limestone is redeposited in the form of a stalactite. A stalagmite may be built up from the floor and the two may meet.

Like $CaCO_3$, magnesite, $MgCO_3$, loses CO_2 on being heated, but does so more readily. The MgO which results is called magnesia; its melting point is 2800° C. It is used principally in the manufacture of refractory blocks for furnace linings and the like, either alone, or combined with such substances as chromite, Cr_2FeO_4, or silica, SiO_2.

The use of dolomite, $MgCO_3 \cdot CaCO_3$, in the manufacture of magnesium was mentioned earlier. A much more important use—in fact, a vital use—is in the hearths of open-hearth furnaces. One and a quarter millions tons annually are calcined into a mixture of CaO and MgO which not only supports the huge pools of molten steel without softening, but is ideal for slagging off the impurities. The MgO can be dissolved from the calcined dolomite by H_2CO_3, the CaO remaining as insoluble $CaCO_3$.

$$\underline{CaO \cdot MgO} + 3H_2CO_3 \rightarrow \underline{CaCO_3} + Mg^{++} + 2HCO_3^- + 2H_2O$$

When the CO_2 is boiled off from this solution, basic magnesium carbonate is precipitated.

$$2H_2O + 2Mg^{++} + 4HCO_3^- \rightarrow \underline{Mg_2CO_3(OH)_2 \cdot 3H_2O} + \overline{3CO_2}$$

The MgO formed by calcining this material is an extraordinarily light, fluffy powder, less than a third as dense as that made by calcining magnesite. Sold as "light calcined magnesia" (the other is "heavy"), it is widely used to insulate steam pipes and furnaces. It is frequently mixed with 15 per cent of asbestos fiber; this is called 85 per cent magnesia. When calcined at a low temperature, it is easily hydrated to $Mg(OH)_2$. $Mg(OH)_2$ can also be prepared more directly from dolomite by virtue of the lower temperature at which $MgCO_3$ decomposes as compared with $CaCO_3$. This low-temperature calcination of dolomite produces a mixture of MgO and $CaCO_3$. Treatment with water hydrates the MgO; its fine, light particles can be easily separated from the larger, denser particles of $CaCO_3$ by hydraulic classification (Fig. 15.4B). However, these methods of preparing $Mg(OH)_2$ are less important than its precipitation from sea water (Section 15.6).

The decomposition of a carbonate by heat into the oxide of the metal and CO_2 is a reversible reaction. If it is carried out in a closed container, equilibrium is reached at a definite pressure of CO_2 which differs for each carbonate. The CO_2 pressure is 1 atm. for $MgCO_3$ at 500° C., for $CaCO_3$ at 898° C., for $SrCO_3$ at 1258° C., and for $BaCO_3$ at 1352° C. Thus stability increases as electronegativity decreases. The stability of the alkali carbonates—they can be melted in an open crucible without decomposing—bears the same relationship to the electronegativities of the metals. Carbonates of the less active (more electronegative) metals are more easily decomposed than $MgCO_3$. This is so because higher electronegativity means greater ability to form covalent bonds. The greater the ability of the metal ion to form bonds with the

O^{--} ion which CO$_3$$^{--}$ tends to release on heating, the more readily the latter ion decomposes.

15.14. Sulfates of the Alkali and Alkaline Earth Metals

Na$_2$SO$_4$ is the ninth manufactured chemical with an output of 1 million tons that we have encountered. (The others are Cl$_2$, H$_2$SO$_4$, NH$_3$, HNO$_3$, H$_3$PO$_4$, NaOH, CaO, and Na$_2$CO$_3$.) More than half of the Na$_2$SO$_4$ is the crude form commonly called salt cake because it is the residue from the manufacture of HCl from NaCl and H$_2$SO$_4$. It is also made by the Hargreaves process; the reaction is as follows:

$$4(Na^+ + Cl^-) + \overline{2SO_2} + 2H_2O + \overline{O_2} \rightarrow 4Na^+ + 2SO_4^{--} + \overline{4HCl}$$

More than 750,000 tons of crude salt cake are used annually in the Kraft process for making pulp for paper and rayon. The lignin is dissolved from the wood chips by means of a solution of Na$_2$S, and the resulting liquor is then burned; most of the Na$_2$S remains and can be dissolved again in fresh water for reuse. The amount of Na$_2$S that is lost is made up by adding salt cake to the liquor before it is burned. The SO$_4$$^{--}$ ion is reduced to S^{--} in the furnace by the carbon compounds in the liquor. For this reason the Kraft process is also known as the sulfate process. Kraft pulp makes stronger paper than sulfite pulp does (*Kraft* is German for strength). Because it was formerly impossible to bleach the pulp to a good white, it was used only for wrapping paper, sacks, and the like. However, the bleaching problem has been solved so successfully by the use of such modern bleaching agents as H$_2$O$_2$, NaClO$_2$, and ClO$_2$ that Kraft pulp can now be used even for rayon; hence its use has been expanding rapidly.

Na$_2$SO$_4$ is also reduced by carbon as an independent source of Na$_2$S for other uses, in competition with the preparation of Na$_2$S from NaOH and H$_2$S.

$$\underline{Na_2SO_4} + \underline{2C} \xrightarrow{\Delta} \underline{Na_2S} + \overline{\underline{2CO_2}}$$

Na$_2$SO$_4$, crystallized from solution, is known as Glauber's salt, Na$_2$SO$_4 \cdot$10H$_2$O. This salt—100,000 tons of it a year—is used in dyeing textiles. Because of its high water content, 56 per cent, it dissolves easily. A small part of the annual output is used medicinally as a purgative.

Glauber's salt effloresces readily; i.e., the water evaporates from the crystals and they disintegrate, forming a fine powder of anhydrous

Na_2SO_4. The glass industry consumes 300,000 tons of this powder, using it as a source of Na_2O just as Na_2CO_3 is used. Although Na_2SO_4 sells for only 1.4 cents per pound, it is slightly more expensive as a source of Na_2O. (Compare the formula weights.) It is used for the same reason that people use a double-action baking powder. The gas released by the Na_2CO_3 imparts a stirring action to the contents of the glass tank. Since Na_2SO_4 is the salt of a stronger acid it requires a higher temperature to react with SiO_2, and a second stirring action occurs at a later stage in the melting process.

$$Na_2SO_4 + SiO_2 \xrightarrow{\Delta} Na_2SiO_3 + \overline{SO_3}$$

Na_2SO_4 is also used as a "builder" in synthetic detergents.

The Carlsbad potash deposits contain carnallite, $KCl \cdot MgCl_2 \cdot 6H_2O$, schönite, $K_2Mg(SO_4)_2 \cdot 6H_2O$, and kainite, $KCl \cdot MgSO_4 \cdot 3H_2O$; Searles Lake brines are even more complex. The development of processes for preparing reasonably pure KCl and K_2SO_4 from these minerals that contain mixtures of these ions was done by physical chemists. Over 2 million tons of K_2SO_4 and 1.5 million tons of KCl (about equal in total K_2O content) are used annually in this country for fertilizer; both are used in small amounts for chemical purposes.

Calcium sulfate occurs as anhydrite, $CaSO_4$, and more commonly as gypsum, $CaSO_4 \cdot 2H_2O$. The transparent crystals of gypsum that form the dunes of White Sands National Monument are called selenite; fibrous crystalline masses are satin spar; and the opaque microcrystalline variety, if of sufficient beauty, is alabaster. Gypsum is soluble in water to the extent of 0.012 M at 40° C.; it is slightly less soluble at higher and lower temperatures. Although this degree of solubility is not enough to make gypsum rocks dissolve rapidly whenever it rains, such a saturated solution would have a hardness of 1200 p.p.m., would taste bitter, and would act as a purgative.

When gypsum is heated at 120 to 130° C. it loses three-quarters of its water. The plaster of Paris which is thus formed is a definite compound, $CaSO_4 \cdot \frac{1}{2}H_2O$, not just partially dehydrated gypsum. When it is mixed with water it quickly solidifies to gypsum, with the evolution of heat.

$$2CaSO_4 \cdot \tfrac{1}{2}H_2O + 3H_2O \rightarrow 2CaSO_4 \cdot 2H_2O + \Delta$$

This is the familiar plaster from which casts are made, but its greatest use is in the manufacture of gypsum wallboard, such as Sheetrock. It is also used for finishing and patching plasters. Blackboard crayons are actually gypsum, not chalk. The addition of 2.5 per cent of gypsum to cement clinker before grinding delays the setting of concrete. If gypsum is used in place of limestone in the manufacture of cement, the SO_4^{--} ion is reduced to SO_2, which can be used in producing H_2SO_4. The substitution of gypsum for limestone is not economical in the United States but is done to some extent in Europe.

In addition to being present in the salts mentioned above as sources of K^+ ion, $MgSO_4$ also occurs in such deposits as kieserite, $MgSO_4 \cdot H_2O$, and Epsom salt, $MgSO_4 \cdot 7H_2O$. It is soluble in water. Besides its well-known use as a purgative, $MgSO_4$ is used in the textile industry in the dyeing and finishing of cloth. However, it is not a very important chemical.

As would be expected from the relative solubilities of $MgSO_4$ and $CaSO_4$, both $SrSO_4$ and $BaSO_4$ are insoluble, the latter extremely so. As a mineral $SrSO_4$ is called celestite; $BaSO_4$ is called barytes, barite, or heavy spar, the last because of its high density, 4.5. Ground barite is used to weight drilling mud. Like Na_2SO_4, it can be reduced to the sulfide by heating with carbon.

$$\underline{BaSO_4} + \underline{2C} \xrightarrow{\Delta} \underline{BaS} + \overline{2CO_2}$$

BaS is somewhat soluble. Its reaction with Na_2CO_3:

$$\underline{BaS} + 2Na^+ + CO_3^{--} \rightarrow \underline{BaCO_3} + 2Na^+ + S^{--}$$

constitutes a third (and minor) source of Na_2S, but its primary purpose is the production of finely divided $BaCO_3$. Although $BaCO_3$ is used in paint, whether it should be called a pigment or a filler poses a question, because it is too transparent to have good hiding power.

A much better pigment called lithopone is made by treating BaS with $ZnSO_4$ solution, made by dissolving any kind of zinc waste in H_2SO_4.

$$\underline{BaS} + Zn^{++} + SO_4^{--} \rightarrow \underline{BaSO_4} + \underline{ZnS}$$

Both products are insoluble and white (ZnS is the only insoluble white sulfide) but they darken on exposure to sunlight; hence lithopone paint is used only for interiors. Even though lithopone is the cheapest white pigment that is good enough to be used by itself, improving it by adding a little titanium dioxide, TiO_2—the most expensive but at the same time the most efficient white pigment—has been found worth while.

15.15. Softening Hard Water

Ordinary soap is the sodium salt of a fatty acid. The fatty acids are derived from edible fats and oils; stearate ion is typical of their anions. In the following formula the hydrogen atoms are covalently bonded to carbon, as are the oxygen atoms; the dots stand for carbon-to-carbon bonds.

$$CH_3 \cdot CH_2 \cdot CH_2 \cdot CH_2 \cdot CH_2 \cdot CH_2 \cdot CH_2 \cdot CH_2 \cdot CH_2 \cdot CH_2 \cdot CH_2 \cdot CH_2 \cdot CH_2 \cdot CH_2 \cdot CH_2 \cdot CH_2 \cdot CH_2 \cdot CO_2^-$$

The anions of other fatty acids may have somewhat shorter carbon chains. In washing, the hydrocarbon end dissolves in grease; the oxygen end and the Na^+ ion remain dissolved in water. This helps to emulsify the grease and remove the dirt. Although the fatty acid salts or soaps of all polyvalent cations are insoluble, the only polyvalent cations present in ordinary water supplies are Ca^{++} and Mg^{++}. When soap is dissolved in water that contains either of these, the corresponding insoluble soap is precipitated.

$$2Na^+ + 2C_{18}H_{35}O_2^- + Ca^{++} \rightarrow \underline{Ca(C_{18}H_{35}O_2)_2} + 2Na^+$$

"Bathtub ring" and "tattle-tale gray" are due to this sticky precipitate in which the dirt is trapped. Water which can thus precipitate soap is called **hard water.**

Water is softened by removing the Ca^{++} and Mg^{++} and replacing them with Na^+ ions, or by sequestering them; these will now be explained.

If a small amount of residual hardness can be tolerated, water is softened by the relatively cheap lime-soda process, in which Ca^{++} is precipitated as $CaCO_3$. This does not mean that all the Ca^{++} is removed, because $CaCO_3$ is not absolutely insoluble. A saturated solution of $CaCO_3$ in pure water is 0.00065 M; if a slight excess of CO_3^{--} is added during the precipitation process, this can be reduced to 0.0005 by the common ion effect. A solution of this concentration contains 50 mg. of $CaCO_3$ per liter (since the formula weight of $CaCO_3$ is 100), or 50 g. per million grams of water. In water analyses the Ca^{++} ion concentration is reported not in terms of molarity but in terms of the corresponding amount of $CaCO_3$, regardless of what anion is present. The above solution might be reported as having a hardness of 50 p.p.m. or 2.9 grains per gallon. (1 grain per gallon = 17 p.p.m.) For many purposes this degree of softening is sufficient.

The molar solubility of $MgCO_3$ is one hundred times that of $CaCO_3$; therefore CO_3^{--} is unsatisfactory as a precipitant for Mg^{++}. Fortunately

Mg(OH)$_2$ is soluble only to the extent of 0.00015 M, 15 p.p.m. (Mg^{++} ion is also expressed in terms of the equivalent amount of CaCO$_3$.) The cheapest source of OH$^-$ ion is lime, Ca(OH)$_2$; the cheapest soluble source of CO$_3^{--}$ ion is soda, Na$_2$CO$_3$—hence the name of the process. The lime needed to remove the Mg^{++} ion is added first, so that the Ca^{++} which is thereby introduced can be removed afterward, along with that already present in the water.

Bicarbonate ion, HCO$_3^-$, is frequently present in water which is to be softened. It reacts with the first portions of lime that are added.

$$2HCO_3^- + Ca^{++} + 2OH^- \rightarrow \underline{CaCO_3} + 2H_2O + CO_3^{--}$$

This is advantageous, because it means that less Na$_2$CO$_3$ is required later on; furthermore, Ca(OH)$_2$ is cheaper than Na$_2$CO$_3$. Thus, sufficient lime is added to neutralize the HCO$_3^-$, and then enough more to precipitate the Mg^{++}.

$$Mg^{++} + Ca^{++} + 2OH^- \rightarrow \underline{Mg(OH)_2} + Ca^{++}$$

Enough Na$_2$CO$_3$ is then added to precipitate the Ca^{++} which was introduced in the preceding step, together with that originally present in the water; allowance is made for the CO$_3^{--}$ produced by the neutralization of the HCO$_3^-$ ion.

$$Ca^{++} + 2Na^+ + CO_3^{--} \rightarrow \underline{CaCO_3} + 2Na^+$$

Many calcium salts, among them CaCO$_3$, are less soluble in hot water than in cold. If water is heated almost to the boiling point before being softened, the residual hardness will be only one-third as great as in the cold process. Furthermore, the precipitate forms more quickly and the particles are larger, obviating the need for large settling basins and huge sand filters. The hot lime-soda process is particularly advantageous when the softened water is to be used immediately for boiler feed, for no heat is wasted.

When water of zero hardness (less than 1 p.p.m.) is required, a cation exchanger is employed. This may be natural or synthetic zeolite, or a synthetic cation-exchange resin. Zeolite is an aluminosilicate mineral; the exchange resins are organic compounds. In either case there is a giant multi-charged three-dimensional anion with a spongelike structure that contains channels through which water and ions can move. In its internal solution, the material always contains enough cations to neutralize its negative charges, but the water outside the granules can trade ions with the water inside in accordance with the mass law. The equilibrium strongly favors polyvalent ions as compared with univalent ions; therefore if hard water is filtered through an exchange bed which contains sodium ions, each of the divalent cations in the water will displace two Na^+ ions from the zeolite or resin. The reversible zeolite reaction can be symbolized as follows, Ze^{--} representing one unit of the giant anion of the zeolite:

$$Ca^{++} + \underline{(2Na^+ + Ze^{--})} \rightleftharpoons 2Na^+ + \underline{(Ca^{++} + Ze^{--})}$$

The bed is exhausted when nearly all its Na^+ ions have been exchanged for half the number of Ca^{++} and Mg^{++} ions. It is then regenerated with saturated NaCl solution. The equilibrium is displaced to the left only in the presence of a huge excess of Na^+ ions; but the molar concentration of Na^+ ions in the brine is 100,000 times as great as that of Ca^{++} ions even in very hard water, so the exchange is reversed. The liberated Ca^{++} and Mg^{++} ions and the excess brine are washed away to the sewer; and the ion exchanger, now regenerated with sodium ions, is ready to soften more water.

Water can be completely de-ionized by treating it with both cation and anion exchangers. The cation exchanger is loaded with H^+ ions instead of Na^+ ions, whereas the anion exchanger is loaded with OH^- ions. Thus the cations in the water are replaced by H^+, and whatever anions are present with the metals are subsequently replaced by OH^-. Since the H^+ and OH^- are necessarily produced in equivalent quantities and neutralize each other, the product is pure water. The cation exchanger is regenerated with H_2SO_4, the anion exchanger with NH_4OH or NaOH.

An ingenious variation of this process is mixed-bed de-ionization, in which the granules of the two resins are intermingled in a single bed. The acid that is released by a cation exchange granule is immediately neutralized by neighboring anion exchange granules, so the H^+ ion concentration never rises enough to cause any mass action reversal of the cation exchange. Regeneration is made possible by having the anion exchange resin considerably lighter than the other resin. The regeneration cycle is shown in Fig. 15.4. In A, a 4 per cent NaOH solution is first run in, followed by rinse water. If R^+ represents the giant cation of the anion exchanger and R^- the giant anion of the cation exchanger, the reaction for the regeneration of the anion exchanger can be written:

$$\text{Na}^+ + \text{OH}^- + (\text{R}^+ + \text{Cl}^-) \rightarrow (\text{R}^+ + \text{OH}^-) + \text{Na}^+ + \text{Cl}^-$$

At the same time the Na^+ ions displace most of the Ca^{++} and Mg^{++} from the cation exchanger just as they do in the regeneration of a simple softener.

$$2\text{Na}^+ + 2\text{Cl}^- + (\text{Ca}^{++} + 2\text{R}^-) \rightarrow 2(\text{Na}^+ + \text{R}^-) + \text{Ca}^{++} + 2\text{Cl}^-$$

Next the backwash separates the light from the heavy particles (*B*). This is called hydraulic classification; the same principle is used in panning gold. The backwash is slowly turned off and the resin granules settle down in two separate layers (*C*). Next, 10 per cent H_2SO_4 is introduced at the top of the lower layer, together with enough water from above to prevent any of the acid from working upward. The reaction is:

$$2\text{H}^+ + \text{SO}_4^{--} + 2(\text{Na}^+ + \text{R}^-) \rightarrow 2(\text{H}^+ + \text{R}^-) + 2\text{Na}^+ + \text{SO}_4^{--}$$

The previous almost complete removal of the divalent ions prevents the precipitation of CaSO_4. After the excess acid has been rinsed out, the resins are remixed by blowing air through the perforated plate at the bot-

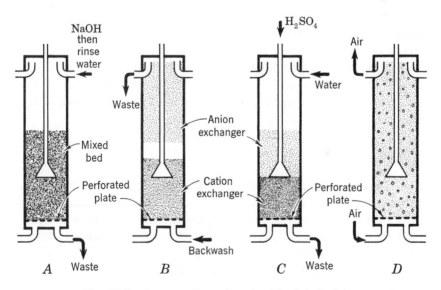

Fig. 15.4. Regeneration of a mixed-bed de-ionizer.

tom (D); they are then drawn quickly down into their original operating position (A). Hard water now enters through one of the upper pipes; the water that comes out at the bottom is practically as pure as distilled water. Being much cheaper, it has replaced distilled water for most purposes.

$$2(H^+ + R^-) + Ca^{++} + 2HCO_3^- \rightarrow (Ca^{++} + 2R^-) + H_2CO_3$$

$$(R^+ + OH^-) + H_2CO_3 \rightarrow (R^+ + HCO_3^-) + H_2O$$

Water may be softened just as effectively by combining the offending ions in the form of complexes as by removing them completely. This process is called **sequestration.** Ca^{++} has so little tendency to form covalent bonds that it was long believed not to do so at all. We now know, however, that a ligand which has several pairs of electrons to be shared, on as many different atoms (a polydentate ligand), can hold an ion much more tightly in a complex than can several monodentate ligands. The long metaphosphate ion $(PO_3^-)_x$, a polydentate ligand, can curl around Ca^{++} ions and coordinate with them in such a way that about one Ca^{++} is sequestered for each six PO_3^- units in the metaphosphate chain. This complex is so stable that it causes calcium soaps that have been previously precipitated to dissolve. Thus if clothes have been washed in hard water and rinsed free of excess soap, a good suds will be produced if they are sloshed around in water containing Calgon (a trade name for sodium metaphosphate, $NaPO_3$, manufactured for household use). $NaPO_3$ will dissolve about its own weight of calcium soap. Mg^{++} ion has a greater tendency to form covalent bonds than Ca^{++} does; therefore it is even more thoroughly sequestered. In softening water, 6 mg. of $NaPO_3$ is added to each liter of water for each part per million of hardness; for water of average hardness (100 p.p.m.), this amounts to 1 heaping teaspoonful per gallon.

15.16. Cation Analysis

When a solution contains several cations—for example, when a sample of a metal alloy is dissolved in acid—it is sometimes necessary to determine exactly which cations are present. This **qualitative analysis** is best made by successively removing from the solutions *groups* of cations in the form of insoluble compounds; see Section 11.12 and Table 11.2. Table 15.3 is a repetition of the earlier table and is given here for convenient reference.

A reagent which causes these insoluble compounds to precipitate is called a **group reagent.** The group reagent for analytical Group I, the sil-

TABLE 15.3. **Cation Analysis by Groups**

(All cations)
|
Add HCl.
|

Precipitate	**Filtrate**
AgCl	Add H_2O_2, then H_2S.
Hg_2Cl_2	
$PbCl_2$	

	Precipitate		**Filtrate**
	CuS	As_2S_5	Boil off H_2S, add $NH_4{}^+$
	HgS	SnS_2	and NH_4OH, then $(NH_4)_2S$.
	PbS	Sb_2S_3	
	CdS		
	Bi_2S_3		

	Precipitate		**Filtrate**
	NiS	$Al(OH)_3$	Add NH_4OH and $NH_4{}^+$,
	CoS	ZnS	then $(NH_4)_2CO_3$.
	MnS	$Cr(OH)_3$	
	$Fe(OH)_3$		
	FeS		

Precipitate	**Filtrate**
$BaCO_3$	Mg^{++}
$SrCO_3$	Na^+
$CaCO_3$	K^+

Group I	**II**	**III**	**IV**

ver group, is Cl⁻ ion; for analytical Group II, the copper-arsenic group, it is H_2S. For analytical Group III, the nickel-aluminum group, there are really two reagents, OH⁻ ion and S⁻⁻ ion.

The filtrate that remains after all these cations have been removed from the solution contains the alkali and alkaline earth metal ions we have studied in this chapter, because neither the sulfides nor the hydroxides of these metals are sufficiently insoluble to precipitate under the conditions of the analysis. Table 15.4 summarizes the analysis of analytical Group IV.

The barium subgroup of this group is precipitated by using $CO_3{}^{--}$ ion as the group reagent, leaving the magnesium subgroup in solution. In order to have plenty of carbonate in the solution to precipitate Ba^{++}, Sr^{++}, and Ca^{++} ions without having too high a concentration of $CO_3{}^{--}$ ions (this would precipitate too much $MgCO_3$), the pH is set at such a level that most of the reagent is in the form of $HCO_3{}^-$ ions. The $[HCO_3{}^-]:[CO_3{}^{--}]$ ratio obeys the expression for the second ionization constant of $H_2CO_3{}^-$:

$$\frac{[H^+][CO_3{}^{--}]}{[HCO_3{}^-]} = K_2$$

TABLE 15.4. **Analysis of Analytical Group IV, the Barium-Magnesium Group**

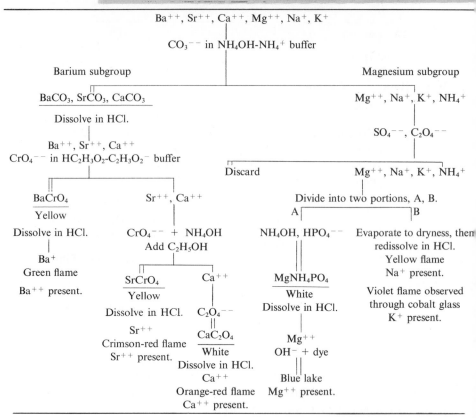

It is governed by an NH_3-NH_4^+ buffer mixture which sets the H^+ ion concentration at the proper point, just as was done previously in controlling the S^{--} concentration. The solubility product of $MgCO_3$ is 4×10^{-5}; those of $CaCO_3$, $SrCO_3$, and $BaCO_3$ are 8×10^{-9}. This means that *at a constant CO_3^{--} concentration,* the solubilities are in the same ratio. It would seem possible to precipitate the three latter, Mg^{++} ion remaining in solution. Unfortunately, in order for the *rate* of precipitation to be satisfactory, such a high CO_3^{--} concentration is required that some $MgCO_3$ also precipitates if a considerable amount was present.

After the carbonate precipitate has been separated from the solution (this may contain Mg^{++}, Na^+, and K^+ ions), it is dissolved in a little HCl. Ba^{++} is then precipitated as the chromate, $BaCrO_4$, leaving the other ions in solution. Here again the concentration of the precipitating ion, CrO_4^{--}, is controlled by a buffer. The situation here is simple enough to permit an illustrative computation. The buffer used in this step is half neutralized acetic acid, for which $K_{ion} = 1.85 \times 10^{-5}$. Since in the expression:

$$\frac{[H^+][C_2H_3O_2^-]}{[HC_2H_3O_2]} = K_{ion}$$

the concentration of $HC_2H_3O_2$ is equal to that of $C_2H_3O_2^-$ ion, the H^+ ion concentration is set at 1.85×10^{-5}. The second ionization constant for chromic acid is:

$$\frac{[H^+][CrO_4^{--}]}{[HCrO_4^-]} = K_2$$

This may be rearranged as follows:

$$\frac{[CrO_4^{--}]}{[HCrO_4^-]} = \frac{K_2}{[H^+]}$$

Substituting the numerical value of K_2, 3.2×10^{-7}, and the above value for $[H^+]$, we have:

$$\frac{[CrO_4^{--}]}{[HCrO_4^-]} = \frac{3.2 \times 10^{-7}}{1.85 \times 10^{-5}} = 1.7 \times 10^{-2}$$

In other words, when the precipitant is added, only 1.7 per cent of it remains in the form of CrO_4^{--} ion; the rest becomes $HCrO_4^-$ ion. Thus when enough K_2CrO_4 is added to make the total molarity 0.02, the concentration of CrO_4^{--} ion is only $0.02 \times 0.017 = 3.4 \times 10^{-4}$. The solubility products for $BaCrO_4$, $SrCrO_4$, and $CaCrO_4$ are respectively 2.4×10^{-10}, 3.6×10^{-5}, and 2.5×10^{-3}. If each cation is present at $0.1\ M$ (the probable maximum), the corresponding ion concentration products will be $10^{-1} \times 3.4 \times 10^{-4} = 3.4 \times 10^{-5}$. Obviously $BaCrO_4$ will precipitate.

The solubility product of $SrCrO_4$, though not exceeded, is closely approached under these conditions. After separation of Ba^{++} ion, the $SrCrO_4$ can be precipitated by increasing the CrO_4^{--} ion concentration. This is accomplished by making the solution just alkaline with NH_4OH.

$$2H^+ + 2CrO_4^{--} \rightleftharpoons 2HCrO_4^- \rightleftharpoons Cr_2O_7^{--} + H_2O$$
(yellow)   (orange)

It can be seen that addition of base will decrease the H^+ ion in the equilibria above and shift them to the left. Thus the solution will change from orange to yellow color as $Cr_2O_7^{--}$ diminishes and CrO_4^{--} increases in concentration. The addition of alcohol, C_2H_5OH, at this stage of the procedure increases the efficiency of the separation of $SrCrO_4$ from Ca^{++} ion. $SrCrO_4$ is less soluble in an alcohol-water solution than in water. The Ca^{++} ion is finally precipitated from the alkaline solution as CaC_2O_4 by use of the reagent $(NH_4)_2C_2O_4$. If the ions are not properly or efficiently precipitated at each stage of the procedure, it is possible that $BaCrO_4$ will precipitate with or in lieu of $SrCrO_4$. Similarly, SrC_2O_4 may precipitate with or in place of CaC_2O_4 (in its absence). Hence it is advisable to make confirmatory flame tests for these ions on precipitates considered to contain them. These are described in the next section.

The filtrate from the barium subgroup contains any magnesium subgroup ions which may be present. Mg^{++} ion is precipitated by adding HPO_4^{--} ion and NH_4OH.

$$Mg^{++} + HPO_4^{--} + NH_4OH \rightarrow \underline{MgNH_4PO_4} + H_2O$$

Since any Group IV ions that were incompletely precipitated also form insoluble phosphates, this precipitate is dissolved in HCl and a confirmatory test is run. The precipitate is $Mg(OH)_2$ in the presence of paranitrobenzeneazoresorcinol, a dye called magnesium reagent, which dyes it blue. A dyed hydroxide precipitate is called a **lake**; a number of them are valuable as pigments.

Na^+ and K^+ ions remain to be identified, if present. Since neither of these forms any very insoluble compound, they are commonly identified by means of flame tests.

15.17. Flame Tests

Many salts, particularly chlorides, when held in a Bunsen burner flame on a platinum wire, evaporate into the flame as independent cations and anions. A flame is full of free electrons, which may be captured by the cations. When an electron falls into a cation the excess energy it possesses is released as radiant energy, i.e., light. The vibration frequency of the light, and therefore its color, is proportional to the amount of this energy. Since the attraction that different atoms have for electrons varies, the colors vary for the different atoms so consistently as to be absolutely characteristic. An electron may fall into an outer orbital first, the light of one color being pro-

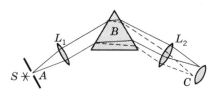

Fig. 15.5. Schematic diagram of a spectroscope. The two lenses serve to form images of the illuminated slit, and deviation by the prism produces separate images for each wave length in the original light. Light from S shines through slit A and is deviated by prism B. Colored images of the slit form at C.*

* From John S. Allen and others, *Atoms, Rocks and Galaxies,* Harper & Brothers.

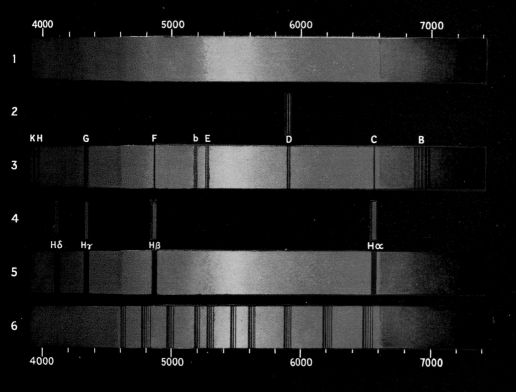

Fig. 15.6. (1) A continuous spectrum from an incandescent solid. (2) Flame spectrum of sodium (at the temperature of an arc a number of other emission lines are shown). (3) Solar spectrum, showing dark lines where relatively cool atoms in the outer atmosphere have absorbed light of that wave length coming from the interior. The dark (or Fraunhofer) lines marked D prove the presence of sodium in the sun. (4) Emission spectrum of hydrogen. Note that the C, F, and G Fraunhofer lines show that there is hydrogen in the sun. (5) Spectrum of Sirius, showing the absorption spectrum of hydrogen. (6) Spectrum of Betelgeuse, a cooler star. The absorption bands are those of molecules, not atoms. (From John C. Duncan, **Astronomy,** Harper & Brothers.)

duced, and then into lower-energy orbitals. The difference in energy being radiated each time as a pulse of light of the corresponding color. Thus the flame is colored crimson by Li^+, yellow by Na^+, lilac by K^+, green by Ba^{++}, signal-flare-red by Sr^{++}, and brick-red by Ca^{++}. The flame coloration imparted by Mg^{++} is in the ultraviolet (high-energy) region, so this ion does not give a flame test in the visible spectrum. Although other ions color flames, these are the only ones for whose identification flame tests are regularly used in qualitative analysis.

Much more energy is available in an electric arc than in a Bunsen flame. When thermally excited in an arc, an ion may lose one or more additional electrons, and regain them later. Many colors of light over the entire spectrum, visible and invisible, are produced by these highly excited ions. If these different colors are separated by a prism or other device, so that they can be seen or photographed independently, each element in a mixture can be identified and the amount of it present accurately measured. A device that enables this to be done is called a spectroscope (Fig. 15.5), a spectograph, or a spectrometer, depending upon whether the separated colors of light are observed visually, photographed, or detected electrically. Fig. 15.6 shows what can be seen with a spectroscope. Each line is an image (or "specter") of the slit through which the light enters the instrument. All the lines from the light emitted by a given element constitute its **spectrum** under the given conditions. Spectroscopic analysis requires expensive instruments and careful standardization, but is unequaled for the speedy detection and measurement of minute traces of impurities. It is indispensable in many branches of industry and chemical research.

If white light, which consists of all frequencies of light, is passed through gaseous sodium (mostly Na, with some Na_2), most of it will be unchanged; but yellow light that is of exactly the same frequency as the Na^+ ions in the flame emit when they capture electrons will be absorbed. As this yellow light is absorbed, it raises the valence electron of the sodium to the orbital from which it fell when the characteristic yellow of the flame test appeared. As these excited atoms drop back to the normal state, the same yellow light will be emitted again, but in all possible direction by different atoms. The amount emitted in any one direction is negligible, so there will be a dark line in the continuous spectrum.

The **absorption spectrum** of any atom is just as characteristic as its **emission spectrum.** This makes the analysis of stars possible. Helium was identified by means of one absorption line in the yellow region of the solar spectrum, long before it was discovered on earth. This fact accounts for its name, the -ium ending, which suggests a metallic nature, being used because most of the elements previously identified in the sun were metals. The spectroscope, of course, gave no indication of its chemical nature.

QUESTIONS AND PROBLEMS

1. In what respects are the alkali metals "extremes"?

2. How does reduction ability vary with atomic number in the alkali and alkaline earth families? Are there any anomalies in this relationship? Explain.

3. Illustrate by balanced equations the reaction of Na with oxygen; hydrogen; ethyl alcohol; water; ammonia; a metal oxide; an acid. Which of these reactions are dangerous? Which are of industrial importance?

4. What are the characteristic oxidation numbers of the alkali and alkaline earth metals? Do these elements ever have other valences? Covalence? Give reasons for your answer.

5. Compare the Dow sea-water process and the ferrosilicon process for preparing metallic magnesium.

6. Which of the "active" metals competes with other industrial metals as far as use is concerned? What are some of the structural applications of this metal?

7. Illustrate the ability of the alkaline earth metals as getters. Which metal is best adapted for this? Are these reactions important commercially?

8. Illustrate the following by means of balanced equations: lime-soda water-softening process; zeolite softening; mixed-bed de-ionization; sequestration.

9. Indicate particular advantages or disadvantages—if there are any—of the processes in question 8.

10. Is there any distinction between sequestration, coordination, and complexation? If so, what is it?

11. Describe how NaOH is prepared commercially by an electrolytic method and a chemical method. What are the advantages and disadvantages of the latter over the former?

12. Which chemical compounds are classified as caustic alkalies and which as alkalies?

13. Show by equations how soda ash and sodium bicarbonate are prepared.

14. What are some of the major uses of the following: $NaOH$; Na_2CO_3; $NaHCO_3$; $Ca(OH)_2$; Na_2SiO_3?

15. Compare the descriptive terms efflorescence, deliquescence, and effervescence.

16. What aspect of the chemical nature of $CaCO_3$ permits the formation of stalagmites? Defend your answer with equations. How is this related to some forms of hard water?

17. What are calcined dolomite and magnesite? Of what use are they?

18. Correlate the electronegativity of the alkali and alkaline earth metals with tendency to form covalent bonds, solubility of hydroxides, thermal stability of carbonates and hydroxides.

19. An unknown containing the following possible ions—Ba^{++}, Ca^{++}, and Mg^{++}— was treated with NH_4Cl-NH_4OH buffer followed by $(NH_4)_2CO_3$. No precipi-

tate formed. When another portion of the unknown was treated with only $(NH_4)_2CO_3$ a white precipitate was obtained. What conclusions do you arrive at? Give reasons for your answer.

20. What is the role of acetic acid-ammonium acetate buffer in controlling the precipitation of chromates of Ca^{++}, Ba^{++}, and Sr^{++}? Which ion precipitates when this mixture is used? What reagent would you add to precipitate the next ion? Which ion would precipitate next? Could you be sure that this precipitate was pure, or would it contain significant quantities of the third ion as chromate?

16

Amphoteric metals, aluminum, chromium, and zinc. Analysis of the aluminum subgroup

16.1. Metals and Non-Metals

The broadest classification of the chemical elements is that which divides them into two categories, metals and non-metals. This classification was originally based on the appearance of the free elements, but was found to go much deeper than that. Most chemical properties can be called exhibitions of metallic or non-metallic behavior. In the chapters on the typical non-metals, we saw that the free elements, which are high in electronegativity, are oxidizing agents and form either monatomic anions or covalently bonded molecules, many of them anions. Typical metals, on the contrary, elements that are low in electronegativity, are reducing agents, form monatomic cations, and do not readily form covalent bonds (Chapter 15).

From the chemical point of view there is no better criterion of a metallic nature than the ability of an atom to exist in solution as a simple cation, more or less strongly hydrated. This ability is closely connected with low electronegativity. In fact, it can be shown that the very property which gives chlorine its high electronegativity—its high kernel charge—would transform into an anion any hypothetical hydrated cation it might form. Suppose, for example, that we could put a Cl^{+7} cation into solution. It would instantly form covalent bonds with the oxygens of four water molecules, drawing an electron pair from each oxygen into one of its s-p orbitals. But the $+7$ charge which drew in the oxygen electrons would simultaneously remove electrons to a considerable extent from the attached hydrogen atoms, and would repel the protons because of the action of like charges on each other. In other words, $Cl(H_2O)_4^{+7}$ would be a strong acid which would react with neighboring water molecules as follows:

$$Cl(H_2O)_4^{+7} + 8H_2O \rightarrow ClO_4^- + 8H_3O^+$$

It would promptly become an anion.

16.2.   Hydrated Cations as Acids

A hydrated cation whose central atom exerted less pull on the electrons in the water molecule and less repulsion on their protons would be a weaker acid. If the central cation is large and has a low charge, it will not form bonds of any appreciable degree of covalence with the surrounding water molecules, and the water molecules, in turn, will be no different chemically from more distant ones. This is the case with all cations that are 1.0 or less in electronegativity. The acidity of hydrated Ca^{++} ion is barely measurable, $K_{ion} = 10^{-13}$; hydrated Mg^{++} ion has a K_{ion} of 2×10^{-12}. An electronegativity of 1.5 corresponds to a noticeable degree of acidity. $Al(H_2O)_6^{+3}$ is an acid of about the same strength as acetic acid, the acid of vinegar; its first ionization constant is 1.3×10^{-5}.

Water molecules are so loosely attached to cations that are low in electronegativity that it is difficult to tell how many molecules of water there are in the hydrated ion. Fortunately this does not matter; Al^{+3} ion is definitely known to have six, as do many others; but four is also common, as in $Cu(H_2O)_4^{++}$ and $Zn(H_2O)_4^{++}$. Definite knowledge about the amount and importance of hydration of cations is rather recent, and it is still not customary to show it in the formula. As was explained in connection with the formulas H^+ and H_3O^+ for hydrogen ion, we use the "dehydrated" formulas for convenience even when we are not compelled to by ignorance. However, one exception should be made; the water of hydration should be shown explicitly when the ionization of a hydrated cation acid is discussed.

16.3. Polyprotic Cation Acids

If a hydrated cation is a sufficiently strong acid so that its solutions are noticeably acid, it can lose a proton from more than one of its water molecules. In other words, it is a **polyprotic acid,** like H_2S and H_3PO_4. Just as it is more difficult to take a proton from the anion produced by the first ionization of an uncharged acid, so it is more difficult to take a proton from the less positive ion that remains after the first ionization of a cation acid. K_2 is always far smaller than K_1, regardless of the original charge. Successively stronger or more concentrated bases are needed for each additional step in neutralizing such an acid. The first ionization of Al^{+3} proceeds to about 1 per cent.

$$Al(H_2O)_6^{+3} + H_2O \rightleftharpoons Al(H_2O)_5OH^{++} + H_3O^+$$

Water is too weak a base to remove a second proton; but with the acetate ion, $C_2H_3O_2^-$, a mild base, the second step of the neutralization goes almost to completion.

$$Al(H_2O)_5OH^{++} + C_2H_3O_2^- \rightleftharpoons Al(H_2O)_4(OH)_2^+ + HC_2H_3O_2$$

A good base like NH_3 removes the third proton completely.

$$Al(H_2O)_4(OH)_2^+ + NH_3 \rightarrow \underline{Al(H_2O)_3(OH)_3} + NH_4^+$$

When the third proton is lost, the charge on the complex becomes zero, the particles no longer repel each other but instead coalesce, and the extremely insoluble aluminum hydroxide precipitates. All hydroxides formed by the neutralization of polyprotic cation acids are insoluble; those formed from trivalent ions are exceedingly so. The insolubility of $Al(OH)_3$, $Cr(OH)_3$, and $Fe(OH)_3$—to use the conventional formulas—is used in the analytical separation of Al^{+3}, Cr^{+3}, and Fe^{+3} ions from solution.

16.4. Amphoteric Hydroxides

Writing the formula of aluminum hydroxide in the conventional way, $Al(OH)_3$, conceals a fact that is obvious from the detailed formula, $Al(H_2O)_3(OH)_3$, namely, that it is still an acid. It should dissolve in a sufficiently strong base and form an anion. OH^- ion is such a base; the reaction is:

$$\underline{Al(H_2O)_3(OH)_3} + OH^- \rightarrow Al(H_2O)_2(OH)_4^- + H_2O$$

A similar reaction occurs with $Cr(H_2O)_3(OH)_3$.

$$Cr(H_2O)_3(OH)_3 + OH^- \rightarrow Cr(H_2O)_2(OH)_4^- + H_2O$$

The formulas of the dehydrated ions, $Al(OH)_4^-$ and $Cr(OH)_4^-$, or even those of the more extensively dehydrated forms AlO_2^- and CrO_2^- are conventionally used. Since aluminum has only one valence, AlO_2^- is called aluminate ion. Chromium has a higher valence as well as the $+3$ valence shown here; so CrO_2^- is chromite ion. A striking difference in these two ions is the green color of the CrO_2^- ion. Color is always to be expected in ions of the transition metals.

An insoluble hydroxide which dissolves in NaOH solution is said to be **amphoteric** (*ampho* = both), because it forms both cations and anions. The ability to dissolve in acids, forming cations, is taken for granted, because the hydroxides are the conjugate bases of the cations in question. Whether or not such a hydroxide will dissolve in NaOH solution, forming anions, depends upon how strong an acid it is. $Cr(OH)_3$ behaves like $Al(OH)_3$, but $Fe(OH)_3$ is too weak an acid to do this, although it dissolves readily in pure melted NaOH; therefore it is not amphoteric. This difference between their hydroxides is used in the analytical separation of Al^{+3} and Cr^{+3} from Fe^{+3}.

16.5. Amphoteric Behavior of Zinc

The size of the charge on a cation is very important in determining its strength as an acid and hence whether its hydroxide is amphoteric, as well as various solubility relations. It is for that reason that Al^{+3}, Cr^{+3}, and Fe^{+3} are very similar chemically, although they are in different groups in the periodic table. Similarly, Cr^{++} and Fe^{++} are more like Mg^{++} than like their own trivalent ions.

Charge is not, however, the whole story. For example, none of the heavier ions in the aluminum family are amphoteric, because their size prevents water molecules from approaching so closely. On the other hand, Be^{++}, the smallest ion in Group II of the periodic table, does form an amphoteric hydroxide, its small size making up for its smaller charge. A third factor of general importance in determining the resemblance of ions to each other is the presence of d electrons in the surface. A d electron has such an elongated orbital that on the average 15 per cent of the time it is farther from the nucleus than an s electron in the following outer layer. The d electron thus shields only 0.85 of a unit of nuclear charge from electrons in the valence layer. This results in a correspondingly increased tendency to form covalent bonds. The two charges on Zn^{++} ion are enough to draw to it only four molecules of water of hydration; but once an electron pair of a water molecule enters the valence layer of the Zn^{++} ion, the electron pair is acted upon by 0.15 of an additional unit of nuclear charge for each of the 10 d electrons in the surface of the Zn^{++} ion. Thus there is a total of 1.5 extra positive charges, in addition to those that constitute the valence charge of the ion. This effective charge of 3.5 exerts such a pull on the electrons of the oxygens that $Zn(H_2O)_4^{++}$ is actually a stronger acid than $Al(H_2O)_6^{+3}$. Its hydroxide, produced by the loss of two protons, is easily soluble in NaOH solution.

$$Zn(H_2O)_2(OH)_2 + OH^- \rightarrow Zn(H_2O)(OH)_3^- + H_2O$$

A fourth proton is lost when the NaOH solution is more concentrated.

$$Zn(H_2O)(OH)_3^- + OH^- \rightarrow Zn(OH)_4^{--} + H_2O$$

These two zincate ions may also be written $HZnO_2^-$ and ZnO_2^{--}.

16.6 Electronegativity and Amphoterism

In the preceding section three factors—high charge, small size, and high effective charge in the valence layer—were listed as contributing to acidity in a hydrated cation and hence to amphoterism in the corresponding hydroxide. All three of these, as a matter of fact, also contribute to the electronegativity of the atom in question. Actually, we can state simply that the electronegativity of an atom governs the acidity displayed by its cation and by its hydroxide. This statement can be checked by observing the properties of solutions of perchlorates, since ClO_4^- ion has no acid or basic properties of its own that would interfere.

If the cation of a perchlorate is below 1.0 in electronegativity, the solution it forms with water will be neutral. The first traces of acidity appear at 1.0 and increase steadily with increasing electronegativity. Simultaneously the solubility of the hydroxide decreases, e.g., $Ca(OH)_2$ and $Mg(OH)_2$. When the electronegativity is 1.5 the solution is distinctly acid. The hydroxide is no longer crystalline; instead, it is gelatinous and quite insoluble, and it is amphoteric. As the electronegativity of the cation rises even more, the salt solution becomes more acid and the basic properties of the hydroxide correspondingly weaker. An electronegativity of 1.9 is the acid boundary of the amphoteric region. For example, Sb_2O_3 (electronegativity 1.8) requires almost concentrated H_2SO_4 to dissolve it, just as $Fe(OH)_3$, at the other boundary, required fused NaOH to dissolve it.

Above this value of 1.8, the hydrated cation is so strong an acid that it cannot exist. Thus there is no $Si(H_2O)_4^{+4}$ or indeed any of the species of cations between it and $Si(OH)_4$. Atoms in the upper half of the electronegativity scale knock a sufficient number of protons from the attached oxygens to remove all the positive charge, even if some of the oxygens must lose both protons. Phosphorus(V) yields H_3PO_4, not $P(H_2O)_4^{+5}$. As the hydroxide becomes more acidic, the insolubility that is characteristic of amphoteric hydroxides disappears; such "hydroxides" as $OP(OH)_3$, $O_2S(OH)_2$, and O_3ClOH are very soluble.

Since so much of the chemistry of aluminum, chromium, and zinc has been discussed under the general subject of amphoterism, it is convenient to continue the study of these three metals in the present chapter. We begin with aluminum.

16.7. History of Aluminum

The first aluminum ever produced sold for about $160.00 a pound. Opera glasses made of this metal were at one time more expensive than those made of silver. This aluminum was made by reducing $AlCl_3$ with potassium amalgam and heating to drive off the mercury, which served only as a solvent for potassium.

$$AlCl_3 + 3K \xrightarrow{\Delta} \underline{Al} + \underline{3KCl}$$

When Deville, a French chemist, used sodium as the reducing agent in 1854, this brought the price down from its then current level of $100 a pound; by 1886 it had dropped to $8 a pound. With the development of the Castner cell, whereby sodium could be produced more cheaply, the price of aluminum dropped to $4 per pound.

Charles M. Hall, while a student at Oberlin College, decided to devote himself to finding an even cheaper method of producing aluminum. He concluded that, in spite of the failure of others to electrolyze Al_2O_3, it was this method which would eventually be successful. However, it is difficult to melt Al_2O_3, and until melted it does not conduct an electric current and cannot be electrolyzed. Therefore he had to find a substance which, in the molten state, would dissolve Al_2O_3; and in cryolite, Na_3AlF_6, he found it. He obtained the direct current he needed by making his own batteries. On February 23, 1886, when he was only 22, Hall proudly showed his sisters a button of metallic aluminum which he had made by fusing cryolite in a graphite crucible and passing an electric current through it. Hall's patents were bought by the Pittsburgh Reduction Company in 1888 after several other concerns had turned them down, and aluminum was soon being produced in greater quantities at a lower price than ever before. Hall's patent barely preceded an attempt to patent the same process by the Frenchman Heroult, who had discovered it independently. Until World War II, the Aluminum Company of America (successor to the Pittsburgh Reduction Company) was the only producer of aluminum in the United States, largely because they had to work so hard to persuade a reluctant industrial world to use the new metal. They were forced to learn so much about its production and properties that when people realized what a good thing Alcoa had, it seemed hopeless to try to compete.

During that war, our aluminum production capacity was expanded sevenfold from the 1939 figure of 163,500 tons. Although most of the new plants were built and operated by Alcoa, the latter's know-how was made freely available to Reynolds, the other operating company. As in the case of magnesium, the production of aluminum soon outran even war needs. The first cutback was made in December, 1943, and a year later the expanded industry was operating at less than half capacity. The vast industrial expansion which followed the war much more than took up the slack. All the government plants passed into private hands, new companies entered the field, and during the decade following the war new plants were built that more than doubled our wartime capacity. At the current rate of production (now 2.13 million tons annually in the United States and Canada), the only metal produced in larger quantity than aluminum is steel. The postwar inflation has about doubled the price of aluminum as well as its production. After reaching a record low of 15 cents per pound in 1947, the price began to rise and at present is approximately double this figure.

16.8. Sources and Production of Aluminum

Aluminum constitutes about 8 per cent of the earth's crust. In many important minerals aluminum and silicon atoms are more or less interchangeable. (Some cation must furnish one positive charge for every aluminum atom present, because the valence of silicon is $+4$). Among the better-known aluminosilicates are the feldspars, micas, shales, clays, zeolites, asbestoses, and spinels. Non-silicate aluminous minerals are less widely distributed. Cryolite, Na_3AlF_6, is found only in Greenland; alunite, $KAl(SO_4)_2 \cdot 2Al(OH)_3$, in Wyoming and a few other places. Large deposits of bauxite, a mixture of varying proportions of diaspore, $AlO(OH)$, and gibbsite, $Al(OH)_3$, but generally written $Al_2O_3 \cdot 2H_2O$, are found in France, British and Dutch Guiana, and Jamaica. (The high-grade portions of deposits in Arkansas were largely exhausted during World War II.) Of these minerals, only bauxite is an economical source of aluminum, although the metal has been made from clay and from alunite.

If bauxite were perfectly pure, it would need only to be calcined to yield the alumina, Al_2O_3, from the electrolysis of which the metal is obtained. Actually bauxite always contains iron(III) and combined silica, which are removed by the Bayer process. The bauxite is treated with lime and soda ash (the equivalent of NaOH solution) under steam pressure in steel containers. The iron oxide, traces of titanium oxide, and most of the silica remain as a red mud; the bauxite dissolves as sodium aluminate.

$$2Na^+ + 2OH^- + 3H_2O + \underline{Al_2O_3} \rightarrow 2Na^+ + 2Al(OH)_4^-$$

When cooled, this solution becomes supersaturated with respect to $Al(OH)_3$.

$$2Na^+ + 2Al(OH)_4^- + 4H_2O \rightarrow 2Na^+ + 2OH^- + \underline{2Al(OH)_3}$$

If the precipitation takes place in the presence of a "seeding" of previously precipitated $Al(OH)_3$, a sandy product is obtained which is easily washed, dried, and calcined to Al_2O_3 (Fig. 16.1). This preliminary treatment is carried out near the supplies of the limestone and coal needed for the lime kilns, and the Al_2O_3 is then shipped to reduction plants located where cheap electricity is available. The aluminum industry is the chief consumer of government-subsidized power in the TVA, Pacific Northwest, and Niagara Falls-St. Lawrence regions; but since it has created power shortages in all these places it is building enormous installations of its own.

Bayer-process red mud contains, in addition to the iron oxide which gives it its color and the $CaCO_3$ formed when the lime is causticized, a mixture of sodium and calcium aluminosilicates. For every pound of SiO_2 which was present in the original bauxite, about a pound *each* of alumina, lime, and soda is carried into the red mud. This is a serious waste and limits the silica content of the bauxite to a maximum of 7 per cent. Since most bauxite has more than 7 per cent silica rather than less, research was pushed and led to the discovery of a method of recovering most of the values from the red mud. A mixture of the mud, soda ash, and quicklime is **sintered** (heated to incipient fusion) and ground. The resulting $NaAlO_2$ is leached out with water. On precipitating $Al(OH)_3$ from this with CO_2, nearly two-thirds of the sodium carbonate used is recovered. Combining this process with the Bayer process makes it possible to use bauxite containing up to 13 per cent SiO_2 and re-

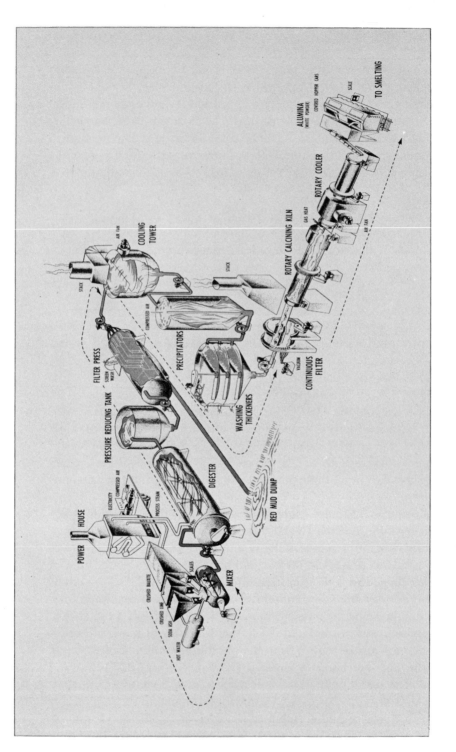

Fig. 16.1. Treatment of aluminum ore (bauxite) to form pure alumina, Al_2O_3, from which aluminum is extracted electrolytically. (Courtesy, Aluminum Company of America.)

cover 95 per cent of the contained alumina—instead of 80 to 85 per cent —at a lower cost for reagents.

16.9. Production of Metallic Aluminum

The purified alumina is dissolved in the fused cryolite bath in the electrolytic plants. The electrolysis chambers are large rectangular iron cells called pots (Fig. 16.2) They are lined with carbon to prevent metallic aluminum from coming in contact with the iron. This lining serves as the cathode. The anodes are made from low-ash petroleum coke, and a double row of them extends into the electrolyte. As the electrodes are used up, any impurities in the anodes fall to the bottom and contaminate the aluminum. Oxygen of the alumina combines with the carbon of the anodes.

$$2Al_2O_3 \xrightarrow{\triangle} 4Al + \overline{3O_2}$$

$$\overline{3O_2} + \text{Carbon anodes} \rightarrow \overline{CO} + \overline{CO_2}$$

The bath is kept at about $1000°$ C., and a thin scum of bauxite usually floats on its surface. The molten aluminum is siphoned from the bottom of the cell at intervals.

About 0.6 lb. of carbon electrode, 2 lb. of bauxite, 0.1 lb each of cryolite and fluorspar, and 10 kw.-hr. of electrical energy are used in producing 1 lb. of aluminum. Maintenance costs on the cells are high; when possible, the plant which manufactures the electrodes is located nearby. If it is necessary to shut down the plant, the electrolyte solidifies, and the pots have to be cleaned out with a pick and shovel.

In Europe, if greater purity than 98 or 99 per cent is required, the aluminum obtained by the Hall process is further refined electrolytically by the Hoopes process. In this process the cell is the anode and has a copper bottom. Molten aluminum is poured in. Above it is a layer of fused fluorides which serve as the electrolyte; however, they are so mixed that its density is less than that of the molten aluminum. Aluminum cathodes are suspended in the electrolyte. When electrons are pulled out of the molten aluminum in the bottom layer, the Al^{+3} ions move from it into the electrolyte above. At the same time the cathodes in the electrolyte force electrons onto Al^{+3} ions, and 99.9 per cent pure aluminum plates out on them. They are kept at a temperature below the melting point of aluminum. The impurities fail to dissolve from the anode pool because they are all more electronegative than aluminum.

In the United States, aluminum of 99.95 per cent purity is obtained, to the extent required, by selective reduction in regular reduction cells.

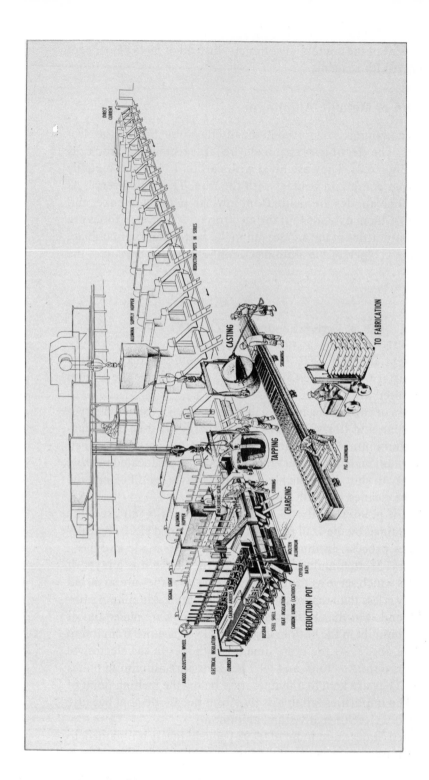

Fig. 16.2. A series of electrolytic cells used to produce aluminum from alumina and cryolite. (Courtesy, Aluminum Company of America.)

6.10. Properties of Aluminum

Aluminum is a soft metal which, curiously, becomes so brittle at high temperatures that it can easily be powdered. It melts at 660° C. and boils at 2057°. It can be rolled into structural forms, sheet or foil, cast, drawn, and stamped. Its density, 2.7, is only about one-third that of steel. Although rather low in electronegativity, 1.5, aluminum surfaces remain bright in the air and resist corrosion by oxidizing agents in general. This is so because any fresh surface that is exposed to the air is immediately covered with a hard, thin, transparent coating of Al_2O_3. When thickened by anodic oxidation this coating can be dyed. Unusual decorative effects can be obtained because a considerable amount of metallic luster shows through.

Aluminum resists the action of weak acids and of concentrated HNO_3, which strengthens the protective oxide coating. When it is dropped into HCl or H_2SO_4 there is a short pause during which the oxide is dissolved; then hydrogen is evolved vigorously.

$$2Al + 6H_3O^+ + 6H_2O \rightarrow 2Al(H_2O)_6^{+3} + \overline{3H_2}$$

If the oxide coating is removed by a solution of NaOH, the clean metal liberates hydrogen rapidly from the water of this solution. However, the other product is not the metal hydroxide, as was the case with the other metals that liberate hydrogen rapidly from water, because the $Al(OH)_3$ dissolves in NaOH to form $Al(OH)_4^-$ as fast as it is formed. The equations are:

$$2Al + 12H_2O \rightarrow 2Al(H_2O)_3(OH)_3 + \overline{3H_2}$$

and $\quad 2Al(H_2O)_3(OH)_3 + 2OH^- \rightarrow 2Al(H_2O)_2(OH)_4^- + 2H_2O$

which add to

$$2Al + 2OH^- + 10H_2O \rightarrow 2Al(H_2O)_2(OH)_4^- + \overline{3H_2}$$

This equation is more commonly written:

$$2Al + 2OH^- + 2H_2O \rightarrow 2AlO_2^- + \overline{3H_2}$$

Aluminum is a powerful reducing agent. Its heat of reaction with many metallic oxides is far more than that required to melt the products. Goldschmidt's thermite welding process takes advantage of this fact to produce molten steel which is hot enough to melt the broken ends of heavy machine parts and rails, thus making it possible to weld them *in situ* (Fig. 16.3). The reaction is:

$$Fe_2O_3 + 2Al \rightarrow 2Fe + Al_2O_3 + \Delta$$

Filings of alloying metals can be added to the thermite mixture so that the welding steel will match that in the broken part. (Thermite incendiary bombs have a magnesium casing; when this is ignited by the

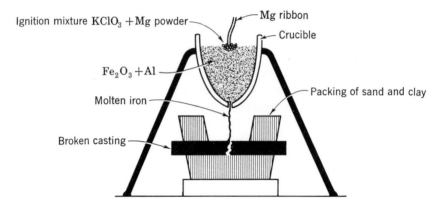

Ignition mixture $KClO_3$ +Mg powder — Mg ribbon

Crucible

Fe_2O_3 +Al

Molten iron

Packing of sand and clay

Broken casting

Fig. 16.3. Thermite welding. Molten iron drips from the crucible. A slag of Al_2O_3 floats to the top.

molten iron, even greater havoc results.) The Goldschmidt process can be used for the commercial production of molybdenum, tungsten, and other expensive metals by substituting the appropriate oxides for the iron oxide. This process also enables the use of aluminum as a scavenger in the purification of other metals. For example, iron(II) oxide dissolves in molten steel with extremely deleterious effects; but a small amount of aluminum added to the melt reacts with the dissolved iron oxide, forming Al_2O_3.

$$3FeO + 2Al \rightarrow Al_2O_3 + 3Fe$$

The Al_2O_3 thus formed is insoluble, most of it floating to the top. The rest nucleates the solidifying metal into a very fine-grained but tough structure. Oxides and other impurities can be removed from other metals in the same way. This process is called **killing,** and steel thus treated is called aluminum-killed steel.

16.11. Uses of Aluminum

The use of aluminum as a chemical reagent, just described, is by no means negligible. For example, about 2 lb. of it are used in deoxidizing the steel used in an automobile—a total of some 7000 tons a year. This amount is small, however, in comparison with what is used as metal, either pure or in alloys. Thus it has been estimated that the average 1961 car contained 50 lb. of aluminum in the engine, transmission, brakes, power units, and trim. Some of the Cadillacs now on the market contain 200 lb. each.

The most familiar use of aluminum—in the manufacture of cooking utensils—was begun in 1914. Although this was the first case of a heavy demand for aluminum, this use now accounts for only a minor part of the output. Its use as a structural material has made great progress. The arguments in favor of it are the same as those for magnesium. Even if it is not as light, it is stronger; this is particularly true of many of its alloys which contain both copper and magnesium. Also, thanks to the pioneering work done by Alcoa, techniques for handling the metal successfully were devised long before similarly successful techniques were available for magnesium. The weight saving made possible by the use of aluminum is very important. The 350 tons of it used in resurfacing an old bridge (Fig. 16.4) reduced the load on the trusses 750 tons. Aluminum bodies on trucks increase the pay load, because most states limit the gross weight of trucks. Aluminum has recently been used for the entire outer wall of a skyscraper, making possible a great saving in the steel frame, greater decorative features, and minimum maintenance costs. Both the metal and its alloys are used extensively in the aircraft industry.

A copper wire carries 50 per cent more current than an aluminum wire the same size, but an aluminum wire will carry twice the current that a copper wire the same *weight* can handle, and at half the cost. All modern high-tension transmission lines use aluminum wire. Its low tensile strength is easily remedied by the use of a steel core.

Pure aluminum is much more resistant to corrosion than its stronger alloys are. Putting a plate of pure aluminum on either side of a thicker plate of alloy made it possible to roll all three out into a single sheet of metal that has the strength of the alloy and the resistant surfaces of the pure metal. This "Alclad" was so successful that the method has been greatly extended and is now used for different purposes. For example, where only surface resistance to corrosion is needed—but not high strength—plain steel can be cladded with stainless. The stainless-

Fig. 16.4. Reconstruction of Smithfield St. Bridge, Pittsburgh. Note that one man is carrying a large piece of aluminum. (Courtesy, Aluminum Company of America.)

clad steel is much cheaper than pure stainless of any considerable thickness.

Aluminum foil is familiar in almost every household as a wrapping material. Aluminum is widely used in the home construction industry as a moisture barrier, as an insulator against radiant heat, and for clapboards on the exteriors of houses. Aluminum is a good conductor of heat between objects with which it is in contact, but it reflects infrared (heat) radiation as well as it does visible light. Sheets of aluminum foil fastened beneath the roof prevent heat from the hot roof from entering in summer and heat being lost by radiation in the winter. Aluminum roofing is common on farm and industrial buildings. Aluminum is an even better reflector of ultraviolet light than silver is; therefore astronomical mirrors are now aluminized rather than silvered. The metal is deposited from the vapor state in a vacuum. An aluminized mirror is not quite as bright to the eye as a *freshly* silvered mirror, but it does not tarnish. The sensitivity of photographic plates to ultraviolet light makes aluminum mirrors more efficient for photography.

Aluminum powder, consisting of tiny flakes, is used in paint. It "leafs out" when applied, forming a shiny coating of overlapping scales. Its imperviousness to moisture makes this paint an excellent protection for steel, and its ability to reflect heat makes it particularly desirable for tanks containing NH_3, gasoline, or liquefied petroleum gases. Aluminized paper used for wrapping is made from either the powder or the foil. This paper, or the foil itself, has completely displaced the expensive tinfoil formerly used for such purposes. Aluminum has also replaced tin for making collapsible tubes for toothpaste, etc. These tubes are extruded through a die. Small machine parts are die-cast from alloys composed mostly of aluminum, and magnesium and zinc base die-casting alloys contain 10 per cent or so of aluminum.

16.12. Ions of Aluminum

As a main-group metal, aluminum has only one valence, $+3$. Anhydrous Al^{+3} ion has a radius of 0.50 A., which puts it on the border line between the medium-sized ions of the familiar metals and the small, highly charged kernels of the non-metals which are always covalently bonded. Accordingly, Al^{+3} occurs in two different states in the minerals in which it is present. When it is surrounded octahedrally by six oxide ions it behaves like such common metal ions as Mg^{++}, Fe^{++}, and Fe^{+3} (Fig. 16.5). When it is surrounded tetrahedrally by four oxygen atoms it is thought to be covalently bonded to them (the distance is shorter)

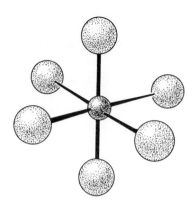

Fig. 16.5. The octahedral $Al(H_2O)_6^{+3}$ or $Al(H_2O)_2(OH)_4^-$ molecule.

and it behaves like the non-metal, silicon. Inability to distinguish these two states was a source of great confusion to mineralogists until rather recently. The situation was clarified by x-ray diffraction photography which made it possible to determine the exact location of each atom in a crystal.

In solution, six molecules of water are firmly attached to the Al^{+3} ion. $Al(H_2O)_6^{+3}$ is a tetraprotic acid. K_2 is 1.3×10^{-5}, in comparison to 1.85×10^{-5} for acetic acid. The equation for the first ionization of $Al(H_2O)_6^{+3}$.

$$Al(H_2O)_6^{+3} + H_2O \rightleftharpoons Al(H_2O)_5OH^{++} + H_3O^+$$

is commonly written:

$$Al^{+3} + H_2O \rightleftharpoons AlOH^{++} + H^+$$

The ionization is therefore usually called a hydrolysis reaction. Note that the water molecule in the second equation is actually one of the molecules that are attached to the Al^{+3} ion, not one of those that are free in the solution as in the first equation. $Al(H_2O)_6^{+3}$ is a strong enough acid to react with any anion that is more than moderately basic. The reaction with acetate ion largely completes the first step of the ionization, but the second step remains incomplete.

$$Al(H_2O)_5OH^{++} + C_2H_3O_2^- \rightleftharpoons Al(H_2O)_4(OH)_2^+ + HC_2H_3O_2$$

The alternate way of writing this equation is:

$$AlOH^{++} + C_2H_3O_2^- + H_2O \rightleftharpoons Al(OH)_2^+ + HC_2H_3O_2$$

A more strongly basic anion, such as CO_3^{--} or S^{--}, sends the third step of the ionization to completion.

$$Al(H_2O)_4(OH)_2^+ + CO_3^{--} \rightleftharpoons \underline{Al(H_2O)_3(OH)_3} + HCO_3^-$$

These reactions show why it is impossible to crystallize aluminum carbonate or sulfide from solution. It is possible to prepare the aluminum salt of a mildly basic anion at a low temperature, but not at a high one. Advantage is taken of this in the use of aluminum acetate in fabric dyeing processes. $Al(OH)_3$ is deposited inside the fibers of a textile, where it absorbs a dye which does not "take" on the fiber. The end result of a dye absorbed in a metallic hydroxide is called a **lake**. The desired design is printed on the fabric with a paste containing $Al(C_2H_3O_2)_3$. Steaming then volatilizes the $HC_2H_3O_2$ which is in equilibrium and sends the reaction to completion.

$$Al(H_2O)_6{}^{+3} + 3C_2H_3O_2{}^- \rightarrow \underline{Al(H_2O)_3(OH)_3} + \overline{3HC_2H_3O_2}$$

or $\qquad Al^{+3} + 3C_2H_3O_2{}^- + 3H_2O \rightarrow \underline{Al(OH)_3} + \overline{3HC_2H_3O_2}$

Since $Al(H_2O)_3(OH)_3$ is too weak an acid to react with even a moderately good base like $CO_3{}^{--}$ ion or NH_3, the $Al(H_2O)_2(OH)_4{}^-$ which is formed by its reaction with OH^- ion is a fairly strong base.

$$\underline{Al(H_2O)_3(OH)_3} + OH^- \rightleftharpoons Al(H_2O)_2(OH)_4{}^- + H_2O$$

or $\qquad \underline{Al(OH)_3} + OH^- \rightleftharpoons Al(OH)_4{}^-$

If the concentration of OH^- ion is reduced by dilution this reaction is reversed, and $Al(OH)_3$ is precipitated in a true hydrolysis reaction.

AlF_3 is insoluble in acids but it dissolves in HF, owing to the formation of the complex fluoaluminate ion, $AlF_6{}^{-3}$. This is an ion cluster that is held together by electrical attraction, for F^- ion has little or no tendency to form covalent bonds. The sodium salt of the fluoaluminate ion is the mineral cryolite, used as the solvent for Al_2O_3 in the manufacture of aluminum, and as an insecticide. The natural supply is inadequate, so most of that used is prepared by the reaction:

$$Al^{+3} + 3NO_3{}^- + 3Na^+ + 3F^- + 3NH_4{}^+ + 3F^- \rightarrow \underline{Na_3AlF_6} + 3NH_4{}^+ + 3NO_3{}^-$$

The coordination number of Al^{+3} for the larger Cl^- ion is 4; therefore the chloroaluminate ion is $AlCl_4{}^-$. The bonding is believed to be largely covalent in this case. Another covalently bonded complex ion of aluminum is aluminohydride ion, $AlH_4{}^-$, a recently introduced selective reducing agent that is a little less powerful than H^- ion itself. Both $AlCl_4{}^-$ and $AlH_4{}^-$ are tetrahedral structures like $PO_4{}^{-3}$, $SO_4{}^{--}$, and $ClO_4{}^-$, in which the aluminum behaves like a non-metal. The hydrogen in $AlH_4{}^-$ is hydride hydrogen; i.e., its oxidation number is -1.

16.13. Aluminum Hydroxide and Aluminum Oxide

$Al(OH)_3$ is precipitated by adding either a base to Al^{+3} or an acid to $Al(OH)_4{}^-$. Since Al^{+3} is an acid and $Al(OH)_4{}^-$ is a base, they can be used to precipitate each other.

$$Al(H_2O)_6{}^{+3} + 3Al(H_2O)_2(OH)_4{}^- \rightarrow \underline{4Al(H_2O)_3(OH)_3}$$

or
$$Al^{+3} + 3Al(OH)_4{}^- \rightarrow \underline{4Al(OH)_3}$$

The gelatinous white precipitate is extremely bulky. A small amount of it in a city water supply will entangle the dirt and bacteria in a large volume of water. Passing the water through a sand filter leaves it clear and almost sterile, with resultant saving of chlorine.

The paper and textile industries use $Al(OH)_3$ as a filler and a **mordant.** The word mordant comes from the French word *mordre,* to bite. A mordant seems to make an otherwise ineffectual dye *bite* into the fabric, though actually, as we saw in the preceding section, it is the mordant that is dyed. Color lakes are also formed separately and used as pigments. Different mordants produce different colors with the same dye.

When $Al(H_2O)_3(OH)_3$ is dried, it begins to lose water of hydration before all the unattached water has evaporated, and OH^- groups begin to dehydrate before all the water of hydration is gone; therefore solids having the composition of either $Al(H_2O)_3(OH)_3$ or $Al(OH)_3$ cannot be prepared by drying. It is possible to precipitate from a boiling solution a form of $AlO(OH)$ which differs from natural diaspore only in crystal habit; it is cubic instead of hexagonal. Aging in basic solution at 60° C. transforms this into gibbsite, $Al(OH)_3$. The formula $Al(OH)_3$ is regularly used, however, for the freshly hydrated precipitate.

The complete dehydration of $Al(OH)_3$ by low-temperature ignition produces Al_2O_3, a soft white powder which is readily soluble in aqueous HCl or NaOH. This material, known as activated alumina, is an excellent dehydrating agent that is easily regenerated by heating. Its activity is due to the fact that the Al^{+3} ions have many empty coordination positions. At higher temperatures the material crystallizes into corundum, the atoms altering their position in such a way as to produce a close-packed array of oxide ions in which each Al^{+3} ion is octahedrally surrounded by six oxide ions. Corundum is soluble only in high-temperature acids and bases, such as fused $NaHSO_4$ and NaOH. A slightly impure form of corundum is prepared by fusing bauxite in an electric furnace, allowing the impurities to settle, cooling, and then crushing the upper part. This material is excellent both as a refractory—it melts at 2020° C.—and as an abrasive, for it is harder than any naturally occurring mineral except diamond. It is sold under such trade names as Alundum and Aloxite.

Transparent corundum crystals that occur in nature are valued as gems; they are known as sapphire if blue or white (colorless), or as ruby if red. Other colors also occur. When the word "oriental" is prefixed to the name of a gem, it means that it is actually corundum but has a color like that of the gem named. Thus amethyst is purple quartz, but "oriental" amethyst is purple corundum; topaz contains Si and F, but "oriental" topaz is yellow corundum; emerald contains Si and Be, but "oriental" emerald is green corundum. Transparent corundum crystals that weigh ounces are now prepared by melting alumina in an oxyhydrogen flame. They are used for jeweled bearings in watches and precision instruments. These crystals can be colored for use as gems by the addition of traces of the same metallic oxides that give the natural stones their color—CrO_3 for ruby; CoO, FeO, or TiO for sapphire, etc. These are true synthetic rubies and sapphires and we might expect them to be valued, like their natural counterparts, on the basis of beauty of color. Instead, an enormous price differential is maintained in favor of the natural stones even though the two can be distinguished only by microscopic examination of the imperfections present in both. These consist of minute bubbles in concentric layers in the synthetic stones, and of both bubbles and inclusions, irregularly arranged, in the natural stones. Star sapphires, both natural and synthetic, contain numerous, regularly arranged crystallites of TiO_2. Balas rubies are red spinel. The spinels are a group of mixed oxides with the general formula, $M_2^{+3}M^{++}O_4$; spinel itself is Al_2MgO_4. Emery, a fine-grained natural mineral used as an abrasive, is an aluminum-iron spinel.

16.14. Aluminum Sulfate and the Alums

The method used in manufacturing $Al_2(SO_4)_3$ depends upon the requirements of the particular industry. If the sulfate must be iron-free, reprecipitated Al_2O_3, like that used in manufacturing metallic aluminum, is used as the initial material and is dissolved in sulfuric acid. If small amounts of iron, etc., are not objectionable, clay is used as the initial material.

$$(Al(OH)_2)_2Si_2O_5 + 3H_2SO_4 \rightarrow Al_2(SO_4)_3 + 2SiO_2 + 5H_2O$$

Evaporating the solution produces crystals of $Al_2(SO_4)_3 \cdot 18H_2O$, tons of which—under the name of filter alum, although it is not an alum—are used as a source of $Al(H_2O)_6^{+3}$ for purifying water, sizing paper, and mordanting cloth.

If a solution containing K^+, Al^{+3}, and SO_4^{--} ions in almost any proportion is evaporated, beautiful octahedral crystals of alum, $KAl(SO_4)_2 \cdot$

$12H_2O$, separate first. This is a double salt, containing K^+ and $Al(H_2O)_6^{+3}$ cations and SO_4^{--} anions. The other six H_2O molecules are an essential part of the crystal and may be hydrogen-bonded to the SO_4^{--} ions. Aluminum has given its name to the alums, a class of double salts of the general formula $M^I M^{III}(SO_4)_2 \cdot 12H_2O$. M^I must be a large univalent cation. In addition to the elements in Group IA, alums are formed by NH_4^+ ion (and numerous ions in which the hydrogens of NH_4^+ are replaced by OH or various hydrocarbon groups), Tl^+, and possibly Ag^+. M^{III} must be a small trivalent cation. Trivalent Al, Fe, Cr, Mn, Ir, Ga, In, Ti, V, Co, and Rh form alums, but the ions of the lanthanides are too large. SO_4^{--} ion may be replaced by SeO_4^{--} ion, but not by $(TeO_4^{--})_x$. All the alums are isomorphous and form mixed and layer crystals; i.e., if the solution contains more than one kind of M^I or M^{III} ions, these will be distributed at random in the crystal in proportion to their concentrations; a crystal of any one alum will continue to grow in a solution of any other. The most common alums, with their commercial names, are as follows:

$$KAl(SO_4)_2 \cdot 12H_2O, \text{ Potash alum}$$
$$NaAl(SO_4)_2 \cdot 12H_2O, \text{ Soda alum}$$
$$NH_4Fe(SO_4)_2 \cdot 12H_2O, \text{ Ferric alum}$$
$$KCr(SO_4)_2 \cdot 12H_2O, \text{ Chrome alum}$$
$$NH_4Al(SO_4)_2 \cdot 12H_2O, \text{ Ammonium alum}$$

Alum is used in styptic pencils to stop bleeding from small cuts; it is also a source of $Al(H_2O)_6^{+3}$ ion. Similarly, other alums are used as a source of M^{III} ions, their advantage being that they can readily be purified by crystallization, whereas the simple sulfates are difficult to crystallize. Thus alum can be obtained free from Fe^{+3} (which imparts dull colors to lakes in mordanting) by reducing the Fe^{+3} in the solution to Fe^{++} with a little SO_2, then recrystallizing the alum. So-called "alum" baking powders actually have sodium aluminum sulfate as their source of Al^{+3} ion; this hydrates to the acid $Al(H_2O)_6^{+3}$ when moistened. Sodium aluminum sulfate is made by drying soda alum.

16.15. Aluminum Chloride

Anhydrous chlorides of elements whose electronegativity is not greater than 1.0 can be prepared by simply evaporating their water solutions. If hydrated salts crystallize out, the water can be driven off by further heating. At an electronegativity of 1.2 it becomes difficult to prevent loss of HCl because of the hydrolysis resulting from the acidity of the cation (Sections 16.2 and 16.12). In the case of aluminum (electronegativity, 1.5) and elements higher in electronegativity, this method of preparation is impracticable or impossible; anhydrous chlorides of such elements are prepared only by methods which do not involve the presence of water in any way. One such method involves the direct combination of the elements. Another widely used method involves reduction of the oxide of an element by carbon in an atmosphere of chlorine. As soon as the element is set free by the carbon it is oxidized by the chlorine. The volatile chloride distills away from the carbon and is not reduced by the CO which is present with it in the gas stream. For example, it is much cheaper to prepare $AlCl_3$ this way than to prepare metallic aluminum and burn it in chlorine.

In fact, $AlCl_3$ became important commercially only after the development of the cheaper method. The equation is:

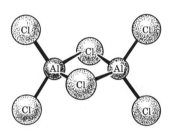

Fig. 16.6. The Al_2Cl_6 molecule consists of chlorine atoms arranged tetrahedrally around the aluminum. Note that two of the chlorine atoms serve as bridges between the two aluminum atoms.

$$\underline{Al_2O_3} + \underline{3C} + \overline{\underline{3Cl_2}} \overset{\Delta}{\rightarrow} \overline{\underline{2AlCl_3}} + \overline{\underline{3CO}}$$

The reaction is carried out in a blast furnace. As soon as the temperature of the effluent gas mixture falls below 750° C. the $AlCl_3$ begins to **dimerize** —i.e., two molecules join to form one—and at 350° C. it is entirely in the form of Al_2Cl_6 while still a gas. This is because the coordination number of Al^{+3} is not satisfied by three chlorines, but requires four. This is achieved by the formation of the molecule Al_2Cl_6. The end chlorine atoms lie in a plane at right angles to the rest of the molecule (Fig. 16.6). Al_2Cl_6 is a covalent compound, not a salt. The fact that it is soluble in many organic solvents and sublimes at 183° C. is evidence of this.

The tendency of a chlorine atom to resist forming more than one covalent bond is responsible for the commercial usefulness of Al_2Cl_6. Any molecule with an electron pair it shares readily can displace an electron pair of one of the bridge chlorines from one of the aluminum atoms. In fact, Al_2Cl_6 behaves chemically almost as though it were

$$: \overset{..}{\underset{..}{C}l} : \\ : \overset{..}{\underset{..}{C}l} : \overset{..}{\underset{..}{A}l} \\ : \overset{..}{\underset{..}{C}l} :$$, the aluminum having one empty valence orbital and hence able

to seize an electron pair of any base. When a base forms a covalent bond, all its electrons must be shifted to some extent in that direction. Very frequently the result is an increase in reactivity, a phenomenon known as **acid catalysis**; it is produced by all ordinary acids in proportion to their strength. G. N. Lewis pointed out that in this case the aluminum atom had the same effect on an electron pair of a base as a proton did. A molecule in which there is an empty orbital that is able to coordinate a base is called a **Lewis acid**. $AlCl_3$ is one of the most important of these, being used to catalyze rearrangements of the atoms of hydrocarbons in petroleum refining and in many smaller-scale procedures for the preparation of organic chemicals. $AlCl_3$ is extremely hygroscopic. Since water molecules are much more basic than Cl^- ions, they readily displace the latter from coordination with Al^{+3}.

$$Al_2Cl_6 + 12H_2O \rightarrow 2Al(H_2O)_6Cl_3$$

The new substance is an ordinary salt. It has no catalytic powers and is insoluble in organic solvents, but dissolves readily in water, yielding $Al(H_2O)_6^{+3}$ and Cl^- ions. Its formula is ordinarily written $AlCl_3 \cdot 6H_2O$ Anhydrous $AlCl_3$, as was stated above, cannot be prepared by any method from any substance in which water is involved. For this reason, it cannot be prepared by the dehydration of $AlCl_3 \cdot 6H_2O$ because HCl is given off more readily than H_2O. A similar but less acute situation was shown to exist in the production of anhydrous $MgCl_2$ (Section 15.6), which does not hydrolyze as readily as $AlCl_3$.

16.16. Production of Metallic Chromium

Nearly all chromium comes from the ore chromite, a chromium-iron spinel, Cr_2FeO_4. Chromite usually contains some of the isomorphous aluminum-iron spinel. Chromite which approximates the formula Cr_2MgO_4 is almost infusible and is used in refractories. The production of chromite ore in the United States is negligible compared with the million tons imported each year from South Africa and New Caledonia.* We consume more than half the world's production of chrome ore but produce less than 0.2 per cent of the output.

Although pure chromium is familiar to everyone as the bright finish used for automobile trim, costume jewelry, and plumbing fixtures, the largest part of our production of it is never separated as the pure metal.

---

*Significant quantities of chromite ore were obtained from Cuba prior to the current political conditions.

Instead, it is obtained as an alloy with iron by smelting a mixture of chromite and coke in an electric furnace at 1200° C.

$$Cr_2FeO_4 + 4C \rightarrow \underbrace{2Cr + Fe}_{\text{Liquid alloy}} + 4CO$$

Ferrochromium thus produced contains 60 to 70 per cent of chromium, 25 to 32 per cent of iron, and small quantities of carbon and silicon.

Pure massive chromium is prepared from the sesquioxide, Cr_2O_3, which is reduced by the Goldschmidt (thermite) process or with sodium. Chromium plate is deposited from a solution of CrO_3 or $Cr_2O_7^{--}$ ion, to which some SO_4^{--} ion may also be added. The preparation of CrO_3 and its salts is discussed in Section 16.19.

16.17. Properties and Uses of Metallic Chromium

The electronegativities of all oxidation states of chromium are probably near the value 1.6 assigned to it in the appendix. As was true in the case of aluminum, the surface of chromium is protected by the instantaneous formation of an invisible coating of oxide. This action depends (1) upon the metal being active—i.e., being low in electronegativity —(2) upon the oxide being neither acidic nor basic enough to react with water, and (3) upon the oxide being impervious to and free from cracks or holes. The factors responsible for the last are not well understood, but chromium not only has this characteristic but can impart it to iron alloys of which it is only a minor constituent. (This characteristic is conspicuously absent in ordinary iron.) The most important of the chrome steels is the one called 18-8, containing 18 per cent chromium and 8 per cent nickel. It is not only stainless but very strong; there are over 100,000 sq. ft. of stainless steel in the exterior of the Empire State Building. Where it is possible to take advantage of its high tensile strength, as in the outer shell of cars for streamliner trains, stainless steel competes with aluminum as far as saving weight is concerned. Its chemical resistance makes it important in the construction of chemical and food-processing equipment.

Pure chromium plating has two physical properties that are almost as important as its chemical resistance—hardness and non-adhesion to many substances. A plating that is as little as a few ten-thousandths of an inch thick will manifest these qualities. Thus when chromium plated, the plates from which magazines with a large circulation are printed will withstand millions of impressions, whereas without that plating they would wear out after several thousand impressions. The chromium plating of cylinders and pistons of automobile engines reduces both wear and friction. Plating the inner surface of the molds in which tires are vulcanized not only makes the molds resistant to attack by hot sulfur compounds, but permits the rubber to be released easily at the completion of the process. This lack of adhesiveness proved a serious difficulty in early attempts at chromium plating, for the plating would peel right off the metal being plated. Fortunately it was found that chromium adheres well to a flash pre-coat of nickel. Even aluminum can now be chromium plated.

16.18. Compounds of Divalent and Trivalent Chromium

Chromium is the first transition metal we have considered in detail. In discussing the properties of its compounds we should pay particular attention to two facts which apply to *all transition metals*. (1) Chromium has *d* electrons that may or may not act as valence electrons. Transition metals are characterized by variable valence, a phenomenon quite unusual with main-group metals. Non-metals regularly have variable valence, depending upon the number of outer electrons that are shared with oxygen, but transition metals never have any unshared electron pairs in the outer layer. (2) Compounds of a given transition element in which the element displays different valences greatly resemble corresponding compounds of main-group elements with those valences, but do not resemble each other. The resemblance to main-group compounds is, however, qualified by two differences—most transition compounds are colored; and transition metal cations, in common with all ions that have *d* electrons in their surface, have a greater tendency to form covalent bonds than do other ions of the same charge and size.

Since chromium is the sixth element in its period, it has 6 more electrons than the preceding inert gas. One of these is in each of the five 3*d* orbitals; the sixth is in the 4*s* orbital in the valence layer. This may be conveniently diagrammed as follows, each dash standing for an orbital and each dot for an electron:

The argon structure is implied at the left of this diagram.

Most transition metals have 2 *s* electrons, losing both at the same time to an oxidizing agent but not losing any d electron if the oxidizing agent is not too strong. In the case of chromium, one of the d electrons must have very nearly the same energy it would have if it were in the normal position in the $4s$ orbital, because no one has yet been able to prepare a Cr^+ ion. Chromium dissolves in non-oxidizing acids such as HCl and dilute H_2SO_4, with the evolution of hydrogen and the formation of blue chromous ion, $Cr(H_2O)_6^{++}$. Anhydrous Cr^{++} ion apparently is colorless.

$$\underline{Cr + 2H^+} \rightarrow Cr^{++} + \overline{H_2}$$

Cr^{++} ion has the following structure:

Its chemical properties are similar to those of Mg^{++} ion. Addition of NaOH solution precipitates the brownish-yellow hydroxide, $Cr(OH)_2$, which does not dissolve in an excess of the reagent. The carbonate and oxalate are insoluble, the sulfate soluble. There are also $CrSO_4 \cdot 7H_2O$, analogous to Epsom salt, and $K_2Cr(SO_4)_2 \cdot 6H_2O$, analogous to schönite.

The one striking chemical difference between Mg^{++} and Cr^{++} ions is that the latter is a strong reducing agent; it loses one more d electron, forming chromic ion, $Cr(H_2O)_6^{+3}$. Moist $Cr(OH)_2$ readily absorbs oxygen from the air.

$$\underline{4Cr(OH)_2} + 2H_2O + \overline{O_2} \rightarrow \underline{4Cr(OH)_3}$$

If protected from the air, it liberates hydrogen.

$$\underline{2Cr(OH)_2} + 2H_2O \rightarrow \underline{2Cr(OH)_3} + \overline{H_2}$$

Cr^{++} ion, useful in quantitative analysis as a reducing agent, remains unchanged in pure water if protected from the air, but liberates hydrogen from acid solutions, especially if in contact with platinum.

$$\underline{2Cr(H_2O)_6^{++} + 2H_3O^+} \xrightarrow{Pt} \underline{2Cr(H_2O)_6^{+3}} + 2H_2O + \overline{H_2}$$

In the trivalent state chromium resembles aluminum as much as it does magnesium when divalent. $CrCl_3$ is obtained as a sublimate of peach-colored scales under the same conditions as $AlCl_3$ is obtained, and is not a salt. The close resemblance of trivalent chromium and Al^{+3} in various hydrated forms was mentioned earlier in this chapter (Sections 16.3, 16.4). The formulas are given for comparison.

$$Al_2(SO_4)_3 \cdot 18H_2O \qquad Cr_2(SO_4)_3 \cdot 18H_2O$$
$$Al(NO_3)_3 \cdot 9H_2O \qquad Cr(NO_3)_3 \cdot 9H_2O$$
$$Al_2O_3 \qquad Cr_2O_3$$

Like Al_2O_3, Cr_2O_3 is a refractory. It is also a grayish-green pigment that is permanent. (This should not be confused with chrome green, a mixture of Prussian blue, $Fe_4(Fe(CN)_6)_3$, and chrome yellow, $PbCrO_4$; it is a much brighter green but is not permanent.) $Cr(H_2O)_6^{+3}$ ion is rather grayish-violet or dull bluish-red in color. The astringent nature of $Al(H_2O)_6^{+3}$ characterized by the puckery taste of alum is displayed to such an extent by $Cr(H_2O)_6^{+3}$ that chrome alum is used to tan leather. Substances used in tanning must be able to convert proteins into insoluble and non-hygroscopic forms. The chrome alum in some fixing baths acts by tanning the gelatin coating of the photographic film. $Cr(OH)_3$ is a mordant like $Al(OH)_3$, but produces different colors.

Cr^{+3} ion has much greater ability to form covalent bonds than Al^{+3} ion does. Part of this is due to the 3 d electrons in its surface, as was explained in Section 16.5 in the analogous case of zinc. This increased bond-forming ability is also due to the fact that two empty d orbitals are available in the Cr^{+3} ion:

They have almost the same energy as the octet (s and p) orbitals. When covalent bonds are formed with all six of these orbitals that have similar energy, they interact with each other, forming six identical orbitals, all at right angles to each other. These *octahedral* bonds—they point toward the vertices of an octahedron—are about 35 per cent stronger than the tetrahedral bonds that are formed when only the s and p orbitals are used. (This is due to the greater extension of the d orbitals mentioned in Section 16.5.) As a matter of fact, the six boxed-in orbitals in the diagram above are *always* occupied by electron pairs shared with ligands. The six ligands may be H_2O, NH_3, Cl^-, CN^-, NO_2^-, and the like—or even such relatively unwilling ones as SO_4^{--} or NO_3^-—in almost any combination. Thus in the presence of concentrated NH_3 and NH_4Cl, blue-gray $Cr(H_2O)_3(OH)_3$ dissolves and forms pink

CrCl(NH$_3$)$_4$H$_2$O^{++} ion. When any Cr(III) salt is heated, its anions usually displace water molecules from the Cr(H$_2$O)$_6$$^{+3}$ ion, forming such green complexes as CrCl(H$_2$O)$_5$$^{++}$, CrCl$_2$(H$_2$O)$_4$$^{+}$, (H$_2$O)$_5$CrSO$_4$Cr(H$_2$O)$_5$$^{+4}$, etc. These revert slowly to Cr(H$_2$O)$_6$$^{+3}$ at room temperature.

6.19. Compounds of Hexavalent Chromium

The most striking chemical difference between Cr^{+3} and Al^{+3} ions is the former's ability to be oxidized. Strong oxidizing agents, particularly in the presence of bases, raise the oxidation number of chromium to +6. Cr(VI) strongly resembles S(VI); e.g., (CrO$_3$)$_x$ and (SO$_3$)$_x$ are both strong Lewis acids. In fact, (CrO$_3$)$_x$ is commonly called chromic acid. Chromate ion, CrO$_4$$^{--}$, forms the same insoluble compounds as SO$_4$$^{--}$ ion does. In solution, HCrO$_4$$^{-}$ ion dehydrates instantly at room temperature to Cr$_2$O$_7$$^{--}$, whereas for the corresponding reaction with HSO$_4$$^{-}$ ion a dry salt must be heated strongly. The acidification of a yellow chromate solution immediately imparts the orange dichromate color. The reverse reaction is as rapid when any base is added.

$$2CrO_4^{--} + 2H^+ \rightleftharpoons Cr_2O_7^{--} + H_2O$$

This reaction of CrO$_4$$^{--}$ ion is responsible for the fact that insoluble chromates are readily soluble in acid, whereas concentrated H$_2$SO$_4$ is required to dissolve insoluble sulfates.

$$\underline{2PbCrO_4} + 2H^+ + 2NO_3^- \rightarrow 2Pb^{++} + 2NO_3^- + Cr_2O_7^{--} + H_2O$$

but $\qquad \underline{PbSO_4} + H_2SO_4 \rightarrow Pb^{++} + 2HSO_4^-$

CrO$_4$$^{--}$ ion is prepared commercially by roasting a mixture of chromite and soda ash.

$$\underline{4Cr_2FeO_4} + \underline{8Na_2CO_3} + \overline{7O_2} \rightarrow 2Fe_2O_3 + 8Na_2CrO_4 + \overline{8CO_2}$$

The Na$_2$CrO$_4$ is then leached out from the Fe$_2$O$_3$. All compounds that contain Cr(VI) are stronger oxidizing agents than the corresponding S(VI) compounds. CrO$_3$ ignites alcohol that is dropped on it. H$_2$Cr$_2$O$_7$ liberates chlorine from concentrated HCl. Chromyl chloride, CrO$_2$Cl$_2$, explodes when in contact with phosphorus and undergoes combustion with sulfur, NH$_3$, and many organic substances. In contrast to S(VI), when Cr(VI) acts as an oxidizing agent it is always reduced to Cr^{+3}, never to any substance corresponding to SO$_3$$^{--}$ or any of the lower valences of sulfur. This is in accordance with the fact, mentioned at the beginning of the preceding section, that there are never any unshared electron pairs in the valence shell of a transition metal, as there would have to be if CrO_3^{--} were formed. When the reducing agent puts 3 electrons into the empty d orbitals of Cr(VI) the size of the kernel is enlarged. Cr(VI) has room for only four oxygen atoms around it; Cr(III) has room for six. Water molecules accordingly move in, and protons are picked up by the original oxygens, there no longer being so high a central charge to repel them. The reduction half-reaction for $Cr_2O_7^{--}$ ion is:

$$6e^- + Cr_2O_7^{--} + 14H^+ + 5H_2O \rightarrow 2Cr(H_2O)_6^{+3}$$

Na_2CrO_4 is the source of other compounds of Cr(VI). Addition of H_2SO_4 produces di-, tri-, and tetrachromates, and finally $(CrO_3)_x$. When Na_2CrO_4 is heated with concentrated H_2SO_4 and a chloride, a deep red vapor of CrO_2Cl_2 distills off and condenses in a cooled receiver to a black-red liquid like bromine. Under the same conditions bromides and iodides do *not* produce chromyl halides; so the formation of CrO_2Cl_2 can be used as a test for the presence of chlorides in bromides and iodides. A small quantity of CrO_2Cl_2 can best be detected, particularly in the presence of quantities of bromine, by collecting the distillate in water, in which it hydrolyzes immediately.

$$2CrO_2Cl_2 + 3H_2O \rightarrow 6H^+ + Cr_2O_7^{--} + 4Cl^-$$

When this is neutralized and Pb^{++} ion is added, yellow $PbCrO_4$ will precipitate.

Several useful pigments are produced from Cr(VI). $(NH_4)_2Cr_2O_7$, which is easily prepared by adding NH_3 to a solution of CrO_3 and crystallizing, decomposes vigorously on heating, evolving nitrogen and steam; there remains a voluminous fluffy residue of dull green Cr_2O_3.

$$(NH_4)_2Cr_2O_7 \overset{\Delta}{\rightarrow} Cr_2O_3 + \overline{4H_2O} + \overline{N_2}$$

A hydrated chromic acid, more nearly leaf-green, is known to artists as viridian; it is the most permanent green pigment known. Chrome yellow is lead chromate, prepared by the reaction:

$$2Pb^{++} + Cr_2O_7^{--} + H_2O \rightarrow \underline{2PbCrO_4} + 2H^+$$

Lighter shades may be prepared by precipitating $PbSO_4$ with it. Chrome red (American vermilion) is basic lead chromate.

$$2PbCrO_4 + 2Na^+ + 2OH^- \rightarrow Pb(OH)_2 \cdot PbCrO_4 + 2Na^+ + CrO_4^{--}$$

When mixed with chrome yellow, it forms chrome orange.

6.20. Peroxy Compounds of Chromium

If a solution of a chromate is acidified with H_2SO_4 and added to H_2O_2 solution, a blue liquid is formed which gives ether a deep indigo-blue color when shaken with it. This reaction is a convenient test for chromates. The water solution contains CrO_7^{--}, in which three of the coordination positions around Cr(VI) are occupied by peroxide groups and the fourth by an oxide ion. As we saw earlier, the corresponding S(VI) compound has three oxides and only one peroxide.

a   b   c   d

Formula *a* is that of peroxymonosulfate. (It is necessary to put mono- in front of sulfate to distinguish it from the peroxydisulfate ion, $O_3SOOSO_3^-$, but it is not needed in front of peroxy because more than one peroxy group is never present.) Formula *b* is that of triperoxychromate ion, the substance in the water solution. (No mono- is needed in front of chromate, because no di- compound exists.) When the triperoxychromate ion is extracted with ether, $O(C_2H_5)_2$, a molecule of ether displaces an O^{--} ion (which takes up protons from the acid solution), forming the uncharged compound whose formula is shown in *c*; there is no simpler name for it than 0,0-diethyl triperoxychromate. When NaOH is added, oxygen is evolved and CrO_4^{--} ion is regenerated.

From an alkaline K_2CrO_4 solution with H_2O_2, red K_3CrO_8 can be crystallized. The anion of this salt, whose formula is shown in *d*, is a tetraperoxy compound of Cr(V), the odd electron which has slipped down into a *d* orbital having been obtained from the oxidation of some H_2O_2. Another compound of Cr(V) is CrF_5, a bright red liquid.

6.21. Production of Metallic Zinc

Zinc ores were used in making brass, a copper-zinc alloy, as early as 1500 B.C. Strabo (7 B.C.) described the preparation of the metal itself, which he called mock-silver, but the art of preparing it was lost in Europe. It was rediscovered by Isaac Lawson in 1730; however, Portuguese traders had been bringing brass from China for the past century.

Zinc ores are found in every state in this country, and the metal is produced in 23 states. The most important zinc-producing regions of the United States are New Jersey, Illinois, Virginia, Kansas, the famous Joplin district in Missouri, and Oklahoma. Zinc and lead ores occur together in many places. Igneous or volcanic rocks contain zinc, lead, and copper. PbS and CuS are insoluble in an acid solution and therefore were precipitated in acid waters. Zinc sulfide is soluble in an acid solution but not in a basic solution, and hence was precipitated when thermal waters passed through a limestone formation. Zinc sulfide, ZnS, is often found in limestone deposits, whereas copper ores are found in veins. ZnS has replaced the $CaCO_3$ in some fossils. Sphalerite, or zinc blende, and wurtzite are different crystalline forms of zinc sulfide and are the more important zinc ores. Others of importance are willemite, Zn_2SiO_4; calamine, $Zn_2SiO_4 \cdot H_2O$; smithsonite, or zinc spar, $ZnCO_3$; zincite, ZnO; and franklinite, Fe_2ZnO_4. Franklinite, a spinel, also contains manganese which is used in steel and is a valuable by-product of zinc smelters.

Zinc is obtained from its ores either by electrolysis or by smelting. With either process if the ore contains a sulfide—and most of them do —it must first be roasted.

$$2ZnS + \overline{3O_2} \xrightarrow{\Delta} \underline{2ZnO} + \overline{2SO_2}$$

The SO_2 is used in the production of H_2SO_4. The roasting process also removes any arsenic which may be present as the volatile oxide As_2O_3.

In the electrolytic process the calcined ore is leached with dilute H_2SO_4 in tanks which are arranged in series so that the acid solution and the ore move through them countercurrent to each other. Fresh acid first encounters nearly exhausted ore; almost spent acid, laden with $ZnSO_4$, is finally used up on the incoming ore. Addition of milk of lime, a suspension of $Ca(OH)_2$, to the solution precipitates the very insoluble hydroxides of the trivalent metals—iron, aluminum, and antimony—which are present as impurities. At the same time small amounts of arsenic and silicon are removed as insoluble calcium salts. After filtration the solution is treated with zinc dust, which reduces the more electronegative Cu^{++} and Cd^{++} ions to the free metals. One more passage through a filter press, and the clear liquid is ready to be electrolyzed. In the electrolysis, oxygen is freed at the lead anodes and zinc is deposited on aluminum cathodes, from which it is stripped daily (Fig. 16.7).

Fig. 16.7. Tankhouse of an electrolytic zinc plant. This building houses 1278 lead-lined cells in which zinc is recovered electrolytically from solution. The workman is hoisting a set of cathodes from a cell. The zinc will be stripped from them elsewhere. (Courtesy, The Anaconda Company.)

$$2Zn^{++} + 2SO_4^{--} + 2H_2O \overset{\triangle}{\rightarrow} \underline{2Zn} + 4H^+ + 2SO_4^{--} + \overline{O_2}$$

In a zinc smelter the calcined ore is mixed with powdered coal and placed in a retort which is heated externally. Zinc distills off and is condensed.

$$\underline{ZnO} + \underline{C} \overset{\triangle}{\rightarrow} \overline{Zn} + \overline{CO}$$

Most of it collects as liquid, which is tapped off and cast into bars; but some of it remains in cooler parts of the condenser as a fine powder mixed with ZnO, called zinc dust. Zinc dust is also prepared intentionally, as small oxide-coated spheres, by atomizing molten zinc with an air blast. A good grade of the dust may contain more than 90 per cent zinc. Smelted zinc that contains iron, lead, and cadmium is called spelter. Very pure zinc can be obtained by fractional distillation of spelter. The zinc and cadmium vaporize off from the iron (b.p. 2800° C.) and lead (b.p. 1620° C.), and the zinc (b.p. 907° C.) is then fractionally condensed from the cadmium (b.p. 767° C.). Production of zinc in the United States ran about 475,000 tons in 1960, and 400,000 tons more are imported each year. The price is as low as 10 cents per pound.

16.22. Properties and Uses of Metallic Zinc

Zinc is most familiar as a coating on the surface of galvanized iron. Cleaned iron in the form of sheets or wire is galvanized by being run through a bath of melted zinc (m.p. 419° C.). The regular pattern of decorative spangles characteristic of galvanized iron is produced by running the sheets as they come from the zinc bath over an iron roller whose surface resembles a waffle iron. The points initiate crystallization of the molten zinc in a pattern which will be large or small according to the roller used. Zinc crystallizes in the hexagonal system. It can be rolled or drawn between 100° and 150° C., but is quite brittle outside that range.

Zinc is alloyed with copper in proportions up to 45 per cent to produce an enormous array of brasses, which frequently contain other metals as well, such as lead, tin, aluminum, manganese, nickel, and iron. About a quarter of all the zinc produced is used in making brasses and die-casting alloys. These alloys contain about 10 per cent or so of magnesium, with some other metals, but no copper. Die casting involves the injection of molten material into permanent, separable molds, and is an efficient mass-production technique for making small metal or plastic parts such as are used in carburetors, fuel pumps, adding machines, builders' hardware, lighting fixtures, toys, etc.

Nearly half the total output of zinc is used in protecting the surface of other metals, iron in particular. The reason for its effectiveness for this purpose is made clear in Section 22.16.

Zinc is a relatively active metal, as is apparent from its vigorous action on dilute acids.

$$\underline{Zn} + 2H^+ \rightarrow Zn^{++} + \overline{H_2}$$

The evolution of hydrogen in this reaction depends upon the presence of particles of iron, copper, or carbon which may catalyze the combination of presumably metallic H atoms into H_2 molecules, a property in which zinc is very deficient. Very pure zinc becomes coated with hydrogen and remains in contact with dilute acid without further action. If it is touched with a platinum wire, electrons from the zinc run up the wire and bubbles of H_2 pour from it rapidly while the zinc dissolves. Ordinary commercial zinc can be made to react like pure zinc by amalgamating its surface with mercury. The film of liquid amalgam covers the specks of impurities from which H_2 would otherwise be liberated; the mercury itself is about as lacking in catalytic properties as zinc. The ability of zinc to remain unaffected when in contact with acid makes it possible to use zinc cans for the acid solution in dry cells; at the same time the zinc serves as the source of electrons. The electrons are not removed from the zinc by H^+ ions, but must flow through the external circuit to reach the oxidizing agent, manganese dioxide.

Though less powerful than all the more active metals—except chromium—that we have discussed, zinc is still a fine reducing agent. This can be demonstrated spectacularly by burning zinc turnings in air, or by igniting a mixture of zinc dust and powdered sulfur which burns with a flash and puff to a white cloud of ZnS. This mixture is a relatively safe propellant for experimental rockets. Its reducing power gives zinc innumerable uses in the chemical industry as well as in the laboratory.

Zinc dissolves readily in hot NaOH solution in the same way aluminum does. Their electronegativities are nearly the same.

$$\underline{Zn} + 2OH^- \rightarrow ZnO_2{}^{--} + \overline{H_2}$$

16.23. Properties of Zinc Ions

Zn^{++} ion, with 10 d electrons in its outside layer:

3d					4s	4p			
∙∙	∙∙	∙∙	∙∙	∙∙	—	—	—	—	—

is well able to form covalent bonds. Its coordination number is 4, corresponding to the vacant octet orbitals. In its anhydrous salts, such as $ZnCl_2$ and ZnS, it is covalently bonded to the anions, which do multiple duty as needed to satisfy the coordination number. In water solutions and in most of its salts it is coordinated to four water molecules. Except for the fact that it is a much stronger acid, $Zn(H_2O)_4{}^{++}$ resembles hydrated Mg^{++} ion. It forms $ZnSO_4 \cdot 7H_2O$, isomorphous with Epsom salt, and $K_2Zn(SO_4)_2 \cdot 6H_2O$, isomorphous with schönite. The former is known as white vitriol. In anhydrous NH_3 solution, and even in aqueous solutions containing any considerable amount of NH_3, zinc exists as $Zn(NH_3)_4{}^{++}$, tetramminezinc ion, more commonly called zinc-ammonia ion. High concentrations of Cl^- ion can displace H_2O from

$Zn(H_2O)_4^{++}$ ion a molecule at a time. Eventually chlorozincate ion, $ZnCl_4^{--}$, is produced; this is analogous to zincate ion, $Zn(OH)_4^{--}$, mentioned in Section 16.5.

16.24. Zinc Oxide

Heating $Zn(OH)_2$ converts it into the white insoluble ZnO. This substance is produced commercially by igniting the basic carbonate and by uniting the elements directly. ZnO has a yellow tinge when hot.

ZnO is an important white pigment. When very pure it is known to artists as Chinese white; the commercial variety is called zinc white. Zinc white has a great advantage over the older white lead (basic lead acetate) in that it is not blackened by the H_2S in the air in industrial cities. Being a base, ZnO reacts a little with vegetable acids in the linseed oil in paint, forming a zinc soap which is gradually washed away by rain. This makes the paint self-cleaning, since its surface weathers away, but this shortens its life to some extent. The covering power of ZnO is only fair, so it is frequently reinforced with some of the much more opaque TiO_2. Another manufactured white pigment consists of a mixture of ZnO and $PbSO_4$; this is called leaded zinc oxide.

A considerable amount of ZnO is used as a filler in white rubber goods, in enamels, glazes, and white glass, and in the manufacture of antiseptic zinc oxide ointment and adhesive tape.

16.25. Zinc Chloride

$ZnCl_2$ can be prepared by the direct union of the elements or by the action of HCl on Zn, ZnO, $ZnCO_3$, or $Zn(OH)_2$. We might expect that only ZnO would be formed when a solution of $ZnCl_2$ is heated, as in the case of $MgCl_2$ and $AlCl_3$; however, as the solution becomes concentrated, Cl^- begins to displace H_2O molecules from the $Zn(H_2O)_4^{++}$ ions, as described in Section 16.23, and $ZnCl(H_2O)_3^+$, etc., are formed. This reduces the concentration of free Cl^- ions and prevents the formation of HCl. Water continues to evaporate even after the composition averages $ZnCl_2(H_2O)_2$, until a melt of the anhydrous salt remains. This is cast into sticks. Anhydrous $ZnCl_2$ freezes at 262° C. It is a high-temperature Lewis acid, which accounts for its largest use, as a flux in soldering. When melted, it dissolves the oxide coatings on metals by forming covalent bond complexes with the oxygen in typical Lewis acid fashion. Thus the oxide coating, which would prevent contact between the metal and the solder, is removed from the surface of the metal.

In similar fashion, the $ZnCl_2$ forms covalent bonds with oxygen atoms in cellulose, but since the oxygens are also attached to the carbon atoms of the cellulose molecule the $ZnCl_2$ is held to the cellulose molecule. If the cellulose is in a piece of timber, the cellulose-zinc chloride film thus formed on the outside protects the wood, for zinc is toxic to both plant and animal life. (If present in any considerable concentration, that is. Trace quantities are necessary for citrus fruit trees, and probably for animals as well.) If the cellulose which is treated with $ZnCl_2$ is in finely divided form, as in cotton or wood pulp, it takes up so much of the chloride that it acquires the hydrophilic properties of $ZnCl_2$. The cellulose takes up water and swells to a gelatinous mass which can be molded into various shapes. The $ZnCl_2$ can be washed out, and the cellulose regenerated in a solid and resistant mass called vulcanized fiber.

$ZnCl_2$ is part of the electrolyte in dry cells. Mixed with ZnO it forms a powder which when moistened with water sets quickly to a hard cement consisting of the basic chloride. This is the cement used in filling teeth. A few thousand tons of $ZnCl_2$ are used as a Lewis acid in oil refining. Our total consumption of $ZnCl_2$ in 1960 was about 30,000 tons.

6.26. Other Zinc Compounds

Zinc sulfate, either anhydrous or the heptahydrate (white vitriol), is the salt usually used to furnish Zn^{++} ions in solution. It is prepared by roasting ZnS under the proper conditions or by dissolving zinc dust or zinc scrap of any kind in dilute H_2SO_4. That which is used in the manufacture of the pigment lithopone (Section 15.14) is never separated as such, but is used in the solution in which it was formed. In 1958 only 62,000 tons of the heptahydrate and in addition 500,000 tons of lithopone were manufactured. $ZnSO_4$ is also used in the textile industry as a filler and mordant, in the manufacture of glue and the preservation of animal hides, in electrogalvanizing, and in dilute solution as an antiseptic and astringent.

ZnS is precipitated in alkaline solution in the separation of analytical Group III. It is actually insoluble enough to be precipitated with analytical Group II in the final treatment with H_2S in 0.3 N acid, but in acid solutions the precipitation of ZnS has a period of induction which is longer the greater the acidity. This would prevent any precipitation of ZnS in analytical Group II but for the unfortunate fact that the precipitation of some of the sulfides in this group—e.g., CuS and CdS—brings about some coprecipitation of ZnS.

Zn^{++} is enough like Mg^{++} ion so that it can be precipitated from solution as $ZnNH_4PO_4$. After drying at 105° C., this can be weighed in the gravimetric determination of zinc.

Zinc stearate, a zinc soap, is an ingredient of an antiseptic powder used to alleviate chafing. Zinc dithionite, ZnS_2O_4, is an important reducing agent, sold under the trade name of zinc hydrosulfite.

16.27. Analytical Properties of Al, Cr, and Zn

The fact that aluminum, chromium, and zinc are around 1.5 in electronegativity and are therefore amphoteric puts them into the same subgroup in analytical Group III. The fact that they are in different groups in the periodic table means that they differ enough in other properties to permit their easy separation.

After analytical Group III has been precipitated as a mixture of divalent sulfides and trivalent hydroxides (Table 15.3), this mixture is washed, redissolved in aqua regia, and treated with NaOH and H_2O_2. The members of the nickel subgroup are converted into insoluble hydroxides or higher oxides, but the members of the aluminum subgroup precipitate as hydroxides and immediately redissolve (Table 16.1).

The $Al(OH)_3$ dissolves in the basic solution by virtue of its amphoteric properties.

$$Al(H_2O)_3(OH)_3 + OH^- \rightarrow Al(H_2O)_2(OH)_4^- + H_2O$$

So does the $Zn(OH)_2$.

$$Zn(H_2O)_2(OH)_2 + 2OH^- \rightarrow Zn(OH)_4^{--} + 2H_2O$$

$Cr(OH)_3$ reacts in exactly the same way as $Al(OH)_3$ does, but as soon as it is in solution the $Cr(III)$ is oxidized to $Cr(VI)$.

$$2Cr(H_2O)_3(OH)_3 + 3H_2O_2 + 4OH^- \rightarrow 2CrO_4^{--} + 14H_2O$$

Al(III) and Cr(III) are so similar that they are very difficult to separate. Advantage is taken of the fact that chromium is in Group VIB of the periodic table; hence Cr(VI) has no resemblance at all to Al(III).

When the solution is acidified, then made alkaline with NH_3, $Al(OH)_3$ precipitates, but $Zn(OH)_2$ does not. The reactions with acid are similar.

$$Al(H_2O)_2(OH)_4^- + 4H^+ \rightarrow Al(H_2O)_6^{+3}$$
$$Zn(OH)_4^{--} + 4H^+ \rightarrow Zn(H_2O)_4^{++}$$

The reactions with NH_3 are not similar.

TABLE 16.1. **Analysis of the Aluminum Subgroup of Analytical Group III**

Al^{+3}, Cr^{+3}, Fe^{+3}, Zn^{++}, Mn^{++}, Co^{++}, Ni^{++}

|
OH^-
|

$\underline{Fe(OH)_3, Mn(OH)_2, Ni(OH)_2, Co(OH)_2}$

$Al(OH)_4{}^-$, $Cr(OH)_4{}^-$, $Zn(OH)_4{}^{--}$

|
H_2O_2
|

Nickel subgroup   Aluminum subgroup

$\underline{Fe(OH)_3, Ni(OH)_2, Co(OH)_3, MnO_2}$ $Al(OH)_4{}^-$, $Zn(OH)_4{}^{--}$, $CrO_4{}^{--}$

|
H^+
|

Al^{+3}, Zn^{++}, $Cr_2O_7{}^{--}$

|
NH_3
|

$\underline{Al(OH)_3}$ $CrO_4{}^{--}$, $Zn(NH_3)_4{}^{++}$

| |
HNO_3 $HC_2H_3O_2$

| |
Al^{+3} $Cr_2O_7{}^{--}$, Zn^{++}

| |
NH_3 + aluminon Ba^{++}

‖ |
$\underline{Al(OH)_3}$ $\underline{BaCrO_4}$ Zn^{++}
Red lake   Yellow

$K_4Fe(CN)_6$
‖
$\underline{Zn_3K_2(Fe(CN)_6)_2}$
White

$$Al(H_2O)_6{}^{+3} + 3NH_3 \rightarrow \underline{Al(H_2O)_3(OH)_3} + 3NH_4{}^+$$

$$Zn(H_2O)_4{}^{++} + 4NH_3 \rightarrow Zn(NH_3)_4{}^{++} + 4H_2O$$

The different behavior shown by zinc is due to its superior ability to form covalently bonded complexes that are characteristic of subgroup elements.

The $Al(OH)_3$ is separated from the solution of $Zn(NH_3)_4{}^{++}$ and $CrO_4{}^{--}$, dissolved in acid, and reprecipitated in the presence of aluminon, a dye (aurintricarboxylic acid). The formation of a red lake confirms the presence of aluminum.

ALUMINUM, CHROMIUM, AND ZINC 475

Like practically all other ions of transition elements, those of chromium are colored. The appearance of the yellow color of CrO_4^{--} ion in the filtrate is sufficient to prove the presence of chromium. Another property of Group VI elements in the periodic table can be used for further confirmation. In the maximum valence which is characteristic of such a group, but only in that valence, there is a strong resemblance between main- and sub-group elements. CrO_4^{--} ion, for example, resembles SO_4^{--} ion in forming insoluble salts with the heavier alkaline earth metal ions and with Pb^{++} ion. Even when the concentration is too low to give the solution a pronounced color, the presence of CrO_4^{--} may be confirmed by the yellow precipitate formed when Ba^{++} ion is added.

$$Ba^{++} + CrO_4^{--} \rightarrow \underline{BaCrO_4}$$

After the removal of $BaCrO_4$, the solution may still contain $Zn(NH_3)_4^{++}$ ion. Its presence is detected by the formation of a precipitate when potassium ferrocyanide, $K_4Fe(CN)_6$, is added. Enough acid must be present to neutralize the NH_3 which is released.

$$12H^+ + 3Zn(NH_3)_4^{++} + 2K^+ + 2Fe(CN)_6^{-4} \rightarrow \underline{Zn_3K_2(Fe(CN)_6)_2} + 12NH_4^+$$

Zinc may also be proven present by precipitating it as the white sulfide, ZnS. $(NH_4)_2S$ can be added directly to the ammoniacal solution.

$$Zn(NH_3)_4^{++} + S^{--} \rightarrow \underline{ZnS} + 4NH_3$$

QUESTIONS AND PROBLEMS

1. Which physical factors and characteristics of metallic ions favor their hydration? Compare Al^{+3} and Ba^{++} in these respects.
2. Why do some hydrated cations display pronounced acid properties, whereas others do not? Give examples.
3. What is meant by amphoterism? Illustrate, starting with the Cr^{+3} ion. What favors the amphoteric character of Be^{++} and Zn^{++} ions?
4. Why is $Zn(H_2O)_4^{++}$ a stronger acid than $Al(H_2O)_6^{+3}$?
5. How do the acid character of hydrated cations and hydroxides and the solubility of the latter vary with the electronegativity of the metal? Use 1.5 as a dividing point and make general comparisons of electronegativity values below, at, and above 1.5.

6. Explain why $Si(H_2O)_4^{+4}$ does not exist, whereas $Al(H_2O)_6^{+3}$ does.

7. Using balanced equations, show how bauxite is purified and aluminum produced from it.

8. Explain why aluminum, low in electronegativity, does not react with pure water to produce hydrogen but does react with water containing NaOH to produce H_2.

9. Distinguish between a mordant and a lake.

10. How are the equilibria of hydrated aluminum ion affected in solution by anions which are weak, medium, and strong bases?

11. Distinguish structurally between AlF_6^{-3} ion and $AlCl_4^-$ ion. Why is there no consistency in the formulas of these halo-complex ions?

12. What are some of the important properties of the oxide and hydroxide of aluminum? Name some uses based on these properties.

13. Write the formula and names of several alums. What is the general formula of an alum?

14. Why is the compound, aluminum chloride, not regarded as a salt? Why can anhydrous aluminum chloride be regarded as an acid?

15. Cr^{++} is like Mg^{++}, and Cr^{+3} is like Al^{+3}. Explain why, and generalize from these comparisons.

16. Write the formulas for some typical complex ions of chromium which display different charges. Include some ions with mixed ligands.

17. Compare CrO_4^{--} with SO_4^{--} ion. What other *common* oxyion of chromium exists?

18. Discuss the importance of chromium, especially in the hexavalent state, as a paint pigment.

19. From the standpoint of s, p, and d orbitals, describe the electronic structures of the following: Cr^{+3}; CrO_4^{--}; $Cr(H_2O)_6^{+3}$; $Cr^{+6}O_3$; CrO_7^{--} (triperoxychromate).

20. Describe by stepwise reactions the production of electrolytic zinc from a sulfide ore.

21. Zinc is above hydrogen in the E.C.S. Explain why *pure* zinc, when immersed in HCl, does not replace hydrogen continuously.

22. Illustrate the amphoteric nature of zinc. Give formulas of common ions containing or consisting of zinc and indicate the oxidation number of zinc in each.

23. What is the coordination number of zinc? Illustrate this coordination with suitable formulas.

24. What are some of the important and unique uses of $ZnCl_2$ and ZnO?

25. The following unknowns contain at least one of these ions: Cr^{+3}, Zn^{++}, and Al^{+3}. Decide from the information given whether the ion is present, absent, or doubtful because of insufficient information.
    a. Unknown A. The colorless solution gave no precipitate with NH_4OH.
    b. Unknown B. The green solution when treated with H_2O_2 and NaOH gave no precipitate. When Ba^{++} was added, a yellow precipitate was obtained and removed. The filtrate gave a white gelatinous precipitate after acidification with HCl and addition of NH_4OH.

17

Manganese and iron

17.1. The 3d Transition Metals

The third analytical group consists of metals whose ions are not precipitated by H_2S in acid solution but come down as sulfides or hydroxides when treated with H_2S in ammoniacal solution. In Chapter 16 we discussed the amphoteric subgroup of these metals. The remaining metals in this group—manganese, iron, cobalt, and nickel—will be treated in this and the next chapter. A glance at the periodic table shows that these elements have consecutive atomic numbers following immediately after chromium, and are in the first transition series. Although the valence layer in them contains only s electrons, successive electrons go into d orbitals in the third shell.

	3d	4s	4p
Mn	. . . . .	. .	— — —
Fe	. . . . .	. .	— — —
Co	. . . . .	. .	— — —
Ni	. . . . .	. .	— — —

Before we continue with the description of specific elements some generalizations about this first transition series are in order (see Fig. 17.1). All electron orbitals tend to decrease

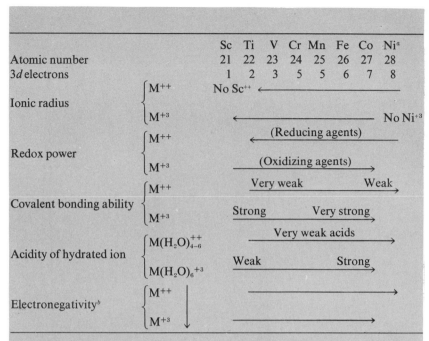

		Sc	Ti	V	Cr	Mn	Fe	Co	Ni[a]
Atomic number		21	22	23	24	25	26	27	28
$3d$ electrons		1	2	3	5	5	6	7	8

Ionic radius
- M^{++} No Sc^{++} ←——————————————
- M^{+3} ←—————————————— No Ni^{+3}

Redox power
- M^{++} ←—— (Reducing agents) ——
- M^{+3} —— (Oxidizing agents) ——→

Covalent bonding ability
- M^{++} Very weak ——— Weak →
- M^{+3} Strong —— Very strong →

Acidity of hydrated ion
- $M(H_2O)_{4-6}^{++}$ Very weak acids ——————→
- $M(H_2O)_6^{+3}$ Weak ——— Strong →

Electronegativity[b]
- M^{++} ——————→
- M^{+3} ——————→

[a] Nickel is the last purely transition metal in this first series. Copper is not a transition metal, since the $3d$ transition is complete; all the $3d$ orbitals are full. However, Cu^{++} contains one half-filled $3d$ orbital and is a typical transition metal ion.

[b] Consult the electronegativity table in the appendix and note that the general trend is an increase as shown with some "level" regions and a minor dip at manganese.

Fig. 17.1. Trends in properties and behavior of 3d transition elements. (Arrows indicate direction of increase.)

in size with increasing atomic number. This tendency is counterbalanced to some extent, as any orbital except s approaches being completely filled, by the repulsion of electrons for each other. These factors account for the shape of the curve for atomic volume in Fig. 17.2. The radii of the atoms in any one period are greatest when a new shell has just been started; they decrease to a minimum near the middle of the period. In the fourth period, the first long period, they are at a minimum when nickel is reached. In the rest of the period the radii of the atoms increase as a result of electron crowding.

The ions of the elements of any given valence change in size in the same way. Thus from scandium to cobalt the trivalent ions decrease in radius from 0.83 A. to 0.55 A., and from titanium to nickel the divalent ions show a similar decrease from 0.85 A. to 0.70 A. All the ions of the

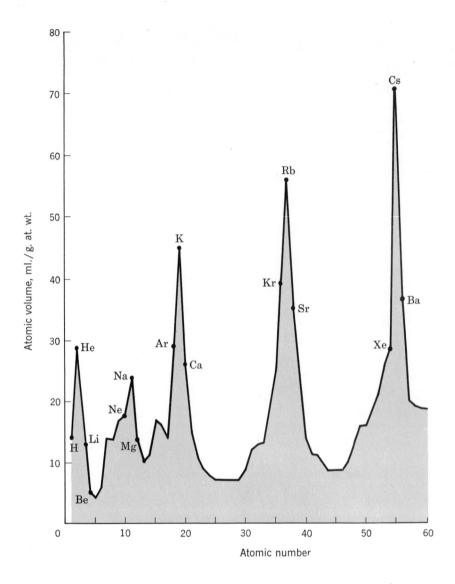

Fig. 17.2. Periodic relationship between atomic number and volume for some of the elements.

divalent series resemble each other in a general way because they have the same valence, and there is a similar resemblance among the trivalent ions. But within each series there is a gradual change in properties because of the decrease in radius and the increase in the number of d electrons, both of which cause an increase in electronegativity. Three properties of special interest which increase with electronegativity are the ability to act as an oxidizing agent, the acidity of the hydrated cation, and the ability to form covalent bonds. Any trivalent ion is to some extent greater in electronegativity than the corresponding divalent ion, not only because of its smaller size, but because of its higher charge. (For a given element, removal of an electron enables the nuclear charge to act with greater effectiveness on the remaining electrons.)

None of the divalent ions is worth mentioning as an oxidizing agent, because they can oxidize only very strong reducing agents. On the contrary, the larger of these ions are good reducing agents. Sc^{++} ion is too good a reducing agent to exist at all, Ti^{++} ion liberates hydrogen from water, and Cr^{++} ion liberates hydrogen from acid solutions in the presence of catalysts. Fe^{++} ion is a mild reducing agent. The acidity of the hydrated cation is weak through Ni^{++}. The ability to form covalent bonds is negligible for the larger divalent ions and does not become important until iron.

The tendency of the simple hydrated cation, $M(H_2O)_6^{+3}$, to act as an oxidizing agent—that is, go to the divalent ion—is zero at the beginning of the series; Sc^{+3} cannot be reduced at all in aqueous solution. But this tendency increases with the atomic number; thus Fe^{+3} oxidizes silver, Co^{+3} liberates oxygen from water, and no simple hydrated Ni^{+3} ion exists. The acidity of the hydrated trivalent cations is marked from the beginning of the series. $Cr(H_2O)_6^{+3}$ is a stronger acid than $HC_2H_3O_2$, and $Fe(H_2O)_6^{+3}$ is almost as strong as H_3PO_4. Similarly, the ability to form covalent bonds becomes noticeable at Cr^{+3} and is highly important from Mn^{+3} on.

The formation of covalent bonds has a striking effect in weakening the oxidizing power of these trivalent ions. This is so because any cation forms bonds by coordination, the ligand furnishing both electrons. Thus each ligand gives some fraction of an electron pair to the central atom, satisfying its electron hunger to that extent. The share of a coordinated electron pair which goes to the central cation depends upon the polarizability of the ligand. F^- ion, the least polarizable of all anions, gives an adjacent trivalent cation so small a share of its electrons that we cannot say that a covalent bond has been formed at all. The oxidizing ability of the cation is thus at its maximum (Fig. 17.3). Oxygen is next to fluorine in electronegativity; hence the polarizability of a water molecule is small. Accordingly the bonds between a cation and its water of hydration are only slightly covalent and the oxidizing ability of the cation is only slightly reduced. In contrast, bonds formed by coordination with cyanide ion, CN^-, may be as much as 50 per cent covalent. A

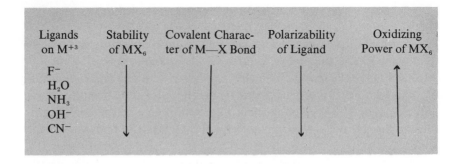

Ligands on M^{+3}	Stability of MX$_6$	Covalent Character of M—X Bond	Polarizability of Ligand	Oxidizing Power of MX$_6$
F$^-$				
H$_2$O				
NH$_3$				
OH$^-$				
CN$^-$				

Fig. 17.3. Properties of a series of complexes MX$_6$ as affected by the nature of the ligand X. (Arrows denote direction of increase.)

100 per cent covalent bond counts as 1 electron for each atom; so each 50 per cent covalent bond would in effect add half an electron to the central cation. Six such bonds would reduce the actual charge on the cation to zero. In such a complex the cation would still have an oxidation number of +3, but its oxidizing power would be very low, even if that of the free cation were high.

17.2. Metallic Manganese

The words manganese, magnesium, and magnet all stem from the same source word, Magnesia, a province in Asia Minor. Here were found magnesia, magnetic oxide of iron, and pyrolusite, an ore of manganese which Pliny (70 A.D.) called magnes, but confused with magnetic oxide of iron. Take a good look at these words so that you will avoid this confusion.

The most important ore of manganese is the black MnO$_2$, the pyrolusite just mentioned. Most of our supply formerly came from Africa and India, for our own deposits are small. At present, however, Mexico and South America are ample sources. A recently discovered deposit is being developed in Canada. Less important ores include psilomelane, (Mn, Ba)O · 2MnO$_2$, lower oxides, MnCO$_3$, MnS, MnS$_2$, and MnSiO$_3$. As its name, rhodonite, indicates, the latter is rose-colored and is used for costume jewelry.

Pure manganese can be obtained from the purified oxide by the Goldschmidt process, but has few uses. It is reddish-white, hard and brittle, and melts at 1260° C. Like chromium and zinc, manganese is an active metal—only slightly less active than aluminum—but unlike those metals it forms no protective coating. It decomposes water slowly, liberating hydrogen.

Even though little pure manganese is used, manganese in the form of alloys is widely used. Manganese ore is regularly smelted in a blast furnace (the blast is now enriched with oxygen to attain the necessary high temperature), along with the amount of iron ore required to produce either of two alloys. The first of these alloys is spiegeleisen (mirror-iron), so called because of the flat shiny crystals which characterize it. It contains 20 to 32 per cent manganese and some carbon, and is added as a deoxidizer to practically all the steel that is made, at the rate of 15 lb. or so per ton. None of it remains in the finished steel; all of it goes into the slag as oxide. The second alloy, ferromanganese, is about 80 per cent manganese and is used in producing manganese steels. Manganese steel containing 12 per cent manganese can be hot-formed by the usual methods, but once cold it work-hardens to a remarkable extent while still remaining extremely tough. The work done by a safecracker's drill on a layer of manganese steel hardens it almost immediately to such a degree that the drill can penetrate no further. Manganese steel switch points, hardened by the pounding of car wheels, outlast several times those made of plain steel. The material is ideal for the jaws of rock crushers.

Manganese bronze, Mn-Cu-Sn-Zn, resists corrosion from sea water and hence is used for propeller blades. Manganin wire, Mn-Cu-Ni, is used for accurate electrical measurements because its electrical conductivity changes little with temperature.

17.3. Manganese(II) (Manganous) Ion

The most stable valence state of manganese is $+2$. Mn^{++} (probably tetrahydrate) is pale pink and shows the expected chemical resemblance to Mg^{++}; it forms a vitriol, $MnSO_4 \cdot 7H_2O$ (though the tetrahydrate is more common), a double sulfate, $K_2Mn(SO_4)_2 \cdot 6H_2O$, and insoluble $Mn(OH)_2$, $MnNH_4PO_4$, and $MnCO_3$. It is the first of the common metal ions considered which has the ability to form a stable insoluble sulfide. Flesh-colored MnS is precipitated in the separation of analytical Group III. It dissolves readily in dilute acids, even acetic, and can be separated from ZnS in this way. $Mn(H_2O)_6^{++}$ is very slightly acid, and $Mn(OH)_2$ is not amphoteric. In acid or neutral solution Mn^{++} can be oxidized only by very strong oxidizing agents such as chlorine (to $MnCl_4^-$) or PbO_2 (to MnO_4^-), but white $Mn(OH)_2$ is rapidly oxidized by atmospheric oxygen to brown $MnO(OH)$.

$$4Mn(OH)_2 + \overline{O_2} \rightarrow 4MnO(OH) + 2H_2O$$

Complex ions of Mn(II), such as $MnCl_4^{--}$ and $Mn(CN)_6^{-4}$, are of little importance.

17.4. Manganese(III) (Manganic) Ion

Almost all the properties of Mn^{+3} ion could be predicted from those of Cr^{+3} ion by applying the principles set forth in Section 17.1. Mn^{+3} is appreciably acidic, hydrolyzing to the amphoteric $Mn(OH)_3$. It forms alums, of which the red $CsMn(SO_4)_2 \cdot 12H_2O$ is the most stable. With Mn^{++} ion it forms the brownish-red spinel Mn_2MnO_4, a manganese ore called hausmannite. (The formula is usually written Mn_3O_4.) The sulfate changes from violet to dark green on dehydration, indicating the formation of a sulfato- complex.

Although such predictions can be relied upon in general, they always need to be checked in the laboratory for the *degree* of change from one element to the next, and for individual peculiarities which the science of chemistry is as yet unable to predict. Actual investigation of Mn^{+3} shows that it is a very strong oxidizing agent. Anhydrous MnF_3 actually liberates fluorine on heating.

$$2MnF_3 \xrightarrow{\Delta} 2MnF_2 + \overline{F_2}$$

$MnCl_3$ is stable only below $-35°$ C. Complex formation (covalent bonding) lowers the oxidizing power, as was explained in Section 17.1. Thus $MnCl_4^-$ is stable in HCl solution almost up to room temperature. Nearly all manganic compounds are covalent. An unpredictable item is the readiness with which the hydroxide dehydrates to $MnO(OH)$. When this dark brown material occurs as a manganese ore it is known as manganite. The black oxide, Mn_2O_3, also occurs naturally as braunite.

17.5. Manganese(IV)

The most important manganese compound is the black dioxide, MnO_2. The name pyrolusite (Gr., *pyr*, fire, + *louein*, to wash) is based on its use in decolorizing normally green ordinary window glass; this color is due to the Fe^{++} ion present as an impurity in the sand from which it is made. The MnO_2 oxidizes this to Fe^{+3}; its pale yellow color is complementary to the purple tinge imparted by the Mn(IV). (If too much MnO_2 is used, the glass will be violet.) As might be expected, Mn(IV) is too acidic to exist as a simple hydrated ion, except perhaps in fairly concentrated H_2SO_4 or an equally acid $HClO_4$ solution. No hydroxide, $Mn(OH)_4$, is known; under treatment which should produce it, Mn(IV) reverts to the dioxide. MnO_2 is weakly acidic, reacting with strong bases to produce manganites such as $CaMnO_3$ and $CaMn_2O_5$. It is a strong oxidizing agent in the presence of H^+ ion, readily oxidizing Cl^- ion to Cl_2. The manganese is reduced to Mn^{++}. This is a minor laboratory use; the largest use of MnO_2 is as an oxidizing agent in dry cells, amounting to about 15,000 tons annually.

The nonexistence of $Mn(OH)_4$, mentioned above, is not an accident, but part of a larger pattern. The more electronegative an element is, the more its hydroxide tends to dehydrate. Thus the hydroxides of the alkali metals, except lithium, and of barium, can be fused without decomposition; $Li(OH)$, $Sr(OH)_2$, and $Ca(OH)_2$ decompose to the oxide at dull red heat, and $Mg(OH)_2$ does so at $100°$ C. Similarly $Al(OH)_3$ loses water on drying at room temperature and Mn(III) precipitates initially as the partially dehydrated $MnO(OH)$. The decomposition of HCO_3^- on heating:

$$2HOCO_2^- \rightarrow H_2O + \overline{CO_2} + CO_3^{--}$$

and the condensation of $H_2PO_4^-$, HSO_4^-, and $HCrO_4^-$ to the corresponding di- acids are manifestations of the same tendency, because in each case two OH groups on different atoms react, with loss of water. This is also true of the ready dehydration of hydroxyacids into their anhydrides. In all these cases some other atom has displaced a proton from a covalent bond with oxygen. This is why dehydration proceeds more readily the greater the electronegativity—and therefore the covalent bond-forming ability—of the displacing atom. All the discussion in this paragraph applies equally to the thermal decomposition of any salt into a metal oxide and a volatile non-metal oxide.

$$\underline{MCO_3} \rightarrow \underline{MO} + \overline{CO_2}$$
$$\underline{M(NO_3)_2} \rightarrow \underline{MO} + N_2O_5$$
$$\quad\quad\quad \overset{\llcorner}{\rightarrow} \overline{2NO_2} + \tfrac{1}{2}O_2$$
$$\underline{MSO_4} \rightarrow \underline{MO} + \overline{SO_3}$$

17.6. Higher Valences of Manganese

Manganese also exhibits oxidation numbers of $+6$ and $+7$.

Mn(VI), MnO₄⁻⁻ ⋮— — — — — [   ] manganate ion, dark green

Mn(VII), MnO₄⁻ — — — — — [   ] permanganate ion, intense purple

When MnO_2 is fused with NaOH, with air having free access or, better, with $NaClO_3$ present, MnO_4^{--} ion is produced.

$$\underline{3MnO_2} + 6Na^+ + 6OH^- + Na^+ + ClO_3^- \rightarrow 7Na^+ + 3MnO_4^{--} + Cl^- + \overline{3H_2O}$$

MnO_4^{--} resembles SO_4^{--} as strongly as Mn^{++} does Mg^{++}, and for the same reasons, i.e., similarity of size, shape, and charge. Thus anhydrous K_2SO_4 and K_2MnO_4 are isomorphous; so are the decahydrates. However, MnO_4^{--} cannot replace SO_4^{--} in alums because the $M^{III}(H_2O)_6^{+3}$ of alums is an acid, and MnO_4^{--} is stable only in strongly basic solution. If the fused manganate mixture is dissolved in too much water, thereby lowering the OH^- ion concentration, the MnO_4^{--} begins to dismute.

$$3MnO_4^{--} + 2H_2O \rightleftharpoons 2MnO_4^- + \underline{MnO_2} + 4OH^-$$

The reaction goes to completion if the OH^- concentration is lowered further by the addition of even so weak an acid as carbonic acid.

$$3MnO_4^{--} + 2H_2O + \overline{4CO_2} \rightarrow 2MnO_4^- + \underline{MnO_2} + 4HCO_3^-$$

MnO_4^{--} can also be oxidized completely to MnO_4^- by ozone or electrolytically. In nitric acid solution Mn^{++} can be oxidized directly to MnO_4^- by sodium bismuthate.

$$2Mn^{++} + \underline{5NaBiO_3} + 14H^+ \rightarrow 2MnO_4^- + 5Na^+ + 5Bi^{+3} + 7H_2O$$

This reaction is used as a confirmatory test for manganese in qualitative analysis. The permanganate color is so intense that even a trace of the permanganate colors the solution pink.

MnO_4^- ion strongly resembles ClO_4^- ion; their corresponding salts are isomorphous, both are weaker bases than water, both yield volatile explosive heptoxides such as Mn_2O_7 on treatment with concentrated H_2SO_4. As in the case of chromium and sulfur, this strong resemblance between main- and sub-group elements is evident only when both display the maximum valence characteristic of that group of the periodic table. MnO_4^- ion is an even stronger oxidizing agent than ClO_4^-. More than 1000 tons of various permanganates—Na, K, Ca, Zn—are used each year in the United States as an oxidizing agent in the chemical industry, dyeing, etc. Both color and power make MnO_4^- ion a favorite reagent in **oxidimetry,** the volumetric determination of a substance by means of a redox reaction. MnO_4^- serves as its own indicator, the color of a single excess drop of 0.1 N solution being visible in 100 ml. of solution after the last of the reducing agent has been oxidized. The half-reaction in acid solution is:

$$5e^- + MnO_4^- + 8H^+ \rightarrow Mn^{++} + 4H_2O$$

whereas in neutral or alkaline solution the half-reaction is:

$$3e^- + MnO_4^- + 2H_2O \rightarrow \underline{MnO_2} + 4OH^-$$

These important equations show that MnO_4^- is a much weaker oxidizing agent in neutral or alkaline solutions.

Traces of manganese compounds are essential for plant growth and in some localities are added to fertilizers. Manganous borate, $Mn(H_2BO_3)_2$, is used as a drier for linseed oil in paints and varnishes. The drying results from oxidation by atmospheric oxygen, which the manganese promotes catalytically by the intermediate formation of higher oxides. MnO_2 is mixed with Fe_2O_3 to give pottery a dark brown glaze.

17.7. Occurrence of Iron

Although the earth's core is believed to be nine-tenths iron, the only metallic iron on the surface is that found in scattered meteorites, 146 million of which are estimated to fall to the earth each year. For a long time iron was more valuable than gold; it was scarcer and much more useful. Meteoritic iron beads were used in Egypt for jewelry before 3400 B.C., but separating the metal from its ore seems to have been achieved by the Hindus about 2000 B.C. The Bible relates how the Philistines maintained a monopoly on the smithy's art. Iron was still rare during the Trojan War; according to Homer, a lump of iron was the prize given to Achilles. In Roman days a man who produced eight pounds of iron in a day's hard work was considered a genius. The chemical symbol for iron, Fe, is derived from its Latin name, *ferrum.*

Only oxygen, silicon, and aluminum are more abundant than iron. Nearly all the colors exhibited by rocks and the soil on any large scale are due to iron. Thus Fe(II) imparts a blue color; Fe(III), red, yellow, and green; a mixture of the two, black. Hemoglobin, the pigment that gives the oxygen-carrying red corpuscles of the blood their color, is an iron compound. Iron is equally essential for plants.

Iron ore is found on every continent and in almost every country. It has been found in all of the United States and is mined in 28 of them. The largest deposits of iron ore are all biological in origin, having been deposited in lake bottoms by microorganisms which concentrated it from the water. These ores include Fe_2O_3, called hematite because of its color; limonite, $Fe_2O_3 \cdot 1\frac{1}{2}H_2O$; and other partially hydrated, geologically younger ferric oxides called bog iron ore. The high-grade hematite ore of the fabulous Lake Superior iron mines, some 2 billion tons of which were used in building the United States and fighting two world wars, is nearing exhaustion. The tremendous new mines that have been developed since World War II in Canada and Venezuela contain hematite. Brown limonite is found in the states along the southern Appalachian Mountains and in Missouri. Sweden and northern Germany are important sources of bog iron ore. The richest iron ore—72.5 per cent Fe—is magnetite, the spinel, Fe_2FeO_4. This mineral gave its name to the magnet, not vice versa. The first magnets known were specimens of Fe_3O_4. (Loadstone, the English name for magnetite, comes from an old form of the verb to lead, and is based on this property—it "leads" iron to itself.) Widely distributed deposits of magnetite in New York, New Jersey, and Pennsylvania furnished much of the iron needed during the Revolutionary and Civil Wars. The iron mines in Utah also contain it. Siderite, $FeCO_3$, is of some importance in England. Strictly speaking, iron pyrites, FeS_2, is not an iron ore. However, when this sulfide is roasted to produce SO_2 for the manufacture of H_2SO_4, there is also an end product of oxides which are smelted for iron. In 1960, 900,000 tons of by-product iron oxides were produced.

Although, as was said earlier, the deposits of high-grade hematite are running low, the Lake Superior mines are actually far from being exhausted. Impure hematite—perhaps five times the quantity of the high-grade ore already mined—still remains, and this can be concentrated by processes now available. In addition, there are some 50 billion tons of taconite, a very hard mineral that runs about 25 per cent iron. Methods of mining and concentrating it were developed during the 1950's by venturous steel companies at a cost of many millions. Whether the process will repay the huge sums invested in it remains to be seen.

17.8. The Blast Furnace

For many centuries little progress was made in working with iron ores because it was impossible to develop sufficient heat to melt the iron. The

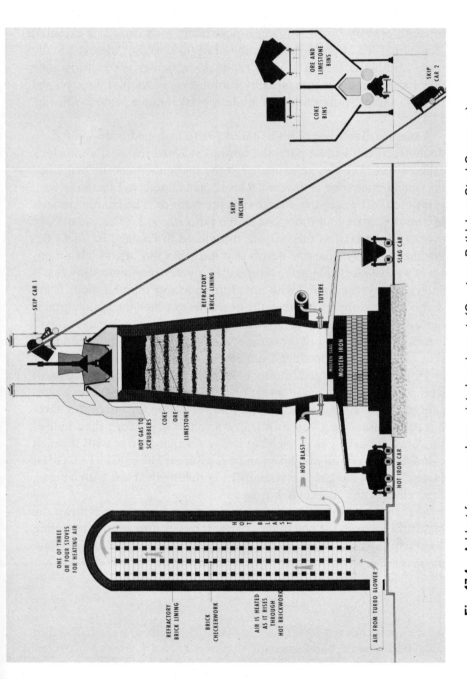

Fig. 17.4. A blast furnace and associated equipment. (Courtesy, Bethlehem Steel Company.)

ore was reduced in a charcoal furnace to a stiff mass which was then shaped by long and repeated heatings and hammerings. Modern technology dates from the invention of the blast furnace in Germany in the fifteenth century, for this made it possible to melt iron. The essential idea is that *hot* air is blown into the blast furnace, but almost equally important is the fact that when the materials enter the melting zone they have already been heated by combustion gases that have passed through them. A diagram of a modern blast furnace is shown in Fig. 17.4.

A blast furnace ranges from 100 to 237 ft. high and is up to 30 ft. in diameter at the widest part, the boshes. It is fed through an air lock called a bell. The charge is loaded at the top and enters the bell when the small upper cone is lowered. This is then closed, and the large cone is lowered, dropping the charge into the furnace. The charge consists of iron ore, coke, and limestone in the ratio 10 : 5 : 3. (The use of coke instead of charcoal as the fuel was introduced in England in 1709.) Below the boshes is a narrow hearth that has holes through which a number of water-jacketed blowing pipes called tuyeres (pronounced "tweers") enter; the tuyeres are fed with hot air from a large annular pipe. There is also a clay-stoppered hole in the hearth from which the molten iron is tapped periodically. A slag notch above this permits the slag to drain off constantly. Operation of the furnace is continuous. Depending on their size, blast furnaces produce from 800 to 1700 tons of iron a day. For every ton of ore charged into it, 1100 lb. of molten iron and 800 lb. of slag are tapped out. Large quantities of slag are sold for use as aggregate in concrete; slag is also blown into rock wool for insulation. Over 3 tons of gases are given off for every ton of ore. More than half of this blast furnace gas is useless nitrogen which carries with it much valuable heat, not all of which can be recovered. The capacity of a blast furnace can be increased materially by enriching the blast with oxygen, thus reducing the volume of nitrogen.

The temperature of the charge increases steadily as it goes down the blast furnace from the bell to the hearth. It passes through the ascending combustion gases, in which all the oxygen has been burned to carbon monoxide.

$$2C + \overline{O_2} \rightarrow \overline{2CO} + \triangle$$

As it approaches red heat (500° to 800° C.), the iron ore is reduced to spongy iron by carbon monoxide.

$$Fe_2O_3 + \overline{3CO} \rightleftharpoons 2Fe + \overline{3CO_2}$$

This reaction is reversible; the partial pressure of CO must be kept twice that of CO_2. Between 700° and 800° C. the limestone is decomposed and some of the CO_2 is reduced to CO by the hot coke.

$$CaCO_3 \rightleftharpoons CaO + \overline{CO_2}$$
$$\underline{C} + \overline{CO_2} \rightleftharpoons \overline{2CO}$$

Any sulfur in the coke goes into the spongy iron, in which FeS is soluble.

$$\underline{Fe} + \overline{SO_2} + \underline{2C} \rightarrow FeS + \overline{2CO}$$

Between 1000° and 1200° C. the reduction of the iron is completed by carbon. The manganese that is usually present is reduced in a similar reaction.

$$\underline{Mn_2O_3} + \underline{3C} \rightarrow 2Mn + \overline{3CO}$$

Any phosphates in the ore are also reduced, the phosphorus being absorbed by the iron. Above 1200° C. the iron becomes saturated with carbon; and some of the silicon that is produced by the reduction of a small part of the gangue, a sandy impurity in the ore, is also dissolved.

$$\underline{SiO_2} + \underline{2C} \rightarrow Si + \overline{2CO}$$

Liquid slag is formed below the boshes.

$$\underline{SiO_2} + \underline{CaO} \rightarrow CaSiO_3$$

The impure iron melts and forms a second, heavier, layer of liquid on the hearth. This iron contains 3.5 to 4.5 per cent carbon and nearly as much of all the other impurities mentioned above. It may be tapped into sand molds and made into pigs for later remelting, or poured into giant ladles and carried in liquid form to the steel furnaces. In either case it is called pig iron, the name now describing the composition rather than the physical state.

Two-thirds of the carbon in the coke that goes into the furnace comes out as CO, a combustible gas. Unless the air for the blast has been dried, the blast furnace gas will also contain up to 4 per cent of H_2 and CH_4, also combustible. This fuel, together with sufficient air for combustion, is burned in three or four enormous stoves (Fig. 17.4), each 100 ft. high, to preheat air for the blast to 600° C. The stoves are iron cylinders lined with firebrick and packed with brick checkerwork. The burning gas passes through the interstices of the checkerwork of one stove until the bricks are red-hot. The gas is then switched to another stove, and the air blast to the tuyeres is sent through the first stove until the topmost bricks begin to cool. Thus the stoves are used in turn as absorbers and emitters of heat.

17.9. Cast Iron

Iron foundries purchase pig iron, remelt it in small cupola furnaces, and pour the molten metal into molds to make castings. Manhole covers for sewers, frames for machines, and many parts of machinery are made of cast iron. The cupola furnace, which looks somewhat like a blast furnace, is lined with clay and has a spout at the bottom. These furnaces hold from one to several tons of iron. Coke is dropped in from the top, and then pig iron, scrap iron, and limestone are put in on top of the coke. The coke is ignited and a blast of air is forced up through it. The iron soon melts and falls to the bottom of the furnace. It is tapped into ladles and poured into molds.

There are two major types of cast iron, white and gray. The white is harder, the gray more brittle. They also differ because in white cast iron the carbon is entirely in the form of iron carbide, called cementite, Fe_3C, whereas in gray cast iron most of the carbon is present as thin curved plates or flakes of graphite. This accounts for the weakening of the structure that makes it extremely brittle. Furthermore, the free carbon gives this iron a dark gray color, in contrast to the silvery gray of white cast iron. Alloying ingredients and casting and cooling procedures are decisive as to which of these types is produced. A casting made of white cast iron can be converted into a malleable iron casting by special high-temperature heat treatment. During this treatment, which may require from hours to several days, some or all of the iron carbide in the white cast-iron casting decomposes into iron and graphite. The graphite is in the shape of spheroids instead of the thin platelets usual in gray cast iron. As a consequence the casting is strong, malleable, and non-brittle. Malleable iron contains about 3 per cent carbon and from 1 to 1.5 per cent silicon. It is used in the automobile industry in wheel hubs, clutch and brake pedals, and rear-axle carriers. Because it is cheaper than steel, it is also used in farm machinery.

17.10. Wrought Iron

A tough form of iron is made by purifying melted pig iron in puddling furnaces. These are small reverberatory furnaces so constructed that heat is reflected down on the pig iron which rests on a bed of iron oxide. As the iron melts, carbon and other impurities react with the oxygen of the iron oxide, and these substances are burned out; the melting point of the iron rises from about 1100° to 1500° C. and the metal becomes plastic. A man called a puddler stirs the iron with a long "rabble." The molten metal is removed from the furnace in balls weighing about as much as a man can lift, and these are hammered or rolled to squeeze out most of the slag. The remaining trace of slag, distributed in the form of a thin coating around fibers of iron, is thought to be responsible for the superior resistance to corrosion exhibited by wrought iron. Where this property is not required, wrought iron is being replaced by low-carbon steel, whose manufacture is much less time-consuming. In order to retain the corrosion resistance of wrought iron prepared by the traditional process and at the same time avoid much of the costly hand labor, the Byers Company pours a fairly pure iron into a premelted slag. The iron is then gathered in much larger masses than can be rabbled and lifted by hand, and the excess slag is hammered or rolled out.

Wrought iron is tough and fibrous. It welds readily; i.e., two pieces that are heated to redness unite when hammered. Its softness is not altered by heating to redness and quenching in water, although this procedure hardens steel.

17.11. Steel

Steel is iron that contains no less than 0.10 per cent carbon (very mild steel) or more than about 1.7 per cent (very hard steel), the carbon and iron being present in the combined form, Fe_3C, or cementite. The impurities of the pig iron are largely removed, but in alloy steels other elements are added. Pig iron is converted into steel by means of Bessemer converters, open-hearth furnaces, and electric furnaces. The steel from any of these furnaces can be further modified into alloy steels by the addition of other metals.

The furnace which is now called the Bessemer converter was designed independently by William Kelly of Kentucky in 1847 and Sir Henry Bessemer of England; the latter patented the process in 1855. Kelly noticed that when air came in contact with pig iron, the metal seethed and boiled, instead of being cooled. He reasoned that the air oxidized the impurities from the metal, and that the reaction was exothermic, the heat thus produced making the metal boil. It occurred to him that the impurities could be removed if air were blown through molten pig iron. Bessemer had the same idea, and a special furnace called a Bessemer converter was developed (Fig. 17.5).

A Bessemer converter is charged with from 12 to 30 tons of molten pig iron at a temperature of about 1200° C., and a blast of air is forced up through the metal. Pig iron contains about 70 lb. of carbon, 20 lb. of silicon, 15 lb. of manganese, and 1 or 2 lb. of sulfur per ton. (Phosphorus-free iron must be used, because this process does not remove phosphorus.) Silicon and manganese burn first and their oxides pass

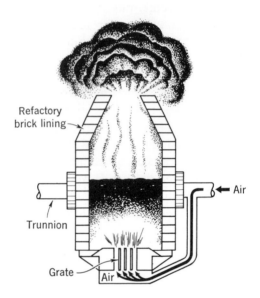

Refactory brick lining

Trunnion

Grate

Air

Air

Fig. 17.5. The Bessemer converter. Excess carbon is burned from the steel by reaction with air. (Courtesy, Bethlehem Steel Company.)

into the slag as $MnSiO_3$; then the carbon is oxidized to CO which burns at the mouth of the converter with an orange-yellow flame edged with blue and shot through with showers of sparks. After 10 to 15 minutes the flame sinks, indicating that all the carbon has been removed. Sufficient heat has been liberated to raise the temperature to about 1900° C., so the iron is still liquid. Enough spiegeleisen (Section 17.2) is added to reduce any FeO that has been formed and to give the desired carbon content. The converter is rotated on its trunnions and emptied into ladles supported by traveling cranes, from which it is poured into molds. At this stage a little aluminum, ferrosilicon, titanium-iron alloy, or other active metal may be added to combine with nitrogen or CO, thus preventing blowholes in the castings. Once the most important method of making steel, the Bessemer process now accounts for only about 2 per cent of our output.

In the Siemens-Martin open-hearth process, a reverberatory or top-heated furnace is used (Fig. 17.6). The fuel and air are supplied through separate regenerators, the direction of flow being reversed three or four times an hour. The saucer-shaped hearth holds as much as 250 tons of steel and is lined with calcined dolomite. This lining must be basic to re-

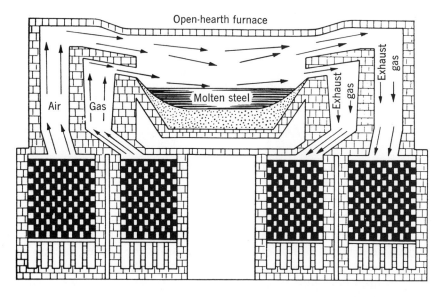

Fig. 17.6. An open-hearth furnace. (Courtesy, General Motors Corporation.)

sist attack by the basic slag used in purifying the charge. The charge consists of pig iron and scrap iron or steel in equal amounts, together with hematite and limestone, and 4 or 5 lb. of CaF_2 per ton of iron, as a flux. (This small amount of CaF_2 consumes half the fluorspar we mine.) The hematite serves as the oxidizing agent and burns out the impurities, just as the Bessemer air blast does. Phosphorus, if present, is oxidized to P_2O_5, which is not volatile at the temperature attained but reacts with the CaO in the slag, forming $Ca(PO_3)_2$, P_2O_5 is also produced in the Bessemer process, but does not react with the acid slag (excess SiO_2); when the air blast stops, the P_2O_5 is reduced again to Fe_2P. This material is soluble in iron and makes the steel brittle at ordinary temperatures; such steel is said to be cold-short. FeS dissolved in steel makes it brittle at red

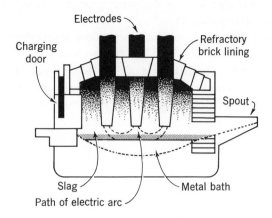

Fig. 17.7. The electric arc furnace used in the production of high-alloy steel. (Courtesy, Bethlehem Steel Company.)

heat, or red-short. Basic slag from the refining of high-phosphorus pig iron is used as a phosphate fertilizer.

From 8 to 12 hours is necessary to refine one "heat" of steel. Toward the end of the refining process the heat may be held constant while samples are analyzed. (This is impossible in the Bessemer process, because there is no external source of heat; the steel must be poured as soon as the impurities have burned out, or it will freeze.) Further analyses may be made after the addition of the spiegeleisen and alloying elements, and the composition corrected if necessary. Because of the better control the process makes possible, open-hearth furnaces now produce 90 per cent of our steel.

Expensive, high-alloy special steels are made in refractory crucibles in an electric furnace. The heat is furnished by an electric arc struck between large vertical carbon electrodes in each crucible. Fig. 17.7 shows that the path of the arc is of such a nature that the surface of the steel is bathed by it. The combination of arc heating and relatively small charge makes possible the accurate temperature and composition control demanded for the production of high-grade alloy steels.

The year 1957 was a record year in steel production, when 113 million tons of all grades were produced in the United States. In contrast, production in 1958 dropped sharply to 85 million tons, or 61 per cent of our potential capacity. In 1960 annual steel production approached 100 million tons.

17.12. Properties of Steel

Any degree of hardness between that of wrought iron, which is very soft, and that of steel files, which are harder than glass, can be obtained in steels by governing the distribution of the Fe_3C in the steel. Fe_3C is soluble in solid steel above 910° C., but insoluble below that temperature; the crystal structure of iron is altered at 910° C. If the steel is cooled slowly, the Fe_3C separates into microscopically fine layers interleaved with layers of iron. The structure, which looks very much like a fingerprint, is called pearlite; pearlite is responsible for the toughness of steel. The quantity of pearlite increases as the carbon content increases. Steel that is 0.83 per cent carbon is 100 per cent pearlitic. If steel has less than this amount of carbon, it consists of a mixture of pearlite and iron; if it has more than this amount, it consists of a mixture of Fe_3C and pearlite. The latter is used for plain carbon-steel tools. If steel is heated above 910° C. and quickly cooled, or quenched, the Fe_3C is dispersed in other forms than pearlite. The various structures obtainable by varying the rate of cooling all are harder than the slow-cooled pearlitic structure. Tempering is a low-temperature heating that follows quenching; it further modifies the structure, hardness, and toughness of the steel. Alloying metals have a twofold effect upon steel. Some affect its properties directly, making it harder, tougher, more resistant to corrosion, less subject to failure from repeated bending, etc. Furthermore, many of them decrease the rate at which high-temperature carbon-dissolving iron assumes the ordinary form in which carbon is nearly insoluble; hence slow cooling may have the same effect on an alloy steel that quenching does on a plain carbon steel. Thus a cutting tool of the proper composition may be used on a lathe operating at such high speed that the tool gets red-hot, but its temper will not be affected.

17.13. Surface Treatment of Steel

Very hard steel is always relatively brittle. If the steel must withstand impact as well as abrasion, it must be **casehardened.** That is, the surface is hardened to a slight depth, the main body of the metal remaining comparatively soft and tough. In the **cementation process** parts made of wrought iron or low-carbon steel are packed in a mixture of carbon and $BaCO_3$ and heated to about 920° C.; they are kept at this temperature until sufficient carbon has dissolved in the surface and diffused to the desired depth. The $BaCO_3$ is an accelerator for the process because it decomposes and forms CO_2, which in turn is reduced by the carbon to CO.

$$\underline{BaCO_3} \xrightarrow{\Delta} \underline{BaO} + \overline{CO_2}$$

$$\overline{CO_2} + \underline{C} \xrightarrow{\Delta} \overline{2CO}$$

CO is an active carburizing—that is, a carbon-giving—agent. It diffuses to every part of the surface of the iron which is not in contact with carbon particles and reacts with it; the reaction is the reverse of the blast furnace reaction.

$$\underline{Fe} + \overline{CO} \rightarrow \underline{FeO} + C \text{ (dissolved in the iron)}$$

In another method of casehardening, the part is heated in a fused salt bath containing cyanide ion, CN^-. This decomposes slowly when in contact with the iron, yielding carbon which dissolves in the iron.

The very hard surface required for automobile cylinders is produced by **nitriding** steel that contains 1 per cent or more of one of the alloying agents—Al, Cr, Mo, V, W, Mn, or Ti. The steel is heated at 450° to 500° C. in an atmosphere of NH_3. The hard crystals of Fe_2N that form at the boundaries of the iron crystals keep them from gliding under stress.

17.14. Properties of Pure Iron

Iron is one of the more difficult metals to purify. In fact, not a single ounce of really pure iron had ever been prepared before World War II, when half a ton of it was prepared as a special war project. The purest commercial iron (Armco) contains about 0.1 per cent of impurities; iron prepared electrolytically for research purposes, 0.03 per cent. Iron prepared by thermal decomposition of iron carbonyl, $Fe(CO)_5$, is relatively pure except for traces of carbon and oxygen. Fusing in an induction furnace with the requisite amount of pure Fe_2O_3 will reduce the carbon below 0.0007 per cent and the oxygen below 0.01 per cent. The density of this pure iron is 7.87. It melts at 1535° C. (1125° C. for pig iron) and boils at around 3000° C. The allotropic modification of iron that is stable at room temperature is called alpha iron. It belongs to the body-centered cubic crystal system. It is easily magnetized, but demagnetizes completely when the external magnetic field is removed. In contrast, hard steel is difficult to magnetize and remains magnetized more or less permanently. Alpha iron loses its magnetic properties at about 760° C. Although it was at first thought to undergo a structural modification to beta iron at this temperature, it is now known that the crystal structure remains unchanged up to 910° C. The high-temperature modification is called gamma iron, and is face-centered cubic. It is non-magnetic. At 1400° C. there is another transformation, to delta iron; this is body-centered cubic and is frequently called high-temperature alpha iron.

Iron is the least active of the metals studied up to this point, but is more active than hydrogen. At red heat it decomposes water in the equilibrium reaction:

$$3\overline{\text{Fe}} + \overline{4\text{H}_2\text{O}} \rightleftharpoons \overline{\text{Fe}_3\text{O}_4} + \overline{4\text{H}_2}$$

Although not attacked by either air or water at room temperature, iron rusts rapidly when exposed to their combined action.

$$\overline{4\text{Fe}} + \overline{3\text{O}_2} + 6\text{H}_2\text{O} \rightarrow \overline{4\text{Fe}(\text{OH})_3}$$

If heated in oxygen, finely divided iron burns with a shower of bright sparks, forming Fe_2O_3. A piece of iron heated in air becomes coated with Fe_3O_4. Quantities of this oxide are produced when white-hot steel billets are rolled into rails, rods, or beams; it is called mill scale. The blued steel finish of gun barrels is Fe_3O_4. Iron dissolves readily in dilute acids, with the evolution of hydrogen and the formation of ferrous ions.

$$\overline{\text{Fe}} + 2\text{H}^+ + \text{SO}_4^{--} \rightarrow \text{Fe}^{++} + \text{SO}_4^{--} + \overline{\text{H}_2}$$

If iron is placed in a concentrated solution of a strong oxidizing agent such as fuming HNO_3, CrO_3, $HClO_3$, or H_2O_2, it becomes *passive,* owing to the formation of an impervious oxide film like that which protects aluminum or chromium. Passive iron does not affect dilute acids, but it loses its passivity immediately if touched with a piece of ordinary iron or struck sharply when in the acid.

7.15. Iron(II) (Ferrous) Ion

Anhydrous ferrous salts are generally white, but the hydrated Fe^{++} ion is pale green. Depending upon circumstances, it apparently can hold four or six molecules of water. For example, it forms the expected Epsom-salt type of heptahydrate (green vitriol, or copperas), but if seeded with $CuSO_4 \cdot 5H_2O$ it produces crystals of the pentahydrate. In both $FeSO_4 \cdot 7H_2O$ and $FeSO_4 \cdot 5H_2O$, one molecule of water is hydrogen-bonded to the SO_4^{--} ion. Fe^{++} is a weak acid and its hydroxide is appreciably soluble only in concentrated NaOH solution. Also as expected, it forms the schönite type of double sulfate. One of these, Mohr's salt, $(NH_4)_2Fe(SO_4)_2 \cdot 6H_2O$, is preferred to $FeSO_4 \cdot 7H_2O$ in the laboratory because it can be weighed in the open without loss of weight, whereas the vitriol is efflorescent. Mohr's salt has the further advantage that its solutions are not as rapidly oxidized by air as are those of simple ferrous sulfate. This is so because of the formation of a complex sulfato-ion. In ferrous sulfate considerable numbers of sulfate ions displace water molecules from the hydrated ferrous ion; the higher concentration of SO_4^{--} ions in Mohr's salt sends this process much further toward completion. Like the other $M^{II}NH_4PO_4$'s, $FeNH_4PO_4$ is insoluble.

Any solution of a ferrous salt, unless made in oxygen-free water and kept in an oxygen-free atmosphere, contains some Fe^{+3} ion. This is definitely different from the general trend mentioned in Section 17.1. Quantitative investigation shows that Mn^{+3} ion:

gains an electron more readily than would be predicted from the regular changes in the four preceding elements. To about the same extent, Fe^{++} ion:

loses an electron more readily than would be expected. We have seen that both of the ions which are more stable than expected—Mn^{++} and Fe^{+3}—have the same structure, with 1 electron in each d orbital.

That this is more than coincidence is suggested by the fact that the free element chromium has the same d structure, at the expense of having only 1 outer s electron instead of the standard 2.

Fe^{++} is the first divalent ion in this series to form a complex ion of any importance. The hexacyanoferrate ion, $Fe(CN)_6^{-4}$, is usually called ferrocyanide ion. Its sodium and potassium salts are known commercially as yellow prussiate of soda and of potash, respectively. One of the CN^- ions can be replaced by various other ligands. If the replacement is a nitrosyl ion, NO^+, $FeNO(CN)_5^{--}$, ordinarily called nitroprusside ion, is formed.

17.16. Iron(III) (Ferric) Ion

$Fe(H_2O)_6^{+3}$ is a very pale purple. However, its color is rarely seen because the ion is so strong an acid—$K_{ion} > 6.3 \times 10^{-3}$, about the same as that of H_3PO_4—that its solutions regularly contain appreciable concentrations of $Fe(H_2O)_5OH^{++}$ ion. The color of any iron(III) complex which includes one or more chloride, bromide, or pseudohalide ions is in the yellow-red-brown series. If one or two OH^- or Cl^- ions are present the color is a light or dark yellow. $Fe(H_2O)_3(OH)_3$ is brown; $Fe(H_2O)_5CNS$ is an intense brownish red that is used as a confirmatory test for Fe^{+3}; $Fe(CN)_6^{-3}$ (ferricyanide or red prussiate) is garnet red; and Fe_2Cl_6 is black.

In addition to its acidity, Fe^{+3} ion shows the expected resemblance to Al^{+3} and the other trivalent ions in this transition series by forming the spinel magnetite, and various alums. The most common ferric alum is $NH_4Fe(SO_4)_2 \cdot 12H_2O$, which is more easily crystallized than the potassium alum. Ferric chloride, the most important ferric salt, is dimeric like Al_2Cl_6 and much like it also in other respects, including volatility and solubility in organic solvents. Although not as acidic as would be expected—it dissolves only in *fused* NaOH—$Fe(OH)_3$ is physically much like $Al(OH)_3$ and is used similarly for water clarification. For this purpose it is usually prepared from chlorinated copperas, $FeSO_4Cl$, which is made by oxidizing $FeSO_4$ with chlorine.

Fe^{+3} is too strong an acid to coexist with such basic ions as CO_3^{--}; the addition of a carbonate solution to a solution of Fe^{+3} precipitates the hydroxide. Similarly, it is too strong an oxidizing agent to form salts with anions which are good reducing agents, such as I^-. Its ability to form covalent bonds with S^{--} ion enables Fe_2S_3 to exist under some conditions, but unless the solution is strongly basic the reaction is:

$$2Fe^{+3} + 3S^{--} \rightarrow \underline{2FeS} + \underline{S}$$

17.17. Iron Pigments

The color of Fe_2O_3 varies widely, depending on physical state and degree of hydration. From prehistoric times this oxide, and clays colored with it, have been valued as pigments. Collectively they are known to artists as earth colors (Table 17.1). Some are natural materials which have been ground fine; others have been heated ("burned") to change the color. In recent years, synthetic pigments have been made that duplicate many of the old earth colors and create new colors. These last are usually called Mars colors. (The alchemists called iron "Mars," after the red planet.) The earth colors are still highly valued for their soft, rich shades and their permanence.

TABLE 17.1. **Earth Colors**

Name	Hue
Ocher	Yellow
Raw sienna	Raw yellow
Burnt sienna	Rich dark brown
Raw umber	Blackish brown
Burnt umber	Almost black
Venetian red	Dark boxcar red
Indian red	A duller red
Light red	Sandstone red
Mars violet	Brownish violet
Terre verte	Gray green

The umbers and terre verte contain manganese in addition to iron; in the latter the iron is $FeSiO_3$.

Another iron color, Prussian blue, is very popular among house painters on account of its tinctorial intensity. However, it cannot be used on exteriors because it is destroyed by sunlight, or directly on plaster because it is converted by bases into $Fe(OH)_3$. Prussian blue is formed by bringing together either Fe^{++} and $Fe(CN)_6^{-3}$ or Fe^{+3} and $Fe(CN)_6^{-4}$ ions. A giant anion is formed in a cubic pattern consisting of one Fe for every three CN^- ions. Both oxidation states of Fe are present, arranged at alternate corners of the cubes in Fig. 17.8. Thus the empirical formula of Prussian blue, $Fe_2(CN)_6^-$, is justified as follows: Note that the Fe in the center of the figure is surrounded by six Fe's. This is true of *each* iron in the lattice and would be more apparent if the figure showed more cubes. Each line that connects an Fe^{++} and an Fe^{+3} represents a CN^- ion. Since it is shared by Fe^{++} and Fe^{+3}, half of it belongs to each. In a more fully extended figure each Fe would be like the center one to which six such lines are connected. Since half of these belong to it, three CN's belong to each Fe and the empirical formula $Fe_2(CN)_6^-$ for the ion is justified. The number of these units is indeterminate. The larger the crystal the larger the molecular ion; therefore the molecular formula is $(Fe_2(CN)_6^-)_n$. Since two reactions produce the same result, it is impossible to tell, once the anion forms, whether it originated from ferro- or ferri-cyanide ions.

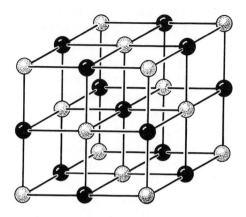

Fig. 17.8. Prussian blue lattice, $Fe_2(CN)_6{}^-$. The closed spheres represent Fe^{+3}; the open spheres, Fe^{++}. The lines represent CN^- ions.

$$Fe^{++} + (Fe^{+3}(CN)_6)^{-3} \rightarrow Fe_2(CN)_6{}^-$$
$$Fe^{+3} + (Fe^{+2}(CN)_6)^{-4} \rightarrow Fe_2(CN)_6{}^-$$

To maintain electrical neutrality, a sufficient number of positive ions —K^+ of $K_4Fe(CN)_6$, or Fe^{+3} from any soluble ferric compound—must occupy some of the cubes, the rest of them being occupied by water of hydration. The precipitation procedure determines which cation will be present. If the Fe^{+3} ion is added to $K_4Fe(CN)_6$ solution, the reaction is that shown in the first equation below. The second equation shows the reaction if the order of addition is reversed. $KFe_2(CN)_6$ is called soluble Prussian blue because it readily forms a colloidal dispersion; this is possibly due to the fact that the particles become charged by losing K^+ ions to the solution.

$$Fe^{+3} + 4K^+ + Fe(CN)_6{}^{-4} \rightarrow \underset{\text{Blue}}{KFe_2(CN)_6} + 3K^+$$
$$4Fe^{+3} + 3(4K^+ + Fe(CN)_6{}^{-4}) \rightarrow \underset{\text{Blue}}{Fe[Fe_2(CN)_6]_3} + 12K^+$$

Similar lattice structures in which all the iron atoms are either ferric (green) or ferrous (white) can be formed, but even the green lattice structure lacks the intense color of Prussian blue. This seems to be no accident, for coloration is always intense whenever two different valences of the same metal are so situated that they can exchange valences by the transfer of an electron. Iron compounds provide other examples. Thus when moist white $Fe(OH)_2$ is exposed to the air, it turns green at the first trace of atmospheric oxidation, and by the time the compound is half oxidized it is a very intense dark green. When oxidation is complete, the color has lightened to the familiar brown of iron rust. Similarly, all spinels that contain the same element in two valence states are intensely colored; Fe_3O_4 is black.

The soluble Prussian blue is used as laundry bluing. The insoluble compound gives blueprints their color. Paper for blueprints is soaked in potassium ferric oxalate or ferric ammonium citrate and $K_3Fe(CN)_6$ and dried in a dark room. Green ferric ferricyanide deposits in the paper. In making the blueprint, the drawing or tracing is placed over the blueprint paper and exposed to a bright light. Wherever light strikes the blueprint paper, the ferric ion is reduced catalytically by the organic matter to the ferrous ion; this reacts with potassium ferricyanide and produces insoluble Prussian blue. After the unchanged salt is rinsed off and the paper is dried, the drawing appears as white lines against a blue background. A solution of a strong base destroys the blue color.

$$Fe(Fe_2(CN)_6)_3 + 12Na^+ + 12OH^- \rightarrow 12Na^+ + 3Fe(CN)_6{}^{-4} + 4Fe(OH)_3$$

17.18. Iron Complexes

Information about the nature of the bonding in the various ferrous and ferric complex ions is obtained by measuring their magnetic susceptibilities. These compounds are found to fall into two classes, depending upon the polarizability of the ligands. If the ligand is low in polarizability—that is, if it does not readily share electrons in a covalent bond (or in an additional covalent bond)—the extent to which the complex ion is attracted by a magnetic field proves that most or all of the d electrons in the iron atoms are unpaired. This is shown diagrammatically as follows:

$$Fe^{++} \quad \cdot\cdot \ \cdot\cdot \ \cdot\cdot \ \cdot\cdot \ \cdot\cdot \qquad\qquad - \quad - \ - \ - \ -$$
$$Fe^{+3} \quad \cdot\cdot \ \cdot\cdot \ \cdot\cdot \ \cdot\cdot \ \cdot\cdot \qquad\qquad - \quad - \ - \ - \ -$$

These diagrams show 4 unpaired electrons in four different d orbitals and a pair of electrons in the fifth d orbital in ferrous ion; and 5 unpaired electrons, one to each d orbital, in ferric ion. When the ligand readily forms covalent bonds—i.e., is highly polarizable—the ferrous complex is not attracted by a magnet at all, the ferric complex only moderately to the extent that corresponds to 1 unpaired electron.

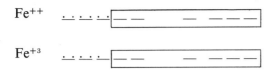

Fe^{++}

Fe^{+3}

In each of these diagrams two d orbitals are not occupied by any of the electrons belonging to the iron atom.

In the first case (p. 504), it is obvious that no d orbitals are available for forming covalent bonds with ligands. To the extent that the ligands form covalent bonds at all, they must use only valence layer orbitals. F$^-$ ion and H$_2$O form complexes of this class. Since fluorine and oxygen are the two most electronegative atoms and therefore the two that least readily share electrons with other atoms, there seems every reason to believe that when F$^-$ and H$_2$O act as ligands they are held to the iron atoms largely by the electrostatic attraction between the positive charge on the iron and the negative charge on the F$^-$ ion or the oxygen end of the water molecule, and that the bonds show very little covalence. This is borne out by the fact that Fe(H$_2$O)$_6$$^{++}$ and Fe(H$_2$O)$_6$$^{+3}$ are very pale in color and FeF$_6$$^{-3}$ is colorless, for color is often a sign of polarization. Accordingly these are referred to as electrostatic or ionic complexes and are characterized by the relative ease with which the ligands can be replaced by others. For example, addition of a large excess of NaF to a solution colored yellow by Fe(H$_2$O)$_5$Cl^{++} decolorizes it because of the formation of FeF$_6$$^{-3}$; but dilution of the excess F$^-$ ions by addition of HCl promptly restores the color.

In the second case above, it is believed that the only reason that all the d electrons are crowded together into three orbitals is that the other two orbitals are occupied by covalent bonds with the ligands. Since the 3d orbitals are intermediate in energy between the 4s and 4p orbitals of the valence octet, and the number of these low-energy orbitals is exactly equal to the number of ligands, all six ligands are believed to form covalent bonds using the six orbitals of nearly identical energy in the iron atoms. This is expressed in the diagrams by the boxes around the orbitals concerned. In the next chapter we will see that when fewer low-energy orbitals are available for bond formation in the central ion, the number and arrangement of ligands are correspondingly altered. Cyanide ion, CN$^-$, is the ligand which most readily forms covalent bonds. Both Fe(CN)$_6$$^{-4}$ and Fe(CN)$_6$$^{-3}$ belong to this class of complexes, commonly called covalent complexes and characterized by very little tendency to dissociate or to replace one ligand by another.

In calling some complexes ionic and others covalent, we do not mean that in the one there is no sharing of electron pairs, and that in the other this sharing is exactly 50-50. The names merely indicate which character is predominant.

17.19. Higher Valences of Iron

In nearly all the groups in the periodic table, the total number of electrons that must be considered in connection with valence phenomena is the group number. In the typical elements these are all s and p electrons in the valence shell. In the transition elements they are s electrons in the valence shell, and d electrons in the shell beneath it. In each case we saw that when all these electrons were lost, or promoted to the valence shell and shared, the element in the subgroup resembled the typical elements which displayed the same valence. This regularity must run aground, so to speak, in Group VIIIB, because iron, for example, could have an oxidation number of $+8$ only by sharing four electron pairs, whereas the elements with 8 electrons in the valence layer are the inert gases, with zero valence. In a hypothetical compound like FeO_4, for example, iron could not resemble the neon atom, even though both would have 8 electrons in the valence shell. The impossibility is even more obvious for the following two elements, cobalt and nickel, with 9 and 10 electrons to consider.

A little consideration should indicate the direction of the deviation from the rule. As the atomic number increased in the $3d$ transition elements we have studied, it became progressively more difficult to oxidize the element to the group valence. Compounds in which the element displayed that valence became stronger and stronger oxidizing agents (Fig. 17.1). So as the atomic number increases still further as we move into Group VIII, it will become almost impossible—for the 8-electron elements, the iron column—and completely impossible—for the 9- and 10-electron elements, the cobalt and nickel columns—to lose all the d electrons.

The actual fact is that although iron has been said to form the compound K_2FeO_5, the elements beyond iron in the fourth period never lose more than 2 d electrons even partially, by sharing; and zinc never loses any d electrons. This is the natural result of the continually increasing positive charge from the nucleus acting upon those electrons.

The highest definitely confirmed oxidation number of iron is $+6$, in the ferrate ion, FeO_4^{--}.

$$\overline{3Cl_2 + 2Fe(OH)_3} + 10K^+ + 10OH^- \rightarrow 10K^+ + 6Cl^- + 2FeO_4^{--} + 8H_2O$$

When Ba^{++} ion is added to the purple solution, red $BaFeO_4 \cdot H_2O$ precipitates. Except for the molecule of water of hydration, the expected resemblance of FeO_4^{--} ion to CrO_4^{--}, MnO_4^{--}, and SO_4^{--} ions is present.

QUESTIONS AND PROBLEMS

1. How do atomic and ionic radii in a transition element series change with increasing atomic number?

2. How does the electronegativity of an M^{++} ion compare for the same element when the ion is M^{+3}? Give reasons for your answer.

3. How do the following properties of ions of the transition metals vary with their electronegativity? Their charge?
   a. Oxidizing ability.
   b. Acid strength of the hydrated ion.
   c. Ability to form covalent bonds.

4. The same general trends are observed in coordination complexes with various ligands, but are modified to some extent depending upon the ligand. What characteristic of the ligand is responsible for this modification? Explain.

5. Why does freshly precipitated white manganese(II) hydroxide turn brown on standing?

6. If it can display amphoterism, does a polyvalent metal necessarily display it in all its valence states? If not, does it display it in high or low valence states? Give reasons for your answer.

7. What are the oxidation states of manganese? In which oxidation state and as what compound is manganese most commonly used? What are the two most common oxidation states for its use in aqueous solutions?

8. Complete and balance the following redox reactions:
   a. $Fe^{++} + Cr_2O_7^{--} + (H^+ + Cl^-) \rightarrow Fe^{+3} + Cr^{+3}$
   b. $Fe^{++} + MnO_4^- + (2H^+ + SO_4^{--}) \rightarrow Fe^{+3} + Mn^{++}$
   c. $Mn^{++} + MnO_4^- \rightarrow \underline{MnO_2}$

9. What are the main metallurgical and chemical uses of manganese?

10. What iron compounds are the main sources of iron in the United States?

11. What is the role of each of the following in the story of steel: blast furnace; open hearth; Bessemer converter; electric furnace?

12. What constituents are charged in each furnace in question 11? Write the essential chemical reactions for the blast furnace.

13. Define each of the following: cast iron; steel; alloy steel; cementite; pearlite; casehardening; tempering.

14. Describe the allotropic modifications of iron and the conditions under which each exists.

15. What is the oxidation state of iron in Fe_3O_4? How is this compound formed?

16. What oxidation state does iron display when it dissolves in acids? Illustrate. Is this state stable? Explain.

17. Compare iron(II) and iron(III) in regard to similarities and dissimilarities. Compare iron with other M^{++} and M^{+3} ions which are similar.

18. What restrictions do the acidity and oxidizing ability of Fe^{+3} impose upon the type of ions that can exist with it in solution?

19. Distinguish between the electronic structures of Fe^{+3} when it forms complex ions with six ligands through the formation of strong covalent bonds and when it forms essentially ionic bonds. What experimental proof is there for these

structures? What characteristics of a ligand favor one type of bonding over the other in forming complex ions? Give examples of each type of complex ion.

20. How do you account for the color displayed by compounds that contain $Fe_2(CN)_6^-$ ion?

21. In higher oxidation states the transition elements resemble main-group elements. Thus MnO_4^- is like ClO_4^-, and CrO_4^{--} is like SO_4^{--}. What difficulty does this trend encounter in Group VIIIB elements? What is the cause of this?

18

Cobalt and nickel. Analysis of the nickel subgroup

18.1. History and Occurrence of Cobalt

Beautiful blue glazes on pottery, and blue glass beads that were imitations of an azure stone called lapis lazuli were in use in Egypt in 1375 B.C. The blue color of these glazes and beads was derived from the cobalt which they contained. Other similar articles from Babylonia are not dated as exactly but probably were made around the middle of the fourteenth century B.C. Some cobalt glass is known from Rome, but most of the ancient blue glazes were colored with $CaCuSi_4O_{10}$. During the Middle Ages Saxony was the largest producer of cobalt compounds. The German miners, believing they had discovered silver ore, attributed their failure to obtain silver from the ore to the mischief of underground gnomes called kobolds. In *De Re Metallica,* the German author Agricola* used the name cobalt for minerals which resembled ores of metals but did not yield the metals un-

---

* His real name was Bauer, but he Latinized it to Agricola; both mean farmer. His book, the most important medieval treatise on mining and metallurgy, was translated into English by former President Herbert Hoover, a mining engineer, and his late wife, a Latinist.

der the usual treatment, giving off As_2O_3 instead. When fused with white sand, SiO_2, and K_2CO_3, the roasted cobalt—an impure form called zaffre, $Co_3(AsO_4)_2$—forms a beautiful blue glass called smalt. The blue color was at first believed to be due to arsenic, but in 1735 George Brandt of Sweden demonstrated that it was due to a new metal, which came to be called cobalt.

Cobalt ores, the most important of which are the arsenides, arseno-sulfides, sulfides, and arsenates, are always associated with other ores. In Cobalt City, Ontario, cobalt ore is present in silver-nickel ores; in Germany it is associated with bismuth; it is a by-product of copper refining in the Congo region; the manganese ore of New Caledonia runs about 2 per cent CoO. The cobalt ores themselves nearly always contain an indefinite mixture of iron, cobalt, and nickel; this should be kept in mind in connection with the formulas which follow. The arsenate, $Co_3(AsO_4)_2 \cdot 8H_2O$, is called erythrite, cobalt ocher, and cobalt bloom; in it the cations have their normal valence of $+2$. In the arsenosulfide ores the valence of the cation is apparently determined by that of the anion. These ores belong to a class of compounds of which the most familiar member is pyrites or fool's gold, FeS_2; in them the anion has the structure $: \overset{..}{X} : \overset{..}{Y} :^{-n}$. If both X and Y are sulfur or selenium, the anion is divalent. Replacement of one atom of sulfur by a Group VA element makes the charge -3; if both atoms are thus replaced, the charge is -4. Thus in pyrites we have Fe^{++}; in cobaltite (cobalt glance), CoAsS, Co^{+3}; and in smaltite (speiss cobalt), $CoAs_2$, Co^{+4}. (Linnaeite, Co_3S_4, may be the sulfur analogue of a spinel that contains two Co^{+3} and one Co^{++} ions, and ordinary S^{--} ions.)

The stabilization of an unusual valence points strongly to covalent bonding, and x-ray investigation proves that this is the case here. These minerals crystallize in a cubic, NaCl type of lattice, with each cation surrounded by six anions and each anion surrounded by six cations. The interatomic distances prove the bonding to be covalent. Each anion shares six electron pairs with six different cations; each cation has six different anions as ligands. When six anions of S_2^{--}, AsS^{-3}, or As_2^{-4} form ligands on a cation they contribute 12 electrons to six empty orbitals of the cation. Thus if the cation can furnish empty d^2sp^3 orbitals (six), the ligands will attach to it. The number of electron vacancies in the valence shell of a cation varies with its oxidation state. Thus Fe^{++} has sufficient vacancies (d^2sp^3), but this is not so of Co^{++} or Ni^{++}. Hence only iron forms a pyrites, FeS_2. Co^{+3}, with 1 electron less than Co^{++}, satisfies the requirement of d^2sp^3 vacancy, and forms a cobaltite CoAsS as does Fe^{+3}, FeAsS. Ni^{+3} has 1 excess electron and cannot meet the vacancy requirement. In the +4 oxidation state even nickel would have sufficient orbital vacancies to accommodate six ligands. Thus all three metals are present in smaltite with the anion As_2^{-4}. The cations have the following structures:

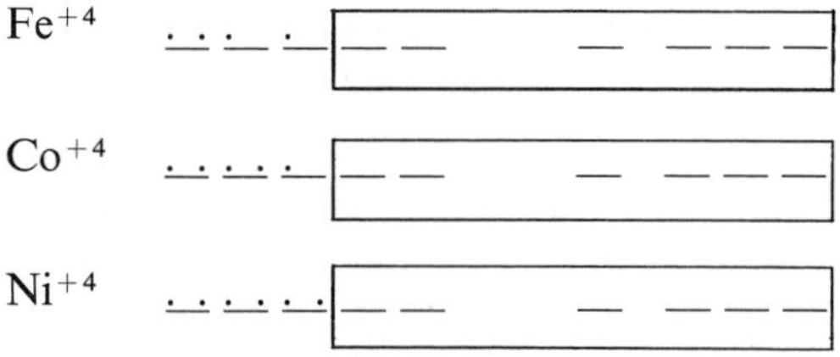

Fe^{+4} ....._[□ □   □ □□□□]

Co^{+4} ....._[□ □   □ □□□□]

Ni^{+4} ....._[□ □   □ □□□□]

18.2. Cobalt Ores and Metallurgy

The presence of arsenic, sulfur, iron, nickel, and many other metals in cobalt ores complicates the metallurgy. At Cobalt City, Ontario, the ore is smelted under such conditions that most of the iron goes into the slag and impure arsenide and antimonide of nickel and cobalt (speiss) settle out. This is roasted to remove arsenic and antimony as volatile oxides at the temperature of the roasting. The metals are now in the form of oxides or, if noble, free metals. Silver is removed by further roasting with salt, followed by its extraction with cyanide solution.

$$4Ag + \overline{O_2} + \underline{4NaCl} + 2SiO_2 \xrightarrow{\Delta} \underline{4AgCl} + 2Na_2SiO_3$$

$$\underline{AgCl} + 2Na^+ + 2CN^- \rightarrow 2Na^+ + Cl^- + Ag(CN)_2^-$$

The residue is boiled with concentrated H_2SO_4 and extracted with water. The water solution is agitated with limestone, which neutralizes the acid and precipitates the residual iron and antimony as hydroxides, and the arsenic as calcium arsenate.

$$Sb^{+3} + \underline{3CaCO_3} + 3H_2O \rightarrow Sb(OH)_3 + 3Ca^{++} + 3HCO_3^-$$

$$2AsO_4^{-3} + 3Ca^{++} \rightarrow \underline{Ca_3(AsO_4)_2}$$

Addition of soda ash to the filtrate removes copper as the basic carbonate.

$$2Cu^{++} + 2H_2O + 3CO_3^{--} \rightarrow \underline{CuCO_3 \cdot Cu(OH)_2} + 2HCO_3^-$$

The cobalt is then precipitated as more or less hydrated Co_2O_3 by adding ClO$^-$ ion.

$$2Co^{++} + ClO^- + 2CO_3^{--} \rightarrow \underline{Co_2O_3} + \overline{2CO_2} + Cl^-$$

Finally nickel is precipitated as basic carbonate by adding more Na_2CO_3; adding NaClO removes the balance of it as Ni_2O_3. The Co_2O_3 is reduced with carbon in an electric furnace, or dissolved in acid and electrolyzed.

Cobalt is strong and malleable; it is easily polished to a high luster that has a slight bluish cast. It is harder, brighter, and less affected by the atmosphere than nickel. It was formerly used for decorative plating, but has now been replaced by chromium. Its density is 8.9; it is magnetic up to 1100° C., and melts at 1495° C. It liberates hydrogen slowly from concentrated HCl.

Prior to 1904 most of the cobalt was produced in Sweden, Norway, and Saxony, but the main sources now are the Congo region and Northern Rhodesia. The Ontario deposits were discovered in 1904 during the construction of a railroad. Annual production of cobalt oxide now approximates 2500 tons, but little of it is produced in the United States. World producers have combined to set the price at a figure which provides optimum volume and profit; the current price is $2 per pound. About half the cobalt oxide produced is reduced to the metal; the remainder is used as such in glass and ceramics, or in making other cobalt compounds.

Cobalt is alloyed with chromium and tungsten to produce Stellite. Extremely hard, even at red heat, and non-corroding, Stellite is used for high-speed cutting tools and surgical implements and in the valves and valve seats of gasoline engines. Alnico, an Al-Ni-Co alloy developed by the General Electric Company in 1936, makes it possible to produce permanent magnets that can lift sixty times their own weight. Vitallium, a stainless alloy containing 65 per cent cobalt, 30 per cent chromium, and 5 per cent molybdenum, is used for gas turbine blades, dental bridgework, and pins, screws, and plates used in bone surgery.

18.3. Cobalt(II) (Cobaltous) Ion

Co^{++} continues the list of divalent cations which form similar compounds. Its vitriol, $CoSO_4 \cdot 7H_2O$, is isomorphous with those of Mg, Zn, Fe, etc., as is the schönite type of double sulfate, $K_2Co(SO_4)_2 \cdot 6H_2O$, etc. It enters into many spinels—for example, Cr_2CoO_4 (green), Al_2CoO_4 (Thenard's blue, used as a test for Al), Co_2CoO_4 (black), and the green compound $CoSnCoO_4$, in which the two trivalent ions normally present in a spinel are replaced by Co^{++} and Sn^{+4} which add up to the same charge.

Co(OH)$_2$ dissolves in hot concentrated KOH solution, but is precipitated when the solution cools. As previously noted, Na$_2$CO$_3$ solution precipitates basic cobaltous carbonate, but the hexahydrated normal salt, CoCO$_3 \cdot$ 6H$_2$O, separates slowly from a cold solution containing Co^{++} and HCO$_3^-$ and saturated with CO$_2$ to keep down the concentration of OH$^-$ ion. Black CoS is not precipitated by H$_2$S from acid solutions but is formed by the action of S^{--} ion in basic solution. It is insoluble in dilute acids, but soluble in concentrated HCl or aqua regia.

The ability to form covalent bonds is present in much greater degree in Co^{++} than in any divalent ion we have studied thus far. In solution or in crystals with colorless anions, Co(H$_2$O)$_4^{++}$ is red or pink, but the water molecules are readily replaced by various anions. A strip of filter paper dipped in CoCl$_2$ solution and dried is a convenient indicator of humidity. In less than 50 per cent humidity the solution dries to the anhydrous salt and the Cl$^-$ ions coordinate with the Co^{++} ions, each doing double duty. The new substance is bright blue. As the humidity rises, this change is reversed, and pink crystals of CoCl$_2 \cdot$ 6H$_2$O are formed. These deliquesce above 80 per cent humidity and wet patches appear on the paper. "Sympathetic ink," CoCl$_2$ solution, works on the same principle. The rather pale pink writing is nearly invisible, but the bright blue produced by warming the paper is easily read. The same blue color is produced by heating CoCl$_2$ solution above 50° C., or by adding concentrated H$_2$SO$_4$, which reduces the water concentration, or concentrated HCl, which increases the Cl$^-$ concentration. This is not a dehydration, as was once believed, but a displacement.

$$Co(H_2O)_4^{++} + 4Cl^- \rightleftharpoons CoCl_4^{--} + 4H_2O$$

This explains why Co(NO$_3$)$_2$ solution does not turn blue when heated or when concentrated H$_2$SO$_4$ is added, but does do so if concentrated HCl is added. Other cobaltous complexes have other colors. CoBr$_2$ is dark green; Co(H$_2$O)$_2$Br$_2$ is purple; CoI$_2$ is black; Co(CNS)$_4^{--}$ is dark blue. With Hg(CNS)$_4^{--}$, Co^{++} forms a bright blue crystalline precipitate analogous in structure to Prussian blue. This precipitation is catalyzed by Zn^{++} ion, and its formation within a specified time is a specific test for Zn^{++}. Anhydrous cobaltous salts containing anions which do not readily form covalent bonds, such as F$^-$, NO$_3^-$, and SO$_4^{--}$, are red.

In all the above cobaltous complexes the Co^{++} ion has the coordination number 4. With CN$^-$ ion, which has very strong coordinating powers, the yellow ion Co(CN)$_6^{-4}$ is formed. This has very peculiar properties. Under proper conditions it liberates hydrogen from water like an active metal; the yellow ion itself is oxidized to Co(CN)$_6^{-3}$. A slightly acid solution of $Co(CN)_6^{-4}$, when boiled in an open dish, reduces atmospheric oxygen to H_2O_2. This is exactly what happens to oxygen when it is bubbled through a solution of metallic sodium in liquid NH_3. As in the case of the pyrites type of iron, cobalt, and nickel ores, this peculiar behavior can be explained on the basis of atomic structure. Co^{++} ion has 7 d electrons, and in most cases this precludes the formation of a 6-covalent complex, but in CN^- the energy of coordination is great enough to *promote* the seventh electron to the 5s orbital. $Co(CN)_6^{-4}$ then has the structure:

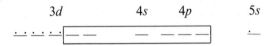

Actually it is structurally analogous to the alkali metals. Conversely the 6-coordinated complexes of Co^{+3} are extraordinarily stable and strongly resist reduction. Either the added electron would have to go into the high-energy 5s orbital, or if it went into the normal 3d orbital two covalent bonds would have to be broken when the coordination number was reduced to 4.

The use of Co^{++} in glass and glazes was mentioned earlier in this chapter. Cobalt acetate, borate, linoleate, and tungstate are used as driers in paints and varnishes. Cobalt is essential to animal nutrition. The fact that adding traces of cobaltous compounds to sheep fodder checked the deadly enzootic marasmus in Australia and the bush-sickness in New Zealand led eventually to the discovery of vitamin B_{12}, a cobalt compound that is essential for the formation of red blood cells.

18.4. Cobalt(III) (Cobaltic) Ion

Co^{+3} is such a strong oxidizing agent that it can be formed only by the supreme oxidizing agent fluorine, or by the practically unlimited power of electrolytic oxidation, unless a complexing agent is present. (Thus in alkaline solution H_2O_2 can oxidize blue $Co(OH)_2$ to black $Co(OH)_3$ because each OH^- in the latter serves as a covalently bonded bridge between two Co^{+3} ions.) Because of this, there is only one case in which Co^{+3} resembles the other trivalent ions—the fact that it forms a typical series of alums (blue). Like the alums, $Co_2(SO_4)_2 \cdot 18H_2O$ apparently contains the simple hydrated cation $Co(H_2O)_6^{+3}$. Anhydrous CoF_3 is green, as is the salt $CoF_3 \cdot 3\frac{1}{2}H_2O$; thus Co^{+3} appears to be able to coordinate even F^- ion. But the degree of covalence in the bonds with either H_2O or F^- ion is so slight that all these compounds are unstable in solution. They oxidize the -2 oxygen of the water to O_2 and some O_3; the Co^{+3} is reduced to Co^{++}.

The ability of Co^{+3} to coordinate F^- ion and its great oxidizing power both indicate that it is relatively high in electronegativity and has a correspondingly great ability to form covalent bonds. This is true. Complexes of Co^{+3} in which it has a coordination number of 6 with both anions and neutral molecules are extraordinarily numerous (over 2000 are known) and stable. The structure of these covalent complexes is:

The charge can range in value from all the way from -3 through 0 to $+3$, depending upon the charges on the ligands. In many cases the starting point is Co^{++}, which, in the presence of the desired complexing agent, is easily oxidized by air or sometimes by the complexing agent itself if it happens to be even a moderate oxidizing agent like NO_3^- and NO. However, it is sometimes possible to displace one ligand by another. The most important of the cobaltic complexes are the cobaltammines, the cobaltinitrites, and the cobalticyanides.

Precipitated $Co(OH)_2$ dissolves in excess NH_3, forming a yellowish-brown solution of $Co(NH_3)_6^{++}$. When exposed to the air this absorbs oxygen, and a pink solution of hexamminecobalt (III) ion is produced.

$$4Co(NH_3)_6^{++} + \overline{O_2} + 4NH_4OH \rightarrow$$
$$4Co(NH_3)_6^{+3} + 4OH^- + 2H_2O + 4NH_3$$

This ion has none of the properties of either Co^{+3} or NH_3. If its chloride is heated with concentrated H_2SO_4, HCl is driven off, but the Co^{+3} is not displaced from its covalent bonds with the NH_3 molecules. The comparative strength with which each holds the NH_3 molecules shows that Co^{+3} is a stronger Lewis acid than the proton.

Mixed cobaltammines can sometimes be formed if other complexing agents are present when the Co^{++} is oxidized. Adding $(NH_4)_2CO_3$ as well as NH_4OH to a solution of $Co(NO_3)_2$ produces a violet liquid in which a CO_3^{--} is presumably already attached to the Co^{++}. If air is drawn through this liquid it is oxidized to blood-red carbonatotetramminecobalt(III) ion, $Co(NH_3)_4CO_3^+$. In this case, though not always, the carbonato- group acts as a *bidentate* ligand, occupying two coordination positions on the Co^{+3}. Mixed complexes can also be formed by displacement. If the above carbonato- complex is heated with excess NH_4Cl and NH_3, chloropentamminecobalt(III) ion is obtained. If concentrated HCl is added, the solid chloride of this cation, $(Co(NH_3)_5Cl)Cl_2$, crystallizes out.

The preparation of hexacyanocobaltate(III) ion, $Co(CN)_6^{-3}$, was described at the end of Section 18.3. (An older name for this ion is cobalticyanide ion.) Although free CN^- ions are easily oxidized, this complex ion is not affected by concentrated HNO_3 or by ClO^- ion. A somewhat less stable complex—it is decomposed by $(NH_4)_2S$—but a more common one is the hexanitritocobaltate(III) (cobaltinitrite) ion, $Co(NO_2)_6^{-3}$, formed by merely adding a nitrite to a cobaltous salt in acid solution.

$$Co^{++} + 7NO_2^- + 2H^+ \rightarrow Co(NO_2)_6^{-3} + \overline{NO} + H_2O$$

This ion is of interest because its potassium salt is one of the least soluble potassium salts. The addition of $AgNO_3$ to a solution of $Na_3Co(NO_2)_6$ makes the latter a still more sensitive reagent for potassium, because $K_2AgCo(NO_2)_6$ and $KAg_2Co(NO_2)_6$ are less soluble than $K_3Co(NO_2)_6$. One part of K^+ ion in 10,000 of water can be detected by the yellow precipitate that forms. Since the charge on a complex is the algebraic sum of the charges of its components, it is perfectly possible for a complex to have a zero charge and to be a non-electrolyte. This is true of trinitritotriamminecobalt(III), $Co(NH_3)_3(NO_2)_3$. Another way to obtain a non-electrolyte complex is to use a bidentate ligand with only one charge. This will be illustrated in connection with nickel. Like other non-electrolytes, these are commonly insoluble in water but many are soluble in organic solvents.

It was known a century ago that when Ag^+ ion is added to a solution of $(Co(NH_3)_5Cl)Cl_2$, only two-thirds of the total chlorine is precipitated as AgCl. In 1893 the Swiss chemist Werner suggested that there must be two different kinds of valence that hold the three chlorine atoms to the cobalt. The two chlorines that could be precipitated were held by ordinary or "principal" valences, like those in $CaCl_2$. The third chlorine and the ammonia were held in an especially tight "inner sphere" by "secondary" valences. Werner had no idea how one kind of valence could be different from another, but fundamentally he was right. His "principal" valence is now known to be electrovalence and his "secondary" valence is covalence. He recognized the fact that each different ion has a characteristic coordination number of secondary (co-) valences, and that very commonly this number is double its principal valence number (charge). He correctly explained the existence of two different dichlorotetramminecobalt(III) ions when he said that in one isomer the two chlorine atoms occupy adjacent positions in the coordination octahedron, whereas in the other isomer the chlorines are not adjacent but diametrically opposite each other (Fig. 18.1). He called them *cis-* and *trans-* isomers, respectively, names which are still used. Werner correctly predicted the number of positional isomers that could be prepared if a complex contained three ligands of each kind, and also that there would be *optical*

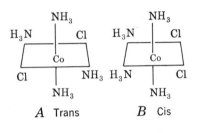

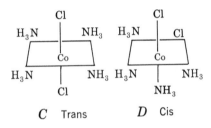

Fig. 18.1. Positional isomerism in an octahedral complex. Each of these diagrams represents a molecule of the same shape as that in Fig. 18.2A. **A** and **B** are different structures, called isomers. **A** is equivalent to **C**, and **B** to **D**. It makes no difference which axis of the molecule is vertical.

isomerism in certain special cases in cis- isomers but never in transisomers. Optical isomerism was already known in carbon compounds. If a molecule is assymmetrical, so that it differs from its mirror image (as a right-hand glove differs from a left-hand glove), the "right" and "left" molecules will have identical chemical properties, except toward other assymmetrical molecules, but the plane of polarization of polarized light will rotate in opposite directions. (**Polarized light** is light all of whose vibrations are in a single plane.) These triumphs of prediction so impressed chemists that to this day these compounds are commonly called **Werner complexes.**

18.5. History and Occurrence of Nickel

Alloys containing copper, zinc, and nickel were first used in China, where they were called *paktong,* meaning white brass. A Bactrian cupronickel coin similar in composition to our own five-cent piece (20 per cent instead of 25 per cent nickel) was coined in 235 B.C. In 1694 the name *Kupfernickel* (false copper) was given to a German mineral which resembled copper ore but yielded no copper. It was NiAs and contained Ni(III). The Swedish chemist Cronstedt studied this ore carefully in 1751 and found that it could be reduced with charcoal to a white magnetic metal which he called nickel. The fact that it was magnetic led to a general belief that the substance was only another form of iron, but it was finally proved to be an element.

The most important nickel deposits are at Sudbury, Ontario, and are worked by both open-pit and underground mining. The ores contain pentlandite, a mixed sulfide of iron and nickel that runs about 22 per cent nickel; pyrrhotite, which contains copper in addition; and chalcopyrite, a copper-iron sulfide. The New Caledonia mines yield garnierite, $(Ni,Mg)SiO_3 \cdot xH_2O$. Nickel is obtained as a by-product of cobalt mining, or vice versa, and of electrolytic copper refining. Meteoric iron often contains some metallic nickel.

18.6. Nickel Metallurgy

The Sudbury ores are first converted partially to oxides by roasting, then melted in open-hearth furnaces, during which much of the iron goes into the slag as $FeSiO_3$. Air is then blown through the liquid in Bessemer converters, and more sulfide is converted to oxide until there is danger of solidification. The product, called matte, is a mixture of copper and nickel oxides and sulfides, with a little iron and manganese. It can be reduced to metal by being heated with carbon, without any attempt at separation; the resulting alloy is called Monel metal and for many purposes is as useful as pure nickel. Nickel that is 99.8 per cent pure is prepared by the **Mond process.** The matte is roasted almost completely to oxides, then leached with dilute H_2SO_4; this removes the copper as sulfate. The residue is treated with water gas $(CO + H_2)$ at 300° to 350° C.; this reduces the NiO to metal, but does not affect the Fe_2O_3. The resultant solid mixture is then treated with CO at 60° C. in a unit called a volatilizer, which converts the nickel and traces of the platinum metals that are present in it to gaseous nickel carbonyl, $Ni(CO)_4$, and platinum metal carbonyls respectively. These substances, being gases at this temperature, readily distill from the undesirable solid im-

TABLE 18.1. Nickel Alloys

Alloy	Percentage of Element (Typical)	Uses
Monel metal	Ni, 67; Cu, 28	Kitchen sinks, fountains, etc.
Invar	Ni, 35; Fe, 64	Low-expansion metal. Seals for light bulbs; surveyors' tape
German silver	Ni, Zn, Cu (varying content)	Jewelry, etc.
Constantan	Ni, 40; Cu, 60	Thermocouples
Manganin	Ni, 4; Cu, 84; Mn, 12	Resistance wire
Nichrome	Ni and Cr (varying content)	Resistance wire
Permalloy	Ni, 78; Fe, 22	Magnetic properties. Ocean cables
Hypernik	Ni, 50; Fe, 50	Transformer cores
Nickel coins	Ni, 25; Cu, 75	Slot machines, parking meters, etc.

purities. The metals, chiefly nickel, are readily obtained from the carbonyls by heating the gases to 180° C., at which temperature they decompose. The nickel and traces of platinum metals are deposited on nickel pellets and the CO is sent back to the volatilizer. The nickel contains sufficient quantities of the platinum metals to make profitable their recovery by electrolytic refining, a process that is described in connection with copper.

Nickel has been in very short supply for years and this situation will not be helped by the Castro government's seizure of the large American plant installed in the late 1950s for the treatment of low-grade ores in Cuba. 120,000 tons of nickel were consumed in the United States in 1960.

Finely divided nickel absorbs hydrogen; apparently it separates the molecules into atoms which behave metallically, forming an alloy. This alloy readily hydrogenates unsaturated edible oils, changing them into solid fats, and then absorbs more hydrogen. Thus the nickel acts as an effective catalyst. The negative plate of the Edison storage cell is spongy nickel.

Nickel has a density of 8.9, is hard and malleable, and takes a high polish. Its silvery luster has the faintest yellow tinge. It is magnetic below 340° C., melts at 1455° C., and boils at 2900° C.

18.7. Nickel(II) Ion

The increase in stability of the divalent ion with atomic number which we have observed in this series of d transition metals reaches such a point with nickel that Ni^{++} is the only free ion formed. Ni(III) and Ni(IV) are found in only a few highly insoluble compounds; they rarely form complex ions.

Nickel dissolves in dilute HNO_3, producing the light green nickel hexahydrate ion, $Ni(H_2O)_6^{++}$. This forms the usual list of salts, including the vitriol, $NiSO_4 \cdot 7H_2O$, and the schönite, $(NH_4)_2Ni(SO_4)_2 \cdot 6H_2O$. These two sulfates are used in making solutions for electroplating and are known to technicians as "single nickel salt" and "double nickel salt" respectively. Surprisingly, nickel hydroxide has no amphoteric properties; as a result, metallic nickel is not attacked by fused NaOH and hence can be used for crucibles for alkali fusions. In fact, $Ni(OH)_2$ is sufficiently basic so that it dissolves even in such a weak acid as NH_4^+ ion. When it dissolves, four or all six of the molecules of water of hydration that Ni^{++} ion normally has are replaced by NH_3 molecules.

$$Ni(OH)_2 + 2NH_4^+ + 2NH_3 \rightarrow Ni(H_2O)_2(NH_3)_4^{++}$$

Both $Ni(H_2O)_2(NH_3)_4^{++}$ and $Ni(NH_3)_6^{++}$ are blue, as are many other compounds in which Ni^{++} is coordinated with nitrogen.

As their magnetic susceptibility shows, all blue or green nickel compounds contain 2 unpaired electrons. The nickel ion, Ni^{++}, has the structure:

It is evident that the ligands do not occupy any d orbitals. Since both nitrogen and oxygen are high in electronegativity, their bonds with Ni^{++} will be largely ionic; so these blue or green compounds are usually said to be ionic complexes. This does not deny the possibility that electrons from the ligands may occupy the octet orbitals of the nickel to some extent—possibly, since there are six ligands, two of the $3d$ orbitals.

The situation is strikingly different in a number of cases in which nitrogen atoms are so situated in bidentate ligands that the geometry is exceptionally favorable for the formation of a five-membered ring with Ni^{++}. Dimethylglyoxime is such a compound. Its structure is:

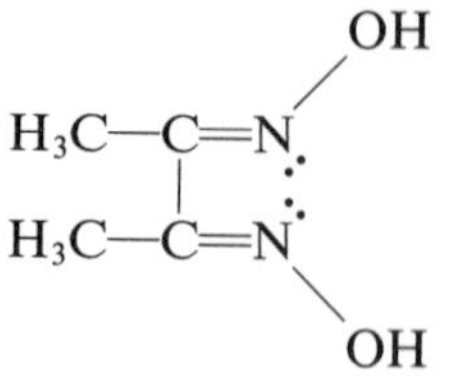

$$
\begin{array}{c}
\text{OH} \\
H_3C-C=N \\
| \\
H_3C-C=N \\
\text{OH}
\end{array}
$$

NH_3 can remove a proton from one of the oxygens, leaving a univalent anion which is bidentate because of the unshared electron on each nitrogen. If Ni^{++} is present when the proton is removed, the stable uncharged complex, nickel dimethylglyoxime, is formed.

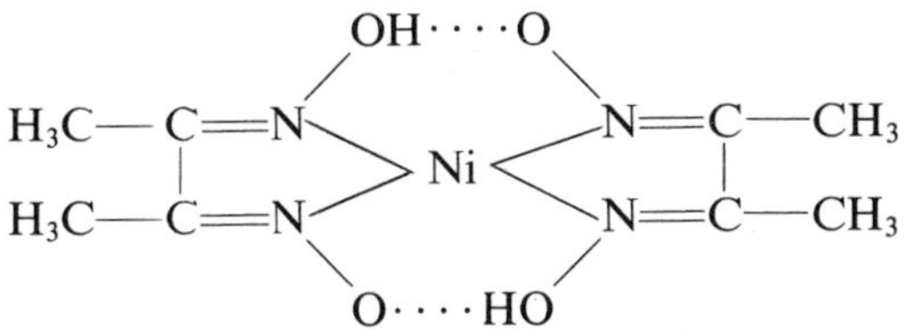

All these atoms, except the hydrogens of the methyl groups, are in the same plane. In addition to the two carbon-containing rings, two hydrogen-bonded oxygen-containing rings are completed by the Ni^{++}. The structure of Ni^{++} in this compound is:

The structure indicates that there are no unpaired electrons, and this is confirmed by the fact that the compound is not attracted by a magnet. A further interesting feature is that the compound is bright red. All non-magnetic nickel complexes are red or yellow, whereas all those that are attracted by a magnet—the *paramagnetic* complexes—are blue or green. The formation of nickel dimethylglyoxime is a sensitive confirmatory test for Ni^{++} in qualitative analysis.

The large number of covalent nickel complexes that exist illustrates the steady increase in electronegativity in even the divalent ions of this series as the number of d electrons has increased.

18.8. Nickel(III) and Nickel(IV)

Nickel arsenide (*Kupfernickel* or niccolite), NiAs, contains Ni(III); the diarsenide (chloanthite or white nickel ore), $NiAs_2$, and the mixed diarsenide smaltite contain Ni(IV). These compounds are used only as ores. More or less hydrated oxides, very insoluble compounds with strong covalent bonding, also have these valences. These compounds have practical uses.

When moderately heated, $Ni(NO_3)_2$ decomposes to black nickelic oxide, Ni_2O_3.

$$4Ni(NO_3)_2 \xrightarrow{\Delta} 2Ni_2O_3 + \overline{8NO_2} + \overline{O_2}$$

Stronger heating results in the formation of nickelous oxide, NiO, which is apple-green. Ni_2O_3 is also formed, together with some NiO_2, by the action of Cl_2 or ClO^- on a suspension of $Ni(OH)_2$; but $Ni(OH)_2$ is not oxidized by atmospheric oxygen as $Cr(OH)_2$, $Mn(OH)_2$, $Fe(OH)_2$, and $Co(OH)_2$ are. Nor is there a nickel spinel. Ni_2O_3 is a strong oxidizing agent; it liberates chlorine from HCl. It forms the positive plate of the Edison storage cell. The formation of NiO_4 by electrolysis has been reported but not confirmed.

18.9. Metal Carbonyls

Nickel carbonyl, $Ni(CO)_4$, formed in the Mond process, is representative of a fairly large class of compounds in which the valence electrons of a free transition metal have been demoted to d orbitals, the octet orbitals and any remaining d orbitals being occupied by coordination with carbon monoxide, $: C : : : O :$. Since the valence electrons have not been lost, the metals in these compounds have an oxidation number of zero. Simple carbonyls that contain only one metal atom are formed by the metals in the chromium subgroup, Cr, Mo, and W; by Fe and by Ru and Os, the two elements directly below Fe; and by Ni, but not Pd or Pt. All these elements have even atomic numbers and all nine of the outer orbitals

contain electron pairs, shared or unshared. If the pairs of electrons shared with CO are counted for the metal atoms, each such atom has become isoelectronic with the following inert gas. (This is not unique. The same thing is true of all the complexes of Fe(II) and Co(III).) This is sometimes described in Langmuir's phrase by saying that the metals have attained the effective atomic number of the following inert gas. The structures of typical simple carbonyls are as follows:

$Cr(CO)_6$

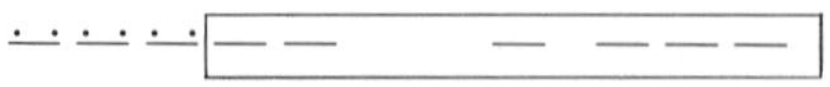

$Fe(CO)_5$

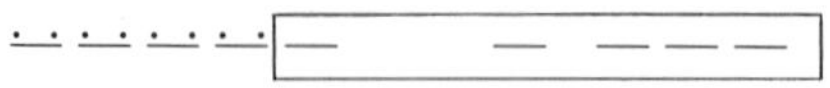

$Ni(CO)_4$

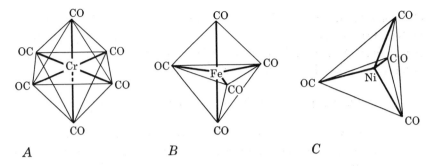

Fig. 18.2. The shape of metal carbonyl molecules. The heavy lines represent the axes of covalent bonds. The light lines are used merely to outline shapes: an octahedron (**A**), a trigonal bipyramid (**B**), and a tetrahedron (**C**). Each of these figures has a metal atom at its center, from which the covalent bonds radiate.

All carbonyls are three-dimensional, the bonds being directed as symmetrically as possible (Fig. 18.2). The first is an octahedron, the second a trigonal bipyramid, the third a tetrahedron. All are volatile and nonpolar, and dissolve readily in non-polar solvents such as benzene.

The transition elements with odd atomic numbers cannot form simple carbonyls that have inert gas structures, but many of them form more complex non-volatile compounds. For example, after cobalt coordinates four CO molecules, it has 1 odd electron, thus:

$Co(CO)_4$ ·· ·· ·· ·· ·–

The odd electrons in two such fragments form a covalent metal-to-metal bond, the result being the dimer, $(Co(CO)_4)_2$. Similarly, rhenium, with 7 electrons, is 1 electron short of the proper number for a pentacarbonyl.

$Re(CO)_5$ ·· ·· ·· ·–

It forms the dimer, $(Re(CO)_5)_2$. Other, more highly polymerized carbonyls exist for transition metals with even as well as odd atomic numbers.

There are other devices than polymerization for completing compounds of this type. Nitric oxide, NO, is built like CO except that it has an extra electron. This it can donate to another atom, itself becoming nitrosyl ion, NO^+. In cobalt nitrosocarbonyl, $Co(CO)_3NO$, this donated electron fills the last d orbital of the metal. The compound is very similar to $Ni(CO)_4$; so is the corresponding iron compound, $Fe(CO)_2(NO)_2$. When $Fe(CO)_5$ is dissolved in $Ba(OH)_2$ and the solution acidified, iron carbonyl hydride, $H_2Fe(CO)_4$, is formed.

$$Fe(CO)_5 + Ba^{++} + 2OH^- \rightarrow H_2Fe(CO)_4 + \underline{BaCO_3}$$

Cobalt carbonyl hydride, $HCo(CO)_4$, is formed from $(Co(CO)_4)_2$ in the same way. Both these compounds are acids; each proton is thought to be covalently bonded directly to the metal. Except for their charge, the anions are similar to $Ni(CO)_4$. In all the compounds mentioned in this paragraph the metal atoms actually have negative oxidation numbers, -2 for iron, -1 for cobalt, because they contain H^+ or NO^+. Other cases of zero and negative oxidation numbers for transition metals are known but are rare. For example, tetracyanonickelate (0) ion, $Ni(CN)_4^{-4}$, is a tetrahedral molecule that is exactly analogous to $Ni(CO)_4$ except for the charge.

18.10. Analytical Properties of Mn, Fe, Co, and Ni

Analytical Group III consists of the ions whose hydroxides or sulfides are precipitated by passing H_2S through a solution that has been made alkaline with NH_3. It is frequently called the ammonium sulfide group. The steps in its analysis are shown in Table 18.2.

For reasons mentioned in earlier sections of this book, the NH_3-NH_4^+ buffer forms complexes with Ni^{++} (Section 18.7), Co^{++} (Section 18.4), and Zn^{++} (Section 16.23, 16.27), but furnishes sufficient OH^- to precipitate the very insoluble hydroxides of aluminum, iron, and chromium. The complex ions in addition to Mn^{++} are successfully precipitated by the alkaline S^- solution. Thus the entire group can be separated from analytical Group IV, whose ions remain in solution under these conditions. To separate the nickel subgroup from the aluminum subgroup, the former is precipitated in a strong alkaline solution as insoluble hydroxides. Under these conditions the aluminum subgroup, as we saw in Section 16.27, remains in solution because of the amphoteric character of the members of this group. Even though present originally as Fe^{++}, iron finally becomes Fe^{+3} as the result of the oxidizing ability of aqua regia.

$$3FeS + 12H^+ + 3NO_3^- \rightarrow 3Fe^{+3} + \overline{3NO} + 6H_2O + \underline{3S}$$

Then $\quad\quad\quad\quad Fe^{+3} + 3OH^- \rightarrow Fe(OH)_3$

TABLE 18.2.

Separation and Analysis of the Nickel Subgroup of Analytical Group III

Al^{+3}, Cr^{+3}, Zn^{++}, Fe^{+3}, Co^{++}, Ni^{++}, Mn^{++}
and Group IV (Ba^{++}, Ca^{++}, Sr^{++}, Mg^{++}, Na^+, K^+)
|
NH_4^+-NH_4OH buffer
|
$Al(OH)_3$, $Cr(OH)_3$, $Fe(OH)_3$
$Co(NH_3)_6^{+3}$, $Ni(NH_3)_6^{++}$, Mn^{++}, $Zn(NH_3)_4^{++}$, and Group IV ions
|
S^{--}
|

| $Al(OH)_3$, $Cr(OH)_3$, ZnS, FeS, CoS, NiS, MnS | Group IV ions, |
| Aqua regia | Table 15.4 |

Al^{+3}, Cr^{+3}, Zn^{++}, Fe^{+3}, Co^{++}, Ni^{++}, Mn^{++}
|
OH^-
|
$Al(OH)_4^-$, $Cr(OH)_4^-$, $Zn(OH)_4^{--}$, $Fe(OH)_3$, $Co(OH)_2$, $Ni(OH)_2$, $Mn(OH)_2$
|
H_2O_2
|

Nickel subgroup   Aluminum subgroup

$Fe(OH)_3$, $Co(OH)_3$, $Ni(OH)_2$, MnO_2	$Al(OH)_4^-$, CrO_4^{--}, $Zn(OH)_4^{--}$,
$(H^+NO_3^-)$	Table 16.1
H_2O_2	

Fe^{+3}, Co^{++}, Ni^{++}, Mn^{++}
|
Divide solution into four portions, A, B, C, D.

A	B	C	D
NH_4SCN	NH_4OH	Solid NaF	Solid $NaBiO_3$
$FeSCN^{++}$	Discard. $C_4H_8N_2O_2$	NH_4SCN	MnO_4^-
Red			Violet-pink
	$(C_4H_7N_2O_2)_2Ni$	$Co(SCN)_4^{--}$	
	Red	Blue	

Cobalt and manganese are also oxidized, but in this case by H_2O_2 in alkaline solution.

$$2Co(OH)_2 + H_2O_2 \rightarrow 2Co(OH)_3$$

$$Mn(OH)_2 + H_2O_2 \rightarrow MnO_2 + 2H_2O$$

$Ni(OH)_2$ remains unchanged even under such strongly oxidizing conditions.

MnO_2 and the hydroxides of the nickel subgroup are dissolved in hot dilute HNO_3. The manganese and cobalt are reduced by the H_2O_2.

$$Fe(OH)_3 + 3H^+ \rightarrow Fe^{+3} + 3H_2O$$

$$Ni(OH)_2 + 2H^+ \rightarrow Ni^{++} + 2H_2O$$

$$2Co(OH)_3 + H_2O_2 + 4H^+ \rightarrow 2Co^{++} + 6H_2O + \overline{O_2}$$

$$MnO_2 + H_2O_2 + 2H^+ \rightarrow Mn^{++} + 2H_2O + \overline{O_2}$$

The nickel subgroup ions can be confirmed in the presence of each other. Fe^{+3} can be tested for in several ways. The buffer mixture of NH_4^+-NH_4OH can only precipitate $Fe(OH)_3$, which is red-brown. Reference to the beginning of Table 18.2 shows what happens to the other ions of this subgroup in the presence of this buffer mixture. Other standard tests for iron involve the use of NH_4SCN or $K_4Fe(CN)_6$. The former results in the formation of $FeSCN^{++}$ ion, which varies in color from a pale brownish-pink to blood-red, depending upon the amount of it produced in solution.

$$Fe^{+3} + SCN^- \rightarrow FeSCN^{++}$$

$K_4Fe(CN)_6$ will produce a precipitate of Prussian blue.

$$Fe^{+3} + K^+ + Fe(CN)_6^{-4} \rightarrow KFe_2(CN)_6$$

This test will also vary, depending upon the amount of Fe^{+3} in the solution. A trace of Fe^{+3} will result in forming a transparent blue solution instead of a precipitate or opaque suspension of Prussian blue. Because of the sensitivity of the latter two tests for Fe^{+3}, even the trace impurity of it usually found in reagents will result in weak positive tests.

The test for nickel involves the use of the reagent dimethylglyoxime (Section 18.7). Since an ammoniacal condition is needed before making the test, the existing acid solution must first be neutralized with concentrated NH_4OH. If iron is present it will precipitate as $Fe(OH)_3$. This precipitate is removed by filtration or centrifugation, and discarded. The dimethylglyoxime is now added and the formation of the red precipitate, nickel dimethylglyoxime, confirms the presence of Ni^{++}.

In spite of the great similarity of Ni^{++} and Co^{++}, when both are present Ni^{++} can be detected without interference from Co^{++}. This is true because Co^{++} cannot exist under the conditions in which nickel dimethylglyoxime forms. In the presence of NH_3, a good complexing agent for Co^{+3}, the Co^{+2} is oxidized by atmospheric oxygen.

$$4Co^{++} + \overline{O_2} + 2H_2O + 24NH_3 \rightarrow 4Co(NH_3)_6{}^{+3} + 4OH^-$$

A sensitive test for cobalt involves the use of the reagent NH_4SCN. A rather delicate blue-colored ion, $Co(SCN)_4{}^{--}$, confirms the presence of Co^{++}. Since the presence of iron would interfere because of forming red $FeSCN^{++}$ with the same reagent, it is necessary to complex the Fe^{+3} in order to prevent this. The addition of solid NaF results in the formation of the colorless fluoro- complex ion of iron.

$$Fe^{+3} + 6F^- \rightarrow FeF_6{}^{-3}$$

This reaction results in decreasing the Fe^{+3} to such a low level that very little, if any, $FeSCN^{++}$ can form.

A high concentration of SCN^- is needed to form the rather easily dissociated blue complex $Co(SCN)_4{}^{--}$. If any of the corresponding Ni(II) complex forms, its color is indistinguishable from the light green of $Ni(H_2O)_6{}^{++}$, so it does not interfere with the identification.

QUESTIONS AND PROBLEMS

1. What physical and chemical characteristics of cobalt make it useful in metallurgy? Name some of its important alloys and their special properties.

2. How similar is Co^{++} to the other divalent ions studied, with respect to types of compound and its covalent bonding character?

3. Using reactions, explain why pink cobalt chloride solution turns blue when heated or when H_2SO_4 or concentrated HCl is added.

4. What is the *dsp* electron distribution in the valence layer of Co^{++} ion and Co^{+3} ion? How does this correlate with the coordination numbers of these ions?

5. In which oxidation state does cobalt show the greatest tendency to form complexes? Why is it difficult to form Co^{+3} ion? Under what conditions does Co^{++} readily oxidize to Co(III)?

6. Draw structural line diagrams of the following complexes:

a. Monochloropentamminecobalt(III) ion.

b. Tetrachlorodiamminecobaltate(III) ion.

c. Trinitritotriamminecobalt(III).

7. How many isomers are there for each complex in question 6?

8. What is unique about the Ni^{++} ion in comparison to other divalent ions in this series?

9. Nickel(II) and cobalt(II) are better complex formers than other elements in this series, nickel being even better than cobalt. Explain.

10. How do colors and magnetic susceptibilities of the complexes of nickel and cobalt correlate with the electronic structure of the metal ion?

11. What are the general formulas of a spinel; a vitriol; a schönite salt; an alum?

12. Which of the compounds in question 11 do cobalt and nickel form? Since the other metals in this transition series also form these compounds, is the fact that Co and/or Ni fail to form any of them indicative of a trend or an inconsistency? Explain.

13. What is a carbonyl complex? In what way do carbonyl complexes of metals having odd atomic numbers differ from those with even atomic numbers?

14. In the following, an unknown was made with one or more of the ions listed in each part. After reading each part, mark an A, B, or C as follows:

A, Those definitely present.

B, Those definitely absent.

C, Those for which there is too little information to make a decision.

Assume that no other ions are present and that ions which are present are more than mere traces.

a. The colored unknown, which was known only to contain ions of the nickel group, formed a darkish pink precipitate with NaOH which darkened when H_2O_2 was added. The precipitate was dissolved in HNO_3 and treated with H_2O_2. Upon the addition of NH_4Cl and NH_4OH no precipitate formed, but the solution became reddish-brown. Treatment with $(NH_4)_2S$ gave a black sulfide which did not dissolve in dilute HCl. The decantate obtained from this last treatment gave a negative test for an analytical Group III ion.

    1. Fe^{+3}.   2. Ni^{++}.   3. Co^{++}.   4. Mn^{++}.

b. The unknown was treated with NH_4Cl and NH_4OH and formed a dark brown-red precipitate. When $(NH_4)_2S$ was added to this the precipitate darkened. The combined precipitate dissolved readily and completely in dilute HCl, forming a green solution. This solution was boiled with a few drops of HNO_3; when treated with excess NaOH, a reddish-brown precipitate and a pale green solution formed. When treated with H_2O_2 the solution turned yellow but the precipitate did not change color.

    1. Fe^{+3}.   2. Mn^{++}.   3. Cr^{+3}.   4. Co^{++}.   5. Al^{+3}.

c. On treatment with NH_4Cl and NH_4OH no precipitate formed and the resulting solution was colorless. When $(NH_4)_2S$ was added, a whitish precipitate formed which readily dissolved in HCl. When NaOH was added, a light precipitate formed which darkened on standing.

    1. Al^{+3}.   2. Mn^{++}.   3. Ni^{++}.   4. Zn^{++}.   5. Cr^{+3}.

d. A yellowish solution known only to contain ions of analytical Groups III and IV gave a reddish-brown precipitate and became colorless when treated with NH_4Cl-NH_4OH. After addition of $(NH_4)_2S$, centrifugation separated the material into a blackish precipitate and decantate A. The precipitate, on treatment with aqua regia followed by NaOH, gave a reddish-brown precipitate which did not darken upon addition of H_2O_2, and a colorless decantate B. Decantate B upon treatment with HNO_3 followed by NH_4OH gave a whitish precipitate. After appropriate preparation decantate A gave no precipitate when treated with NH_4OH-$(NH_4)_2CO_3$; its flame test was violet-colored. Assume excellent techniques, observation, and ideal behavior of reactions.

1. Fe^{+3}. 2. Ni^{++}. 3. Co^{++}. 4. Mn^{++}. 5. Al^{+3}. 6. Cr^{+3}. 7. Zn^{++}. 8. Na^+. 9. K^+. 10. Mg^{++}. 11. Ca^{++}. 12. Ba^{++}. 13. Sr^{++}.

19

Cadmium, mercury, tin, and lead

19.1. The Soft Metals; Periodic Table Relationships

In Chapters 17 and 18 we discussed hard, strong metals that are in common use. The present chapter is concerned with four soft metals with relatively low melting points—cadmium, mercury, tin, and lead. These, together with magnesium, aluminum, and zinc, which were studied in earlier chapters for reasons of chemistry, constitute the soft, low-melting metals in everyday use. Their relative grouping in the periodic table and their relationship to other soft metals are shown in Table 19.1, which is a section of consecutive groups from the long form of the periodic table.

Cadmium and mercury constitute the remainder of the zinc subfamily in Group IIB of the periodic table. Study of the properties of these three elements reveals the fact that their *electronegativity increases with atomic weight;* the reason for this is one of the unsolved problems of chemistry. This increase in electronegativity is the exact opposite of what holds true for all the main families. It is very characteristic of the subgroup families, the only distinct exceptions being niobium, tantalum, and tungsten. (The

TABLE 19.1. **Soft Metals and Their Melting Points (°C.)**

IB	IIB	IIIB	IVA	VA
Cu	Zn	Ga	Ge	As
1083°	419°	30°	959°	814° at 36 atm.
Ag	Cd	In	Sn	Sb
961°	321°	156°	232°	631°
Au	Hg	Tl	Pb	Bi
1063°	−39°	302°	327°	271°

elements rhenium through platinum seem in each case to have the *same* electronegativity as do the elements above them, respectively. Note, however, that electronegativities are given to only two significant figures. It is possible that the value for palladium, for example, may be 1.76 and that for platinum 1.84, although both are given as 1.8.) Whatever the reason for it, the relatively high electronegativity, and the corresponding readiness to form covalent bonds, is the keynote of the chemistry of the heavy transition metals.

Generalizations in regard to main and subgroup elements frequently do not hold good for Group IV. It is, in fact, difficult to decide which family is the main and which the subgroup.

From the viewpoint of both the long and the short form of the periodic table, either the titanium or the germanium group could be the subgroup without disrupting formalized generalizations, logic, or trends in either table. Shifting carbon and silicon to the titanium group in the long form would mean that Group IVA would be preceded by IIIA and followed by the VB subgroup, and that Group IVB would be preceded by IIIB and followed by VA. In the short form of the table, interchanging the letters A and B in Group IV would extend the grouping sequence, A followed by B, through Group IV instead of through Group III, and the sequence, B followed by A, would start with Group V instead of with Group IV.

From the point of view of electron structure, the titanium group should be the subgroup, for they are transition elements; each has two d electrons in the shell next to the valence shell. This argument seems to be justified in the case of titanium, which has divalent and trivalent ions like those of the typical subgroup elements which follow it in the $3d$ transition series—V, Cr, Mn, Fe, Co, and Ni. But in the titanium group the electronegativity *decreases* as we move down the family. This is main-group behavior. With the decreasing electronegativity, the two d electrons come to be lost almost as readily as the s electrons. The $+2$ valence is difficult to obtain for zirconium and hafnium. Thorium shows only the group valence, $+4$, like a main-group element.

The anomalous behavior of the electronegativity in the titanium group finds an echo in that of the germanium group. Instead of decreasing as we go downward, it remains constant (at least to two significant figures) at the 1.8 value of silicon. This is similar to the behavior of the electronegativity in typical subgroups, but in other respects these elements resemble the type elements, carbon and silicon, more closely than the titanium elements do.

It is natural that this confusion between main and subgroups should exist at Group IV because the elements are all equidistant from the nearest inert gas, i.e., the preceding inert gas in the case of the titanium elements and the following one in the case of the germanium elements.

19.2. Cadmium

In 1817 Stromeyer, investigating why a sample of ZnO was yellow, was surprised to find that the color was due not to Fe_2O_3 but to a small amount of the brown oxide of a new metal. He named the metal cadmium, from *cadmia,* the old name of the zinc ore in which he discovered it.

No cadmium is obtained as a primary product; it is always a by-product of the copper, lead, and zinc industries. Although most zinc ores contain cadmium, it seldom runs more than 3 per cent; the average is less than 0.5 per cent. Its separation from zinc was described in Section 16.21. Because of its volatility, any cadmium that is present in lead or copper furnaces is in the flue dust. It is reduced like zinc, but reduction is easier.

Cadmium is a soft, bluish-white metal which oxidizes slowly in air, forming a protective coating. A very thin cadmium plating protects iron and steel from rust. Its bright surface gave it an advantage over galvanized articles as far as appearance was concerned, but this was lost when a process to give zinc a bright electroplating was devised; moreover, cadmium costs about twelve times as much as zinc. Small amounts of cadmium are added to some casting alloys to lower the melting point, and to some extent it can replace tin in bearing metals and solders.

19.3. Cadmium Ion

Cadmium dissolves slowly in dilute non-oxidizing acids and readily in dilute HNO_3 to form colorless, poisonous $Cd(H_2O)_4^{++}$. Although this ion differs considerably from the divalent ions we studied earlier, it is most like Zn^{++}. Its sulfate forms neither a vitriol nor a schönite; instead, it crystallizes as $3CdSO_4 \cdot 8H_2O$. Its halides are said to be weakly ionized salts; in other words, there is a strong tendency for halide ions to displace water molecules from $Cd(H_2O)_4^{++}$, forming uncharged complexes like $Cd(H_2O)_2Cl_2$, together with smaller amounts of $Cd(H_2O)_3Cl^+$ and $Cd(H_2O)Cl_3^-$. In the presence of a high concentration of halide ions, particularly I^-, all the water molecules are displaced, yielding CdX_4^{--}. Insoluble cadmium salts—e.g., CdS—dissolve readily in KI solution.

$$\underline{CdS} + 4K^+ + 4I^- \rightarrow 4K^+ + S^{--} + CdI_4^{--}$$

The precipitation of CdS may be prevented in analytical procedures by having too high a Cl^- ion concentration—thereby reducing the Cd^{++} ion concentration through the formation of chloro- complexes—as well as by having too high an H^+ ion concentration, and thus too low a concentration of S^{--} ions. Cd^{++} forms an ammonia complex like that of zinc; $Cd(OH)_2$ dissolves readily in NH_3.

$$\underline{Cd(OH)_2} + 4NH_3 \rightarrow Cd(NH_3)_4^{++} + 2OH^-$$

There are two unexplained peculiarities in the behavior of Cd^{++}. (1) An ion with such strong ability to form covalent bonds would be expected to form a strongly acid hydrate and an amphoteric hydroxide. On the contrary, neither $Cd(OH)_2$ nor cadmium metal dissolves in NaOH. (2) CN^- ion ordinarily forms tighter complexes than the halide ions, to which it is very similar; but $Cd(CN)_4^{--}$ ion is sufficiently dissociated so that CdS can be precipitated in the presence of a considerable concentration of CN^- ion. Both these facts are analytically important.

Bright yellow CdS is precipitated from acidic solutions containing Cd^{++} ion if the H^+ ion concentration is not above 1.3 N. It is used by artists under the name of cadmium yellow and is an excellent and permanent pigment. Lighter shades are obtained by diluting it with barium sulfate. Orange to deep red shades result from admixture of the selenide, CdSe.

19.4. Mercury

The only ore of mercury is cinnabar, HgS, found in Almadén, Spain; in Idria and Monte Amiata, Italy; and in the volcanic part of California. There are less important deposits in Peru, Mexico, China, and Japan. Spain and Italy produce about 75 per cent of the world's supply. The

United States ranks third, but our consumption is over twice our production. The ores now mined rarely contain over 0.4 per cent mercury, and the outlook for the future is not promising. When World War II cut off most of our foreign supply, the consequently skyrocketing prices put a swarm of marginal one- and two-man diggings back into production. In a couple of years, however, all our domestic needs were supplied and a two-year stockpile was built up; as a result, the price went down to around the old rate of $90 a flask, and the little mines closed down. Our postwar prosperity and high wages prevented their reopening, even though the price has gone above $250 a flask. Mercury is sold in iron bottles, or flasks, that contain 3 arrobas, or 76 lb. (The *arroba* is an old Spanish unit of weight.) One flask (approximately $2\frac{1}{2}$ l. capacity) on each side of a pack saddle constitutes a full load for a mule because the density of mercury, 13.6, is so high.

Mercury is obtained from cinnabar by roasting.

$$\underline{HgS} + \overline{O_2} \xrightarrow{\Delta} \overline{Hg} + \overline{SO_2}$$

The flue gases are passed through coolers where the mercury vapor condenses and liquid mercury collects. Commercial mercury contains lead and sometimes zinc, tin, and bismuth. It leaves a "tail" when it runs over glass, and forms a black scum when shaken with air. It is purified by being run as a fine stream of globules through a column of 5 per cent HNO_3 that contains a little mercurous nitrate (Fig. 19.1). For scientific instruments required for exacting work, it is then distilled in a vacuum; the surface is kept still, for if the mercury boils, impurities are carried over in spray.

Most liquid metals dissolve other metals, and compounds are frequently formed. Mercury is no exception. Alloys in which it is an important part are called amalgams, a name that has pertained to mercury since ancient times. The joining of mercury and other metals to form amalgams (alloys) is called **amalgamation.** Mercury amalgamates readily with most metals, but not with the iron group or platinum. Its ability to amalgamate gold was extensively used to recover fine particles of free gold from sand or crushed ore that is carried over the surface of the mercury by a stream of water. However, extraction by NaCN solution is displacing the amalgamation process. Similarly, silver has replaced the amalgam of mercury and tin formerly used for coating mirrors. Dental amalgam consists of mercury with which is mixed an alloy consisting of 3 parts of silver to 1 of copper, with a little zinc and tin. The largest current application based on the solvent property of mercury is in mercury cathode electrolytic cells for sodium and chlorine.

Although for a metal, mercury is a poor conductor of electricity, its resistance being about seventy times that of silver, this does not interfere with its use in electrical contacts for small currents in scientific instruments. Mercoid silent wall switches do not heat up, because the current travels so short a distance through the mercury drop which closes the circuit when the switch is moved to the "on" position. An arc through mercury vapor produces mainly high-frequency light—blue, violet, and a large amount of ultraviolet. This high-energy light is very efficient for photochemical processes such as suntanning, sterilization, and photoengraving; it can be used for general illumination if the ultraviolet is transformed into the proper proportions of red to green light by a fluorescent coating on the lamp tube. When the arc is condensed into a small tube it becomes white and can be used for motion-picture projection. If the vapor from a dish of warm mercury is placed between a mercury vapor light and a fluorescent screen its shadow can be seen on the screen, since mercury vapor absorbs the same frequencies of light that excited mercury atoms emit. Mercury should never be heated in the open, for its vapor is extremely poisonous.

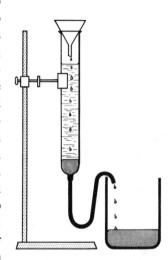

Fig. 19.1. Purification of mercury.

About 25 per cent of the mercury produced is used in the manufacture of the many mercury drugs that are on the market. Inorganic chemicals of some importance that are produced from mercury include calomel, corrosive sublimate, and fulminate of mercury.

19.5. Mercury(II) (Mercuric) Ion

Mercury is more electronegative than hydrogen, so it is not attacked by any non-oxidizing acid. It is readily oxidized to Hg(II) by nitric acid. The increase in tendency to form covalent bonds that we noted between magnesium and zinc, and between zinc and cadmium, continues between cadmium and mercury. Covalent bonding is the rule, not the exception, in compounds of mercury. The chloride, for example, is a typical covalent compound. It is more soluble in ether than in water, does not form HCl with hot concentrated H_2SO_4, and is not oxidized to chlorine by nitric acid. It sublimes at $277°$ C. (b.p. $302°$ C.), probably as

$$Cl—Hg \overset{\displaystyle Cl}{\underset{\displaystyle Cl}{<\;>}} Hg—Cl,$$ since the coordination number of Hg^{++} can be

either 3 or 4. In water it yields the uncharged complex $Hg(H_2O)Cl_2$ and 1 per cent or so of $Hg(H_2O)_2Cl^+$ and Cl^-. The amount of simple hydrated mercuric ion is very small.

$HgCl_2$ is a useful antiseptic and a dangerous poison. A 0.1 per cent solution is used to sterilize objects which cannot be boiled, including hands. When taken internally, the drug, which coagulates protein, in effect cauterizes the entire lining of the stomach. Immediate administration of egg white—this provides a protein for the $HgCl_2$ to act on—and an emetic, sometimes saves a life. Besides its use as an antiseptic, $HgCl_2$ is used in tanning. It is commonly called bichloride of mercury or, more appropriately, corrosive sublimate.

The only mercuric salts that contain water of crystallization are $HgF_2 \cdot 2H_2O$, $HgSO_4 \cdot H_2O$, and $Hg(NO_3)_2 \cdot \frac{1}{2}H_2O$. In all probability some of the coordination positions on the Hg^{++} are filled by anions in all three of these compounds, for there are not enough water molecules in any of them to satisfy the coordination number of Hg^{++}. The fact that all three salts can be crystallized only from their respective concentrated acids makes this all the more probable. If their solutions in concentrated acid are diluted only slightly, basic salts precipitate. We may imagine that as soon as a water molecule displaces one of these reluctant ligands (F^-, SO_4^{--}, or NO_3^-) from Hg^{++}, the molecule is so strongly acidified that it ionizes one or both protons immediately. $Hg(OH)F$, $Hg_3O_2(NO_3)_2$, and $Hg_3O_2SO_4$ are the compounds formed. The basic fluoride is the only instance of an OH group attached to Hg^{++}. There is no hydroxide. If one attempts to precipitate the hydroxide, he obtains the oxide instead.

$$Hg^{++} + 2NO_3^- + 2Na^+ + 2OH^- \rightarrow HgO + H_2O + 2Na^+ + 2NO_3^-$$

Zinc oxide is soluble in NaOH solutions, presumably by forming the hydrated hydroxide (e.g., $Zn(H_2O)_2(OH)_2$), which, being a weak acid, reacts further with the NaOH to form zincate ion, $Zn(OH)_4^{--}$. HgO has no tendency to hydrate, and is not amphoteric. HgO can also be prepared by heating mercury a long time at $350°$ C. in contact with air. Thus prepared, it is a dense red crystalline powder which turns black on being heated to a temperature near its decomposition point; the reaction is reversible. When precipitated from solution, HgO is yellow because of the small size of its particles.

Complex halo- anions of Hg(II) are readily formed. The crystalline compounds $HHgCl_3$, $KHgCl_3$, and Na_2HgCl_4 are known. Scarlet HgI_2 is precipitated from a Hg(II) solution by the addition of I^- ion.

$$HgCl_2 + 2K^+ + 2I^- \rightarrow \underline{HgI_2} + 2K^+ + 2Cl^-$$

It dissolves readily in an excess of the precipitant, forming colorless HgI_3^- or HgI_4^{--}. HgO dissolves in KI solution.

$$\underline{HgO} + 3K^+ + 3I^- + H_2O \rightarrow 3K^+ + HgI_3^- + 2OH^-$$

HgI_2 changes reversibly into a yellow crystalline form at 126° C. Ag_2HgI_4 undergoes a similar change at 60° C.; the colors are reversed. A piece of 6-mm. glass tubing filled with Ag_2HgI_4, sealed at both ends, and used as a stirring rod turns red at the end that is stuck into hot water; the other end stays yellow.

Passing H_2S through even a strongly acid solution containing Hg(II) precipitates black HgS, which is extremely insoluble.

$$HgCl_2 + \overline{H_2S} \rightarrow \underline{HgS} + 2H^+ + 2Cl^-$$

If the addition of H_2S is stopped while $HgCl_2$ is present in the solution, the black precipitate may become white $HgCl_2 \cdot 2HgS$. Resuming the addition of H_2S turns this white precipitate first red, then back to black HgS. Sublimation of amorphous HgS or its digestion with Na_2S solution produces the less soluble crystalline scarlet form, the pigment known as vermilion. HgS is insoluble in boiling concentrated HCl or dilute HNO_3. It dissolves slowly in hot concentrated HNO_3, which oxidizes the S^{--} to SO_4^{--}, and quickly in aqua regia because the Hg^{++} is also removed by complexing with Cl^- ion.

$$\underline{HgS} + 8H^+ + 8NO_3^- + 4Cl^- \rightarrow SO_4^{--} + HgCl_4^{--} + 4H_2O + \overline{8NO_2}$$

HgS is easily soluble in a mixture of NaOH and $(NH_4)_2S$, forming the colorless dithiomercurate(II) ion, HgS_2^{--}. It is unusual to find the sulfide amphoteric when the oxide is not. Amphoteric sulfides (thioamphoterism) will be discussed in Chapter 20.

Hg(II) readily takes up NH_3 from a water solution, forming compounds in which NH_3 takes the place of the water of crystallization (e.g., $HgCl_2 \cdot 2NH_3$), NH_2^- replaces OH^- (as in $Hg(NH_2)Cl$), and NH^{--} substitutes for O^{--}. One example of the latter, $(—Hg—O—Hg—NH—)_x$, is explosive, as are many other compounds of heavy metals with N^{-3}. Compounds of the type described in this paragraph are common enough, but are usually formed in anhydrous liquid NH_3 solution and are decomposed by water. When these compounds contain mercury, they are unique in that they form in the presence of water. Mercuric amido chloride, $Hg(NH_2)Cl$, the second compound mentioned above, is valuable in qualitative analysis, as we shall see. An amusing if not useful mercury-nitrogen compound is the thiocyanate, $Hg(CNS)_2$. A small pellet of this material, when ignited, burns slowly, producing poisonous fumes of mercury and SO_2, and a long wormlike mass of a polymerized cyanogen product known as Pharaoh's serpent. Of great use as a detonator, although dangerous, is mercuric isocyanate, or fulminate, $Hg(ONC)_2$, which is used in blasting caps to detonate high explosives, and in rifle and revolver cartridges—around the rim of rim-fire and in the cap of center-fire cartridges. It is sensitive both to heat and to shock or friction.

19.6. Mercury(I) (Mercurous) Ion

The most curious manifestation of the ability of Hg(II) to form covalent bonds is the fact that it can coordinate the pair of valence electrons in the s orbital in the outside shell of a free mercury atom and form the unique mercurous ion, Hg_2^{++}. With the bonding electron pair largely concealed between the two atoms, from either end this ion looks much like an Au^+ or Ag^+ ion. Like them, it has a set of completely filled d orbitals in its surface, and a charge which, if not $+1$, is $+1$ *per atom*. Accordingly, it behaves much like Ag^+ ion; in particular, it forms insoluble halides. The simple hydrated cation is only slightly acid and forms ordinary salts, including the carbonate.

The striking difference between Ag^+ and Hg_2^{++} is the way the latter dismutes into Hg(II) and free mercury on the addition of any reagent which bonds strongly with Hg(II). Thus its reaction with H_2S is:

$$Hg_2^{++} + H_2S \rightarrow \underline{Hg} + \underline{HgS} + 2H^+$$

The analogous mixture of Hg and HgO was once thought to be Hg_2O, which does not exist. This ability to dismute is used to distinguish AgCl from Hg_2Cl_2. When NH_3 is added, AgCl dissolves, forming $Ag(NH_3)_2^+$, but Hg_2Cl_2 dismutes.

$$Hg_2Cl_2 + 2NH_3 \rightarrow Hg + Hg(NH_2)Cl + NH_4^+ + Cl^-$$

Although $Hg(NH_2)Cl$ is white, its mixture with finely divided mercury is black. This reaction with NH_3 is responsible for calomel (Gr., *kalomelas,* beautiful black), the common name of Hg_2Cl_2. Calomel is used in medicine as a purgative. Hg_2Cl_2, like AgCl, is somewhat soluble in HCl because of the formation of a chloro- complex.

Hg_2^{++} ion in solution is readily oxidized to Hg(II). Unless some free mercury is kept in contact with the solution, any solution containing a mercurous salt will give a positive analytical test for Hg(II). The reduction of $HgCl_2$ to calomel by means of stannous ion, Sn^{++}, is the standard confirmatory test for Hg(II). If only a drop of $SnCl_2$ is added, the white precipitate of Hg_2Cl_2 forms. If an excess of the reducing agent is added, the precipitate turns gray and then black as it is reduced to metallic mercury.

$$2HgCl_2 + Sn^{++} + 2Cl^- + 2H^+ + 2Cl^- \rightarrow Hg_2Cl_2 + H_2SnCl_6$$

$$Hg_2Cl_2 + Sn^{++} + 2Cl^- + 2H^+ + 2Cl^- \rightarrow 2Hg + H_2SnCl_6$$

Tests like this are double-barreled. If Sn^{++} can be used to test for Hg^{++}, then Hg^{++} can be used to test for Sn^{++}.

19.7. History and Occurrence of Tin

Tin articles are known at least as early as the 18th Dynasty (ca. 1400 B.C.) in Egypt. Homer called tin *kassiteros* and Pliny *plumbum candidum* ("white lead," in contrast to *plumbum nigrum,* "black lead"); Homer stated that it came from the Cassiterides in the Atlantic. (The Cassiterides, or Tin Islands, were the British Isles; the Cornish tin mines were worked into modern times.) The metal was later called *stannum,* whence the symbol Sn.

The only important ore of tin is cassiterite, or tinstone, SnO_2, which is found in veins and alluvial deposits (stream tin) mainly in Southeast Asia, but also in Bolivia and in uncertain quantities in Africa. In the 1930's dire predictions were being made of the imminent exhaustion of the world's supply of tin, since no new ore deposits had been found in many years. Fortunately for the Allies, after the fall of Singapore it was found possible to expand Bolivian tin mining enough to take care of minimum requirements. Nevertheless, the situation remains tight and the outlook for the future not too bright. The price of tin—nearly a dollar a pound—reflects the present necessity of working even marginal deposits. Practically no tin is produced in the United States, but we rank first as a user, consuming some 60,000 tons a year. The can companies estimate that we use about 10 billion tin cans each year. The term tin can does not mean that the can is made from tin; the very thin tin coating on the steel seldom amounts to over 2 per cent, by weight, of the can.

The opportune perfecting of an electrolytic method for depositing extremely thin yet perfect coatings of tin was all that prevented the shortage of tin during World War II from being disastrous. It made possible the saving of two-thirds of the tin formerly used in the hot-dip process. The trouble with early attempts to electroplate tin was the annoying fact that a very thin coat of tin consisted of separate crystals of tin, with bare steel between them. The saving invention used the idea of passing the coated tin through a high-frequency alternating electrical field (electronic heating) which melted the tin crystals just long enough to permit them to flow out and coalesce before they solidified again.

Curiously, tin gives better protection to the inside of a can of tomatoes or fruit than it does to the outside. The outside protection is merely inert coating protection, whereas the inside protection is galvanic (Section 22.16). This is because tin, although less active than iron when in contact with neutral or alkaline solutions, is more active than iron when in contact with acid. A trace of acid is added to many neutral foods when they are canned, in order to take advantage of this fact.

Tin ores are nearly always low grade; many that are worked do not contain over 0.5 per cent tin. SnO_2 is quite heavy and can be separated from the pulverized ore by floating away the impurities. If the ore contains sulfur or arsenic, it is roasted first; otherwise the concentrate is smelted without further treatment.

Although a few blast furnaces are used in Germany and India, most of the ore is smelted in reverberatory furnaces. One of these large furnaces in Singapore can produce 30,000 to 50,000 tons of tin per year. Another furnace, in Texas City (the only one in the United States, built during the war), now smelts all American purchases of Bolivian tin ore. A mixture of SnO_2 ore, powdered coal, and flux is heated on the furnace floor until the tin oxide is reduced to molten metallic tin which is collected in settling basins. The tin in these basins is kept in the molten state to bring the slag to the surface. Some tin is volatilized, necessitating equipment for collecting the dust. Since the first-run slag may contain 10 to 25 per cent tin, it is returned to the furnace and resmelted.

Tin is refined by heating the crude tin just enough to melt the pure tin. The hard brittle residue which remains usually contains iron, arsenic, sulfur, lead, and 20 per cent tin, and is known as hard lead. This can be purified further.

The molten high-quality tin is further purified by stirring with poles made from green wood. The gases produced bring the impurities to the top and reduce back to metal some of the SnO_2 which always forms on the surface when molten tin is exposed to the air.

Some 3000 tons of tin are recovered annually in this country from scrap tin plate. During World War II used tin cans also were salvaged and detinned, yielding 27,000 tons of tin a year. Although this was a lifesaver during the wartime shortage of tin, the amount salvaged does not pay the cost of collecting the tin cans in peacetime. Tin plate is detinned with chlorine, which forms volatile $SnCl_4$ at too low a temperature for iron to be attacked. The residue of scrap iron is baled and smelted.

19.8. Metallic Tin

Tin is a soft, bright, white metal with a density of 7.3. Metallic tin is stable between 13° and 161° C. and is malleable. Formerly it was rolled for use as tin foil, but aluminum foil has now replaced it almost completely. When a rod of white tin is bent, it creaks as the crystals slip. **Slip** in crystals is the movement of sheets or planes of atoms as they slide over each other, much as individual cards in a deck slide over each other when the top edge of the deck is pushed gently.) This "cry of tin" is characteristic of tin, though cadmium exhibits it to some extent. Zinc "cries" to a small extent, but breaks. Above the 161° C. transition point the crystalline structure of tin changes; this modification has the appropriate name of brittle tin, for this tin can be broken into pieces by the blow of a hammer. Below 13° C. the stable form of tin is known as gray tin. White tin is metastable below that temperature, but eventually it crumbles to a gray powder with a lower density, 5.8. The change is most rapid at −50° C. Once initiated, it continues as long as the temperature is below the transition point. This change is known as tin pest or tin disease.*

Tin is not attacked by air or water, separately or together, or by dilute H_2SO_4. It is attacked very slowly by dilute HCl, and rapidly by hot concentrated HCl.

---

*Tin disease has caused museum pieces to crumble to powder in a short time. Some of the many stories about it concern the tin pipes of an organ in Russia which crumbled, the Russian government's block tin which was found to be a powder, and the tin buttons which turned to powder just before they were to be sewed on the soldiers' uniforms.

$$\underline{Sn} + 2H^+ + 4Cl^- \rightarrow SnCl_4^{--} + \overline{H_2}$$

Dilute HNO_3 reacts slowly.

$$\underline{4Sn} + 10H^+ + 10NO_3^- \rightarrow 4Sn^{++} + NH_4^+ + 9NO_3^- + 3H_2O$$

Concentrated HNO_3 oxidizes it to a partially hydrated tin(IV) oxide called metastannic acid; the reaction is violent and the oxide is insoluble in dilute acids. Aqua regia readily dissolves tin, forming H_2SnCl_6.

$$\underline{Sn} + 4H^+ + 4NO_3^- + 6H^+ + 6Cl^- \rightarrow H_2SnCl_6 + \overline{4NO_2} + 4H_2O$$

Tin does not liberate hydrogen from water with appreciable speed below red heat. Probably for this reason, tin is attacked only slowly by boiling concentrated NaOH solution, although both its oxides dissolve readily in bases. All metals that dissolve in NaOH solution do so by liberating hydrogen from water, not from OH⁻ ion.

Tin plate is so commonly called tin that tin ingots or anything made of pure solid tin is distinguished by the name block tin. Block tin is

TABLE 19.2 **Percentage Composition of Alloys of Tin**

	Tin	Anti-mony	Lead	Cop-per	Zinc	Cad-mium	Bis-muth	Phos-phorus
Babbitt metal	90	7	...	3	...	...	...	...
Britannia metal	86	10	...	1	3	...	...	...
Old pewter	79	1	20	...	...	...	...	...
Modern pewter	89	7	...	2	...	...	2	...
Type metal (British)	10	30	60	...	...	...	...	...
Type metal (American)	10	18	70	2	...	...	...	...
Linotype metal	3	$13\frac{1}{2}$	$83\frac{1}{2}$	...	...	...	...	...
Monotype metal	5	15	80	...	...	...	...	...
Fine solder	67	...	33	...	...	...	...	...
Soft solder	50	...	50	...	...	...	...	...
Cheap solder	30	...	70	...	...	...	...	...
Rose's metal 94°	25	...	25	...	...	...	50	...
Wood's metal 71°	$12\frac{1}{2}$	...	25	...	...	$12\frac{1}{2}$	50	...
Lipowitz' metal 60°	$13\frac{1}{3}$	...	$26\frac{2}{3}$	...	...	10	50	...
Bronze (gun metal)	10	...	...	90	...	...	...	...
Speculum metal	$33\frac{1}{3}$	...	...	$66\frac{2}{3}$	...	...	...	...
Bell metal	20	...	...	80	...	...	...	...
Coin bronze	1	...	...	98	1	...	...	...
Phosphor bronze	5–15	...	...	82–95	...	...	...	$\frac{1}{4}$–$2\frac{1}{2}$

sometimes used in laboratories for distilled water lines, but copper heavily plated with tin is more common when the characteristic properties of tin are required. The real importance of tin, however, is its use in alloys. The composition of a number of tin alloys is given in Table 19.2.

19.9. The Inert Pair of Electrons

The outer electronic structure of tin and lead is:

From our study of the non-metals in Groups V, VI, and VII of the periodic table we should expect tin and lead to complete the valence octet by forming covalent compounds of the SnH_4 and $SnCl_4$ type. This they do, although the hydrogen compounds are very unstable and the chlorides have unexpected Lewis acid properties. But in these metals we encounter for the first time a new type of behavior—the complete loss of p electrons. Carbon, the first element in this family, is a non-metal; but its electronegativity is only 2.5 and the first traces of metallic properties are evident in the black color, the semimetallic luster, and the electrical conductivity of one of its forms, graphite. Tin and lead have a value of 1.8 in electronegativity, and the free elements are definitely metallic; hence we should expect strong metallic properties to be evident in their chemistry. But how? The loss of 4 valence electrons is too much to look for with 10 d electrons in the surface of the kernels, for the effective charge acting on the valence electrons is considerably more than $+4$. Therefore only the p electrons are lost, and Sn^{++} and Pb^{++} ions are formed. The remaining 2 valence electrons fill the spherical s orbital in the outer shell; this means no incomplete subshells, no d electrons in the outer layer, a moderate ionic charge, and perfect spherical symmetry. This sounds like the description of a main-group ion, but one in Group II, not Group IV. The properties of the Sn^{++} and Pb^{++} ions actually do resemble those of the ions in Group II, being intermediate between the main-group and subgroup properties. Sn^{++} is more like Zn^{++}, whereas Pb^{++} more closely resembles Ba^{++}.

When a non-metal completes its valence octet by sharing, any unshared pairs of electrons behave geometrically as though they were shared, moving in orbitals symmetrical to those of the shared pairs; compare NH_3, H_2O, H_3O^+, ICl_4^-, IF_5, etc. But although Sn^{++} and Pb^{++} have considerable ability to form covalent bonds, the s electrons in their valence shells are *stereochemically inert*. These electrons are called an inert pair because they have no effect on the shape of any complex which the ion may form.

The loss of all p electrons, while retaining the pair of s electrons, is characteristic of the elements on either side of tin—indium and antimony—and of lead—thallium and bismuth.

19.10. Tin(II) (Stannous) Ion

As was stated above, Sn^{++} ion resembles Zn^{++} ion considerably. It is very acidic; if $SnCl_2 \cdot 2H_2O$ (tin salt) is dissolved in more than a small amount of water, $Sn(H_2O)_4^{++}$ ionizes sufficiently so that a basic chloride begins to form; if there is a great deal of water, $Sn(OH)Cl \cdot \frac{1}{2}H_2O$ precipitates. If HCl is added, the dilute acid solution remains clear; in concentrated HCl, the Cl^- ions replace water molecules, as is true of $Zn(H_2O)_4^{++}$, and $SnCl_4^{--}$ is formed. The stable salt, ammonium chlorostannite, $(NH_4)_2SnCl_4$, can be crystallized.

The gelatinous white stannous hydroxide, $Sn(OH)_2$, is precipitated by the addition of NaOH; it dissolves in excess NaOH to stannite ion, $Sn(OH)_4^{--}$, or the dehydrated form of stannite ion, SnO_2^{--}. The dehydration of $Sn(OH)_2$ to black SnO is easily done by heating. SnO is readily oxidized to SnO_2 and both stannous and stannite ions are good reducing agents. The half-reactions are, respectively:

$$SnCl_4^{--} + 2H^+ + 2Cl^- \rightarrow H_2SnCl_6 + 2e^-$$
$$Sn(OH)_4^{--} + 2OH^- \rightarrow Sn(OH)_6^{--} + 2e^-$$

The use of the reaction in acid solution was described at the end of Section 19.6 as a test for Hg(II). The reaction in basic solution is used as a confirmatory test for Bi(III) as described in Section 20.9.

Dark brown SnS is precipitated when H_2S is passed through an acidified solution of Sn(II). SnS is soluble in hot concentrated HCl but not in $(NH_4)_2S$. It is easily oxidized to SnS_3^{--} ion by S_2^{--} ion.

$$\underline{SnS} + 2NH_4^+ + S_2^{--} \rightarrow 2NH_4^+ + SnS_3^{--}$$

Hence SnS dissolves in yellow ammonium sulfide.

19.11. Tin(IV) (Stannic) Ion

The gas SnH_4 is prepared only with considerable difficulty. It is stable for some days at room temperature but decomposes rapidly above 150° C. SnO_2, prepared by oxidizing tin with either air or concentrated

HNO_3, is a white powder (putty powder) that is soft to the touch because of its small particle size; but the individual crystallites are hard enough for it to be used as a fine polishing powder; it is also used in opacifying milk glass and white glazes. Massive native SnO_2 is as hard as steel and nearly infusible. $SnCl_4$ is a volatile liquid that hydrolyzes to stannic hydroxide, an acid.

Qualitatively, all these statements about the chemistry of tin(IV) describe typical non-metallic behavior, but behavior exhibited in an extremely non-typical degree. That tin(IV) is barely classifiable as non-metallic is indicated by the instability of the hydride, the insolubility of the oxide, and the weakness and indefinite composition of the acid. The properties and to some extent the composition of stannic acid depend upon how it is prepared. The coordination number of Sn(IV) for small atoms is 6; so the formula of the hydroxide should be $Sn(H_2O)_2(OH)_4$, and the hydroxide should be a diprotic acid. Actually the stannate ion, $Sn(OH)_6^{--}$, is well known, although the formula is usually written in the dehydrated form, SnO_3^{--}. But the hydroxide itself loses water and condenses into polystannic acids; there is much disagreement about the nature of these acids. Alpha-stannic acid is prepared by oxidizing tin with HNO_3; it dries at 100° C. to a substance whose simple empirical formula is H_2SnO_3, but the true molecule, $(H_2SnO_3)_x$, is certainly a complex substance, for only part of its protons are replaceable. It dissolves in HCl to form chlorostannic acid, which is identical with a solution of $SnCl_4$ in HCl.

$$H_2SnO_3 + 6H^+ + 6Cl^- \rightarrow H_2SnCl_6 + 3H_2O$$

On standing, this solution slowly deposits beta-stannic acid, or metastannic acid, which is approximately identical with alpha-stannic acid in composition, but is insoluble in dilute acids and shows other differences in behavior. Chlorostannic acid is a simple monomer that forms well-defined salts.

Even $SnCl_4$ does not behave entirely like a non-metal chloride; it forms the crystalline hydrate, $SnCl_4 \cdot 5H_2O$. This hydrate is prepared commercially from the $SnCl_4$ obtained in the detinning of tin-plate scrap, and is used as a mordant and weighting agent for silk. $SnCl_4$ combines directly with Cl^- ion, forming chlorostannates.

$$SnCl_4 + 2NH_4Cl \rightarrow (NH_4)_2SnCl_6$$

This reaction shows that $SnCl_4$ is a Lewis acid. The salt $(NH_4)_2SnCl_6$ was formerly used as a mordant with madder red and pink dyes and was known commercially as pink salt; however, it has been replaced by $SnCl_4 \cdot 5H_2O$.

In weighting and fireproofing silk with SnO_2 the cloth is soaked in a solution of $Na_2Sn(OH)_6$ and then dried. If it were now treated with HCl, a gelatinous precipitate of stannic hydroxide would form on the surface and prevent the HCl from penetrating to the inside of the fiber until it had been dissolved to H_2SnCl_6 by increasing the concentration of the acid. This difficulty has been solved ingeniously by using an acid that is too weak to react with the stannate ion at room temperature, namely, NH_4^+ ion. The cloth is soaked in a solution of $(NH_4)_2SO_4$, the NH_4^+ ions easily penetrating everywhere there are $Sn(OH)_6^{--}$ ions. Heat is then applied, whereupon the proton transfer takes place, the stannic acid is dehydrated, and the residual NH_3 is driven off. The Na_2SO_4 is washed out of the cloth, leaving the insoluble SnO_2.

$$2Na^+ + Sn(OH)_6^{--} + 2NH_4^+ + SO_4^{--} \rightarrow Sn(H_2O)_2(OH)_4 + \overline{2NH_3} + 2Na^+ + SO_4^{--}$$
$$\hookrightarrow \underline{SnO_2} + \overline{4H_2O}$$

Stannic oxide is important as a mordant, and several patents have been taken out for ways of depositing it on cloth. A rough check on the amount of SnO_2 in silk is made by weighing the piece of cloth, burning it, and weighing the ash; the SnO_2 usually makes up more than 50 per cent of the total weight.

Pale yellow SnS_2 is formed by passing H_2S through moderately acid solutions of stannic salts, i.e., those containing $SnCl_6^{--}$, $Sn(OH)_6^{--}$, or some intermediate; no cation containing $Sn(IV)$ exists. SnS_2 is soluble in excess acid; it dissolves easily in $(NH_4)_2S$, forming thiostannate ion.

$$\underline{SnS_2} + S^{--} \rightleftharpoons SnS_3^{--}$$

Acidification of a thiostannate solution removes the S^{--} ion which is in equilibrium with it and reprecipitates the SnS_2. Note that in analysis a very similar-looking precipitate of sulfur is obtained by acidifying a solution of yellow ammonium sulfide that contains S_2^{--} ion.

$$2H^+ + S_2^{--} \rightarrow \overline{H_2S} + \underline{S}$$

19.12. History and Occurrence of Lead

A small lead statue in the British Museum is attributed to the First Dynasty in Egypt (3400 B.C.), and lead is mentioned in the Bible. In ancient days it was sometimes confused with tin; thus the little use the Greeks made of it suggests that they considered it tin. The Romans, however, used large quantities of *plumbum,* as they called it, for water pipes. Indeed, it is this word *plumbum* that is responsible for our word plumbing. Although the manufacture of lead pipe still constitutes one of the largest single uses of the metal, lead is now used mostly for waste and sewer pipes rather than for incoming water pipes. Below 100° C., lead is not attacked by dry air or by pure water, but it is appreciably dissolved by water containing air and CO_2. Ordinarily SO_4^{--} ion is also present and the lead soon forms an impervious protective coating of basic lead sulfate. In the absence of SO_4^{--} an almost equally efficient protective coating of basic carbonate usually forms.

$$2Pb + \overline{O_2} + H_2O + \overline{CO_2} \rightarrow \underline{Pb(OH)_2 \cdot PbCO_3}$$

But if an unusual amount of CO_2 is present and SO_4^{--} is absent, enough of this coating can dissolve to put a dangerous amount of Pb^{++} into solution.

$$\underline{Pb(OH)_2 \cdot PbCO_3} + H_2O + \overline{3CO_2} \rightarrow 2Pb^{++} + 4HCO_3^-$$

In fact, almost any measurable amount of Pb^{++} is dangerous in drinking water, because its poisonous action is cumulative. Water that has this unusual solvency for lead occurs occasionally; the resultant poisonings are responsible for present-day objections to the use of lead for pipes that are in contact with any drinking water.

No such excess of CO_2 can be present in water that is exposed to the open air, although rain water contains enough CO_2 to assure the formation of the protective basic carbonate coating. Lead roofing (Fig. 19.2) is therefore practically everlasting. In spite of its weight (density 11.35) and its cost, lead is still used in some cases to roof buildings which are expected to last indefinitely; the National Cathedral in Washington, D.C., has a lead roof.

The chief ore of lead is galena, PbS, a dense (7.5) mineral that cleaves cubically into flat faces that have a brilliant, dark gray metallic luster. Galena is widely distributed. The town of Galena, Missouri, was named for it because of rich veins in the vicinity. The United States consumes half the world's output of lead and formerly produced a third of it. Because of the exhaustion of the richest veins during World War II, we now import nearly a million tons a year but produce only some 300,000 tons. The price of lead is unstable, ranging between 10 and 30 cents per pound.

19.13. Metallic Lead

Lead ore which has been roasted to a mixture of PbO and $PbSO_4$ is usually mixed with additional unroasted ore and lime for a flux for a blast furnace charge. The PbS does most of the reduction.

Fig. 19.2. Lead roofs on St. Sophia, Istanbul, which were installed between 532 and 537 A.D. (From Gendreau, New York.)

$$PbS + 2PbO \xrightarrow{\Delta} 3Pb + \overline{SO_2}$$
$$PbS + PbSO_4 \xrightarrow{\Delta} 2Pb + \overline{2SO_2}$$

CO in the blast furnace gas also reduces some of the PbO and $PbSO_4$. Any excess PbS is reduced in the hearth of the furnace when it comes in contact with molten iron, produced from Fe_2O_3 that is present in the ore as impurity or is added intentionally.

$$PbS + Fe \rightarrow Pb + FeS$$

548 THE NATURE OF ATOMS AND MOLECULES

The crude lead contains small amounts of several other metals whose ores were not completely separated from the lead ore during its concentration. They make the metal hard. It is softened by being left, melted, on the hearth of a reverberatory furnace until the copper, antimony, bismuth, and iron, along with a little of the lead, are oxidized and form a scum on top, which is then removed. Most galena contains from 0.01 to 0.1 per cent of silver; in fact, it is a major source of silver. The **Parkes process** is one method of recovering this valuable metal. It is based on the fact that lead and zinc dissolve in each other to the extent of only 1 per cent, but silver is much more soluble in zinc than in lead; it forms an alloy with the zinc that melts at a temperature above the melting point of zinc. Hence, if a small amount of zinc is mixed with silver-bearing lead (base bullion or lead bullion), it extracts the silver, together with any gold or copper that may be present, and rises to the surface. When cooled, it solidifies into a crust that can be skimmed off and worked for its content of precious metals. The zinc which remains in the lead is removed as the oxide by blowing air and steam through the desilvered lead. The lead can be further purified by adding a little calcium as a scavenger; it combines with non-metallic impurities and forms alloys with others, producing a floating scum or dross. Excess calcium, which would make the lead brittle, is removed by blowing chlorine through the lead; this also removes any traces of bismuth that may be present.

Another method of refining lead bullion is the **Betts electrolytic process.** In it, thick anodes of the lead bullion are suspended in a bath of fluosilicic acid, H_2SiF_6, and lead fluosilicate, $PbSiF_6$; pure sheet lead is used for the cathodes. At the voltage used in this process, active metals like iron and zinc remain in solution. The less active metallic impurities, such as copper, gold, silver, and bismuth, do not dissolve in the electrolyte; they drop beneath the anode and form the anode mud. Although the Parkes process is cheaper, the Betts process is widely used because many industries require electrolytic lead in which total impurities can easily be limited to 0.01 per cent.

A freshly cut surface of lead has an almost silvery luster, but it rapidly becomes a dull bluish-gray as the protective coating forms. Lead is plastic, especially when hot. In making pipe joints in plumbing, it can be "wiped" into shape with a leather "palm"; the lead pipe itself is formed by extrusion. When greater strength is required, lead can be hardened by the addition of a little antimony. As was said earlier, lead is used mainly for protective purposes. However, in some cases its flexibility is also an advantage. For example, both suspended and underground telephone cables are made watertight and weatherproof by means of a seamless lead covering that is extruded around the cable as the wires pass through the center of the die. A particularly valuable property of lead is its resistance to H_2SO_4, because of the insolubility of $PbSO_4$; this makes possible the lead chamber process for producing H_2SO_4, and the use of lead for acid lines in chemical industries. In the familiar automobile storage battery, not only the active substance in the negative plate, but the plates themselves are lead because the electrolyte is H_2SO_4. Steel coated with lead is called terne plate.

19.14. Lead Ion, Pb++

Lead is insoluble in dilute HCl or H_2SO_4, or in concentrated HNO_3, because of the formation of protective coatings of the respective salts. It dissolves readily in dilute HNO_3 or hot concentrated H_2SO_4.

$$\underline{3Pb} + 8(H^+ + NO_3^-) \rightarrow 3Pb^{++} + 6NO_3^- + 4H_2O + \overline{2NO}$$
$$\underline{Pb} + 3(H^+ + HSO_4^-) \rightarrow Pb^{++} + 2HSO_4^- + 2H_2O + \overline{SO_2}$$

In the latter case $PbSO_4$ is precipitated on dilution.

The Pb^{++} ion which is formed is less acidic than Sn^{++} ion and has less tendency to form covalent bonds. Hence it greatly resembles Ba^{++} ion. However, in Ba^{++} ion both these properties are so weak as to be negligible, which is not the case with Pb^{++} ion. The resemblance to Ba^{++} ion is evident in the isomorphism of the nitrates and the insolubility of the sulfates and chromates. ($PbCrO_4$ is the least soluble lead salt.)

The difference between Ba^{++} and Pb^{++} ions in regard to covalent bond formation begins to show up in the halides. Less than 1 per cent of $PbCl_2$ dissolves in cold water, but 3.2 per cent dissolves in boiling water. $PbBr_2$ and PbI_2 are even less soluble in cold water and more soluble in hot. PbI_2 is colored; it separates in golden-yellow spangles as the hot solution cools. All the lead halides are soluble in the presence of a *large* excess of halide ion, forming complex ions such as $Pb_2Cl_5^-$ and PbI_3^-.

The most important complex salt of lead is the acetate, $Pb(C_2H_3O_2)_2 \cdot 3H_2O$. It is known as sugar of lead because of its sweet taste, but like other soluble lead salts it is poisonous. It is used in the manufacture of other lead compounds and as a mordant in dyeing. Paper soaked in lead acetate solution is used as a test for H_2S, because traces of the gas turn the paper brown or black; there is frequently a metallic luster on the surface that calls to mind the luster of galena. Curiously enough, little is known about the exact molecular species present in a lead acetate solution, but presumably practically all the Pb^{++} ions are attached to one, two, or three $C_2H_3O_2^-$ ions, the remaining coordination positions being occupied by water molecules. At any rate, $C_2H_3O_2^-$ can lower the concentration of simple hydrated lead ion to such an extent that all the insoluble lead salts except the chromate and the sulfide dissolve in warm concentrated $NH_4C_2H_3O_2$ solution. (This is a means of distinguishing between $PbSO_4$ and $BaSO_4$.)

Gelatinous white $Pb(OH)_2$ is obtained when a base is added to a lead salt. It dries to $Pb_2O(OH)_2$ and when heated to 145° C. dehydrates to the tan-colored oxide PbO, known commercially as litharge. All three of these compounds dissolve in NaOH solution, forming plumbite ion, PbO_2^{--}.

$$\underline{PbO} + 2Na^+ + 2OH^- \rightarrow 2Na^+ + PbO_2^{--} + H_2O$$

Lead glass is made by melting PbO, SiO_2, and K_2O together. Litharge is used as an accelerator in the manufacture of rubber, as a dryer in varnishes, and in assaying gold and silver. For assays, powdered litharge and charcoal are mixed with the crushed ore and the mixture is heated. The lead formed by the reducing action of carbon on PbO forms an alloy with gold and silver and the molten mixture is poured off. When the lead is oxidized and removed, pure gold and silver remain. Lead oxide is used in glazes in the pottery industry. Litharge is used in the manufacture of lead storage batteries, and also in making certain insecticides, chrome pigments, and "Doctor solution." "Doctor solution," or sodium plumbite, Na_2PbO_2, is used in petroleum refining to remove complex organic sulfur compounds by precipitating the sulfur as insoluble lead sulfide. Na_2PbO_2 is made by agitating a solution of caustic soda and litharge at 30° C. with compressed air.

H_2S precipitates PbS from a moderately acid solution of a lead salt. If there is a good deal of HCl the precipitate may at first be yellow or red $PbS \cdot PbCl_2$; but with additional H_2S this becomes black PbS. Hot concentrated HCl dissolves this, with the evolution of H_2S. With boiling dilute HNO_3 the reaction is:

$$\underline{3PbS} + 8(H^+ + NO_3^-) \rightarrow 3Pb^{++} + 6NO_3^- + \overline{2NO} + \underline{3S} + 4H_2O$$

Some grains of PbS may become embedded in the sulfur and give it a black or gray color.

19.15. Lead(IV) Compounds

Although tin and lead have the same electronegativity, the +4 valence of lead is less stable than that of tin. Lead dioxide, PbO_2 (sometimes miscalled peroxide), is a powerful oxidizing agent; it oxidizes

Mn^{++} to MnO$_4^-$, ignites sulfur when the two are rubbed together, and becomes red-hot when warmed in SO$_2$; PbSO$_4$ is formed. PbCl$_4$, a liquid, decomposes, sometimes explosively, when warmed, liberating chlorine. A compound which may be regarded, with question, as a derivative of PbH$_4$ is tetraethyllead, Pb(C$_2$H$_5$)$_4$; it has enormous practical importance. A liquid, it boils at 202° C. and is miscible with organic solvents such as petroleum. Some years ago it was discovered that adding small quantities of the liquid to gasoline raised the octane rating of the fuel and decreased the pre-ignition knocking that occurred when the fuel was burned in motors. Its use has made possible the operation of high-compression motors, thereby increasing efficiency and indirectly preserving our supply of crude petroleum. When lead tetraethyl burns in a motor the lead combines with the bromine of ethylene dibromide and is volatilized as PbBr$_2$. Hundreds of tests show that the concentration of fumes from this source is not sufficiently high to be toxic to garage mechanics; carbon monoxide is a far greater hazard.

Pb(C$_2$H$_5$)$_4$ can be prepared by the action of ethyl halides on a lead-sodium alloy.

$$4C_2H_5Cl + \underset{\text{(alloy)}}{4NaPb} \xrightarrow[\text{catalyst}]{Zn} \underset{\text{(liquid)}}{Pb(C_2H_5)_4} + 4NaCl + 3Pb$$

PbO$_2$ is obtained by heating Pb$_3$O$_4$ with concentrated nitric acid, or PbO with an alkaline hypochlorite solution.

$$Pb_3O_4 + 4H^+ + 4NO_3^- \rightarrow 2Pb^{++} + 4NO_3^- + PbO_2 + 2H_2O$$

$$PbO + Na^+ + ClO^- \rightarrow PbO_2 + Na^+ + Cl^-$$

(No oxidation or reduction takes place in the first of these equations; Pb$_3$O$_4$ contains both di- and tetravalent lead.) PbO$_2$ always forms when a lead storage battery is being charged. Very pure PbO$_2$ can be obtained by electrolyzing a lead salt between platinum electrodes; the PbO$_2$ collects at the anode. The dioxide is used on the striking surface of safety-match boxes.

Red lead or minium, Pb$_3$O$_4$, is prepared by roasting litharge at 400° C. If heated to 500°, it decomposes.

$$2Pb_3O_4 \rightleftharpoons 6PbO + O_2$$

Pb$_3$O$_4$ is not a spinel. Its formula may be written PbO$_2 \cdot$ 2PbO; x-ray examination of its crystal structure shows that each layer of PbO$_2$ is sandwiched between two layers having the litharge structure. Most of the annual production of Pb_3O_4 goes into the manufacture of storage batteries; the next largest use is in paint manufacturing. Red lead paint is used as a rust-preventing coating on structural steel. Minium was the red pigment commonly used for illumination in old manuscripts. A "miniature" was originally a painting done with minium; the meaning, small size, came later, by association.

19.16. Lead Paints

Paint has been used for centuries both for its beauty and for the protection it gives to a surface. A good paint should have a high covering capacity, adhere firmly to the surface for a long time, and not discolor. Manufacturers of paint list the constituents under the heading of pigment, vehicle, dryer, thinner, and filler. The choice of pigment depends upon the atmospheric conditions to which the paint is to be exposed. A typical white paint might contain white lead, zinc oxide, lithopone, or titanium dioxide as the pigment. The vehicle should dry rapidly and form a tenacious film; its drying involves its oxidation and polymerization from a liquid to a solid compound. Linseed oil is the most common vehicle, although tung and other oils are also used. Metal oxides, such as manganese, cobalt, and nickel, are used as dryers because they react with the oil to form metallic soaps which catalyze the drying process. The most popular thinner is turpentine; it evaporates and leaves a more viscous film of vehicle and pigment. Any cheap inert substance can be used as a filler to bring the solids content of the paint film up to the value that yields the greatest durability; among the more common are limestone, gypsum, kaolin, powdered silica, barium sulfate, and asbestine. The latter, a fibrous magnesium silicate, is useful in preventing the pigment from settling out.

Among the lead pigments are:

Red lead (and orange mineral, another form of red lead)
Basic lead carbonate (white lead)
Sublimed blue lead (mixture of $PbSO_4$, $PbSO_3$, PbS, ZnO, and carbon)
Sublimed white lead (mixture of $PbSO_4$, PbO, and ZnO)
Lead chromate
Basic lead chromate

Until recently, most of the white lead paint was made by the old "Dutch process," described by Theophrastus in 300 B.C. This process requires about 90 days for the preparation of a single batch of white lead.

Thin perforated disks or buckles of metallic lead 6 to 8 in. in diameter are placed in earthenware pots which are so constructed that the buckles are kept a few inches from the bottom of the pots; and dilute acetic acid is then poured in. Spent tanbark is stacked between the pots; as it ferments, heat and carbon dioxide are liberated. The heat vaporizes the acetic acid; and this, the atmospheric oxygen, and the CO_2 all react with the lead in a complicated series of reactions whose exact nature is unknown. A complex with the acetate ion appears to play an intermediate role. The final product can be formulated $Pb(OH)_2 \cdot 2PbCO_3$.

The newer white lead processes are modifications of the Dutch process. For example, the same reactions are used in the Carter process, but only two weeks are required. Powdered lead is placed in large rotating wooden cylinders and sprinkled with acetic acid; hot air and carbon dioxide are forced through the cylinders. In the Euston process, basic lead acetate is first made by dissolving lead in a solution of lead acetate. Electrolytic white lead is manufactured in a diaphragm cell. Pb^{++} ions are liberated from a lead anode and kept in solution, while traversing the anode compartment, by the acetate ions which it contains. The cathode compartment contains sodium carbonate solution. As the Pb^{++} ions, migrating through the porous diaphragm, meet the CO_3^{--} and OH^- ions migrating in the opposite direction, basic lead carbonate is formed. The supply of hydroxyl ions, originally produced by hydrolysis of the carbonate, is maintained by the liberation of H^+ ions at the iron cathode.

Basic lead sulfate or sublimed white lead is made of $PbSO_4$, PbO, and ZnO (maximum 9 per cent). In one process the native mineral, galena, is oxidized. The pure sulfate can be obtained by atomizing molten lead in excess air and sulfur dioxide.

Sublimed blue lead gets its color from the lead sulfide and carbon which are present. It is used in painting steel, for it has excellent covering power and is effective in preventing the formation of rust.

Red lead, a standard metal paint, is the second most widely used paint pigment.

Lead chromate pigments are available in many different colors. The normal chromate, $PbCrO_4$, is precipitated from a solution of a soluble lead salt by the addition of a soluble dichromate. It is brilliant yellow in color and is called medium chrome yellow. If a little sulfuric acid is added to the original mixture, some white $PbSO_4$ forms with the $PbCrO_4$ and the precipitate is known as lemon chrome yellow. Orange chrome yellow is prepared by adding NaOH to the dichromate solution. Prussian blue (ferric ferrocyanide) and lead chromate are precipitated together for the chrome green pigment. Basic lead chromate made from litharge is the orange paint which is the official color for airway markers all over the world; this paint was used for the final coat on the Golden Gate Bridge because of its brilliant, long-lasting color. Chinese scarlet is a basic lead chromate that is made from white lead.

QUESTIONS AND PROBLEMS

1. Compare the main groups and subgroups in the periodic table with respect to variation in electronegativity with increasing atomic number. In which groups are these trends peculiar?

2. What valence does cadmium have as an ion? How does this differ from the valences of transition metals? Can you suggest a reason for this?

3. What is unusual about the following chemistry of cadmium?

$$Cd(CN)_4^{--} + S^{--} \rightarrow \underline{CdS} + 4CN^-$$

but
$$\underline{CdS} + 4I^- \rightarrow CdI_4^{--} + S^{--}$$

4. In attempting to precipitate CdS, which ions should be avoided in solution in excess? Why?

5. What is an amalgam? Which common metals do not form amalgams? What are some important uses of amalgams?

6. In the subgroup Zn-Cd-Hg, which is the most electronegative? Which displays the greatest tendency toward forming covalent bonds? What are the oxidation states of these elements? Which are amphoteric?

7. What experimental evidence is indicative of covalent bonding in mercury(II) compounds?

8. What very common compound of metals does not exist for mercury? Is there an explanation for this?

9. Compare the dissolving of CdS and HgO by I^- ion. Is this analogy logical? Why or why not?

10. List compounds of mercury whose colors change as a result of heating or of a variation in the concentration of some critical ion. What colors are commonly observed?

11. Compare the electronic structure of mercury(I) ion and Ag^+. How does this account for their chemical similarity?

12. Write balanced chemical equations illustrating the reactions used to confirm the presence of Hg_2^{++}, Hg^{++}, and Sn^{++} in solutions.

13. What is meant by an inert electron pair? Which elements besides tin have such electron pairs? Which group ions do Sn^{++} and Pb^{++} approach in characteristics?

14. Compare the molecular species in dilute water solutions of $ZnCl_2$ and $SnCl_2$, and also in concentrated HCl.

15. What strong chemical characteristic is displayed by tin(II) both in the simple cation and in the negative ions, chlorostannite and stannite? Illustrate this for each ion with balanced equations.

16. Demonstrate by chemical equation the amphoteric nature of Sn^{++} toward OH^- ion. Since S^{--} is also a strong base, should a similar reaction occur between it

and SnS? Should Sn(IV) be more non-metallic? Can you explain why SnS is dissolved more readily by persulfide ion, S_2^{--}?

17. Demonstrate the use of lead compounds as oxidizing and reducing agents in smelting operations to produce metallic lead.

18. What are some of the outstanding uses of lead and tin metals and alloys? Name the particular properties which lead to these uses.

19. In what respects is Pb^{++} similar and not similar to Ba^{++} and Sn^{++}?

20. What ion (salt) successfully complexes the available Pb^{++} ion which is in equilibrium in solution with an insoluble lead salt, forcing the salt to dissolve? Give an example of this for lead sulfate.

20

Arsenic, antimony, and bismuth. Analysis of analytical group II

20.1. From Non-Metal to Metal

If a 100-g. weight is put on one pan of a chemical balance, the pan will sink. If salt is poured in a slow, steady stream onto the other pan, there will be no change in the position of the pans for a long time. But when the hundredth gram of salt is added, the pans move rapidly to the balanced position and less than a gram more of salt is needed to reverse the original positions. Another 100 g. of salt may then be added without further change in the position of the pans. The way all the interesting part of this simple experiment is concentrated in the middle of it illustrates a phenomenon that is rather common in chemistry. An already familiar example is acid-base titration, in which the complete color change of the indicator takes place during the addition of only a few drops of the titrant. So also, a large part of the change from metallic to non-metallic character that occurs as elements increase in electronegativity takes place in a small, intermediate range of electronegativity.

The complete range of the electronegativity scale, the inert gases being omitted, is about 3.5 units, from francium to fluorine. Non-metallic chemical behavior sufficiently marked to be worth noting appears for the first time at an electronegativity of 1.5. The amphoteric area in which non-metallic properties increase and metallic properties fade out extends over barely half a unit of electronegativity. Only the faintest traces of a metallic nature are apparent in any of the elements of the main groups by the time they have reached an electronegativity of 2.1. This instructive shift in chemical properties can be observed broadly in either of the two eight-element periods, but not in detail because the change in electronegativity from element to element is too great. There is the further complication of the change in valence in two elements with consecutive atomic numbers. By proceeding downward in a properly chosen family of the periodic table we can follow the change in electronegativity in small steps without being troubled by changes in the number of valence electrons. The nitrogen family is ideal for this purpose because the large drop in electronegativity between the first two elements brings it down to 2.1 for the second element; after this it falls a total of 0.2 unit the rest of the way. The first two thoroughly non-metallic elements in this family were discussed in Chapter 12. In this chapter we shall discuss the remaining elements in this family, with particular reference to the disappearance of non-metallic and the appearance of metallic properties with decrease in electronegativity.

20.2. The Hydrogen Compounds

The formation of covalent compounds with hydrogen is a characteristic part of the chemical behavior of non-metallic elements. Our study of the halogen family showed that their hydrogen compounds underwent regular changes as the electronegativity of the halogen decreased. They became less stable and more strongly acidic; i.e., they dissociated more easily, both thermally and ionically. The general truth of these statements was confirmed by the behavior of H_2O, H_2S, H_2Se, and H_2Te, but the level of acidity was much lower. We saw further that the least acidic of these compounds, H_2O, has appreciable basic properties. In Group V we find a further large decrease in acidity. NH_3, the least acid of the hydrogen compounds in this group, is actually a good base; its acid properties are almost undetectable. Examination of arsine, AsH_3, stibine, SbH_3, and bismuthine, BiH_3, shows that they too become more acidic and less stable in that order.

Since the first member of the series, NH_3, is a good base, and the second, PH_3, is a weaker base than water, it is not surprising to find that AsH_3 has no basic properties. Its acidic properties are difficult to detect, but it does react with $HgCl_2$, yielding intermediate yellow and brown compounds and finally, in the very sensitive Gutzeit arsenic test, the black mercuric arsenide, Hg_3As_2. When AsH_3 is passed into Ag^+ ion solution the Ag^+ is reduced to the metal, but SbH_3 produces silver antimonide.

$$SbH_3 + 3Ag^+ \rightarrow \underline{Ag_3Sb} + 3H^+$$

Since SbH_3 is a better reducing agent than AsH_3, this reaction is an indication that it is also a stronger acid. Although still a very weak acid, BiH_3 is at least acidic enough to be more soluble in NaOH solution than in water.

The gradual loss of non-metallic properties with decreasing electronegativity as we proceed down this family is clearly shown in the decreasing stability of the hydrogen compounds. While PH_3, like NH_3, can be formed from the elements under pressure, though only at a lower temperature, the remaining three require stronger reducing agents—zinc for AsH_3 and SbH_3, and magnesium for BiH_3. AsH_3 decomposes into the elements at 230° C.; the other two decompose still more easily.

This difference in stability is used in the Marsh test to distinguish arsenic from antimony. The test is used for detecting arsenic in the internal organs of a person whose death may have been due to arsenic poisoning. It is also used for estimating the amount of residue of arsenical insecticides; it detects as little as a few milligrams of arsenic per bushel of apples. For the Marsh test, the suspected material is put into a flask in which special arsenic-free zinc and acid are generating hydrogen (Fig. 20.1). Under these conditions any arsenic compound is reduced to the −3 valence state and picks up protons, forming AsH_3 which is carried off with the hydrogen through a glass delivery and drying tube. A flame heats one spot on the tube, and a bright metallic black-brown mirror forms beyond the heated spot if the slightest trace of arsenic is present.

$$As_2O_3 + \underline{6Zn} + \underline{12H^+} \rightarrow \overline{2AsH_3} + 6Zn^{++} + 3H_2O$$
$$\overset{\Delta}{\longrightarrow} \underline{2As} + \overline{3H_2}$$

If antimony is present, SbH_3 is formed and decomposed in the same way; but part of the decomposition takes place before the gas reaches the hottest part of the tube, and the mirror is deposited on both sides of the flame. The antimony mirror is not as bright as the arsenic mirror. Several chemical tests are available to confirm the identification. A solution of ClO^- ion dissolves arsenic but not antimony; tartaric acid dissolves antimony but not arsenic; with $(NH_4)_2S$ both elements form sulfides, but the arsenic sulfide is yellow, whereas Sb_2S_3 is orange. No BiH_3 is obtained under the above conditions. A magnesium-bismuth alloy must be treated with 4 N H_2SO_4. Even under the best conditions only a trace of BiH_3 can be obtained, and *all* of it decomposes before the hottest part of the tube is reached, a brown stain being deposited.

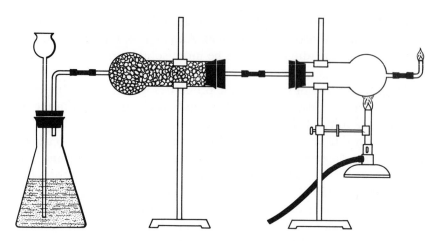

Fig. 20.1.   The Marsh test for arsenic.

20.3.   The Halides

The gradual loss of non-metallic properties from arsenic to bismuth is indicated equally well by the change in the properties of the halides. All non-metal halides hydrolyze completely and irreversibly when brought into contact with water, producing hydrogen halide and the acid of the non-metal. Phosphorus chlorides, for example, react as follows:

$$PCl_3 + 3H_2O \rightarrow H_3PO_3 + \overline{3HCl}$$
$$\underline{PCl_5} + 4H_2O \rightarrow H_3PO_4 + \overline{5HCl}$$

$AsCl_3$ hydrolyzes in a similar reaction, but this reaction is reversible. When As_2O_3 is boiled with concentrated HCl solution, $AsCl_3$ distills. $AsCl_5$, however, cannot be produced in this manner. This is in agreement with the important general principle that *a higher valence of any element is always more electronegative (and thus more non-metallic) than a lower valence.*

$SbCl_3$ is a soft crystalline solid (butter of antimony) that melts at 73° C. and dissolves in HCl to form such ions as $SbCl_4^-$, $Sb_2Cl_7^-$, $SbCl_5^{--}$, and $SbCl_6^{-3}$. If this solution is diluted, hydrolysis occurs and antimonyl chloride, SbOCl, is precipitated. Hydrolysis may be completed by treatment with a base, Sb_2O_3 being formed. $SbCl_5$ is not immediately hydrolyzed by ice-cold water; instead it forms crystalline hydrates. Hot water hydrolyzes it to Sb_2O_5, but it dissolves in HCl, forming $SbCl_6^-$, $SbCl_7^{--}$, and $SbCl_8^{-3}$ ions.

$BiCl_3$ behaves similarly to $SbCl_3$, but less concentrated acid can be used to reverse the hydrolysis; there is no pentachloride. The pentavalent state of arsenic is more easily reduced than that of phosphorus; $SbCl_5$ begins to dissociate into $SbCl_3$ and Cl_2 at 150° C. Bi(V) is an extremely strong oxidizing agent, stronger than MnO_4^-. It exists only in BiF_5 and in impure preparations of Bi_2O_5 and BiO_3^-. This increasing tendency not to assume the higher, more non-metallic valence is further evidence of the increase in metallic nature as we go down this group.

20.4. The Oxides

The oxides of the non-metals and metals at the extreme ends of the periodic table dissolve readily in water. The former hydrate upon dissolving and form oxyacids, whereas the oxide ions of the latter react with water to form OH^- ions. As we move from one side of the table toward the other, the oxides show a decreasing solubility in water and tend to react less readily with it. This trend is accompanied by a gradual increase in amphoteric character.

Unlike phosphorus, arsenic burns in oxygen only to the lower oxide. As_2O_5 is formed by oxidizing this oxide with concentrated HNO_3.

$$2H_2O + \underline{As_2O_3} + 2H^+ + 2NO_3^- \rightarrow 2H_3AsO_4 + \overline{NO} + \overline{NO_2}$$

The product is then dehydrated at 200° C. As_2O_5 behaves in general like P_2O_5, although it hydrates much less vigorously, forming AsO_3^-, $As_2O_7^{-4}$, and AsO_4^{-3} ions that are more basic than the corresponding phosphate ions. Arsenic acid, H_3AsO_4, is a good enough oxidizing agent to liberate iodine from iodides. Like all soluble arsenic compounds, it is poisonous. A number of arsenates are used as insecticides. As_2O_3 is analogous to P_2O_3 in structure (its molecular formula is As_4O_6) and reactions, but is much less acidic. It is not easily moistened by water and dissolves only slowly, forming a solution barely acid enough to turn litmus pink. The extremely poisonous white powder is known commercially as white arsenic, or simply arsenic. It dissolves in bases and forms various arsenite ions, including the normal orthoarsenite ion, AsO_3^{-3}. (H_3PO_3, remember, is a diprotic acid, one H being attached to phosphorus instead of oxygen.) Arsenites are also used as insecticides, particularly the brilliantly colored Paris green, $Cu_2(AsO_2)(C_2H_3O_2)$, a mixed acetate-meta-arsenite. Scheele's green, $CuHAsO_3(?)$, is subject to attack by molds; volatile organic derivatives of AsH_3 are produced. Its use as a pigment on wallpaper has produced arsenic poisoning in damp locations and is now prohibited in the United States.

The oxides of antimony are definitely less acidic than those of arsenic. The higher oxide of antimony is only about equal to the lower oxide of arsenic as far as acidity is concerned. Antimonate ion is structurally different from AsO_4^{-3} and PO_4^{-3} ions; its formula is $Sb(OH)_6^{-}$. $NaSb(OH)_6$ is interesting as one of the least soluble sodium salts (1 : 350). Sb_2O_3 is almost insoluble in water, though it is still acidic enough to dissolve in bases; it forms such antimonites as $NaSbO_2 \cdot 3H_2O$ and KSb_3O_5. But Sb_2O_3 is also a base. It dissolves easily both in dilute HCl, forming a solution that contains the covalently bonded chloro- anions mentioned in Section 20.3, and in tartaric acid; here also it forms a covalently bonded complex. In view of the covalent nature of the products, these two reactions are not too good evidence of the basic nature of Sb_2O_3. But it also dissolves in hot concentrated H_2SO_4, and $Sb_2(SO_4)_3$ crystallizes on cooling. This is probably a true salt, and its solution in the acid may contain the actual Sb^{+3} ion.

Bismuth is enough more metallic than antimony for its trioxide not to be ordinarily considered amphoteric. Although readily soluble in acids, in bases it is soluble only in *concentrated* NaOH. Further evidence of increasing basicity is the fact that adding a base to a bismuth salt precipitates a hydroxide, $Bi(OH)_3$, which does not lose water below 100° C. The fact that bismuth does not readily assume its higher, more non-metallic oxidation state may also be taken as evidence of increasing metallic character. The formation of Bi_2O_5 or BiO_3^{-} ion requires the presence of concentrated or even fused NaOH and a powerful oxidizing agent such as chlorine or oxygen. Bismuthic acid is very weak; its salts are hydrolyzed by water with the precipitation of Bi_2O_5. Treating this with acid produces a solution that contains Bi^{+3}; and either the acid is oxidized—e.g., HCl to Cl_2—or oxygen is liberated.

20.5. The Elements

Arsenic, antimony, and bismuth are all high enough in electronegativity so that their oxides can readily be reduced by carbon to the free elements; however, due precautions must be taken on account of their appreciable volatility. As_2O_3 and Bi_2O_3 are obtained mainly from the flue dust of copper, lead, and tin smelters; Sb_2O_3, from roasting the ore stibnite, Sb_2S_3. The gradual shift from non-metallic to metallic character is apparent in the elements themselves as well as in the three series of compounds we have already studied. To observe this shift, we first consider the change in the relative stability of their allotropic modifications with increasing electronegativity. The very definite non-metals have small molecules (one to eight atoms), are soluble in inert solvents, and form brittle, non-conducting solids if temperatures are low enough. The very definite metals form gas molecules which are diatomic (Group I) or monatomic (Group II) but in the solid state seem to contain neither discrete molecules nor even atoms. Rather, metal cations are held together by a cloud of electrons none of which can be said to belong to any specific ion. Ductility, electrical conductivity, and metallic luster are the result. Fundamentally, the physical properties of non-metals result from electrons being held strongly between specific atoms by covalent bonds; in metals, these properties result from electrons being held loosely as a whole by all the ions as a whole. The gradual disappearance of non-metallic physical properties which accompanies a gradual decrease in electronegativity is marked by a gradual weakening of the covalent bonds, a loosening of the constraints which hold the electrons.

A result of the weakening of bonds in a non-metal is the appearance of modifications of giant molecules. If the bonds are weak enough to be broken frequently and the element is in a *condensed*—i.e., solid or liquid —state, the bonds are as likely as not to form again between atoms in adjacent molecules, tying the whole mass together. This was seen in plastic sulfur and amorphous phosphorus. Thus these amorphous modifications are characteristic of elements with moderate electronegativity. The fact that plastic sulfur soon changes into S_8 under ordinary conditions, whereas P_4 irreversibly changes into amorphous (red) phosphorus, shows that phosphorus is below sulfur in electronegativity.

If atoms are crushed so closely together that the electrons in a given bonding pair are influenced by several other atoms in addition to the two they are holding together, the fields of the various atoms pull in different directions and cancel each other. The electrons cease to be localized and a conducting metallic modification results. In the case of phosphorus, a pressure of 12,000 atm. is required to produce this form. Neither this nor the amorphous non-metallic form is soluble in CS_2.

Both arsenic and antimony are non-metallic enough to have a yellow, soluble tetraatomic form. But As_4 rapidly assumes the metallic form when exposed to light, and Sb_4 becomes amorphous antimony when warmed above $-90°$ C. In the gaseous state As_4 begins to dissociate into As_2 above 450° C. (P_4 is stable to 700° C.) Antimony is not volatile at such temperatures, but in solution in lead at 325° C. it completely dissociates into Sb_2. Bismuth is too metallic to have any non-metallic modification.

Arsenic vapor condenses into the giant-molecular amorphous form, instead of into the yellow form as phosphorus vapor does. At 360° C., this amorphous black arsenic becomes metallic arsenic, with a strong evolution of heat. Amorphous antimony is obtained by the slow electrolysis of $SbCl_3$ in HCl solution. It looks like polished graphite; if scratched, or warmed to 200° C., it explodes violently, and metallic antimony forms.

The metallic modifications of phosphorus, arsenic, antimony, and bismuth are isomorphous. All are black when finely divided, as is true of all metals. In the usual crystal size arsenic is gray, but it can be obtained as tin-white crystals. Antimony is silver-white; bismuth is equally lustrous, but reddish-white. Although antimony and bismuth are metallic in appearance and arsenic can be, all are poor metals, brittle and with relatively low electrical conductivity. This agrees well with their mixture of metallic and non-metallic chemical properties. The progressively weaker bond strength which accompanies the decrease in electronegativity and the onset of metallic properties is further evident in the drop in melting point. Arsenic sublimes if heated in the open; but if the tube is closed, it melts at 814° C. The melting point of antimony is 631° C.; of bismuth, only 271° C. These last two elements have the very unusual property of expanding when solidified, a property probably dependent upon a residual tendency to form localized covalent bonds. Antimony is added to type metal not only to lower the melting point, but also, and more important, to give the alloy this property of expanding when solid, so that sharp type faces and full mold-sized bodies can be made without the use of external pressure. Because of their intermediate electronegativity, none of these elements are metallic enough to dissolve in a nonoxidizing acid, though all are oxidized by HNO_3. But their electronegativity is low enough so that they burn in oxygen and even in chlorine, if heated sufficiently for the reaction products to volatilize. Powdered arsenic and antimony, whose chlorides boil at 130° and 223° C. respectively, ignite when dropped into chlorine.

Metallic arsenic, antimony, and bismuth are used only in the form of alloys. Alloyed with copper, arsenic increases corrosion resistance and raises the temperature at which work-hardened copper anneals, or becomes soft again. This latter accounts for its use in automobile radiators that are soldered together. Lead shot, the lead plates in ordinary storage batteries, and lead-tin bearing metal are all hardened by the addition of 1 per cent or so of arsenic, and sometimes antimony as well. In the case of lead shot the arsenic not only hardens the metal but makes the shot more spherical. If the droplets of metal freeze too quickly after falling through the screen at the top of the shot tower, they will be irregular in shape. The arsenic lowers the freezing point enough so the drops can become spherical before they solidify. About 100 tons of arsenic are used annually in the United States.

Over half our consumption of antimony goes into the manufacture of storage batteries, cable coverings, bearings, and type metal. Much of this antimony is recovered and used again. The hard lead used in batteries, bullets, and shrapnel contains 12 to 15 per cent antimony. Our requirements for new antimony exceed the 750 tons mined annually in the United States.

Bismuth is used principally to lower the melting point of alloys. Plugs of fusible alloys are used as safety devices in hot-water heaters; they melt and release the pressure if the water gets too hot. In automatic fire sprinkler systems the sprinkler head is held shut by a valve which is opened by the water pressure as soon as a bit of fusible solder melts. Fig. 20.2 shows one type of sprinkler head. The composition of the fusible alloy can be chosen so that the melting point is so low that the alloy will melt when a sheet of newspaper is burned on the floor beneath it, or so high that the alloy will not melt until a predetermined danger point is reached. Of our 621-ton annual consumption of bismuth in 1958, 244 tons went into these alloys. The rest is used for

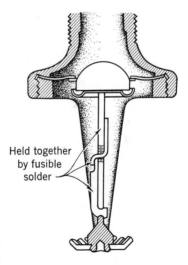

Held together by fusible solder

Fig. 20.2. A fire sprinkler.

the manufacture of bismuth compounds. The prices of arsenic, antimony, and bismuth, per pound, are 60 cents, 30 cents, and $2.25 respectively.

20.6. The Sulfides

Arsenious sulfide, As_2S_3, which occurs as a mineral, has been known at least since A.D. 500. It is bright yellow, as is indicated by its old name, orpiment (L., *auri pigmentum*, pigment of gold). It is used as an insecticide, but it has been replaced by chrome yellow as a pigment. However, both it and the similar-looking arsenic sulfide, As_2S_5, are of more interest in analytical chemistry, for they are precipitated from even *strongly acid* solutions of arsenious and arsenic acids by hydrogen sulfide.

$$2H_3AsO_3 + 3H_2S \rightarrow \overline{As_2S_3} + 6H_2O$$

$$2H_3AsO_4 + 5H_2S \rightarrow \overline{As_2S_5} + 8H_2O$$

As_2S_5 is so insoluble that it precipitates as a colloidal suspension unless precautions are taken. Crystallization nuclei form everywhere in the solution and precipitation is complete before any of the particles have grown to a size that makes filtration or centrifugation possible. Precipitation is prevented by having the solution so strongly acid—i.e., the S^{--} ion concentration so low—that only a moderate number of nuclei form and have time to grow to appreciable size before the solution is exhausted of its arsenic content. Both As_2S_5 and As_2S_3 can be dissolved readily by adding an oxidizing agent to oxidize the sulfide ion to free elemental sulfur. As(III) is oxidized to As(V) at the same time.

$$3As_2S_3 + 10H^+ + 10NO_3^- + 4H_2O \rightarrow 6H_3AsO_4 + \overline{10NO} + \overline{9S}$$

$$3As_2S_5 + 10H^+ + 10NO_3^- + 4H_2O \rightarrow 6H_3AsO_4 + \overline{10NO} + \underline{15S}$$

Since antimony is more metallic than arsenic, Sb(III) does not exist in ordinary HCl solutions as an oxyanion; instead, it is present as the complex ion $SbCl_6^{-3}$. The reaction of this ion with H_2S is:

$$2SbCl_6^{-3} + 3H_2S \rightarrow \overline{Sb_2S_3} + 6H^+ + 12Cl^-$$

That this reaction is reversible becomes evident when the H^+ ion concentration is increased. Therefore the acidity of the solution must be reduced to a moderate value before Sb_2S_3 can be precipitated. If the acidity is lowered enough for SbOCl to precipitate, the equation for the reaction with H_2S is:

$$2SbOCl + 3H_2S \rightarrow \underline{Sb_2S_3} + 2H_2O + 2H^+ + 2Cl^-$$

This reaction can be reversed by adding acid not only because of the H^+ ion on the right but because the SbOCl is soluble in acid.

$$\underline{SbOCl} + 2H^+ + 5Cl^- \rightarrow SbCl_6{}^{-3} + H_2O$$

As precipitated, Sb_2S_3 is bright orange. It can be converted into a grayish-black crystalline modification, the mineral stibnite. Red varieties of rubber contain Sb_2S_3 as a pigment and vulcanizing agent. Sb_2S_5 is of no importance.

Bi(III) is sufficiently metallic so that its simple hydrated cation, Bi^{+3}, can exist in acid solutions. (The number of molecules of water of hydration is not known definitely.) It can therefore form salts with non-complexing anions such as $NO_3{}^-$; it is the only member of this family that can do so. $Bi(NO_3)_3 \cdot 5H_2O$ is the most important bismuth salt. Bi(III) also forms complex chloro- anions like those of Sb(III), and other anions such as $BiI_4{}^-$ and $Bi(S_2O_3)_3{}^{-3}$. H_2S precipitates dark brown Bi_2S_3 from all of these if the solution is not too acid. The simplest equation is:

$$2Bi^{+3} + 3H_2S \rightarrow \underline{Bi_2S_3} + 6H^+$$

Bi_2S_3 is soluble in 3 M HNO_3.

20.7. Thioamphoterism

Since sulfur is a member of the oxygen family, all sulfides should strongly resemble the corresponding oxides. Accordingly, the sulfides of arsenic, antimony, and bismuth should be acidic, and their acidity should diminish in that order. This is actually the case. The arsenic sulfides dissolve in NH_3 and even in such a weak base as $(NH_4)_2CO_3$. Sb_2S_3 does not dissolve in such weak bases but will dissolve in hot concentrated Na_2CO_3, which is a stronger base than $(NH_4)_2CO_3$ because the acidic $NH_4{}^+$ ion is absent. Bi_2S_3 does not dissolve even in NaOH.

When an acidic or amphoteric sulfide dissolves in a base, the sulfur is not completely displaced as free S^{--} ion, but remains attached by one electron pair to the other element, say arsenic. The remaining coordination positions on the arsenic are usually filled by O^{--} ions. The equation for the reaction of As_2S_5 with NaOH may be written:

$$As_2S_5 + 6OH^- \rightarrow AsS_3O^{-3} + AsS_2O_2^{-3} + 3H_2O$$

Many chemists, however, prefer tᴐ assume that the di- and tri-thioarsenates *disproportionate* into arsenate and tetrathioarsenate (usually called simply thioarsenate) ions. In this case the equation is:

$$4As_2S_5 + 24OH^- \rightarrow 5AsS_4^{-3} + 3AsO_4^{-3} + 12H_2O$$

If the base is CO_3^{--} ion, the products are the same as far as the arsenic is concerned.

$$4As_2S_5 + 24CO_3^{--} + 12H_2O \rightarrow 5AsS_4^{-3} + 3AsO_4^{-3} + 24HCO_3^-$$

But if the base is S^{--} ion, only thioarsenate ion is produced.

$$As_2S_5 + 3S^{--} \rightarrow 2AsS_4^{-3}$$

In most cases an amphoteric sulfide dissolves more readily in a solution containing S^{--} ion than would be expected merely from considering the basicity of the solution. Thus the sulfides of arsenic and antimony dissolve readily in ammonium sulfide solution which, although commonly written $(NH_4)_2S$, actually contains mostly hydrosulfide ions, HS^-, and is only slightly more basic than a solution of $NaHCO_3$. Similarly, Bi_2S_3, although insoluble in $(NH_4)_2S$, will dissolve in concentrated K_2S solution even though Bi_2O_3 is not amphoteric. (The same is true of HgS and HgO.) This may be ascribed to the fact that S^{--} ion forms covalent bonds more readily than O^{--} ion does. Tin(II) is an unexplained exception to this rule. SnO dissolves readily in OH^- but SnS does not dissolve in HS^-. The more acidic SnS_2 dissolves readily enough (Section 19.11).

Such thioarsenite and thioantimonite ions as AsS_3^{-3}, $As_2S_5^{-4}$, AsS_2^-, SbS_3^{-3}, $Sb_4S_7^{--}$, and SbS_2^-, and the thioarsenate and thioantimonate ions AsS_4^{-3} and

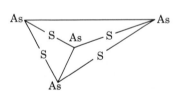

Fig. 20.3. Realgar, As_4S_4. The four arsenic atoms are still in the tetrahedral arrangement of yellow arsenic, As_4. Each sulfur atom lies outside an edge of the tetrahedron, although for simplicity they are shown on the edges in this figure. The sulfur atoms serve as a bridge between two arsenic atoms, replacing an As—As bond. The S—As—S valence bond angle is 93°.

SbS_4^{-3} can all be prepared from the corresponding sulfides under proper conditions, and all reprecipitate the sulfides on acidification.

Arsenic forms another sulfide, realgar (Arabic, *raj al ghar,* powder of the mine), which is red. Its formula is As_4S_4; its molecule has a curious structure (Fig. 20.3). Each arsenic atom has one covalent bond with another arsenic atom and two such bonds with sulfur atoms. Each sulfur is bonded to two arsenic atoms. There is an unshared electron pair on each arsenic atom; so each atom in the molecule has a complete valence octet of electrons.

20.8. Basic Salts

Arsenic is not metallic enough to form basic salts, nor is Sb(V) or Bi(V); but Sb(III) and Bi(III) form several. When $SbCl_3$ solution in HCl is poured into a little water, SbOCl precipitates; with a larger amount of water the product is $Sb_4O_5Cl_2$.

$$SbCl_4^- + H_2O \rightarrow 2H^+ + 3Cl^- + \underline{SbOCl}$$

$$4SbCl_4^- + 5H_2O \rightarrow 10H^+ + 14Cl^- + \underline{Sb_4O_5Cl_2}$$

Both of these oxychlorides are basic antimony(III) chlorides. SbOCl may also be called antimonyl chloride. Although it is thought of as being derived from the antimonyl ion, SbO^+, there is no evidence that any such ion exists in solution. $SbBr_3$ behaves like $SbCl_3$, but only $Sb_4O_5I_2$ is precipitated from SbI_3. If Sb_2O_3 and cream of tartar—potassium hydrogen tartrate, $KHC_4H_4O_6$—are boiled together, soluble potassium antimonyl tartrate, or tartar emetic, is formed. This compound is used medicinally to induce sweating and vomiting; it is also used as a mordant. The formula of the solid, which contains water of crystallization, is usually written $(K(SbO)C_4H_4O_6)_2 \cdot H_2O$, but the complete formula with the exception of the potassiums may represent a single complex divalent ion.

Bismuth (III) forms a similar series of bismuthyl halides. BiOCl resembles AgCl in being light-sensitive, but when it darkens it goes through gray shades, not violet like AgCl. It is first precipitated as $Bi(OH)_2Cl$, and loses water when heated gently. Bi^{+3} is too strong an acid to form a normal carbonate; but the basic carbonate, $(BiO)_2CO_3 \cdot \frac{1}{2}H_2O$, is precipitated when a solution of $Bi(NO_3)_3$ is neutralized with CO_3^{--} ion. This is the "bismuth meal" given before the digestive tract is x-rayed. The high atomic number of bismuth makes its compounds opaque to x-rays. When a solution of $Bi(NO_3)_3$ is poured into a large amount of water, basic bismuth nitrate is formed. When first precipitated, its formula is $Bi(OH)_2NO_3$. Washing converts some of this to $Bi(OH)_3$; when this is dried, a portion of both substances dehydrates to the corresponding bismuthyl compounds. The commercial product, known to pharmacists as bismuth subnitrate, contains about 15 moles of $Bi(OH)_2NO_3$ to 5 of $BiONO_3$ and 4 of $BiO(OH)$. It is used to soothe stomach irritation, and also in ointments. Many basic bismuth salts of organic acids are also used in medicine.

Bismuthyl hydroxide is readily reduced to metallic bismuth by stannite ion; this reaction is used as a confirmatory test for bismuth.

$$2BiO(OH) + 3Sn(OH)_4^{--} + 2H_2O \rightarrow 2Bi + 3Sn(OH)_6^{--}$$

20.9. Analysis of the Copper-Arsenic Group

Analytical Group II consists of the elements which are not removed as insoluble chlorides in Group I, but can be precipitated as sulfides by introducing H_2S into their *acid* solutions; therefore it is frequently called the hydrogen sulfide group. Table 20.1 shows the procedure for analyzing this group. The group includes the elements discussed in this and the preceding chapter, and Cu^{++} in addition. There are eight of these elements—mercury(II), lead, cadmium, tin, copper, arsenic, antimony, and bismuth. Of these, tin(IV), arsenic, and antimony constitute a subgroup by virtue of the fact that their sulfides are amphoteric and easily soluble in $(NH_4)_2S$. Tin(II) is not analyzed separately from tin(IV), but is oxidized to tin(IV) by preliminary treatment with H_2O_2.

$$Sn^{++} + H_2O_2 + 2H^+ + 6Cl^- \rightarrow SnCl_6^{--} + 2H_2O$$

Incidentally, this treatment oxidizes arsenite to arsenate.

$$H_2AsO_3^- + H_2O_2 \rightarrow H_2AsO_4^- + H_2O$$

The solution containing the ions of this group is treated with H_2S, first in the presence of a high concentration of H^+ ions (this is necessary to prevent the formation of colloidal As_2S_5, as noted in Section 20.6), and again after the H^+ concentration has been lowered to precipitate the more soluble sulfides. Typical equations are:

TABLE 20.1. Analysis of Analytical Group II, the Copper-Arsenic Group

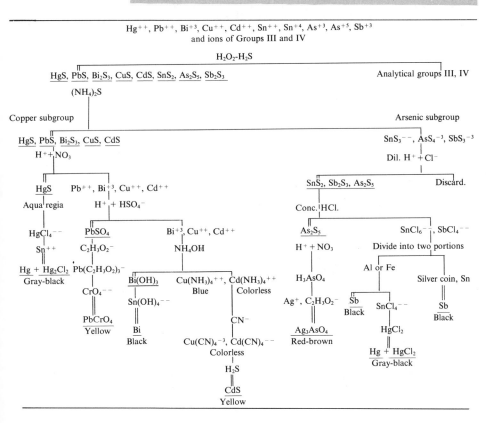

$$Pb^{++} + H_2S \rightarrow \underline{PbS} + 2H^+$$

$$2H^+ + 2H_2AsO_4^- + 5H_2S \rightarrow \underline{As_2S_5} + 8H_2O$$

$$2SbCl_4^- + 3H_2S \rightarrow \underline{Sb_2S_3} + 6H^+ + 8Cl^-$$

The H_2S may be obtained from outside sources and the gas bubbled through the solution. Some laboratories use commercial cylinders of liquefied H_2S, others prepare it by the action of acid on FeS. A more common means of obtaining the H_2S is heating test-tube-sized batches of "Aitchtuess," a mixture of sulfur and paraffin that has enough asbestos fiber to keep the mass porous. This method is safer because the production of H_2S stops as soon as the flame is removed. Whenever H_2S is bubbled through a solution, avoid breathing any of the gas which issues from the test tube, for it is as poisonous as carbon monoxide. A completely safe method of precipitating analytical Group II is to generate the needed small amount of H_2S in the solution by the hydrolysis of thioacetamide.

$$CH_3 \cdot C \begin{smallmatrix} SH \\ \\ \\ NH \end{smallmatrix} + 2H_2O \rightarrow C_2H_3O_2{}^- + NH_4{}^+ + \overline{H_2S}$$

In the acidic solutions actually used, the rather basic acetate ion immediately takes up a proton, forming acetic acid, $HC_2H_3O_2$. The hydrolysis is negligible at room temperature but rapid at 75° to 90° C. The test tube containing the thioacetamide may be suspended in a beaker of boiling water for a few minutes.

The amphoteric sulfides are extracted from the others as thio- anions by $(NH_4)_2S$ solution.

$$\underline{SnS_2} + S^{--} \rightarrow SnS_3{}^{--}$$

$$\underline{As_2S_5} + 3S^{--} \rightarrow 2AsS_4{}^{-3}$$

$$\underline{Sb_2S_3} + 3S^{--} \rightarrow 2SbS_3{}^{-3}$$

As_2S_3 may be present as a result of the reduction of $AsO_4{}^{-3}$ by H_2S.

$$2H_3AsO_4 + 5H_2S \rightarrow \underline{As_2S_3} + 8H_2O + \underline{2S}$$

It behaves like Sb_2S_3.

Acidification of the solution containing the thio- anions produces the corresponding thio- acids. These promptly lose H_2S and precipitate the sulfides just as oxyacids lose H_2O and form oxides, but usually at higher temperatures.

$$2H_3AsO_4 \rightarrow \underline{As_2O_5} + 3H_2O$$

$$2H_3AsS_4 \rightarrow \underline{As_2S_5} + 3\overline{H_2S}$$

Unless the $(NH_4)_2S$ was freshly prepared, it will contain some $S_2{}^{--}$ ion because of atmospheric oxidation. The H_2S_2 formed from this will decompose with the liberation of sulfur.

$$H_2S_2 \rightarrow \overline{H_2S} + \underline{S}$$

All these reactions emphasize well the resemblance between -2 oxygen compounds and those of -2 sulfur.

The fact that arsenic sulfides are practically insoluble in acids, whereas the sulfides of the metals are more soluble, makes it possible to separate the antimony and tin from the sulfide mixture by treating it with concentrated HCl.

$$Sb_2S_3 + 6H^+ + 8Cl^- \rightarrow 2SbCl_4^- + \overline{3H_2S}$$

$$SnS_2 + 4H^+ + 6Cl^- \rightarrow SnCl_6^{--} + \overline{2H_2S}$$

The yellow precipitate that remains after the Sb_2S_3 and SnS_2 are dissolved does not prove the presence of arsenic; it may be just sulfur. Accordingly, the residue is oxidized with HNO_3; any arsenic that is present goes into solution as H_3AsO_4. Adding Ag^+ ion does not produce an immediate precipitate because H_3AsO_4 is a weak acid. When it is neutralized by the weak base, $C_2H_3O_2^-$ ion, the concentration of AsO_4^{-3} ion is increased enough so that reddish-brown Ag_3AsO_4 precipitates.

$$H_3AsO_4 + 3Ag^+ + 3C_2H_3O_2^- \rightarrow \underline{Ag_3AsO_4} + 3HC_2H_3O_2$$

If a piece of aluminum or iron is put into the acid solution which contains the antimony and tin, the latter will be reduced to the metallic state while the aluminum or iron is dissolving. The reactions are as follows, when aluminum is used:

$$\underline{Al} + SbCl_4^- \rightarrow \underline{Sb} + Al^{+3} + 4Cl^-$$

$$4\underline{Al} + 3SnCl_6^{--} \rightarrow 3\underline{Sn} + 4Al^{+3} + 18Cl^-$$

After all the aluminum is dissolved, holding the solution a couple of minutes at the boiling point redissolves the tin.

$$\underline{Sn} + 2H^+ \rightarrow Sn^{++} + \overline{H_2}$$

Any antimony remains unchanged, as a black residue. The presence of Sn^{++} ion in the solution may be verified by its ability to reduce $HgCl_2$ to Hg_2Cl_2 or mercury (Section 19.6).

After the original H_2S precipitate has been extracted with $(NH_4)_2S$, there is a residue of non-amphoteric (copper subgroup) sulfides. Some of these can be easily redissolved by increasing the H^+ ion concentration and thus lowering the S^{--} ion concentration. Others are so insoluble that it is impossible to lower the S⁻⁻ ion concentration sufficiently to dissolve them, even with the maximum attainable H⁺ ion concentration. When S⁻⁻ is oxidized to free sulfur by HNO_3, its concentration is reduced to a value far lower than can be achieved simply by increasing the acidity. Therefore 3 M HNO_3 will dissolve many sulfides that resist HCl. HgS, however, is so insoluble that it is not affected even by HNO_3. Accordingly it remains when the other copper subgroup sulfides are dissolved in HNO_3, and thus can be separated from them. In order to dissolve HgS, the concentrations of *both* Hg⁺⁺ and S⁻⁻ ions must be reduced to extremely low values. The Hg⁺⁺ ion concentration is reduced by aqua regia. The Cl⁻ ion in the aqua regia turns the Hg⁺⁺ ion into a complex ion, $HgCl_3^-$ or $HgCl_4^{--}$.

$$3HgS + 2NO_3^- + 8H^+ + 12Cl^- \rightarrow 3\overline{HgCl_4^{--}} + 2\overline{NO} + 4H_2O + 3\underline{S}$$

(The sulfur may be further oxidized, but this is irrelevant.) The presence of mercury in the solution is confirmed by the $SnCl_2$ test.

Pb⁺⁺ is separated from the other ions in the HNO_3 solution by precipitating it as the sulfate. This can be done only after the HNO_3 has been driven off, for excess acidity prevents HSO_4^- ions from ionizing sufficiently to SO_4^{--} ions.

$$Pb^{++} + HSO_4^- \rightleftharpoons \underline{PbSO_4} + H^+$$

For a further test, the $PbSO_4$ can be dissolved in $NH_4C_2H_3O_2$ and reprecipitated as the less soluble chromate.

$$\underline{PbSO_4} + 3C_2H_3O_2^- \rightarrow Pb(C_2H_3O_2)_3^- + SO_4^{--}$$

$$Pb(C_2H_3O_2)_3^- + CrO_4^{--} \rightarrow \underline{PbCrO_4} + 3C_2H_3O_2^-$$

The solution remaining from the precipitation of the $PbSO_4$ is made alkaline with NH_3.

$$Cu^{++} + 4NH_3 \rightarrow Cu(NH_3)_4^{++} \quad \text{(intense blue)}$$
$$Cd^{++} + 4NH_3 \rightarrow Cd(NH_3)_4^{++} \quad \text{(colorless)}$$
$$Bi^{+3} + 3NH_4OH \rightarrow \underline{Bi(OH)_3} + 3NH_4^+$$

The white $Bi(OH)_3$, after it is separated from the solution, is identified by its reduction to jet-black metallic bismuth with stannite ion.

$$2Bi(OH)_3 + 3Sn(OH)_4^{--} \rightarrow 2\underline{Bi} + 3Sn(OH)_6^{--}$$

The dark blue color of tetramminecopper(II) ion is sufficient as a test for copper. Before testing for cadmium, copper(II) must be removed by reduction to copper(I).

$$2Cu(NH_3)_4^{++} + 9CN^- + H_2O \rightarrow 2Cu(CN)_4^{-3} + CNO^- + 6NH_3 + 2NH_4^+$$
Colorless

Cadmium is recognized by the bright yellow precipitate that forms when H_2S is added.

$$Cd(CN)_4^{--} + H_2S \rightarrow \underline{CdS} + 2HCN + 2CN^-$$

Even though $Cu(CN)_4^{-3}$ is present in the same solution, no Cu_2S precipitates, because the copper(I) complex is much less dissociated than the cadmium complex. An alternative method of preventing copper(II) from interfering with the cadmium test is to reduce it to free metal with dithionite ion, $S_2O_4^{--}$.

$$Cu(NH_3)_4^{++} + 2H_2O + S_2O_4^{--} \rightarrow \underline{Cu} + 2SO_3^{--} + 4NH_4^+$$

QUESTIONS AND PROBLEMS

1. Make the following correlations, relative to general trends, for elements in main Groups V, VI, and VII of the periodic table:
   a. Electronegativity against atomic number, vertically and horizontally.
   b. Acid strength of hydrogen compounds against atomic number.
   c. Stability of these compounds against atomic number.

2. Why is it necessary to use arsenic-free zinc in the Marsh test?

3. There follows a series of reaction pairs. Describe what they indicate as far as trends in this family are concerned, as well as the specific chemical nature of each halide. Give reasons for your answers.

$$PCl_3 + 3H_2O \rightarrow H_3PO_3 + \overline{3HCl}$$
but $\quad$ $$H_3PO_3 + HCl \rightarrow No\ reaction$$

$$AsCl_3 + 3H_2O \overset{\Delta}{\rightleftharpoons} H_3AsO_3 + 3HCl$$
$$SbCl_3 + H_2O \underset{HCl}{\rightleftharpoons} \overline{SbOCl} + 2HCl$$

$$SbCl_3 + 3NH_4OH \rightarrow \underline{Sb(OH)_3} + 3(NH_4^+ + Cl^-)$$

$$SbCl_5 + H^+ + Cl^- \rightarrow SbCl_6^- + H^+$$

4. Compare ortho-, pyro-, and meta-phosphate ions to the corresponding arsenic ions as far as basicity is concerned. What generalization for this family does this indicate? If corresponding ions of antimony and bismuth existed, what would their basic nature be? Why? What common oxyions of these do exist?

5. Which of the Group V elements form salts in which the particular element is a positive ion? What generalization is this based on?

6. Oxides of elements in higher oxidation states are more acidic than oxides of the same element in a lower oxidation state. Support this statement with suitable examples and comparisons with the Group V elements.

7. Correlate some of the properties of the *free* elements P through Bi with electronegativity. Consider such properties as metallic nature, crystallinity, electrical conductivity, strength and nature of bonds, and melting point.

8. Are there any restrictions as to the type of compound from which the sulfides of As, Sb, and Bi can be precipitated?

9. Illustrate, with balanced chemical equations, the effect of the bases NaOH and $(NH_4)_2S$ on As_2S_3. Why does this effect also appear with Sb_2S_3 but not with Bi_2S_3?

10. The K_{sp} of CdS is 1×10^{-28} and that of ZnS is 1×10^{-23}. How many moles of HCl are required, in 1 l. of solution saturated with H_2S, to prevent the precipitation of ZnS but permit the precipitation of CdS? $Cd^{++} = Zn^{++} = 0.05\ M$. $K_{12}H_2S = 1.1 \times 10^{-22}$. Saturated $H_2S = 0.1\ M$.

11. The following unknowns are given limited tests. On the basis of these tests, decide whether each of the ions listed is present or absent, or whether the data are insufficient for a decision.

a. A blue solution is known to contain one or more of the following Group II ions:

    1. Cu^{++}.   2. Sb^{+3}.   3. Hg^{++}.   4. Bi^{+3}.   5. Cd^{++}.

The solution was appropriately treated with H_2S and gave a darkish precipitate that was insoluble in $(NH_4)_2S$. The precipitate dissolved partially in dilute HNO_3, leaving a black residue and a colored decantate. Adding an excess of NH_4OH produced a clear blue solution that gave a black precipitate when $(NH_4)_2S$ was added.

b. A colorless solution is known only to contain one or more of the following Group II ions:

    1. AsO_4^{-3}.   2. Sb^{+3}.   3. Cd^{++}.   4. Bi^{+3}.   5. Sn^{++}.

On dilution with water the solution became cloudy but cleared up when HCl was added prior to treatment with H_2S. After appropriate treatment with H_2S a yellowish precipitate was obtained which was partially soluble in $(NH_4)_2S$; it gave a decantate (I) and a yellow residue (II). The residue (II) was completely soluble in dilute HNO_3. The decantate (I) gave a yellowish precipitate with dilute HCl which was completely soluble in concentrated HCl. After proper treatment with HCl and Al, this solution formed a white precipitate when $HgCl_2$ solution was added.

c. An unknown consisting of a mixture of solid chlorides, known to contain only metals of the copper-arsenic group, dissolved readily and completely in cold water, giving a clear, pale blue solution. The regular treatment with H_2S resulted in a brownish precipitate. This precipitate was partially soluble in $(NH_4)_2S$. The residue did not dissolve in $(NH_4)_2S$ but was completely soluble in warm dilute HNO_3.

    1. Sn^{++}.   2. Bi^{+3}.   3. Cu^{++}.   4. Hg^{++}.   5. Pb^{++}.   6. Sb^{+3}.   7. Cd^{++}.
    8. AsO_4^{-3}.

12. Following is a list of five pairs of solid compounds, and five reagents. From the list of reagents, select one for each unknown that is suitable for identifying at least one member of the pair. A reagent may be used for more than one pair.

a. CdS and SnS$_2$. A. NH$_4$OH.

b. Bi(OH)$_3$ and Cd(OH)$_2$. B. HCl.

c. SbCl$_3$ and BiCl$_3$. C. (NH$_4$)$_2$S.

d. As$_2$S$_3$ and Sb$_2$S$_3$. D. HNO$_3$.

e. HgS and CuS. E. H$_2$O.

21

Copper, silver, and gold. Analysis of analytical group I

21.1. History

Copper, silver, and gold have been known and used longer than any other metals. Objects of hammered copper 8000 years old are known from Egypt, and specimens of cast copper from Egypt and Babylonia date from 4000 B.C. An Egyptian temple dating from 2750 B.C. was uncovered in 1907; in it were found 1300 feet of 1.85-in. copper drain pipe. The pipe seams were hammered, not soldered. Silver also was known in Egypt at least 6500 years ago, but was so rare that it was valued more highly than gold for a long time. The use of gold is older than modern civilization; gold ornaments are found in Neolithic remains. All three of these metals have been used for money since coinage began (900 to 800 B.C.), wherefore they are frequently called the coinage metals. Their relatively high electronegativities are responsible both for their long history and for the high esteem in which they have been and are still held. In a metal, high electronegativity means low activity. Accordingly the coinage metals are often found free in nature (native), and objects made from them are largely or completely resistant to atmospheric attack.

During the last Ice Age in America, native copper was broken off from exposed lodes in the Great Lakes region by glacial action and scattered southward over an area of 70,000 sq. mi. The Indians used copper for ornaments and many other objects which could not be made from flint. They are believed to have moved a 3-ton boulder of nearly pure copper for two miles; it is now in the National Museum in Washington, D.C. John Winthrop started a brass foundry in 1664, and in 1666 pins were made from native copper in Lynn, Massachusetts. A copper mine was opened in Connecticut in 1709. An attempt to mine copper in the Lake Superior region in 1771 failed; successful copper mining there dates from 1846.

Comparatively few people know that the Paul Revere who made the famous midnight ride was an artisan in gold and silver and the founder of the malleable copper industry in this country. He discovered the secret process, hitherto known only in England, whereby copper could be made sufficiently malleable to be hammered hot. His foundry, established in the 1780's, had become a large enterprise by 1800, casting bronze bells and brass cannon, and manufacturing much-needed bolts, spikes, and nails for shipbuilders. The government loaned him $10,000 with which to buy a water-power site at Canton, Massachusetts. Two years later the Navy alone bought $93,000 worth of Revere copper and brass.

21.2. Occurrence of Copper

Besides occurring free in nature, copper in quantities sufficient to be mined is found as sulfides, oxides, carbonates, silicates, sulfates, oxychlorides, sulfarsenides, and sulfantimonides. The sulfides are by far the most important, the oxides, carbonates, sulfates, and silicates following in that order. One of the finest exhibits of copper ores is the Gallagher collection at the Montana School of Mines in Butte, Montana. The names and formulas of some of the copper ores are as follows:

Sulfides: Chalcopyrite, $CuFeS_2$; bornite, $FeS \cdot (Cu_2S)_2 \cdot CuS$; covellite, CuS; chalcocite, Cu_2S.
Oxides: Melaconite, CuO; cuprite, Cu_2O.
Carbonates: Malachite, $CuCO_3 \cdot Cu(OH)_2$; azurite, $(CuCO_3)_2 \cdot Cu(OH)_2$.
Silicate: Chrysocolla, $CuSiO_3 \cdot 2H_2O$.
Sulfates: Chalcanthite, $CuSO_4 \cdot 5H_2O$; brochantite, $CuSO_4 \cdot (Cu(OH)_2)_3$.
Oxychloride: Atacamite, $Cu_2Cl(OH)_3$.
Arsenic and antimony compounds: Enargite, Cu_3AsS_4; tetrahedrite, $(Cu_2S)_3 \cdot Sb_2S_3$.

Copper compounds instead of iron compounds serve as oxygen carriers in the blood of oysters and lobsters. Therefore these two sea foods are one source of the traces of copper compounds which our bodies require.

21.3. Metallurgy of Copper

Northern Michigan is the only part of the United States in which native copper is mined in any quantity. The metal content of the ores averages only about 1.5 per cent, and each ton contains on the average 0.006 oz. of gold and 0.25 oz. of silver.

Copper sold in the market is known as Lake, electrolytic, and casting copper. Lake copper consists of lumps of native copper dispersed in rocks, the lumps ranging from very small particles to masses weighing several tons. The ore is hoisted to the surface of the ground and crushed. It is then shipped to the concentrating mill, where the copper is separated from the gangue, or waste, by jigs, tables, and ore flotation machines. The concentrate is shipped to the smelter and melted in reverberatory furnaces; the molten copper sinks to the bottom and the waste material floats on the top and is thrown away. Air is blown through the molten copper to oxidize other impurities; any copper oxide that forms is reduced with carbon. The molten copper is then cast into billets, cakes, or ingots.

The year 1864 saw the development of the first mines in Butte, Montana, the placer gold mines. Gold mining soon proved unsuccessful and was followed by silver mining. In 1875 copper mines in that region were systematically developed for the first time, and copper mining has continued from that time to the present. To date, over 5 million tons of the metal have been taken from this section. The entire city of Butte is undermined by the 700 miles of drifts or horizontal passages that have been constructed. The shafts extend approximately 4000 ft. into the ground.

The copper ore is found as bands and streaks in quartz and altered granite. The principal ores of the Butte deposits are chalcocite, bornite, and enargite. Associated with them are iron sulfide, about 0.6 oz. of silver per 1 per cent of copper, gold so small in quantity that it has a value of about 10 cents per ton of ore, zinc sulfide or sphalerite, galena, PbS, and two manganese minerals, rhodochrosite, $MnCO_3$, and the dioxide, pyrolusite.

Underground mining is expensive. In Bingham, Utah, and in Bisbee and Morenci, Arizona, it has proved more practical to mine whole mountains containing innumerable small ore veins and large bodies of low-grade ore. An average copper content of 0.5 per cent is sufficient to make such an operation profitable. The ore is crushed and ground to such fineness that any one particle is either mostly ore, or entirely barren rock. The crushed ore is then concentrated by **flotation** (Section 14.7). The pulverized "pulp" is fed into tanks of water with canvas bottoms through which air is blown. Minute quantities of chemicals, carefully chosen so as to wet the ore particles but not the barren rock, are added to promote frothing. The ore is moved into the froth and coats each bubble in it. The gangue is carried away by the water; the froth is skimmed off, broken up by acid, and dried, leaving a high-grade concentrate. This process, developed through research directed by the noted mining engineer Herbert Hoover before he became President, is the only method of recovering not only copper ore but many other valuable minerals from very low-grade deposits.

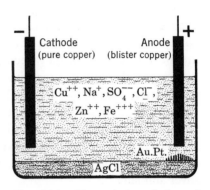

Fig. 21.1. Electrolytic refining of copper.

The concentrate, which contains about 27 per cent copper, is roasted to remove part of the sulfur and then smelted in reverberatory furnaces. The matte from these furnaces contains about 45 per cent copper and is dumped into converters. The molten impure copper from the converters is cast into anodes and shipped to electrolytic refineries. "Blister copper" anodes are about 99.3 per cent copper, and contain iron and zinc, and traces of gold, silver, and antimony.

In electrolytic refining, sheets of pure copper are the cathodes, and blister copper is used as the anodes, as shown in Fig. 21.1. The bath contains $CuSO_4$, H_2SO_4, and NaCl. Metallic copper goes into solution as Cu^{++} ions at the anode and plates out at the cathode. Zinc and iron go into solution along with the copper, but the voltage is low enough so that the Fe^{++} and Zn^{++} ions are kept in solution. Silver goes into solution as Ag^+ ions, but precipitates as AgCl, which forms a sludge in the electrolysis cell. The noble metals, such as gold and platinum, do not dissolve; they fall to the bottom when released from the copper. The value of the anode mud about pays for the refining. Electrolytic copper contains 99.95 per cent copper.

Sulfur dioxide from the roasting ovens is converted into sulfuric acid.

Arsenic, zinc, lead, and traces of other elements are recovered from the flue dust.

21.4. Occurrence and Metallurgy of Silver and Gold

Lead, zinc, cobalt, and copper ores nearly always contain small quantities of silver. Galena, for example, frequently contains as much as 1 per cent silver. Outcroppings of such argentiferous ores that have been exposed to weathering and leaching by ground waters for a long time are so depleted in their content of the less noble metals, whose compounds are more soluble, that they become silver ores. Most of the silver is in the form of the sulfide, argentite or silver glance, Ag_2S, or the chloride, cerargyrite or horn silver, $AgCl$. Important quantities of these compounds may be reduced to the metallic state. For this reason, most silver mines are relatively rich in silver near the surface, gradually becoming lead mines, etc., deeper down. There are no longer any important silver mines in the United States, although we still produce 1600 tons of silver annually.

Gold is nearly always found free in nature, although the ore Au_2Te gave its name to the mining town of Telluride, Colorado. Gold is frequently found alloyed with small amounts of silver or copper, but small amounts of gold are present in many ores and in pyrites.

The recovery of silver and gold as by-products of various metallurgical operations has already been described. The concentration of relatively coarse gold from alluvial deposits by placer and hydraulic mining, and from crushed quartz veins by hydraulic classification, is too largely mechanical to warrant description here. There is, however, a purely chemical method of extracting silver and gold, native or combined, which can be used with the tailings from flotation plants and with ores or alluvial deposits that contain "flour gold"—gold in specks too small to settle out of moving water. This is the **cyanide process.**

Although silver and gold are ordinarily not affected by air, they can be dissolved by atmospheric oxygen in the presence of ions which can coordinate with their oxidation products to form covalently bonded complexes. Cl^-, Br^-, and I^- are increasingly effective in that order; but the pseudohalide ion, CN^-, is perhaps the most efficient of all the complexing agents, and is, moreover, relatively cheap. The material to be treated, in particles no larger than grains of sand, is loaded into huge concrete tanks that hold several thousand tons each. Fire hoses wet it down with dilute $NaCN$ solution which is thoroughly aerated in the process. Silver can be substituted for gold in the following equations. The H_2O_2 formed as an intermediate compound speeds up the reaction.

$$2Au + \overline{O_2} + 4CN^- + 2H_2O \rightarrow 2Au(CN)_2^- + 2OH^- + \cancel{H_2O_2}$$

$$2Au + \cancel{H_2O_2} + 4CN^- \rightarrow 2Au(CN)_2^- + 2OH^-$$

$$\overline{4Au + O_2 + 8CN^- + 2H_2O \rightarrow 4Au(CN)_2^- + 4OH^-}$$

The CN^- ion reduces the concentrations of all subgroup metal ions to such low values by the formation of complex ions that even their most insoluble compounds, such as chalcocite and argentite, dissolve along with the free silver and gold. The equation for argentite is typical.

$$Ag_2S + 4CN^- \rightarrow 2Ag(CN)_2^- + S^{--}$$

The precious metals are precipitated from the solution by zinc.

$$2Au(CN)_2^- + Zn \rightarrow 2Au + Zn(CN)_4^{--}$$

The mixture of metals which is obtained may be separated by electrolytic refining, or chemically. If the alloy does not contain more than one-third gold, the silver may be dissolved out of it by boiling HNO_3 or concentrated H_2SO_4. This procedure may be used with richer metal by first alloying it with enough silver to bring the gold content down to 25 per cent. In another procedure, the alloy is dissolved in aqua regia (HNO_3 + HCl), which precipitates the silver as AgCl. The gold is then precipitated by Fe^{++} ion.

$$Au + 3H^+ + 3NO_3^- + 4H^+ + 4Cl^- \rightarrow H^+ + AuCl_4^- + \overline{3NO_2} + 3H_2O$$
$$AuCl_4^- + 3Fe^{++} \rightarrow Au + 3Fe^{+3} + 4Cl^-$$

21.5. Physical Properties and Uses of the Coinage Metals

Gold, silver, and copper are too familiar to require detailed description. All are extremely ductile and malleable; gold can be beaten into leaf that is less than 0.0001 mm. thick. All three are outstandingly good conductors of heat and electricity, silver being the best of any metal in this respect, with copper next. In the case of copper, even traces of such impurities as arsenic, silicon, and phosphorus seriously lower its conductivity; hence the importance of electrolytic refining.

Cu_2O is soluble in copper and has a harmful effect on its properties, but it can be removed by mild reducing agents. For ordinary purposes the molten copper is stirred with green wooden poles to remove the oxygen. The melting of copper under a layer of magnesium produces oxygen-free copper. Fused silver dissolves up to twenty times its volume of oxygen, but this is liberated when the metal begins to solidify. The silver "spits," spurting out liquid so that the solid has a rough surface. Gold is not affected by oxygen.

Alloying with other metals or with each other hardens the coinage metals, for they are too soft for most purposes. Copper is alloyed with zinc to form brass, and with other metals to form bronzes. Copper pennies contain 2.5 per cent each of tin and zinc. Our nickels are 25 per cent nickel; Monel metal, about 60 per cent. Ordinary bronze—bell metal, etc.—contains from 10 to 20 per cent tin. The tensile strength of annealed copper is only 30,000 p.s.i., but this may be doubled by work-hardening. In strength, the alloys range from 60,000 through 105,000 p.s.i. for aluminum bronze (5 per cent Al) up to a remarkable 175,000 p.s.i. for beryllium bronze (2 per cent Be). Springs made from beryllium bronze practically never fail from fatigue; the alloy is also used for non-sparking tools. Sterling silver contains 7.5 per cent copper, and 10 per cent copper is used to harden silver and gold coins. The fineness of gold that is used for jewelry is expressed in carats (abbreviated K, from karat, the old spelling); a carat is a twenty-fourth part. Pure gold is 24K, and the gold used in high-grade jewelry 18K; 14K gold is commonly used for rings because they have to withstand hard wear. The rest of the alloy is usually copper, which gives the gold its red color. Gold may be whitened with silver or platinum; adding 1 per cent aluminum produces green gold; and the compound, $AuAl_2$, containing 21.5 per cent aluminum, is purple. Table 21.1 lists some of the physical properties of the coinage metals.

Although our production of copper varies, it has run around 1 million tons annually in recent years—about one-third of the world output. We import about half as much as we produce. Electrical equipment accounts for about 50 per cent of the copper we use, brass and other alloys for about 20 per cent more. The building trades—sheet and pipe—and chemical construction—vats, stills, condensers for chemicals, food, and beverages—use another 10 per cent. The price of copper is extremely variable; from 37 cents per pound in 1917 it fell to 5 cents in 1932, rose to 54 cents in 1956, and was down to half that amount the following year.

Neither price nor demand has much influence on our production of silver. Rather our output depends on the production of other metals of

TABLE 21.1. **Physical Properties of the Coinage Metals**

	Copper	Silver	Gold
Density, g./cc.	8.92	10.5	19.3
Melting point, °C.	1083	960.8	1063
Boiling point, °C.	2336	1950	2600
Atomic radii, A.	1.173	1.339	1.336
Ionic radii (M$^+$), A.	0.96	1.26	1.37
Electronegativity	1.9	1.9	2.4

which silver is a by-product. The United States Treasury is currently buying 5000 tons of silver per year; U. S. production is 1000 tons. Only about half of this is used in coinage; the rest goes into the immense hoard which the Treasury has been accumulating since 1934 in accordance with Congressional action. These purchases by our Treasury, at prices fixed by law, have been the major factor in setting the world price of silver, which is currently 91 cents per troy ounce or $9 per pound avoirdupois.

The 50 tons of gold which we now annually produce on an average is small compared with the world output of almost 1000 tons. The United States Treasury purchased 470 tons for $400 million in 1957; this was stored in Fort Knox. The government's fixed price of $35 per troy ounce represents a purchasing power which has gradually diminished as a result of inflation. This is reflected in the 20 per cent decrease in gold production between 1947 and 1961.

21.6. Chemical Properties of the Coinage Metals

The coinage metals are characterized by and valued for their low reactivity. Even copper, the most active of the three, is below hydrogen in the E.C.S., and does not react with H$^+$ ion to liberate hydrogen unless a complexing agent is present. It is stable in dry air and pure water; but if exposed to the weather it gradually forms a coating of verdigris, $CuCO_3 \cdot Cu(OH)_2$, which in urban atmospheres that contain H_2S may be blackened because of the formation of CuS. Copper objects buried in moist earth eventually—after many centuries—are completely corroded.

Although more resistant to chemical attack than copper is, silver tarnishes in air that contains H_2S.

$$4Ag + \overline{2H_2S} + \overline{O_2} \rightarrow 2Ag_2S + \overline{2H_2O}$$

It liberates hydrogen from concentrated hydriodic acid, owing to the formation of AgI_2.

$$2Ag + 4H^+ + 4I^- \rightarrow 2H^+ + 2AgI_2^- + \overline{H_2}$$

Both of these reactions are similar in principle to the extraction of silver and gold by the cyanide process. That is, the metal is dissolved by an oxidizing agent that ordinarily would not attack it, because the resulting metal ion is removed by precipitation or the formation of complex ions. In similar reactions, both copper and silver dissolve in warm dilute HNO_3.

$$3Cu + 8H^+ + 8NO_3^- \rightarrow 3Cu^{++} + 6NO_3^- + 2\overline{NO} + 4H_2O$$

$$3Ag + 4H^+ + 4NO_3^- \rightarrow 3Ag^+ + 3NO_3^- + \overline{NO} + 2H_2O$$

They also dissolve in hot concentrated H_2SO_4.

$$Cu + 3H_2SO_4 \rightarrow Cu^{++} + 2HSO_4^- + \overline{SO_2} + 2H_2O$$

$$2Ag + 3H_2SO_4 \rightarrow 2Ag^+ + 2HSO_4^- + \overline{SO_2} + 2H_2O$$

Gold is not affected by any atmospheric condition. As was mentioned in connection with the cyanide process, it dissolves only when attacked simultaneously by a strong oxidizing agent and a complexing agent. In aqua regia, for example, concentrated HNO_3 serves as the oxidizing agent, and the Cl⁻ ion of the concentrated HCl as the complexing agent.

$$Au + 7H^+ + 3NO_3^- + 4Cl^- \rightarrow HAuCl_4 + 3\overline{NO_2} + 3H_2O$$

A few strong oxidizing agents produce their own complexing agents as reduction products and hence can dissolve gold without any additional complexing agent. In chlorine water, a mixture of HClO and HCl, the oxidizing agent is Cl(I) in HClO, and the Cl⁻ from the HCl is the complexing agent; the result is $AuCl_4^-$. In HIO_3 the iodine has an oxidation state of $+5$ and oxidizes gold, forming the complex AuI_4^-.

21.7. The Monovalent Ions

Cuprous, argentous, and aurous ions are ions of the pseudo-inert gas type, like Zn^{++}, Cd^{++}, and Hg^{++}; there are 10 d electrons in their surface. The single s electron in the valence shell has been lost; hence the charge is $+ 1$. For Cu^+, Ag^+, or Au^+, the outer electron structure is:

Because of their d electrons, these ions have considerable ability to form covalent bonds, but their low charge usually limits the number of ligands to two. Cu^+, the smallest ion, can actually take on four ligands, and Ag^+ ion to some extent three, in the presence of a high concentration of complexing agent. The chlorides, bromides, and iodides of all three ions are insoluble because each halide ion in the crystals forms bonds with cations on both sides of it; the bonds are covalent to some degree. This effect increases in the order Cl^-, Br^-, I^-.

Further generalizations about these ions are not worth while because of one striking—and unexplained—difference between them. Ag^+ is to such an extent the most stable valence of silver that it is ordinarily called silver ion. In water solution, however, both Cu^+ and Au^+ dismute into the free metals and a higher valence ion if their concentration rises to more than a minimal value—10^{-4} M in the case of Cu^+ ion. This means that neither of them can exist except in complex ions or highly insoluble compounds, in both of which the valence is stabilized by the formation of covalent bonds. Cu(I) complex ions include $CuCl_3^{--}$, $Cu(CN)_4^{-3}$, $Cu(NH_3)_3^+$, CuI_2^-, and $Cu(S_2O_3)_2^{-3}$. The common insoluble compounds are the halides and pseudohalides, Cu_2O and Cu_2S; explosive cuprous acetylide, Cu_2C_2, is also of interest. Au(I) forms similar compounds, except that its covalence is never more than 2. Since only the octet orbitals are concerned in the formation of the complex ions and contain no unshared electron pairs, the shape of the complex ions is simple. If there are two ligands, the molecule is linear; if there are three, it is a plane triangle with the metal at the center; if four it is tetrahedral.

Silver ion forms the same complex ions and insoluble compounds as gold and copper do. It also forms many compounds that are only moderately insoluble, several that are on the border line, and a few salts that are very soluble. The border-line compounds, characterized by solubilities around 1 per cent, include $AgC_2H_3O_2$, $AgMnO_4$, $AgBrO_3$, and Ag_2SO_4. Ranging from moderately to extremely soluble are $AgClO_3$, $AgClO_4$, $AgNO_3$, and AgF. Simple hydrated Ag^+ ion, having no unpaired d electrons, is colorless and forms colorless—white—salts except with anions that are highly polarizable and that therefore have a high tendency to form covalent bonds. Ag^+ ion has too low a charge for it to be acidic to any considerable degree, as witness the fact that it can coexist with CO_3^{--} ion, forming the normal carbonate, Ag_2CO_3. Ag^+ ion is a slightly better oxidizing agent than Fe^{+3} ion but not quite as good as HNO_3 in equal concentrations. Cu^+ and Au^+ ions are comparable in this respect with iodine and MnO_4^- ion respectively, but neither can be obtained in more than extremely dilute solutions.

21.8. Photography

When solid AgCl is exposed to bright light, its color quickly changes from the original white, through shades of lavender, to black. The first step in this photochemical reaction is the knocking off of an electron from a Cl⁻ ion by a quantum of light. (A **quantum** of radiant energy, or light, is a discrete quantity regarded as a unit.) These ejected electrons are called **photoelectrons.** The uncharged chlorine atom thus produced may recombine with its own or another electron to form Cl⁻ again, or it may combine with another chlorine atom to form the molecule Cl_2, which evaporates. If not captured by chlorine, the photoelectron can convert silver ion into metallic silver. The following reactions summarize these possibilities:

$$AgCl + Light \rightarrow Ag^+ + \underline{Cl} + e^-$$
$$\underline{Cl} + e^- \rightarrow Cl^-$$

or

$$Cl + Cl \rightarrow \overline{Cl_2}$$
$$Ag^+ + e^- \rightarrow \underline{Ag}$$

AgBr, the most commonly used sensitive material, behaves in the same way, but more slowly, because its bonds are more covalent; its color changes from its original cream color through greenish shades, in darkening. AgI is also photosensitive. Nearly all photography is based on these reactions, but the actual process is much more complicated.

The silver halides, chiefly AgBr, are precipitated in a warm gelatin solution by the reaction:

$$Ag^+ + NO_3^- + K^+ + Br^- \rightarrow \underline{AgBr} + K^+ + NO_3^-$$

The very small AgBr crystals which are produced in this way do not settle out but remain in permanent suspension as a creamy emulsion. This emulsion is coated on a transparent support, such as glass or film, upon which it solidifies. By suitable control in its preparation, the grain size of the AgBr can be varied over limits that make possible fine- to coarse-grained emulsions. As will be seen, the coarse grains increase the sensitivity of the film.

Very little of the metallic silver which is present in the finished image of the negative and print is the direct result of the reduction of Ag^+ by photoelectrons. Indeed, to accomplish this would require a tremendous intensity of photons and a great amount of time. Fortunately, the emulsions are sensitized by the presence of specks of Ag_2S in the AgBr crystals. The Ag_2S is due to the sulfur which is a natural constituent of the gelatin. The photoelectrons that are produced on exposure to light are trapped in irregularities of the AgBr crystals caused by specks of Ag_2S. The trapped photoelectrons constitute what is called a **latent image** of the object photographed. They are held in this image until they combine with Ag^+ ions which come into contact with the Ag_2S and convert the Ag^+ ions into metallic silver. It has been shown that as few as three silver atoms thus produced can render an entire AgBr grain developable, because of the catalytic effect of the metallic silver on the development of the remainder of the Ag^+ ions in the grain.

Development is the chemical process in which Ag^+ is reduced to metallic silver in the light-struck grains of AgBr; it is an all-or-nothing phenomenon. That is, every unexposed grain is left untouched by the developer, which is a weak reducing agent; and every light-struck grain, whether large or small, is completely *reduced*. This is why, other things being equal, a coarse-grained film is more sensitive than a fine-grained film. The amount of image blackening, or density, depends upon the number of light-struck grains which in turn is determined by the number of light quanta that struck a given region of the film. The developer, which converts the latent image into the final observed image, contains a reducing agent, Br^- ions to minimize the action of the reducing agent on unexposed grains (fogging), a base to neutralize H^+ ions liberated during the reaction, and SO_3^{--} ion to reduce the used oxidized developer which otherwise would be colored and cause film staining and also catalyze further film development (Section 11.17). The action of the developer is stopped at the proper time by dropping the film into a bath of dilute $HC_2H_3O_2$.

Before the film can be exposed to light, the unchanged silver halide must be removed; otherwise it too will soon turn black. This process, called **fixing,** entails complexing the silver ion with thiosulfate ion.

$$\underline{AgBr} + 2S_2O_3^{--} \rightarrow Ag(S_2O_3)_2^{-3} + Br^-$$

The source of this ion is $Na_2S_2O_3 \cdot 5H_2O$; this is erroneously still called hypo because in the early stages of the art of photography it was thought to be sodium hyposulfite, Na_2SO_2.

The fixing solution also contains agents which harden or tan the gelatin in order to increase its scratch resistance. The tanning agents are aluminum or chromium alums. $HC_2H_3O_2$ is added to maintain the proper acidity for tanning. Under these conditions the $S_2O_3^{--}$ tends to decompose.

$$S_2O_3^{--} + H^+ \rightleftharpoons HS_2O_3^- \rightleftharpoons HSO_3^- + \underline{S}$$

This is prevented by adding a considerable amount of $Na_2S_2O_5$ which establishes a high concentration of HSO_3^- ion in solution as a product of the following equilibrium, thus reversing the decomposition.

$$S_2O_5^{--} + H_2O \rightleftharpoons 2HSO_3^-$$

For this reason $Na_2S_2O_5$ is usually though erroneously called sodium bisulfite by photographers instead of being given its correct name, pyrosulfite.

Photographic images may be reduced or intensified in density or opacity. Some of the silver may be dissolved by oxidizing it with Fe^{+3} or MnO_4^-. This reduces the intensity of the image. If the photograph is dipped in a solution containing Ag^+ ion and a developer, more silver will be deposited in the regions which already contain metallic silver. This is due to the catalytic reducing effect of silver on Ag^+ ion, and is called "physical" intensification. An interesting example of "chemical" intensification involves the use of $HgCl_2$ in solution.

$$\underline{2Ag} + 2HgCl_2 \rightarrow \underline{2AgCl} + \underline{Hg_2Cl_2}$$

The reaction occurs wherever silver is already present in the photograph. Redevelopment results in the formation of metallic mercury and silver, actually twice as much metal in each region as there was formerly. This can be repeated as often as desired, intensification being increased each time. Other intensification treatments involve various ions and compounds, the principles being similar to those discussed here.

Toning and colorations are achieved by causing the silver atoms to displace a less active metal, such as platinum or gold, from a solution containing it. Or the silver may be oxidized in the presence of a suitable anion which immediately precipitates a silver salt of the desired color. Here again there are too many variations in procedure for us to consider them here.

21.9. Analysis of Analytical Group I

The first general group reagent used in making a qualitative cation analysis of an unknown solution is dilute HCl. This precipitates the ions that form insoluble chlorides (Table 21.2).

$$Ag^+ + Cl^- \rightarrow \underline{AgCl}$$

$$Hg_2^{++} + 2Cl^- \rightarrow \underline{Hg_2Cl_2}$$

$$Pb^{++} + 2Cl^- \rightarrow \underline{PbCl_2}$$

TABLE 21.2.　**Analysis of Analytical Group I, the Silver Group**

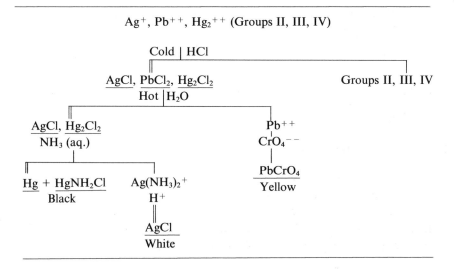

Although they also form insoluble chlorides, the other monovalent ions of the non-inert gas type—Cu^+, Au^+, and Tl^+—are not included because they either cannot be obtained in solution or are rare. $PbCl_2$ will be precipitated in this analytical group only to the extent that its concentration exceeds about 1 per cent. If lead is found in analytical Group I, it should also be found in Group II; but the reverse is not true. HCl must not be used in excess, for AgCl and $PbCl_2$ are soluble in concentrated HCl, forming $AgCl_2^-$ and $PbCl_4^{--}$ ions respectively.

$PbCl_2$ is three times as soluble in boiling water as it is in cold water. Hence enough of it can easily be washed out of the mixed chloride precipitate with boiling water to give the characteristic yellow precipitate of $PbCrO_4$ when a drop of CrO_4^{--} solution is added.

$$Pb^{++} + CrO_4^{--} \rightarrow \underline{PbCrO_4}$$

AgCl is dissolved from the remaining mixed chloride precipitate by NH_3 solution.

$$\underline{AgCl} + 2NH_3 \rightarrow Ag(NH_3)_2^+ + Cl^-$$

When the NH_3 solution is neutralized and acidified, if the silver-ammonia ion is present it will revert to Ag^+ ion and precipitate as AgCl.

$$Ag(NH_3)_2^+ + Cl^- + 2H^+ \rightarrow \underline{AgCl} + 2NH_4^+$$

At the same time that the NH_3 is removing the AgCl, it blackens the remainder of the chloride precipitate, if it contains any Hg_2Cl_2. This is the calomel reaction (Section 19.6).

$$\underline{Hg_2Cl_2} + 2NH_3 \rightarrow \underline{Hg} + \underline{HgNH_2Cl} + NH_4^+ + Cl^-$$

If Hg_2^{++} is proved to have been present in the unknown, at least a trace of Hg^{++} should be present in analytical Group II.

21.10. Higher Valences of the Coinage Metals

The monovalent ions of the coinage metals are colorless and of the pseudo-inert gas type. They can lose one or two d electrons from the completed subgroup in their surface. The ions that result are of the non-inert gas type; they are colored, and in chemical properties resemble other non-inert gas types of ions with similar valence.

The reaction at the top takes place readily with copper, only with great difficulty with silver, and not at all with gold. The reverse is true of the reaction below. Thus only silver has three valences, but only silver is restricted so strongly to a particular valence. None of the elements which follow these three elements in their respective periods ever loses a d electron. Thus Group IB elements are the only ones whose valence is ever more than the group number.

21.11. Copper(II) (Cupric) Ion

When copper is oxidized by heating it in air, or with HNO_3 or hot concentrated H_2SO_4 (Section 21.6), Cu(II) is produced, although when it burns in the vapor of boiling sulfur the oxidation goes only to Cu_2S. Since Cu^{++} is the only ion of copper that is ever encountered in appreciable concentration, Cu^{++} is called copper ion much more commonly than either cupric or copper(II). Anhydrous $CuSO_4$ is white, but Cu(II) is regularly coordinated to four ligands and is colored. $Cu(H_2O)_4^{++}$ is light blue; other colors are produced if the water molecules are displaced by one or more other ligands. $Cu(H_2O)_2Cl_2$ is light green, and $Cu(H_2O)_2 Br_2$ is dark green. $CuCl_4^{--}$ is yellow; $CuBr_4^{--}$ dark brown. There are no iodides for two reasons—Cu(II) is comparable to I_2 as an oxidizing agent, and Cu^+ and I_2, the products of the reaction, are held at very low concentrations by precipitation and complexing respectively.

Or simply
$$2Cu^{++} + 5I^- \rightarrow 2CuI + I_3^-$$
$$2Cu^{++} + 4I^- \rightarrow 2CuI + I_2$$

This reaction is the basis of the important iodide method for the quantitative determination of copper. The liberated iodine is titrated with thiosulfate.

When Cu(II) is coordinated with nitrogen atoms, a dark blue color is produced; this color is most familiar in the tetramminecopper ion, $Cu(NH_3)_4^{++}$. Although this color is by no means as intense as the starch-iodine color whose disappearance indicates the end point of the thiosulfate titration just mentioned, it is strong enough so that its disappearance indicates the completion of the following reaction, sometimes used in analyzing copper ores:

$$2Cu(NH_3)_4^{++} + 3CN^- + H_2O \rightarrow 2CuCN + CNO^- + 6NH_3 + 2NH_4^+$$

This reaction is similar to the preceding reaction in principle, corresponding to the fact that cyanide ion is a pseudohalide and cyanogen a pseudo hypohalite. In the presence of excess CN^- ion, the precipitate dissolves by forming the complex $Cu(CN)_4^{-3}$ ion (p. 575). Copper phthalocyanin gives the most intense copper blue and is the finest and most stable blue pigment known. The phthalocyanin ion, $C_{32}H_{20}N_8H_2^{--}$, resembles a lace doily in shape. At its center, four nitrogen atoms are arranged in a square; there is just enough room between them for a Cu^{++} ion. Each of the four nitrogen atoms has an electron pair that can coordinate with the Cu⁺⁺ ion. The resulting uncharged complex is insoluble and very stable; it sublimes unchanged at 500° C. The formation of a square coordination compound shows that one d orbital is used, as in the square complexes of Ni⁺⁺. Since the atomic number of copper is one unit higher than that of nickel, Cu⁺⁺ ion has one more electron than Ni⁺⁺ ion. It is forced into the p orbital that is empty in the nickel complexes; this requires only a very small promotion in energy. Cu(II) as in $Cu(NH_3)_4^{++}$, etc., is:

Because Cu⁺⁺ ion tends strongly to have a coordination number of 4, Cu(II) salts differ in crystalline form, and in the amount of water of hydration, from the corresponding salts of other divalent cations of the non-inert gas type. For example, it forms no schönite, because one unit in the crystal of double salts of the type $K_2SO_4 \cdot MSO_4 \cdot 6H_2O$ is $M(H_2O)_6^{++}$, where M⁺⁺, as we have seen, can be Mg⁺⁺, Mn⁺⁺, Fe⁺⁺, Co⁺⁺, Ni⁺⁺, Zn⁺⁺, or Cd⁺⁺. The true vitriols, $MSO_4 \cdot 7H_2O$, also contain $M(H_2O)_6^{++}$ ions; the seventh water molecule is hydrogen-bonded to the SO_4^{--} ion. Thus the most familiar copper salt, $CuSO_4 \cdot 5H_2O$, although called blue vitriol, is not a true vitriol. In it the H_2O molecule is hydrogen-bonded to the SO_4^{--} ion, but the cation is a square tetrahydrate instead of an octahedral hexahydrate, and the crystal symmetry is accordingly different. The number of molecules of water which hydrate a cation is sometimes subject to the influence of other ions in the crystal that is forming. If a mixture of Cu(II) and Fe(II) sulfates is being crystallized from solution, mixed crystals will be formed, the two kinds of cations being arranged at random in each crystal; the proportion depends upon their relative concentration in the solution. If the iron predominates, the crystals will be the true vitriol, $(Fe,Cu)SO_4 \cdot 7H_2O$. But if there is considerably more copper than iron, the pentahydrate, $(Cu,Fe)SO_4 \cdot 5H_2O$, will be formed. A mixture of Cu⁺⁺ and Zn⁺⁺ ions behaves similarly.

Like Zn⁺⁺ ion, Cu⁺⁺ ion is too strong an acid to form a normal carbonate; but two basic carbonates—deep blue azurite, $Cu(OH)_2 \cdot 2CuCO_3$, and bright green malachite, $Cu(OH)_2 \cdot CuCO_3$—are common surface ores of copper. Both make attractive costume jewelry. Many other basic salts can be formed. Normal salts are formed with any anion that is neither strongly basic nor a fairly good reducing agent. Adding NH_3 to $Cu(H_2O)_4^{++}$ solution first removes two protons; the pale-blue gelatinous hydroxide, $Cu(H_2O)_2(OH)_2$, is precipitated. This is insoluble in NaOH solution but dissolves readily in excess NH_3, because the NH_3

molecules displace the H_2O and OH^- molecules, forming tetramminecopper ion, $Cu(NH_3)_4^{++}$.

$$Cu(H_2O)_4^{++} + 2NH_3 \rightarrow \underline{Cu(H_2O)_2(OH)_2} + 2NH_4^+$$

$$\underline{Cu(H_2O)_2(OH)_2} + 4NH_3 \rightarrow Cu(NH_3)_4^{++} + 2OH^- + 2H_2O$$

21.12. Gold(III)

Gold does not have an oxidation number of 2. Compounds in which it apparently has this number have been shown to contain equal numbers of Au(I) and Au(III) atoms. An example is the double salt whose empirical formula is $CsAuCl_3$; its actual formula is $Cs_2(AuCl_2)(AuCl_4)$. The first anion contains Au(I) and is therefore linear. The second contains Au(III); this has the same number of d electrons as Ni(II), and is therefore square. Au^{+3} is unknown except in AuF_3, where it proves to be a very strong oxidizing agent. In all other auric compounds the gold atom has four covalent bonds, in complete accordance with what we should expect from its relatively high oxidation number and the fact that it is a sixth-period transition metal. In compounds of the type AuX_3, where X^- is a halide or pseudohalide, and Au_2Y_3, where Y^{--} is a member of the oxygen family, non-metal atoms do double duty, forming covalent bonds with two gold atoms. In color, these compounds range from yellow through red to brown or black. Although insoluble in water, they dissolve readily in an excess of the anion, forming complex anions. In most of these compounds gold has a covalence of 4, as in chloraurate ion, $AuCl_4^-$; the substance commonly sold as gold chloride is $HAuCl_4$. $Au(OH)_3$ is amphoteric; the formula of sodium aurate may be NaH_2AuO_3. All gold compounds decompose when gently heated, yielding metallic gold.

QUESTIONS AND PROBLEMS

1. Outline the extractive chemistry and treatments for producing pure copper.
2. What outstanding physical properties of copper make it so important as a metal and a constituent of alloys?
3. Name some of the common alloys of copper. What are their most important uses?
4. What oxidation states do the coinage metals have? Which are most common for each metal?

5. Using balanced equations, show how the coinage metals are dissolved by acid, complexation, and aqua regia. Use a different metal in each case.

6. Show by orbital dots the pseudo-inert gas type of electronic structure of the monovalent ions of these metals.

7. Are silver salts generally soluble or insoluble? Examples? Name some complexes formed with Ag^+ ion.

8. Explain the photosensitivity of the silver halides.

9. What part do acetic acid and hypo play in the development of films?

10. Each of the following three unknowns contains all or some of the metallic ions listed, but no other cations. Decide in each case, on the basis of the limited test results, whether the ion or compound is present or absent, or whether the information is insufficient for a decision.

   a. When a solid unknown was added to water, a white residue was left. This was separated by filtration and the residue was completely dissolved in concentrated NH_4OH.
      1. $Pb(NO_3)_2$. 2. $AgNO_3$. 3. $HgCl_2$. 4. $Hg_2(NO_3)_2$.

   b. When a colorless unknown was acidified with HCl, a precipitate and a decantate were formed. The precipitate dissolved in NH_4OH. The decantate was divided into three portions. The first portion gave a white precipitate when diluted with water. The second portion, when properly treated with H_2S, gave a blackish precipitate, none of which dissolved in $(NH_4)_2S$. The third portion gave a grayish precipitate on the addition of $SnCl_2$.
      1. Ag^+. 2. Hg_2^{++}. 3. Cu^{++}. 4. Bi^{+3}. 5. Hg^{++}. 6. Sb^{+3}.

   c. A colorless unknown contained only ions of analytical Groups I and II. When HCl was added, a white precipitate and a colorless decantate were formed. The precipitate turned black when NH_4OH was added. After appropriate preparation and treatment with H_2S, etc., the decantate gave a yellowish precipitate which was centrifuged and washed. Part of this precipitate dissolved in $(NH_4)_2S$, giving an amber-colored decantate and a distinctly yellow residue. This residue dissolved almost completely in dilute HNO_3, leaving a whitish residue which was not soluble in aqua regia. The amber-colored decantate formed a yellowish precipitate when dilute HCl was added; this precipitate was partially soluble in concentrated HCl, leaving a residue which proved to be sulfur.
      1. Ag^+. 2. Hg_2^{++}. 3. Pb^{++}. 4. Cu^{++}. 5. Bi^{+3}. 6. Hg^{++}. 7. Cd^{++}.
      8. Sn^{++}. 9. AsO_4^{-3}. 10. Sb^{+3}.

11. How many and what kind of ligands does Cu^{++} coordinate with? How do these complexes vary in color? Explain the fact that $CuSO_4$ is white; when dissolved in water it is blue; and in concentrated HCl it is green.

12. Is Cu^{++} an oxidizing or a reducing agent? Why cannot CuI_2 exist?

13. Compare the coordination ability of Cu^{++} with that of other ions, M^{++}, of the non-inert gas type. Is this sufficient to account for the fact that copper does not form the schönite type of salts? Is the name blue vitriol appropriate for $CuSO_4 \cdot 5H_2O$?

14. Cations that are acidic in type do not form normal carbonates or any normal salt containing a strong base anion. How does Cu^{++} behave in this respect?

22

Electrochemistry and corrosion

22.1. Electrochemical Reactions

Chemical reactions which occur at the surface of the immersed electrodes during electrolysis are induced by the electrical energy that is imparted to the electrodes. They are normal redox reactions involving electron transfer. When the chemical substances available lack the requisite electronegativity to bring about the particular redox reaction involved, the limitless power of electricity is more than ample to do this.

Electrolysis was mentioned frequently in earlier chapters as the means by which many elements and compounds are produced on an industrial scale. Its importance was stressed in connection with the production of hydrogen, oxygen, fluorine, chlorine, sodium, magnesium, calcium, aluminum, zinc, nickel, and copper, as well as such compounds as the oxyhalogen salts of sodium, sodium hydroxide, and hydrogen peroxide. Electrolytic processes are well adapted for the cheap mass production of such substances, even though the same substances can also be produced with conventional chemical reactions. The by-products that form at one or both electrodes often make electrolysis more attractive financially. For example, in the electrolysis of brine to produce hydrogen and chlorine, sodium hydroxide is produced simultaneously. Which is the major product and which the by-product in a case like this often depends on the industrial demand.

The complex cells designed for special electrolytic processes operate on the same simple principles and show the same quantitative electrochemical relationships as do simple cells used in the laboratory. Complexity of design is generally due to the need to satisfy unique demands for convenient continuous separation of products from the electrolytes and for the prevention of contamination.

Electrochemistry is also concerned with the exact opposite of electrolysis, namely, the generation of electricity by means of appropriate redox reactions at the surfaces of electrodes. A cell in which this occurs is called a **galvanic** or **voltaic cell**. The functioning of batteries such as the dry cell, lead storage battery, nickel hydroxide cell, etc., depends upon fundamental principles underlying simple voltaic cells and the electrochemical series which will be developed in this chapter.

One other facet of electrochemistry is concerned with corrosion. We will see how simple principles that have been developed for studying galvanic cells enable a better understanding of at least some corrosion processes and of corrosion prevention in these instances.

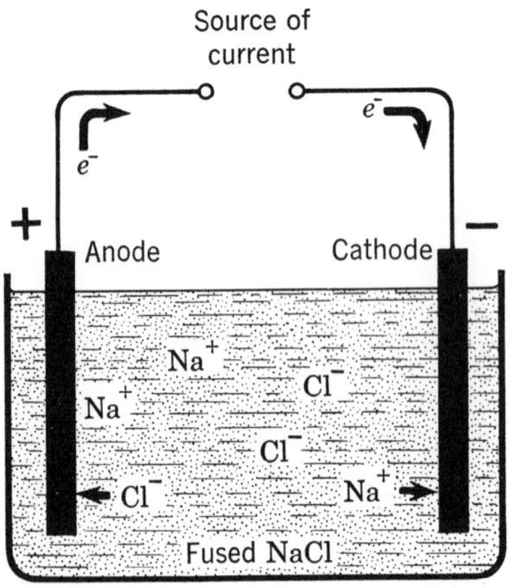

Fig. 22.1. Electrolysis of NaCl. A simple cell is shown in order to illustrate the fundamental components and principles of an electrolytic cell.

22.2. Electrolysis

The fundamental principles underlying electrolysis reactions can be demonstrated by means of the simple cell and reaction for fused NaCl (Fig. 22.1). Since only two kinds of ions are present, Na^+ and Cl^-, complexities which are due to mixtures of similarly charged ions are avoided. In the simple cell used in this reaction, two electrodes—the positively charged anode and the negatively charged cathode—are immersed in the electrolyte. A source of direct current supplies the charges on the electrode. The voltage, which measures the concentration of electrons or electrical "pressure" used, is dependent upon the difficulty of discharging the ions. (See the E.C.S.) The amount of energy used is the product of the voltage and the quantity of electricity—i.e., the number of electrons—driven through the cell.

As we saw earlier, sodium and chlorine react exothermically.

$$2Na + \overline{Cl_2} \rightarrow 2(Na^+ + Cl^-) + \triangle$$

Since in electrolysis we wish to reverse this reaction, the electrical energy used must be at least equal to the energy ($\triangle$). The voltage needed is often greater than that called for by the E.C.S. because of complexities arising from the nature of discharge reactions on various electrode surfaces and because of heat losses due to resistance in the cell. This will not be considered in this text. Because the anode is positively charged, the negative anions, Cl⁻, that move at random in the electrolyte will have a migrational trend toward this electrode; this was shown schematically in Fig. 9.5. Similarly, because of attraction between opposite charges, the cations, Na⁺, move toward the negative cathode. Two half-reactions occur, one at each electrode.

$$
\begin{array}{rll}
\text{Cathode:} & 2Na^+ + 2e^- \rightleftarrows 2Na & \text{(reduction)} \\
\text{Anode:} & \underline{2Cl^- - 2e^- \rightleftarrows \overline{Cl_2}} & \text{(oxidation)} \\
\text{Over-all reaction:} & 2Na^+ + 2Cl^- \rightleftarrows 2Na + \overline{Cl_2} &
\end{array}
$$

Thus the cathode reaction in electrolysis is *always a reduction reaction* and the anode reaction is *always an oxidation reaction*. The same number of electrons are involved at each electrode. In fact, the electrons picked up by the Na⁺ ions have been stripped from the Cl⁻ ions by the force—the voltage—supplied. The battery or dynamo which provides this voltage acts as a pump, moving the electrons around the circuit onto the cathode and then to the Na⁺ ions. Hence this is a true redox reaction even down to the "balanced" electrons.

22.3. Faraday's Laws

Inspection of the redox equations for reactions during electrolysis shows that the symbol for the electron represents quantities of electrons in the same sense that symbols for ions and molecules represent specific quantities of ions and molecules. It is obvious from our earlier discussion of reactions, valence, and valence changes that the electrons react in whole-number quantities, not fractions. Just as we do not use half atoms in our discussion, so we do not use any fraction of an electron. Thus we can say that the reaction:

$$Na^+ + e^- \rightarrow Na$$

specifies that one sodium ion gains one electron and forms one sodium atom; the more common interpretation is that one gram-atomic weight of sodium ions (N ions) gains N electrons and forms one gram-atomic weight of sodium (N atoms). Similarly in the reaction:

$$Mg^{++} + 2e^- \rightarrow Mg$$

2N electrons are involved per gram-atomic weight of magnesium, or N electrons per equivalent weight (Mg/2) of magnesium. In fact, in all redox reactions, whenever a *single* electron is involved, equivalent weights of every other substance in the reaction are involved. For example:

$$Cl^- - e^- \rightarrow Cl$$
$$\frac{Al^{+3}}{3} + e^- \rightarrow \frac{Al}{3}$$
$$\frac{Cu^{++}}{2} + e^- \rightarrow \frac{Cu}{2}$$

Thus the quantity of electricity represented by the symbol e is of fundamental importance. Since this is N or 6×10^{23} electrons, it is a respectable amount of electricity. The **coulomb** is used to measure small quantities of electricity; it is the amount of electricity that a current of 1 ampere transmits in 1 second. In the above equations, on a gram-atomic basis e^- is N electrons, or 96,500 coulombs. This quantity is called a **faraday.** The same quantity of electricity can be produced with other combinations of current and time. The equation is:

$$Q = i \times t$$

where Q is the number of coulombs, i is the rate of electron flow (current in amperes), and t is the time in seconds. Thus, if Q is 100 coulombs:

$$
\begin{aligned}
Q = 100 \text{ coulombs} &= i \times t \\
&= 1 \times 100 \\
&= 2 \times 50 \\
&= 4 \times 25 \\
&\quad \text{etc.}
\end{aligned}
$$

This discussion enables us to understand the laws known as **Faraday's laws,** formulated by Michael Faraday in 1832–1833 on the basis of experimental observations.

1. Chemical action of electricity is proportional to the absolute quantity of electricity which passes through a conductor.

2. The weights of ions deposited by the passage of the same quantity of electricity are proportional to their chemical equivalents.

The latter is often worded as follows: *Every 96,500 coulombs of electricity deposits, creates, or decomposes one equivalent weight of each substance involved in electrolysis.* The word "decompose" does not of course mean annihilate. That Cl^- becomes Cl_2 during electrolysis is a case of decomposition and creation.

22.4. Application of Faraday's Laws

Faraday's laws can be used in many kinds of electrochemical calculations of either theoretical or practical interest. Thus we can calculate the quantities of substances decomposed or created in a fixed interval of time by a specified current, or the time or current required to deposit fixed quantities of substances. There are a fixed number of variables in these calculations; and if all but one are known, the unknown can be calculated by appropriate substitution in the Faraday relationships. For example: How many grams of copper will be deposited in two hours by the electrolysis of $CuSO_4$, the current being 10 amp.?

The quantity of electricity used is:

$$Q = i \times t$$
$$= 10 \times (2)(60)(60) = 72{,}000 \text{ coulombs}$$

$$\text{Grams deposited} = \text{Grams/Coulomb} \times \text{Coulombs}$$
$$= \frac{\frac{63.5}{2} \times 72{,}000}{96{,}500} = 23.7 \text{ g.}$$

These general relationships hold:

$$\text{Grams deposited} = \frac{\text{Eq. wt.} \times \text{coulombs used}}{96{,}500} \qquad [1]$$

$$\text{Volume (gas)} = \frac{\text{Eq. vol.} \times \text{coulombs used}}{96{,}500} \qquad [2]$$

By using Faraday's laws, an electroplater can calculate how long silver should be electroplated on a spoon to reach a prescribed thickness. The surface area of the spoon times the desired thickness gives the volume of metal to be plated. This figure times the density of the metal gives the weight. From Eq. 1 he can calculate the coulombs required to produce the specified weight and then calculate the time in seconds needed for the electrolysis. By means of the electrodeposition of chromium, expensive but worn parts such as large stamping dies can be built up to proper size again. Calculations like the preceding provide information so that the part can be rebuilt to the exact dimensions.

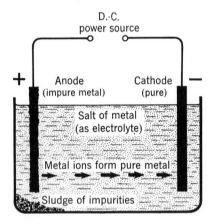

Fig. 22.2. Electrolytic refining of metals.

Many metals are refined electrolytically. Chapter 21 showed this as a necessary step in the production of copper. The impure copper metal serves as the anode and is immersed in $CuSO_4$ solution (Fig. 22.2). During electrolysis the copper dissolves.

$$Cu \xrightarrow{\triangle} Cu^{++} + 2e^-$$

The Cu^{++} ions thus made available replace those removed from solution by electrodeposition on the pure metal cathode.

$$Cu^{++} + 2e^- \xrightarrow{\triangle} Cu$$

Insoluble impurities settle out as a sludge, or anode mud. Soluble impurities—other metal ions—remain in solution because the operating voltage is selected so it will be insufficient for their deposition. If this

is impossible on a practical basis, other ions may be added which selectively complex or precipitate the impurity ions, thus preventing their
electrodeposition.

22.5. Redox Reactions as a Source of Energy

The electron transfers discussed in connection with ordinary chemical and electrochemical reactions actually occur; they are not just a
tool to make possible the balancing of a chemical equation. Any individual half-reaction is also a reversible reaction, although in most cases
only one direction is shown because under the particular conditions the
reaction goes to completion. For example, when sodium and chlorine
react,* forming sodium chloride:

$$2Na + \overline{Cl_2} \rightarrow 2Na^+ + 2Cl^- + E$$

The reaction is exothermic, meaning it liberates an amount of energy E.
This energy results from two half-reactions:

$$2Na - 2e^- \rightarrow 2Na^+ \quad \text{(oxidation)}$$
$$\overline{Cl_2} + 2e^- \rightarrow 2Cl^- \quad \text{(reduction)}$$

The reverse of these reactions occurs in electrolysis.

$$2Na^+ + 2e^- \overset{\triangle}{\rightleftharpoons} 2Na \quad \text{(reduction)}$$
$$2Cl^- - 2e^- \overset{\triangle}{\rightleftharpoons} \overline{Cl_2} \quad \text{(oxidation)}$$
$$\overline{2Na^+ + 2Cl^- \overset{\triangle}{\rightleftharpoons} 2Na + \overline{Cl_2} - E}$$

Note that when the reactions are reversed the labeling is reversed. The
former oxidation reaction becomes a reduction reaction and the reduction reaction becomes an oxidation reaction. Furthermore, though it is
still the same in magnitude, the over-all energy of the reaction is reversed
in sign; the reaction is endothermic. The $-E$ used in this discussion replaces the usual $\triangle$ used in electrolysis equations. It must be understood
that the over-all energies of the two processes can be compared only if
all conditions are comparable. For example, the formation of crystalline
NaCl in the first reaction would not involve an energy comparable to
that used up for the electrolysis of an equivalent amount of *molten* NaCl,

---

* The letter E in the following discussion actually differs from the heats of reaction because
it has been corrected for certain amounts of energy connected with volume and other changes
which are only incidental to the reactions. These energies are called **free energies**.

due to the contribution of lattice energy and heat of fusion to the over-all energy.

Sodium reacts more vigorously with chlorine than iron does.

$$2Na + \overline{Cl_2} \rightarrow 2Na^+ + 2Cl^- + E$$
$$Fe + \overline{Cl_2} \rightarrow Fe^{++} + 2Cl^- + \varepsilon$$

This does not mean that sodium contributes more energy to the reaction but that it absorbs less of the available energy to form Na^+ ion than the more electronegative Fe does to form Fe^{++} ion. As a consequence, there is more *net* free energy that can be evolved. It is this net free energy which can be utilized to do work. For example, if the electrons involved in a redox reaction pass through an electrical circuit they can light a bulb or drive a motor. The net free energy released in this manner is electrical energy. The amount released, per electron or per equivalent, is measured by the voltage of the cell. The voltage from the vigorous sodium-chlorine reaction would be greater than that from the less vigorous iron-chlorine reaction.

22.6. Voltaic (Galvanic) Cells

A device for obtaining an electric current from a redox reaction is called a **voltaic** or **galvanic cell.** The operation of this cell depends on the fact that redox reactions occur on the surface of an electrode that is in contact with the oxidizing or reducing agent just as they do when the two reagents are mixed together. We saw that redox reactions between electrodes and reagents occurred in electrolysis. These are endothermic reactions; hence energy must be provided by the source of the current. Similar reactions occur in voltaic cells; however, these are over-all exothermic reactions, and the reaction provides the energy. The negative electrode is in contact with the reducing agent and obtains electrons from it. These flow through a circuit into the positive electrode which is immersed in the oxidizing agent; the latter accepts the electrons from the positive electrode.

For optimum energy yield in such a cell, the reducing and oxidizing agents must be kept from coming in contact with each other; otherwise electron transfer will occur directly between them instead of via the electrode-circuit path. For this reason each reagent is in a separate container with its electrode. The electrode and the solution in which it is immersed are known as a **half-cell.** The reducing agent will lose electrons to the electrode, because positive ions are forming in the solution or negative ions are losing their charge; hence a positive charge will develop in this solution. By the same token a negative charge will develop in the oxidizing solution because it accepts electrons from its electrode in order to discharge positive ions or create negative ions. The charges in these solutions interfere with the free flow of electrons in the external circuit because the negative solution repels the electrons attempting to reach the surface of its electrode, whereas the positive solution attracts the electrons attempting to leave its electrode. This is illustrated in the Zn-Cu cell in Fig. 22.3A. In this cell the zinc electrode is the reducing agent since Zn^{++} ions form on its surface, liberating electrons to carry on the reduction process. The Cu^{++} ions in the other part of the cell constitute the oxidizing agent since they accept electrons. Some means for ion transfer between the half-cells must be provided in order to restore electrical neutrality. This is done by means of a tube filled with a solution of an electrolyte such as KCl dissolved in gelatin. Such a link between half-cells is called a **salt bridge** (Fig. 22.3B). When the positive charge tends to accumulate in the zinc half-cell, anions move through the salt bridge to the left and cations move through it to the right in numbers to keep both half-cells electrically neutral. Thus sufficient electrons can now move freely in the external circuit. As a result, the voltmeter deflects and records, for this particular cell, approximately 1.1 v.; this is the net driving force of the reaction:

$$\underline{Zn} + Cu^{++} \rightarrow Zn^{++} + \underline{Cu}$$

A shorthand notation for such a cell is as follows:

$$\begin{array}{ccc} (-) & \xrightarrow{\ e^-\ } & (+) \\ Zn \mid Zn^{++} & \mid\mid & Cu^{++} \mid Cu \end{array}$$

$$
\begin{array}{ll}
\underline{Zn} \rightarrow Zn^{++} + 2e^- & E = +0.76 \\
Cu^{++} + 2e^- \rightarrow \underline{Cu} & E = +0.34 \\
\hline
Cu^{++} + \underline{Zn} \rightarrow Zn^{++} + \underline{Cu} & E = +1.10 \text{ volts}
\end{array}
$$

The single vertical bar represents the electrode, and the double bar the salt bridge. The reducing agent, Zn in this case, is always written at the left. The left-hand electrode is always $(-)$, and electrons flow in the external circuit from the left electrode to the right electrode. This technique leads to uniformity of labeling cells.

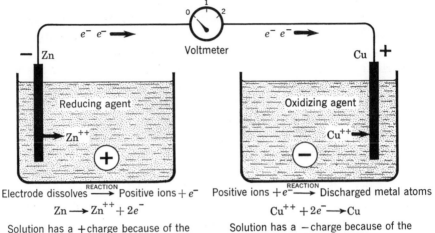

Electrode dissolves $\xrightarrow{\text{REACTION}}$ Positive ions $+ e^-$

$$Zn \longrightarrow Zn^{++} + 2e^-$$

Solution has a $+$charge because of the formation of Zn^{++} ions. Therefore electrons cannot leave this half-cell.

Positive ions $+ e^- \xrightarrow{\text{REACTION}}$ Discharged metal atoms

$$Cu^{++} + 2e^- \longrightarrow Cu$$

Solution has a $-$charge because of the depletion of Cu^{++} ions. Therefore electrons are repelled and cannot enter this half-cell.

A

$$Zn \longrightarrow Zn^{++} + 2e^-$$

$$Cu^{++} + 2e^- \longrightarrow Cu$$

$$\overline{Zn + Cu^{++} \longrightarrow Zn^{++} + Cu}$$

B

Fig. 22.3. Zinc-copper cell. **A,** Without salt bridge; **B,** with salt bridge.

22.7. Half-Cells and the E.C.S.

Various half-cells can be combined to make up a single cell. Metals are usually immersed in 1 m solutions of their salts—for example, a Zn electrode in a 1 m $ZnSO_4$ solution. If the concentration of the solution is not 1 m, the voltage from the half-cell will be different (see Section 22.15). Gases can also be used in conjunction with an inert electrode such as platinum or graphite; the electrode is immersed in a 1 m solution of the ion of the gas. Thus the hydrogen electrode consists of hydrogen gas at 1 atm. pressure, which is bubbling over a platinum surface immersed in 1 m HCl, and therefore 1 m H^+ ion.

The reactions in a voltaic cell often amount to simple substitution reactions which would be predicted from the E.C.S. Certainly we could predict that Zn would displace Cu^{++} ion from solution and that the reverse would not occur. Likewise Zn would displace H_2 gas from H^+ ion, but copper would not because it is below hydrogen in the E.C.S. These are not mysterious coincidences. On the contrary, the E.C.S. is based on cell reactions and the voltages associated with each half-cell when measured against the hydrogen electrode.

22.8. Standard Electrode Potentials

The voltage of a cell is the algebraic sum of the voltage supplied by each half-cell. Since most metals displace hydrogen from HCl—that is, they reduce H^+ ion—the hydrogen electrode was adopted as a reference half-cell. The voltage it supplied to the over-all voltage was arbitrarily set at zero. Thus the total voltage of a cell in which the hydrogen electrode is one of the half-cells will be the voltage of the other electrode. For example:

$$(-) \xrightarrow{\quad e^- \quad} (+)$$
$$\text{Zn} \mid \text{Zn}^{++} \mid\mid \text{H}^+ \mid \text{Pt}(\text{H}_2 - 1 \text{ atm.})$$

The total voltage of this cell is $+0.76$ v. (In this and all other cases the ionic concentration is 1 m.)

$$\text{Voltage of Zn half-cell} + \text{Voltage of hydrogen half-cell} = +0.76$$
$$x \qquad\qquad + \qquad\qquad 0 \qquad\qquad = +0.76$$
$$\text{Therefore: } x = +0.76$$

So the voltage of the reaction:

$$\underline{\text{Zn}} \rightarrow \text{Zn}^{++} + 2e^-$$

is 0.76 v. This is called the **standard electrode potential** of zinc for the reaction shown. In the reverse reaction the voltage will be the same but opposite in sign.

$$Zn^{++} + 2e^- \rightarrow \underline{Zn}$$
$$E = -0.76 \text{ v.}$$

All metals above hydrogen in the E.C.S. (Fig. 22.4) behave like zinc relative to the hydrogen electrode. They all liberate electrons in the spontaneous cell reaction with the hydrogen electrode and are reducing agents. The metals below hydrogen, however, accept electrons from the hydrogen electrode and therefore behave as oxidizing agents. The voltages supplied by these half-cells to the total voltage is (+) *for the reactions shown.* For any half-cell reaction opposite to that shown, the voltage is negative. The voltages decrease as we approach hydrogen; this is in accord with the following principles as we progress down the E.C.S. series:

1. The metals become more electronegative.
2. More energy is required to remove their valence electrons; hence less *net* energy is available as voltage of a cell.
3. The metals are successively poorer as reducing agents.
4. They are therefore less reactive chemically.

The voltage of any cell made by combining two half-cells is obtained by the algebraic addition of the individual half-cell potentials. In the zinc-copper cell:

$$(-) \qquad\quad \xrightarrow{e^-} \qquad\quad (+)$$
$$Zn \ \big|\ Zn^{++} \ ||\ Cu^{++} \ \big|\ Cu$$

$$
\begin{array}{ll}
\underline{Zn} \rightarrow Zn^{++} + 2e^- & E = +0.76 \\
Cu^{++} + 2e^- \rightarrow \underline{Cu} & E = +0.34 \\
\hline
Zn + Cu^{++} \rightarrow Zn^{++} + \underline{Cu} & E = +1.10 \text{ volts}
\end{array}
$$

If both half-cells are above hydrogen, the one nearer the top will, as usual, act as the reducing agent and the other will act as the oxidizing agent. For example, in the zinc-lead cell:

$$(-) \qquad\quad \xrightarrow{e^-} \qquad\quad (+)$$
$$Zn \ \big|\ Zn^{++} \ ||\ Pb^{++} \ \big|\ Pb$$

$$
\begin{array}{ll}
\underline{Zn} \rightarrow Zn^{++} + 2e^- & E = +0.76 \\
Pb^{++} + 2e^- \rightarrow \underline{Pb} & E = -0.13 \\
\hline
Zn + Pb^{++} \rightarrow Zn^{++} + \underline{Pb} & E = +0.63 \text{ volt}
\end{array}
$$

Reductant		Oxidant				Potential
Li	$\rightarrow$	Li^+	$+$	e^-		$+3.02$
K	$\rightarrow$	K^+	$+$	e^-		$+2.92$
Ba	$\rightarrow$	Ba^{++}	$+$	$2e^-$		$+2.90$
Sr	$\rightarrow$	Sr^{++}	$+$	$2e^-$		$+2.89$
Ca	$\rightarrow$	Ca^{++}	$+$	$2e^-$		$+2.87$
Na	$\rightarrow$	Na^+	$+$	e^-		$+2.71$
Mg	$\rightarrow$	Mg^{++}	$+$	$2e^-$		$+2.34$
Al	$\rightarrow$	Al^{+3}	$+$	$3e^-$		$+1.67$
Mn	$\rightarrow$	Mn^{++}	$+$	$2e^-$		$+1.05$
Zn	$\rightarrow$	Zn^{++}	$+$	$2e^-$		$+0.76$
Cr	$\rightarrow$	Cr^{++}	$+$	$2e^-$		$+0.71$
Fe	$\rightarrow$	Fe^{++}	$+$	$2e^-$		$+0.44$
Cd	$\rightarrow$	Cd^{++}	$+$	$2e^-$		$+0.40$
Co	$\rightarrow$	Co^{++}	$+$	$2e^-$		$+0.28$
Ni	$\rightarrow$	Ni^{++}	$+$	$2e^-$		$+0.25$
Sn	$\rightarrow$	Sn^{++}	$+$	$2e^-$		$+0.14$
Pb	$\rightarrow$	Pb^{++}	$+$	$2e^-$		$+0.13$
H	$\rightleftharpoons$	H^+	$+$	e^-		0.00
Sb	$\leftarrow$	Sb^{+3}	$+$	$3e^-$		$+0.10$
Bi	$\leftarrow$	Bi^{+3}	$+$	$3e^-$		$+0.20$
As	$\leftarrow$	As^{+3}	$+$	$3e^-$		$+0.30$
Cu	$\leftarrow$	Cu^{++}	$+$	$2e^-$		$+0.34$
2Hg	$\leftarrow$	Hg_2^{++}	$+$	$2e^-$		$+0.80$
Ag	$\leftarrow$	Ag^+	$+$	e^-		$+0.80$
Br^-	$\leftarrow$	$\frac{1}{2}Br_2$	$+$	e^-		$+1.06$
Cl^-	$\leftarrow$	$\frac{1}{2}Cl_2$	$+$	e^-		$+1.36$
Au	$\leftarrow$	Au^+	$+$	e^-		$+1.68$
F^-	$\leftarrow$	$\frac{1}{2}F_2$	$+$	e^-		$+2.85$

Increasing Reducing Power (left margin, upward)

Increasing Electronegativity and Oxidizing Power (right margin, downward)

Fig. 22.4. Standard electrode potentials, 25° C. and 1m solutions; also called the E.C.S. and standard oxidation-reduction potentials. The series shown here is abbreviated. For additional potentials, consult a handbook.

Since the lead electrode reaction is the opposite of that shown in the E.C.S., its voltage is negative. The result is a difference between the potentials when the algebraic addition is made. This is also the case when both half-cells are below hydrogen. In the bismuth-silver cell:

$$(-) \qquad \xrightarrow{e^-} \qquad (+)$$
$$\text{Bi} \ \boxed{ \ \text{Bi}^{+3} \ || \ \text{Ag}^+ \ } \ \text{Ag}$$

$$\begin{array}{ll} \text{Bi} \rightarrow \text{Bi}^{+3} + 3e^- & E = -0.20 \\ 3\text{Ag}^+ + 3e^- \rightarrow 3\text{Ag} & E = +0.80 \\ \hline \text{Bi} + 3\text{Ag}^+ \rightarrow \text{Bi}^{+3} + 3\text{Ag} & E = +0.60 \end{array}$$

22.9. The Hydrogen Ion-Zinc Cell

Although the production of electricity in a chemical reaction was first observed by Galvani in 1790, the first cell capable of producing any considerable amount of it was constructed by Volta in 1800. He used zinc as his reducing agent; it is so excellent for this purpose that it is still used in more cells than any other agent. His oxidizing agent was the H^+ ion of dilute H_2SO_4; this is a rather poor oxidizing agent. Hence the voltage of his cell is only 0.76 v. In Fig. 22.5 the zinc, which is the negative electrode, is immersed in the acid, which not only provides the ionic connection between the electrodes but is also the oxidizing agent. Offhand, we would expect the zinc and acid to react directly, with hydrogen being liberated on the surface of the zinc and the energy going to waste as heat. Instead, in this case all the hydrogen is liberated on the carbon electrode and the reaction ceases when the wire is disconnected. If ordinary zinc is dropped into acid it will indeed dissolve, and hydrogen will be liberated. But close inspection during the reaction under discussion shows that most of the surface of the zinc is insulated from the solution by an adhering layer of gas, and that most of the hydrogen bubbles escape from specks on the surface of the zinc. If the zinc is very pure and the acid dilute, there will be no appreciable evolution of hydrogen unless some other conducting material touches the surface. If, for example, a piece of copper wire is put down into the acid until it touches the zinc, bubbles of hydrogen immediately appear along the entire submerged surface of the wire. The copper remains unchanged, but the zinc goes into solution as Zn^{++} ions. Graphite and platinum are just as good as copper. Actually, any conducting material that is a good catalyst for the formation of H_2 mole-

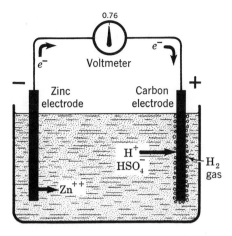

Fig. 22.5. The zinc-acid cell.

cules from H atoms can be used. Zinc is not this kind of catalyst; the layer of monatomic hydrogen that slowly forms hydrogen gas on its submerged surface effectively separates it from the oxidizing agent (H^+ ions) in the solution. In Fig. 22.5, the connection from the catalytic surface to the zinc is made above the solution through the external circuit, but serves the same purpose. All that is necessary is to provide a path along which the electrons can travel from the zinc to where H^+ ions can pick them up and they can combine into H_2 molecules. It was with a battery of these cells, hooked up in series to obtain sufficient voltage, that Davy discovered sodium and potassium in 1807 by electrolyzing their melted hydroxides.

22.10. The Dry Cell

Leclanché improved the zinc-hydrogen cell by substituting ammonium chloride for hydrochloric acid as the source of protons. The ammonium ion is a far weaker acid than the hydronium ion, so it is possible to have a high concentration of it in the solution without its directly attacking the zinc. Around the carbon rod he introduced powdered manganese dioxide as a depolarizer. **Polarization** is the accumulation around an electrode of products which tend to stop or reverse the reaction; in this case the product was H_2. Leclanché expected it to react with the manganese dioxide according to the equation:

$$\overline{H_2} + \underline{MnO_2} \rightarrow \underline{MnO} + H_2O$$

He found that he had not merely improved the operation of the cell but had approximately doubled the voltage. It was really a new cell, in which the powerful oxidizing agent MnO_2 replaced the moderate oxidizing agent H^+.

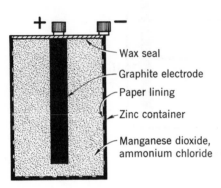

Fig. 22.6. The dry cell.

Leclanché's combination is the basis of the familiar dry cell shown in Fig. 22.6. The dry cell is not really dry, it is moist; if no water were present the necessary migration of ions could not take place. The container is made of zinc and is marked $(-)$ because electrons are emitted from it. The graphite (carbon) rod is marked $(+)$ because electrons flow into it. The electrolyte, NH_4Cl solution, is mixed with some porous material (sawdust or charcoal) and manganese dioxide. A paper lining keeps the MnO_2 from coming into contact with the zinc, and a wax or pitch seal keeps the cell from leaking, drying out, or taking up moisture from the air. If the terminals are connected, electrons flow in the external circuit from zinc to carbon. The equations for the reaction at the zinc pole (electrode) are simple.

$$\underline{Zn} \rightarrow Zn^{++} + 2e^-$$
$$Zn^{++} + 4H_2O \rightarrow Zn(H_2O)_4{}^{++}$$

The $Zn(H_2O)_4{}^{++}$ ions migrate toward the carbon pole. The reaction at the other pole (which really consists of the entire surface of the MnO_2, all of which is in electrical contact with the graphite electrode) is probably:

$$2e^- + \underline{MnO_2} + 4NH_4{}^+ + 4Cl^- \rightarrow Mn^{++} + 4Cl^- + 2H_2O + 4NH_3$$

As fast as the new $Zn(H_2O)_4{}^{++}$ ions meet the ammonia they react with it and form the complex zinc-tetrammine ion.

$$Zn(H_2O)_4{}^{++} + 4NH_3 \rightarrow Zn(NH_3)_4{}^{++} + 4H_2O$$

This reaction lowers the concentration of zinc ion and thereby further increases the voltage of the cell. The total cell reaction is thus:

$$Zn + MnO_2 + 4NH_4{}^+ + 4Cl^- \rightarrow Zn(NH_3)_4{}^{++} + Mn^{++} + 4Cl^- + 2H_2O$$

Even though the production of hydrogen gas is prevented, polarization is still possible, because the zinc ions and the ammonia molecules have to move through the cell before they can react with each other. If a flashlight is used too long at one time the light becomes dim because Zn^{++} and NH_3 accumulate at their respective electrodes. If the light is given a rest, diffusion remedies this polarization and the light is brighter when next used.

22.11. The Lead Storage Cell

A cell in which the original active materials can be regenerated by forcing a current through in the opposite direction to that in which it flows during discharge is called a **storage cell.** No electricity is actually stored; during both discharge and charge, as many electrons come out one electrode as go into the other. What *is* stored is chemical energy produced in the cell from the electrical energy of the recharging current.

The lead storage cell is extremely useful, for it is sturdy, capable of recharge, and relatively inexpensive. The construction of a lead cell is illustrated in Fig. 22.7. Although only two plates are shown in this figure, the battery consists of many plates joined together in parallel, thus increasing the capacity of the cell. The plates, often called grids, are made of lead or an alloy of lead and antimony. One plate is coated with red-brown lead dioxide, PbO_2; this is the positive pole. The other is coated with spongy lead; this is the negative pole. These plates are dipped into sulfuric acid of sp. gr. about 1.3 and 40 per cent H_2SO_4 by weight. If the two terminals are connected, electrons flow in the external circuit from the lead plate to the plate coated with PbO_2; when fully charged, the cell develops about 2.2 v. Six of these cells are connected in series to form a standard 12-v. automobile battery.

Reaction at the lead plate	$Pb + SO_4{}^{--} \rightarrow PbSO_4 + 2e^-$
Reaction at the PbO_2 plate	$2e^- + PbO_2 + 4H^+ + SO_4{}^{--} \rightarrow PbSO_4 + 2H_2O$
Total reaction	$Pb + PbO_2 + 2H_2SO_4 \rightarrow 2PbSO_4 + 2H_2O$

During the discharge of a lead storage battery the active material in each plate is used up, the concentration of sulfuric acid in the cell decreases, and insoluble white lead sulfate forms at each pole. The cell is exhausted when any one of the reactants has been consumed. To *recharge* a "dead" battery, electrons must be forced to flow in the oppo-

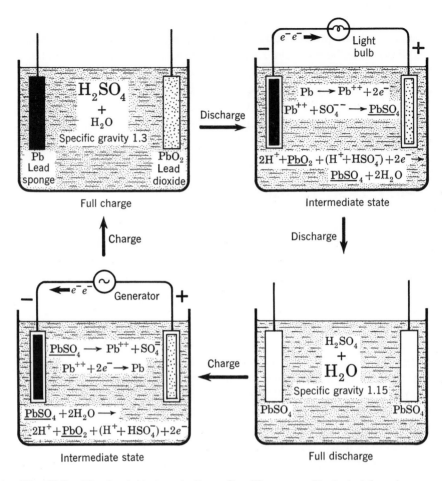

Fig. 22.7. The lead storage battery. Conditions are illustrated for charge-discharge cycles.

site direction, thereby *reversing each* of the reactions which occurred during discharge. The concentration of sulfuric acid in a charged battery is much higher than in a discharged battery; hence the statement that a charged battery never freezes in cold weather—the sulfuric acid lowers the freezing point of the solution. Fig. 22.7 shows what happens in a lead storage cell at various stages of charge and discharge. Compare this with the discussion and equations above.

A speedy method for testing whether a battery is charged involves determining the specific gravity of the solution in the cell. This is done with a **hydrometer** (Fig. 22.8). The float in the hydrometer is calibrated to record accurately the specific gravity of solutions over a limited range. The usual limits are a specific gravity of 1.3 for a charged battery and 1.15 for a "dead" one. Some water is electrolyzed during the charging process, for the battery is functioning as an electrolytic cell. The more nearly charged it is, the greater the amount of hydrogen liberated. The storage battery attendant usually says that the battery is charged if it is "gassing well."

22.12. Nickel(III) Cells

The next most popular storage cells are the **Edison** and **Nicad cells.** The positive plate of the charged Edison cell consists of black $Ni(OH)_3$; the negative plate, of iron sponge. The electrolyte is a 20 per cent solution of KOH, with some LiOH. The cell reactions on discharge are:

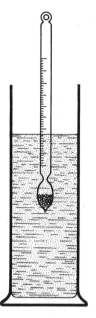

$$\underline{Fe + 2OH^- \rightarrow Fe(OH)_2 + 2e^-}$$
$$\underline{2Ni(OH)_3 + 2e^- \rightarrow 2Ni(OH)_2 + 2OH^-}$$

The Nicad cell has specially prepared cadmium-coated electrodes instead of iron. The reactions for this battery are similar, except that Cd is substituted for Fe in the above equations.

Fig. 22.8. A specific gravity spindle.

As with the lead cell, these reactions are reversed during the recharging of the cell by inducing a flow of electrons in the opposite direction. The electrolyte does not change when the cell is charged or discharged. Whether the cell is charged cannot be determined with a hydrometer. Instead, the voltage which can be maintained with a standard current flow is measured, for this falls off fairly rapidly as the cell is discharged.

The voltage of these alkaline cells, when fully charged, is well below that of a lead cell, and a battery with equal voltage and capacity is considerably more expensive. However, there are several compensating advantages. Because the alkaline cell is much stronger mechanically, there is less danger of its being damaged by shock or vibration. It can be left uncharged indefinitely without danger of deterioration or freezing, whereas the lead cell, even if it does not freeze, will become "sulfated." That is, the amorphous $PbSO_4$, not being completely insoluble in the

H_2SO_4, gradually crystallizes, and the cell is very difficult to recharge. The discharged electrode materials in the alkaline cells are too insoluble in the electrolyte for this to happen, even when they remain uncharged for long periods. Furthermore, overcharging does not harm this type of battery. Moreover, their ability to deliver full capacity at high discharge rates makes them especially suitable for starters and auxiliary electrical sources in railroad, marine, bus, and truck service.

Recent developments in the construction of Nicad automobile batteries may makes this type competitive with the lead storage cell. Nicad car batteries have a potential life of fifteen to twenty years; hence one battery may outlive several automobiles, instead of the reverse, which is true at present. Both the Edison and Nicad cells have an average working voltage of about 1.2 v. during discharge, but this voltage is maintained for a larger proportion of the total discharge time when cadmium is used. The cadmium cells also undergo less self-discharge than the iron cells, and function better at low temperatures.

22.13. The Silver-Zinc Cell

The reducing agent in a silver-zinc cell is zinc; the oxidizing agent is a mixture of Ag_2O and AgO, both in sponge form. The electrolyte is KOH solution. The discharging cell reactions are:

$$\underline{Zn} + 4OH^- \rightarrow \underline{Zn(OH)_4^{--}} + 2e^-$$

and

$$2e^- + \underline{Ag_2O} + H_2O \rightarrow \underline{2Ag} + 2OH^-$$

or

$$2e^- + \underline{AgO} + H_2O \rightarrow \underline{Ag} + 2OH^-$$

Which of the latter two occurs depends upon the state of oxidation of the silver. If the cell is to be used as a secondary or storage cell, the zinc electrode is wrapped in cellophane to prevent the zincate ion from diffusing, and the recharging is regulated to stop with Ag_2O. When built as a primary or single-use cell, the cellophane is omitted and the positive plate is charged largely to AgO. This cell maintains a remarkably constant voltage of 1.4 until 75 per cent discharged. Its most important advantage, however, is that it can deliver 50 watt-hours of energy per pound of battery, or four or five times as much as a lead or nickel cell can deliver. This accounts for its uses in guided missiles and hand-held power devices. A 15-lb. battery can run a 1-hp. motor for an hour.

22.14. Other Cells

The mercury-zinc cell depends on the reaction:

$$HgO + Zn \rightarrow Hg + ZnO$$

The electrolyte is KOH which has been saturated with $K_2Zn(OH)_4$ so that the ZnO which is produced in the reaction will not dissolve. This cell maintains its voltage fairly well during discharge; the average is 1.2 v. for small currents. Its high energy content, 40 watt-hours per pound, made possible the walkie-talkie during World War II; the cell is being used at present in hearing aids. It is also being used in oil well surveying instruments because it can operate in temperatures over 135° C., owing to the high concentration of its electrolyte and the correspondingly high boiling point.

In an air cell, electrons from heavy wedges of zinc move to a porous carbon electrode where they are taken up by atmospheric oxygen which diffuses in.

$$2Zn + \overline{O_2} + 2H_2O + 4OH^- \rightarrow 2Zn(OH)_4{}^{--}$$

Naturally it is impossible for such a cell to deliver a heavy current, but at a discharge rate of 0.1 amp. it can maintain a constant voltage of 1.28 for 6000 hours.

The extreme in this type of cell is the vanadium pentoxide-cadmium cell. It is used only where current drain is negligible, as in maintaining the grid bias in a vacuum tube, but it can maintain a constant voltage for ten years.

A few other specialized cells are in use or being developed. In the future they may be as common as those already mentioned.

22.15. Concentration Cells

When a piece of metal is dipped into a solution that contains its ions, a few atoms of metal go into solution as ions, their electrons remaining in the mass of metal. On the other hand, metal ions that strike the metal take electrons from it and plate out as metal atoms. The equilibrium state of charge of the metal depends on its electronegativity, the energy of hydration of its ions, and the concentration of the ions in the solution. If the solution is 1 m, this charge is called the **standard electrode potential** of the metal. If the concentration is higher, there will be a greater tend-

ency for the ions to take electrons from the metal; the metal will then become less negative, and will be positive in relation to the electrode in the
1 m solution. The reverse will be true if the metal is put into a more dilute solution than 1 m.

Any two electrode systems which have a different potential (voltage)
can be combined in a cell which will yield current. When the half-cells
differ only in ion concentration, the cell is called a **concentration cell.**
For example, with iron, the oxidation reaction in such a cell is:

$$\underline{Fe} \rightarrow Fe^{++} + 2e^-$$

The reduction reaction is:

$$Fe^{++} + 2e^- \rightarrow \underline{Fe}$$

Since the iron is the same in both cases, the reaction will proceed by
way of the first equation in the solution in which the concentration of
Fe^{++} is low, and by way of the second equation in the solution in which
the concentration of Fe^{++} is high. This tends to equalize the concentration of the two solutions; when the concentrations actually become
equal the current stops flowing. Although of no importance as a source
of current, concentration cells are tremendously important in connection with the corrosion of metals which occurs when such cells are accidentally set up.

22.16. Corrosion

It is estimated that corrosion is responsible for replacement costs in
the United States amounting to approximately $5.5 billion a year. Few
giant industries can claim a dollar volume of business such as this per
year. All of us are familiar with some form of corrosion; a brief glance
at the cars in a parking lot provides ample evidence of this chemical-
metallurgical phenomenon.

There are many causes of corrosion, some of which are not thoroughly understood. Corrosion proceeds readily whenever a non-noble
metal or alloy is exposed to an oxidizing atmosphere in the presence
of water. A considerable variation in conditions is possible. The oxygen of the air provides a suitable oxidizing atmosphere for corrosion,
and even "dry" air contains sufficient water for the process. Corrosive
gases in the atmosphere—HCl, Cl_2, SO_2, etc., for example—speed up
the rate of corrosion either by attacking directly or by providing more

concentrated electrolytic solutions or films on the corroding surface. The extreme of this condition is seen when metal is directly submerged in salt water or splashed by slush from salted roads during the winter. Other factors such as impurities in metals and residual stresses due to fabrication may also increase the rate of corrosion. In this section we consider the role of electrolytic or galvanic processes in corrosion.

In electrolysis, and especially in galvanic cells, one electrode of the system may dissolve. This is mainly responsible for the pitting, and in some cases even the disappearance, of metal during corrosion. Electrolytic corrosion is not as common as galvanic corrosion but may occur whenever faulty electrical connections cause electricity to pass through a metal conductor into an electrolytic solution. Underground cables and pipelines that run through salt marshes and other damp earth containing dissolved minerals are subject to this type of attack. If nearby electrical "grounds" are present in the earth, an "electrolytic cell" miles in diameter may be set up. To the embarrassment of the city engineers of an eastern city, some iron water mains in a salt marsh were electrolyzed in a matter of months as the result of the current from a trolley line passing through the ground and the water mains on its way back to the powerhouse.

When covered with a film or solution of electrolyte, virtually any metal surface furnishes dissimilar electrodes to complete a galvanic cell. Such a cell may be microscopic in size. The neighboring grains in a metal surface, especially in alloys, may be sufficiently different in composition to constitute two electrodes; this is even more apparent in a weld joint or a connection between two dissimilar metals. The CO_2 of the atmosphere dissolved in the solution in contact with the "electrodes" furnishes the electrolyte as H^+ and HCO_3^- ions. Other atmospheric gases such as Cl_2 and SO_2 may provide a higher concentration of ions. Iron and steel corrode in accordance with the following equations:

$$Fe \rightarrow Fe^{++} + 2e^-$$
$$\tfrac{1}{2}O_2 + 2e^- \rightarrow O^{--}$$
$$O^{--} + H_2O \rightarrow 2OH^-$$

The iron dissolves, forming $Fe(OH)_2$. Fe^{++} ion is readily oxidized further by atmospheric oxygen to Fe^{+3} ion. Red-brown $Fe(OH)_3$ is ultimately deposited as rust. This is one of the most common cases of corrosion. In processes involving exposure to atmospheric oxygen, the oxygen serves as the electron acceptor or oxidizing agent, and the metal as the electron donor or reducing agent. If there is more than one metal in the corroding cell, the more active metal, the stronger reducing agent, will react, rather than the less active metal. Thus in the case of galvanized iron—iron coated with zinc—the more reactive zinc will dissolve and form zinc ions. Corrosion still takes place, but the dusty whitish zinc hydroxide or oxide is not the eyesore that rust is. Pinholes in the zinc coating increase the rate of reaction because the voltage drive between zinc and iron electrodes is greater than that between two slightly dissimilar grains of zinc. Zinc is a "sacrificial" metal in this case; it is present to be corroded instead of the iron. Similarly magnesium is used with iron so that it and not the iron will corrode. For this purpose magnesium rods and blocks are installed in hot-water tanks, on ships' hulls, and periodically on transcontinental pipelines. The magnesium inserts can be replaced more easily and cheaply than the major iron installation which they protect.

Various protective coatings such as those resulting from plating, anodizing (electrolytic oxidizing), painting, etc., are used to protect against corrosion. In the main, such procedures slow up corrosion by decreasing the chance of any contact between oxygen or other gases and the metal. These coatings minimize the demand for electrons to form oxide ions and hence the need for metals to dissolve in order to furnish these electrons. The effect of the surface of the electron donor on the rate of corrosion is illustrated in the case of galvanized nails used on copper gutters. The immense copper surface which acts as the positive electrode with respect to zinc transfers to the oxygen the electrons furnished by zinc. Since many oxygen molecules strike this large surface, the demand for electrons is great. Consequently the very small amount of zinc on the surface of the nails must supply these electrons.

$$\underline{Zn} \rightarrow Zn^{++} + 2e^-$$

As a result, the nails dissolve within a few days and the gutters fall. It would be better to use galvanized gutters and copper nails, or still better to have the nails and gutters of the same metal. Whenever two dissimilar metals must be used in contact with each other under such conditions of exposure, the best results will be obtained if the minimum surface consists of the less active metal. By the same token, it is the less active metal that should be painted.

QUESTIONS AND PROBLEMS

1. Draw the simple cell used for electrolyzing an aqueous solution of $CuCl_2$. Label each part, and indicate the sign and direction of electron flow. Write each reaction and identify it with respect to the electrode at which it occurs, and whether it is oxidation or reduction.

2. Repeat the preceding question, using a sodium sulfate solution.

3. How many grams of aluminum and what volume of oxygen would be obtained in eight hours by the electrolysis of bauxite with a current of 20 amp.? (Disregard the secondary reaction of oxygen to form CO.)

4. How long would it take to produce a ton of copper by the electrolysis of $CuSO_4$ with a current of 50 amp.?

5. How many grams of copper oxide can be reduced with the hydrogen produced when water is electrolyzed for 150 minutes if the current is 5 amp.?

6. How many moles, equivalents, and grams of each of the following will be produced by 2.5 faradays of electricity?

a. Cu from Cu^{++}.   c. Hg from Hg_2^{++}.

b. Cu from Cu^+.   d. O_2 from OH^-.

7. a. Write the equation for the substitution reaction of magnesium metal with a solution containing silver ion.

b. Write the cell designation of the cell obtained by combining magnesium and silver half-cells.

c. Write the redox half-reactions for this cell.

d. Which electrode is positive? Which negative?

e. On the basis of the relative position of the two metals in the E.C.S., which reacts as the oxidizing agent? The reducing agent?

f. What is the voltage of this cell?

8. Write equations for the reactions that occur in the dry cell. What is the purpose of the MnO_2? In which direction do the electrons flow in the external circuit? What is polarization? What causes it in the dry cell?

9. Write equations for the charging of a lead storage battery. Which is the negative pole during discharge? What is the role of the specific gravity of the H_2SO_4 with respect to charge? Can you charge the battery by adding H_2SO_4? Why or why not?

10. What are the advantages and disadvantages of other secondary cells relative to the lead storage battery?

11. In what respects is a corrosion cell similar to a galvanic cell?

12. Explain how a bar of iron rusts.

13. Do bars of aluminum and magnesium corrode? Why may these more active metals be exposed to the atmosphere unprotected, whereas iron cannot?

14. Chromium is corrosion-resistant. Why? Why do chromium-plated automobile bumpers usually "rust" fairly readily?

15. If you had an aluminum outboard motor, would you prefer the exposed nuts and bolts to be made of aluminum, steel, or magnesium alloy? Give reasons for your answer. Why did you not decide on one of the other materials?

23

Carbon; organic chemistry

23.1. The Unique Nature of Carbon

The number of carbon compounds is many times as great as that of all the compounds which do not contain carbon. Until Wöhler synthesized urea, $CO(NH_2)_2$, from the salt ammonium cyanate, NH_4CNO, in 1828, it was thought that only living organisms were capable of producing carbon compounds of the type found in plant and animal tissues. The study of carbon compounds was therefore called **organic chemistry,** a name still used even though around a million organic compounds have been synthesized since Wöhler's day. College curricula allot eight to ten semester hours to the study of elementary organic chemistry, an amount of time that both professors and students find all too short. The astounding prolificness of carbon in forming compounds is not due to the mysterious "vital force" which was once thought to reside in it, but to the combination of special values of three familiar properties. These are electronegativity, covalence, and size.

The electronegativity of carbon is 2.5. This value is high enough so that carbon is able to form strong covalent bonds, but not so high that molecules containing C—C bonds show any tendency to be oxidizing agents. In fact, even C—O bonds have very little oxidizing ability. This is one reason why carbon far surpasses all other elements in its ability to form chains of identical atoms.

Carbon has 4 valence electrons and therefore forms four covalent bonds. This has two results. In the first place, it protects a carbon chain by coating it with strongly bonded atoms which are themselves resistant to chemical attack. C—H, C—Cl, and C—F bonds are all stronger than C—C bonds. A covalently bonded hydrogen atom has no unshared electrons to be attacked, and chlorine and fluorine hold their electrons too tightly to permit loss. A chain such as

$$H : \overset{\overset{\displaystyle H}{..}}{\underset{\underset{\displaystyle H}{..}}{C}} : \overset{\overset{\displaystyle H}{..}}{\underset{\underset{\displaystyle H}{..}}{C}} : \overset{\overset{\displaystyle H}{..}}{\underset{\underset{\displaystyle H}{..}}{C}} : \overset{\overset{\displaystyle H}{..}}{\underset{\underset{\displaystyle H}{..}}{C}} : \overset{\overset{\displaystyle H}{..}}{\underset{\underset{\displaystyle H}{..}}{C}} : H$$

is thus much less reactive than $H : \overset{..}{\underset{..}{S}} : \overset{..}{\underset{..}{S}} : \overset{..}{\underset{..}{S}} : \overset{..}{\underset{..}{S}} : \overset{..}{\underset{..}{S}} : H$, even though carbon and sulfur have the same electronegativity. In the second place, the fact that the covalence of carbon is 4 gives rise to innumerable possibilities of replacing the hydrogen atoms in the above formula with all sorts of other atoms, *including carbon.* The insertion of a carbon atom makes the chain branch and produces a whole new array of possibilities. Thus a single carbon atom may be bonded to one, two, or even three or four other carbon atoms. In the following examples, the lines represent single covalent bonds.

Propane   **Tetramethylmethane (neopentane)**   **Dimethyl ethylmethane (isopentane)**

Remember that molecules such as these which are conveniently shown in a line or with right angles are not flat or planar. The single covalent bonds of carbon form the tetrahedral angle of 109°. As a consequence there is some "puckering" or staggering in the three-dimensional configurations.

In addition to chains and branched chains, ring structures are also common. Rings may consist of three or more carbon atoms, five- or six-membered rings being most common because the bond angle of carbon enables rings consisting of these numbers to be closed with the least strain on the bonds. Combinations of chains and rings are also common.

Cyclopropane **Cyclohexane** **Methylcyclopentane**

Atoms other than carbon and hydrogen may be attached to a chain or inserted in a ring. The most common of these atoms are oxygen, the halogens, and nitrogen. Such molecules are called **derivatives** of the hydrocarbons. There are many kinds of derivatives; the formulas of three of them follow.

Monochloropropane **Aminopropionic acid** **Diethyl ether**

Derivatives are, in general, more important than the simple hydrocarbons from which they are formed.

The carbon atom is small; it is therefore able to form multiple bonds. In addition to ordinary single bonds, it can form double or triple bonds with oxygen, nitrogen, and other carbon atoms. Obviously the possibility of introducing multiple bonds here and there along a carbon chain, and of connecting the chain to oxygen or nitrogen by multiple instead of single bonds, increases the possible number of compounds manyfold. Not at all obvious is the fact that entirely different molecules are formed when two or more double bonds are **conjugated,** or yoked together. Double bonds are conjugated when there are overlapping p orbitals with parallel axes on several adjacent atoms. There is then an intercommunicating system of p orbitals such as was described for SO_3 in Section 11.22 and for NO_3^- ion in Section 12.14. The intercommunication may be through a central atom as in NO_3^- ion; CO_3^{--} ion, for example, is isoelectronic with NO_3^- ion, and is identical in construction.

A series of conjugated double bonds may also appear along a chain. The simplest example of this is butadiene. The formula of this molecule is conventionally written $CH_2{=}CH{-}CH{=}CH_2$; its actual structure is shown in Fig. 23.1. The straight lines represent the ordinary bonds that

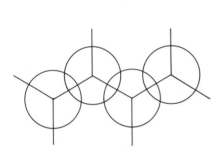

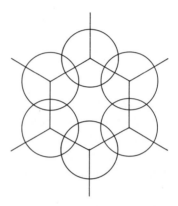

Fig. 23.1. Butadiene, $CH_2{=}CH{-}CH{=}CH_2$, a four carbon conjugated system. A carbon atom is understood to be at the center of each circle, and a hydrogen atom at the end of each projecting line. The intercommunicating **p** orbitals contain two electron pairs.

Fig. 23.2. Benzene, C_6H_6, a six-carbon conjugated ring system. The intercommunicating **p** orbitals contain three electron pairs.

join the four carbon atoms; the center of each atom is where the lines join. The hydrogen atoms are at the free ends of these lines. All the atoms lie in the plane of the paper. The axis of the remaining p orbital of each carbon atom is perpendicular to that plane, one lobe of the orbital being above the paper and one below it. The circles represent the projection of these lobes onto the plane of the paper and show how the p orbitals overlap. Obviously, if a pair of electrons is introduced into the region between the first and second carbon atoms where their p orbitals overlap, and another pair into the corresponding region between the third and fourth carbon atoms, both pairs of electrons will extend considerably into the region between the second and third carbon atoms. In the symmetrical molecule of benzene, C_6H_6 (Fig. 23.2), three pairs of electrons

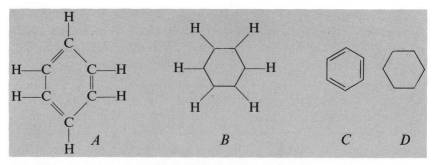

Fig. 23.3. Various ways of representing the benzene molecule. **B, C,** and **D** are abbreviations and have certain implications. Since each carbon has four bonds, **B** must have multiple bonding in the ring, **C** must have hydrogens attached to the ring since the multiple bonding is shown, and **D** must have multiple bonds as well as hydrogens attached to the ring. Generally **A** is the preferred representation, and **C** the preferred abbreviation.

are distributed evenly throughout the overlapping p orbitals; hence each pair of adjoining carbon atoms is connected by $1\frac{1}{2}$ bonds. Formulas of this sort, usually called Kekulé formulas, can be shown conveniently by bond line diagrams like those in Fig. 23.3. The expansion of these electrons into double the normal volume releases energy; so molecules containing conjugated double bonds are more stable, less reactive, than they would be if the bonds were too far apart for conjugation. Thus size is the third factor which vastly increases the number of possible carbon compounds.

23.2. Isomerism

The enormous number of possible organic compounds cannot be appreciated unless we realize that if two molecules differ even slightly in structure they are molecules of two different substances. This holds true even if both molecules contain exactly the same number of the same kinds of atoms. For example, the three pentanes have the formula C_5H_{12}, but are as much different substances as "read," "dear," and "dare," that have the same letters, are different words.

$$CH_3 \cdot CH_2 \cdot CH_2 \cdot CH_2 \cdot CH_3 \qquad CH_3 \cdot CH_2 \cdot CH \bigg\langle \begin{array}{c} CH_3 \\ CH_3 \end{array} \qquad \begin{array}{c} CH_3 \\ \diagdown \\ CH_3 \diagup \end{array} C \begin{array}{c} CH_3 \\ \diagup \\ \diagdown \\ CH_3 \end{array}$$

Normal pentane   **Isopentane**   **Neopentane**

Normal pentane boils at 37° C.; isopentane, at 30° C.; and neopentane, at 9.5° C. To cite a more familiar example, normal octane (unbranched chain) is a typical component of kerosene; it boils at 125° C. and causes serious knocking even in a low-compression motor. But another octane, 2,2,4-trimethylpentane, boils at 99° C.

$$CH_3 \cdot \overset{\displaystyle \overset{CH_3}{|}}{CH} \cdot CH_2 \cdot \overset{\displaystyle \overset{CH_3}{|}}{\underset{\displaystyle \underset{CH_3}{|}}{C}} \cdot CH_3$$

2,2,4-Trimethylpentane

It is the standard for rating antiknock gasoline. Substances which are different but have the same molecular formula are called **isomers**. The number of possible isomers increases rapidly as the number of atoms in the molecule increases, becoming astronomical even when the size of the molecules is still quite reasonable.

The number of possible isomers also increases rapidly if hydrogen atoms are replaced by other atoms or groups. A moment's study of the formulas of the pentanes shows that every hydrogen atom in neopentane has the same position relative to the carbon atoms and the other hydrogen atoms, whereas there are three positions for the hydrogens in normal pentane (viz., on the carbon at either end, on the carbon next to the end, and on the middle carbon) and four for those in isopentane. If one hydrogen atom is replaced by an —OH group, the resultant molecule is an alcohol; there will be only one alcohol from neopentane, but three from normal pentane and four from isopentane, a total of eight isomeric alcohols from three isomeric pentanes. Alcohols of the pentanes are called pentanols. Can you verify the fact that these in turn can lead to 31 monochloropentanols?

Isomers are impossible with the small molecules methane, CH_4, ethane, $CH_3 \cdot CH_3$, and propane, $CH_3 \cdot CH_2 \cdot CH_3$. Similarly, most of the inorganic molecules studied earlier in this text are too small and simple to display isomerism. However, isomers are possible with more complicated inorganic molecules.

23.3. Hydrocarbons

Compounds that consist of carbon and hydrogen alone are called **hydrocarbons**. If there are no multiple bonds in the molecule of a hydrocarbon it is relatively unreactive. This is the basis of the name *paraffin* for this class of hydrocarbon, from Latin words meaning *too* *little* (chemical) *affinity*. Hydrocarbon molecules with one or more multiple bonds have greater thermal stability than the paraffins because of the extra strength of the bonds; but the multiple bonds readily take up hydrogen and form paraffins or other molecules—Br_2, HCl, etc.—and form derivatives of the paraffins. For that reason these hydrocarbon molecules are called **unsaturated compounds.** The paraffins are alternatively referred to as **saturated hydrocarbons.** Hydrocarbons have systematic names derived from the Greek name for the number of carbon atoms in their molecules.

Table 23.1 lists the common names and formulas of saturated and unsaturated hydrocarbons containing up to four carbon atoms in the molecule. When there are more than four carbon atoms in the molecule, systematic names are used which indicate the number of carbon atoms and the state of saturation. The number of carbon atoms is designated by a prefix, and the state of saturation by a suffix; e.g., *-ane* denotes a saturated hydrocarbon, *-ene* denotes one containing one or more double bonds, and *-yne* designates an unsaturated hydrocarbon that contains triple bonds. Thus pentane is C_5H_{12}; hexane, C_6H_{14}; pentene, C_5H_{10}; hexyne, C_6H_{10}, etc. Many substances have unsystematic names which were given them before the systematic nomenclature was adopted. Some of these are listed in Table 23.1.

TABLE 23.1. **Common Names in Regular Use**

Formula	Name	Formula	Name
CH_4	Methane	$CH_2 : CH_2$	Ethylene
$CH_3 \cdot CH_3$	Ethane	$CH_3 \cdot CH : CH_2$	Propylene
$CH_3 \cdot CH_2 \cdot CH_3$	Propane	$CH_3 \cdot CH_2 \cdot CH : CH_2$	Butylene
$CH_3 \cdot CH_2 \cdot CH_2 \cdot CH_3$	Butane	$CH \vdots CH$	Acetylene

Several of the substances listed in Table 23.1 are familiar in everyday life. The natural gas transmitted in pipelines is almost entirely methane. Propane and butane and various mixtures of the two are sold as LPG (liquefied petroleum gases) in cylinders for domestic use. Ethylene, an anesthetic, is used mainly as an intermediate in the preparation of other substances such as alcohol, permanent types of antifreeze, and a plastic, polyethylene.

The prefix *cyclo-* denotes a ring molecule, a chain whose ends are connected to each other. The valuable anesthetic cyclopropane has the formula:

$$\begin{array}{c}
\text{CH}_2 \\
\diagup \quad | \\
\text{H}_2\text{C} \quad | \\
\diagdown \quad | \\
\text{CH}_2
\end{array}$$

Note that this is an isomer of propene, $\text{CH}_3 \cdot \text{CH} : \text{CH}_2$.

The source of most of our hydrocarbons is the complex mixture called petroleum, and the natural gas which is associated with it. Many hydrocarbons are present in the mixture; others are obtained at oil refineries by rearranging the molecules at high temperatures in the presence of catalysts. Acetylene is also obtained from the reaction of water with calcium carbide.

$$\underline{\text{CaC}_2} + 2\text{H}_2\text{O} \rightarrow \underline{\text{Ca(OH)}_2} + \overline{\text{C}_2\text{H}_2}$$

23.4. Active Groups

A C—H bond has negligible polarity because of the small difference in electronegativity (0.4) between carbon and hydrogen. In hydrocarbon molecules even this cancels out because of the symmetry of the bonds. The introduction of a more electronegative atom in place of hydrogen anywhere in a hydrocarbon molecule produces a polar bond which destroys this symmetry; as a result, a polar molecule is formed. Bonds between carbon and nitrogen or chlorine (difference in electronegativity, 0.5) are considered to be only 6 per cent ionic in character, but a C—O bond (difference in electronegativity, 1.0) is 22 per cent ionic. Such a substitution therefore makes the material much more like water; i.e., its boiling point is higher in proportion to the molecular weight, its solubility in water is appreciable or complete, and it may be able to dissolve salts to some extent. (In moderately polar liquids salts dissolve as ion pairs rather than as independent ions.) Furthermore, every polar group in an organic molecule provides a region of increased chemical reactivity in the molecule. Some of the most important of these groups are listed in Table 23.2, R representing a hydrocarbon group.

23.5. Inductive Effect

The substances in Table 23.2 can all be regarded as derivatives of water or ammonia. The substitution of a hydrocarbon group (R) for a hydrogen atom has very little effect on the behavior of the remaining atoms because carbon is only a little above hydrogen in electronegativity. An alcohol is therefore a very weak acid and a very weak base—not too

TABLE 23.2. **Some Common Active Groups**

Active Group Formula	Characteristic Name	Examples
—C—OH	Alcohol	Ethanol (ethyl alcohol), CH_3CH_2OH
—C (with H and =O)	Aldehyde	Benzaldehyde, (structure); Propanal, CH_3CH_2C (with H and =O)
—C—O—C—	Ether	Ethoxyethane (diethyl ether), $CH_3CH_2OCH_2CH_3$; Methoxypropane, $CH_3OCH_2CH_2CH_3$
—C—C—C— (with =O)	Ketone (also carbonyl)	2-Propanone (dimethyl ketone), CH_3COCH_3; 2-Butanone (methyl ethyl ketone), $CH_3COCH_2CH_3$
—C—OH (with =O)	Carboxyl (acids)	Propanoic acid, CH_3CH_2COOH; Benzenecarboxylic (benzoic) acid, (structure)
—C—NH₂	Amine	Ethylamine, $CH_3CH_2NH_2$; aniline, (structure) —NH_2
—C—NH₂ (with =O)	Amide	Ethanamide (acetamide), CH_3C (with =O) —NH_2

different from water in this respect. An ether or a ketone shows only weak basic properties. An amine is a slightly stronger base than ammonia. But if the group which replaces a hydrogen atom is not a simple hydrocarbon radical, the situation is different. A carbon atom bonded to a highly electronegative atom is itself considerably more electronegative than a carbon atom which is bonded only to hydrogens or other hydrocarbon groups. This is true because of the *inductive effect* of the highly electronegative atom in removing electrons from the carbon. In a doubly bonded oxygen, this effect is considerable; it amounts to the carbon atom being given nearly half a unit of positive charge.

The effect of induction is plain in compounds containing the last two carboxyl and amide groups in Table 23.2, where the presence of two electronegative groups on the same carbon atom so modifies the properties of both groups that a special name is given the combination. The carboxyl group may be considered as being formed by the substitution of a keto- group for one of the hydrogens of water. The effect on the —OH group which remains is about the same as that produced by sub-

stituting the $H : \overset{\displaystyle :\overset{..}{O}:}{\underset{\displaystyle :\overset{..}{O}:}{P}}$ group, and much greater than that produced by

substituting $: \overset{..}{\underset{..}{Cl}}$. In other words, the acid $R \!-\! C \!\! \begin{array}{c} O \\ \diagup\diagup \\ \diagdown \\ OH \end{array}$ (or RCOOH)

is about as strong as $H_2PO_3^-$ and much stronger than ClOH (or HClO). The —OH group has a reciprocal effect on the carbonyl oxygen, reducing its basic properties almost to the vanishing point. Similarly, the amide group has negligible basic properties and a measurable degree of acidity.

The carboxyl group is an example of conjugation (Fig. 23.4). Each oxygen atom forms a partial second bond with the carbon atom, but not to the same extent; the hydrogen prevents its oxygen from sharing an electron pair to the same extent as the other oxygen does. The carboxylate anion, on the other hand, is perfectly symmetrical, each oxygen forming $1\frac{1}{2}$ bonds with the carbon. The electron cloud of the conjugated system is in a much lower energy state than it was when the proton drew it over to one side. The greater stability of the carboxylate ion in comparison to the carboxyl group accounts for the strength of a carboxylic acid as much as the inductive effect does. The structural for-

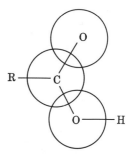

Fig. 23.4. A carboxylic acid. The three-atom conjugated system is not completely symmetrical because the hydrogen atom prevents its oxygen from contributing as much of an electron pair to the p orbital of the carbon atom as the other oxygen atom does. The carboxylate ion, R·COO⁻, is perfectly symmetrical.

mulas of the acid and anion are written $R-C\begin{smallmatrix}O\\ \\OH\end{smallmatrix}$ and $\left[R-C\begin{smallmatrix}O\\ \\O\end{smallmatrix}\right]^-$

for historical reasons. The fact that the latter could just as well be writ-

ten $\left[R-C\begin{smallmatrix}O\\ \\O\end{smallmatrix}\right]^-$ should remind you that the bonds actually are equal.

Even in the case of the acid the difference probably amounts only to about 1.6 bonds for the carbonyl group as against 1.4 for the hydroxyl group.

23.6. Inductive Effect on the C—H Bond

Ordinary hydrocarbons have no acid properties; this is reflected in the fact that the hydrogen is customarily written last in their formulas, e.g., C_2H_6. In view of the abrupt decreases in acid strength which occur between HF and H_2O and between H_2O and NH_3, it is not surprising to find that CH_4 is not an acid at all. The hypothetical carbanion,

$R:\overset{\displaystyle R}{\underset{\displaystyle R}{\ddot{C}}}:^-$, is evidently a tremendously strong base.

The fundamental reaction of a base is the offering of an electron pair to be shared. The more electron pairs the base is compelled to share, and the larger its part of each electron pair that it has to relinquish to the ligand, the more the base is weakened; compare the series O^{--}, OH^-, HOH, and ClOH. In other words, the more of its electrons that are taken away from it, the less willing the base is to share the remainder. Accordingly it should be possible to impart detectable acid properties to a hydrogen—even though it is attached to a carbon atom—if sufficiently electronegative groups are also attached to that same atom.

This is actually the case. For example, chloroform, $HCCl_3$, has traces of acid properties. The electronegative groups can be carbon atoms which themselves have electronegative substituents. The carbonyl group

is very effective this way. In acetylacetone, $\begin{smallmatrix}CH_3\cdot CO\\ \\CH_3\cdot CO\end{smallmatrix}>CH_2$, one of the

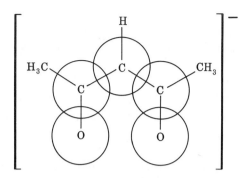

Fig. 23.5. Acetylacetonate ion, $CH_3 \cdot CO \cdot -CH \cdot CO \cdot CH_3{}^-$, a five-atom conjugated system which includes oxygen atoms as well as carbon atoms. Intercommunication between the **p** orbitals of the two CO groups becomes possible only on removal of one of the two hydrogen atoms originally on the central carbon atom in acetylacetone, $CH_3 \cdot CO \cdot CH_2 \cdot CO \cdot CH_3$.

central hydrogen atoms can readily be removed by a strong base. The loss of the proton releases an electron pair on the central carbon atom which permits a conjugated system to be established; this is shown in the structure of the ion in Fig. 23.5. This fact can be represented equally well by either of the following structural formulas:

The perfect symmetry of this anion further increases the acid strength of the parent compound. The acetylacetonate ion is very effective in forming complexes with metal cations. Fig. 23.5 shows that a metal cation approaching the two oxygen atoms would be in a position to accept both of them as ligands.

A hydrogen atom which is activated by the presence of a carbonyl oxygen on the *same* carbon atom, $-\overset{\displaystyle O}{\underset{\displaystyle H}{\overset{\|}{C}}}$, not only is acidic enough to

be lost in certain reactions (see the discussion of Bakelite in Section 24.10), but can readily be oxidized to —OH, yielding the carboxyl

group, $-\overset{\displaystyle O}{\underset{\displaystyle OH}{\overset{\|}{C}}}$. It is for this reason that aldehydes are distinguished

from ketones (Table 23.2).

23.7. Carbon Monoxide

Carbon monoxide is isoelectronic with N_2, the two structures differing only in that the electron distribution in CO favors oxygen a trifle. In diatomic molecules that contain a triple bond the unshared electron pair on each atom projects outward along the axis of the molecule. The dot formula is $: C ::: O :$. It is the unshared pair of electrons on the carbon atom that is accepted by nickel in forming $Ni(CO)_4$. This pair is also accepted by the iron atom in the hemoglobin molecule just as are the similarly projecting electrons in the O_2 molecule when blood is aerated in the lungs. Unfortunately a tighter bond is formed with CO than with O_2; so hemoglobin which has taken up carbon monoxide is permanently out of action. The oxygen supply of a person who is breathing air contaminated with carbon monoxide is gradually shut off just as though he were trying for an altitude record in an unpressurized jet and had no oxygen mask. Breathing air that contains 0.1 per cent CO is fatal in about half an hour. H_2S and HCN, which are similarly taken up, are about equally toxic but far less dangerous because of their odor; CO is odorless. Newspapers commonly refer to CO as "monoxide gas."

Carbon monoxide is always produced when any fuel burns in an insufficient supply of oxygen or when combustion is incomplete for any other reason. Almost as inert as nitrogen at room temperature, carbon monoxide is an excellent reducing agent at high temperatures. It is CO, not coke, that reduces iron ore in the blast furnace. The carbon monoxide produced by the water gas reaction is used as fuel. CO is oxidized to CO_2 by oxygen. In the presence of suitable catalysts it is oxidized by chlorine to carbonyl chloride (phosgene), $COCl_2$, a useful reagent in the synthesis of dyes, etc. It was used as a poison gas in World War I, being considerably more toxic than chlorine, and easier to handle (b.p. = 8° C.).

23.8. Carbon Dioxide

The CO_2 molecule is linear, with carbon in the middle. Two carbon p orbitals perpendicular to the molecular axis overlap similarly oriented p orbitals of the oxygen atoms *on either side*. Thus each end of the molecule looks like a CO molecule. However, a single electron pair lies between the carbon atom and its *two* neighbors in each of these conjugated groups of p orbitals. The total bonding effect is the same as that of a double bond between carbon and each oxygen, and structural formulas are

ordinarily written $: \ddot{O} :: C :: \ddot{O} :$ or $O = C = O$.

CO_2, a colorless, odorless gas, is produced when fuels burn in the presence of excess oxygen. It is exhaled in the breath of animals, and is produced in many fermentations. One-third of the carbon in sugar is liberated as CO_2 in alcoholic fermentation.

$$C_6H_{12}O_6 \xrightarrow{\text{enzymes}} 2C_2H_5OH + \overline{2CO_2}$$

In drilling for oil it is not uncommon to strike a pocket or even a well of carbon dioxide. Some of these wells are used in the production of solid carbon dioxide, or dry ice.

The physical properties of the oxides of carbon are shown in Table 23.3. The values of the various constants for CO are nearly identical with those for nitrogen; the molecular weights of the two are the same. Since the critical temperature of CO_2 is above room temperature, it can be shipped as a liquid in cylinders. Because the freezing point is above

TABLE 23.3.	**Properties of Carbon Dioxide and Carbon Monoxide**				
	Melting Point	Boiling Point	Critical Temperature	Critical Pressure	Solubility in Water in cc./cc.
Carbon dioxide	$-56.6°$ [a]	$-78.5°$ [b]	$31.1°$	73 atm.	1.79 at 0°
Carbon monoxide	$-207°$	$-192°$	$-139°$	35 atm.	0.035 at 0°

[a] At 5.3 atm.
[b] Sublimes.

the boiling point—i.e., the vapor pressure is above 1 atm. at the freezing point—liquid CO_2 boils if the pressure is decreased, until enough heat has been absorbed to freeze it; the solid sublimes until the temperature has been lowered to about $-80°$ C. Solid CO_2 is used in laboratories when so low a temperature is needed. Commercially it has the advantages of leaving no residue and being able to absorb about fifteen times as much heat as an equal weight of ice can. Because the body's automatic breathing mechanism is actuated by the accumulation of CO_2, oxygen used for resuscitation contains 5 per cent CO_2 to stimulate breathing.

CO_2 is the anhydride of carbonic acid, H_2CO_3, and is itself a Lewis acid. It adds directly to bases, as shown in the following equations:

$$\overline{CO_2} + O^{--} \rightarrow \overline{CO_3}^{--} \qquad \text{(carbonate ion)}$$

$$\overline{CO_2} + OH^- \rightarrow \overline{HCO_3}^- \qquad \text{(bicarbonate ion)}$$

$$\overline{CO_2} + H_2O \rightarrow \overline{H_2CO_3} \qquad \text{(carbonic acid)}$$

$$\overline{CO_2} + 2NH_3 \rightarrow NH_4H_2NCO_2 \qquad \text{(ammonium carbamate)}$$

If the base is strong, the product is a base; if weak, the product is a weak acid. The slightly sour taste of the weak acid H_2CO_3 is familiar in plain carbonated water.

CO_2 is a very poor oxidizing agent. It oxidizes white-hot carbon.

$$\overline{CO_2} + \underline{C} \overset{\Delta}{\rightarrow} \overline{2CO}$$

It supports the combustion of magnesium.

$$\overline{CO_2} + \underline{2Mg} \rightarrow \underline{2MgO} + \underline{C} + \triangle$$

For this reason CO_2 cannot be used to extinguish magnesium or other more reactive metals that are on fire. It is an excellent extinguisher in the case of other fires. Liquid CO_2 is applied from a portable cylinder with a flared nozzle, the idea being not to freeze the fire out, but to exclude oxygen from it by the blanket formed by the dense, inert gas. One great advantage of CO_2 is the fact that it cannot damage anything around it.

Fire extinguishers that must be inverted for use are filled with a concentrated solution of $NaHCO_3$, above which is a container of sulfuric acid that spills when tilted. When this comes in contact with the $NaHCO_3$ solution it is used up; the reaction is:

$$H^+ + HSO_4^- + 2Na^+ + 2HCO_3^- \rightarrow 2Na^+ + SO_4^{--} + 2H_2O + \overline{2CO_2}$$

A stream of $NaHCO_3$ solution is forced out through the small hose by the pressure exerted by the CO_2. This solution liberates CO_2 onto the fire in accordance with the reaction used in the Solvay process for making sodium carbonate.

$$\underline{2NaHCO_3} \xrightarrow{\Delta} \underline{Na_2CO_3} + \overline{H_2O} + \overline{CO_2}$$

Foamite fire extinguishers operate on the same principle, but the acid is a solution of Al^{+3} ion. When this is neutralized by the HCO_3^- ion, gelatinous $Al(OH)_3$ is produced; this forms a thick froth with the escaping bubbles of CO_2. The foam is stabilized by a substance obtained from licorice root after the flavor has been extracted. This foam floats on and blankets burning oil or gasoline, whereas water would fall directly to the bottom.

23.9. Alcohols

Some of the alcohols are familiar substances that are manufactured in huge quantities. Methanol, CH_3OH (commonly called methyl alcohol), is a non-permanent antifreeze, but is used in much larger amounts as a solvent. It is very toxic; even when not fatal it causes blindness. Its non-chemical name, wood alcohol, refers to the fact that it is one of the products of the pyrolysis or heat decomposition of wood. It is now manufactured by a catalytic process in the apparatus used for the Haber process for ammonia synthesis. The reaction is:

$$\overline{CO} + \overline{2H_2} \xrightarrow{\text{catalyst}} \overline{CH_3OH}$$

Ethanol, $CH_3 \cdot CH_2OH$, is more commonly called ethyl alcohol or simply alcohol; it is often called grain alcohol in contrast to wood alcohol. Much beverage alcohol is produced by the fermentation of sugar resulting from the action of malt enzymes upon the starch in various grains. A greater quantity of alcohol is produced by the fermentation of the residual sugar in molasses and is either purified for commercial use or sold in the impure state as rum. Some alcohol is fermented in Europe from sugar made by the hydrolysis of wood or of potato starch. In the United States the alcohol produced by adding water to ethylene equals that produced from all other sources. If alcohol is pure, it is impossible to identify the source. Most beverage alcohol is flavored by substances derived from the raw material or from the charred wood barrels in which it is stored. Gin is pure alcohol flavored with juniper, etc.; vodka is simply dilute alcohol. A mixture of equal volumes of alcohol and water (50 per cent solution by volume) is just strong enough to burn when ignited. This test for the strength of liquors led to the use of the term proof spirits for alcohol of this strength. "86 Proof" on the label of a bottle means that the alcoholic strength is 86 per cent as great as that of proof spirits, or 43 per cent by volume.

Like methanol, ethanol is used industrially by the hundred million gallons as a solvent. Both alcohols are also used in large amounts as raw materials in the manufacture of other chemicals.

Three other alcohols, although of lesser importance, are also familiar

in everyday life. Isopropyl alcohol, $\begin{matrix} CH_3 \\ \diagdown \\ CH_3 \end{matrix} CHOH$, is commonly used as

rubbing alcohol. Glycol (ethylene glycol, Prestone, etc.), $CH_2OH \cdot CH_2OH$, is familiar as a permanent antifreeze. Glycerol (glycerine) was used as a permanent antifreeze before the commercial development of glycol, but a large quantity was required because of the high molecular weight corresponding to the formula, $CH_2OH \cdot CHOH \cdot CH_2OH$. It is still used as a humectant to maintain the desired moisture content in hand lotions, tobacco, photographic prints, etc.

23.10. Esters

One chemical property common to all alcohols is the ability to react with acids, inorganic as well as carboxylic, and form esters. In this reaction a proton from the alcohol joins an —OH group from the acid and is eliminated as water; the remainder of both molecules unites covalently. The equation shows the formation of ethyl acetate from ethyl alcohol and acetic acid.

$$CH_3 \cdot CH_2 \cdot O|H + HO| \cdot CO \cdot CH_3 \rightarrow CH_3 \cdot CH_2 \cdot O \cdot CO \cdot CH_3 + H_2O$$

The problem as to which molecule furnishes the oxygen was solved by using alcohol labeled with the isotope [18]O as a tracer. Although esters are covalent compounds, they are named as though they were salts, just as were the non-metal halides, e.g., phosphorus trichloride and carbon tetrachloride.

Esters are pleasant-smelling, when volatile. A number of them are used as perfumes or flavorings, the most familiar being methyl salicylate, oil of wintergreen. Edible oils and fats are glyceryl esters of long-chain carboxylic acids. Other esters are used as solvents, and as plasticizers in plastics or as plastics themselves. Under the incorrect name of nitroglycerin, glyceryl nitrate is well known as an explosive and as a heart stimulant. Glycol nitrate is also used in dynamite.

23.11. Phenols

Owing to its unsaturated nature, the carbon skeleton of benzene, C_6H_6 (Section 23.1), is considerably more electronegative than the carbon skeletons of saturated hydrocarbons. Its protons are therefore more active, and can be replaced more readily by other groups. The electronegativity of the phenyl radical, C_6H_5—, is sufficient to produce appreciable acidity in an —OH group if one is attached to it. This is why phenol, C_6H_5OH, is not considered an alcohol. It is nearly as strong an acid as HCO_3^- ion; in fact, it is commonly called carbolic acid. It is a powerful antiseptic and poison. The slow-healing burns it produces are due to its specific action on proteins, not to the very mild acidity. Phenol is a raw material for many dyes and certain pharmaceuticals, but most of it is used in the manufacture of the Bakelite type of plastics.

Creosote, a strong-smelling antiseptic and wood preservative obtained from coal tar, contains three methylphenols called cresols. The formulas are shown below, the hexagon representing the benzene ring and its attached hydrogen atoms. The groups substituted for hydrogen are shown, but the $1\frac{1}{2}$ bonds between the carbon atoms of the ring are implied by the conjugated double bond system shown here (see Section 23.1). As is usual, the unoccupied ring positions belong to hydrogens.

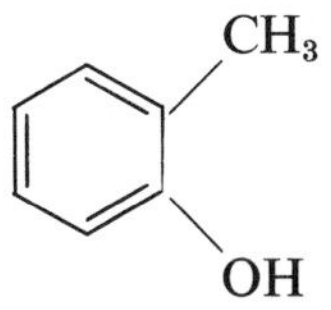

| Ortho- | Meta- | Para- |

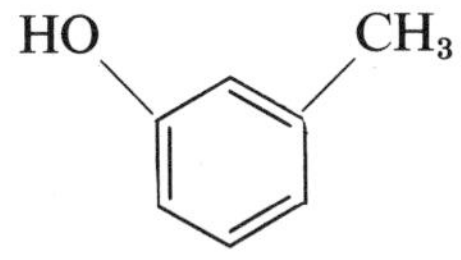

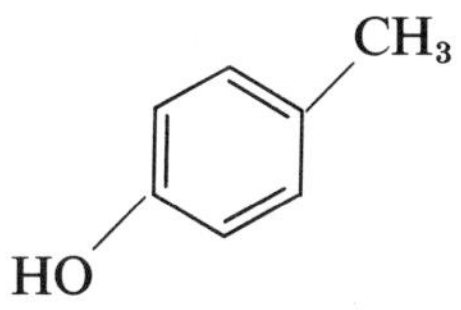

The three isomers differ in melting point by as much as 32° C., and also in chemical properties. The above prefixes that are used to distinguish them show the relative positions of the substituents in *all* disubstituted benzenes.

Phenols familiar to photographers as developing agents include hydroquinone (para-dihydroxybenzene), and pyrogallol (1,2,3-trihydroxybenzene). The numbering system is necessary when there are three substituents. The carbon atoms in the ring are numbered consecutively; hence in pyrogallol there is an—OH group on each of three consecutive carbon atoms.

23.12. Carboxylic Acids

The names of the carboxylic acids are mostly historical, indicating their source rather than their structure. Thus formic acid, $HCOOH$, is responsible for the sting in the bite of an ant (L., *formica*); a 5 per cent solution of acetic acid, $CH_3 \cdot COOH$, is vinegar (L., *acetum*). $HCOOH$ is a moderately weak acid, comparable with HNO_2. Acetic acid (generally written $HC_2H_3O_2$ or HAc by inorganic chemists) is somewhat weaker; it has about the same strength as $Al(H_2O)_6^{+3}$. Both $HCOOH$ and $HC_2H_3O_2$ are miscible with water. As the length of the hydrocarbon chain increases, the strength of the acids diminishes still further, and they become completely insoluble in water. Collectively they are called fatty acids. The name refers to both source and appearance of the acids.

Only acids with an even number of carbon atoms occur in nature. If the chain is saturated, the acids from C_{10} (capric acid, so called because of its goatlike smell) on up are solids; the C_{18} acid (stearic, from *stearin,* the Greek word for tallow) is used to make candles but is more important as a lubricant on the surface of dies through which wire is drawn in order to reduce its diameter. The sodium salts of the C_{16} and C_{18} acids are the main constituents of soap. The introduction of a double bond in the middle of the C_{18} chain, with the accompanying loss of two hydrogen atoms, produces a liquid called oleic acid (L., *oleum,* oil). Olein (glyceryl oleate) is also a liquid; it is the main constituent of the salad oils obtained from olives, corn, peanuts, cottonseed, etc. Linoleic acid contains a pair of conjugated double bonds which make its glyceryl ester, linseed oil, a drying oil. It "dries" not by evaporation but by reacting with oxygen, forming a solid film on paint and linoleum.

The simplest dicarboxylic acid, $HOOC \cdot COOH$, is called oxalic acid after the plant oxalis (wood sorrel) in which it occurs. The sour taste of the $HOOC \cdot COO^-$ ion is readily apparent in both leaves and flowers; they should not be eaten in any quantity because the acid and both anions are poisonous. Oxalic acid is oxidized quantitatively by MnO_4^- ion in acid solution and is used to standardize permanganate solutions for oxidimetry.

$$6H^+ + 5H_2C_2O_4 + 2MnO_4^- \rightarrow 2Mn^{++} + 8H_2O + \overline{10CO_2}$$

It forms a complex with Fe^{+3} ion and hence is used to remove rust stains. It should be used with great care because not only is it a dangerous poison, but it is a strong enough acid to roughen the glaze on porcelain enamel and to weaken cotton fibers.

Because of the inductive effect of the two carboxyl groups on each other, $H_2C_2O_4$ is almost a strong acid. The first ionization is three times as strong as the ionization of HSO_4^- ion. The Cl_3C- group shows a similar and even more powerful inductive effect. Trichloracetic acid, $Cl_3C \cdot COOH$, is three times as strong as oxalic acid; it is 73 per cent ionized in 0.1 M solution. This inductive effect decreases rapidly to zero as the chain is lengthened.

Other dicarboxylic acids of interest include tartaric acid, from grapes; malic acid, from apples; and adipic acid, used in nylon. Cream of tartar is potassium hydrogen tartrate.

$$HO \cdot CH \cdot COOH$$
$$|$$
$$HO \cdot CH \cdot COOH$$

Tartaric acid

$$CH_2 \cdot COOH$$
$$|$$
$$HO \cdot CH \cdot COOH$$

Malic acid

$$HOOC \cdot (CH_2)_4 \cdot COOH$$

Adipic acid

Citric acid comes from lemons and can also be produced by a special fermentation process for sugar. It is a tricarboxylic acid and has the following formula:

$$HOOC \diagdown \qquad \diagup CH_2 \cdot COOH$$
$$C$$
$$HO \diagup \qquad \diagdown CH_2 \cdot COOH$$

23.13. Aldehydes

An aldehyde is usually named from the acid into which it is oxidized so easily. The most important of the aldehydes is the gas, formaldehyde, HCHO; huge quantities are produced by the partial oxidation of methanol. The 37 per cent solution sells for about 5 cents per pound in tank-car lots. It is one of the raw materials of Bakelite. Under the name of formalin, the solution is used in embalming, in preserving and hardening museum specimens, and as a disinfectant.

Formaldehyde has a very strong, sharp, unpleasant, burning odor. Many of the higher aldehydes, however, have very pleasant odors. This is particularly true of aldehydes whose formulas contain the benzene ring, and is part of the reason why the whole class of benzene derivatives became known as *aromatic compounds.* Familiar aromatic aldehydes include benzaldehyde, cinnamaldehyde, and vanillin.

Benzaldehyde   **Cinnamaldehyde**   **Vanillin**

The first of these is almond flavor; the second and third are the most important ingredients of cinnamon and vanilla respectively.

23.14. Ethers

The ethers have the formula R_2O; the R's may be the same or different. Methyl ether, $CH_3 \cdot O \cdot CH_3$, is isomeric with ethanol; but since it has no acidic hydrogen to engage in hydrogen bonding, its boiling point is more than 100° lower than that of alcohol, $-24°$ C. instead of 78° C. Every ether is isomeric with an alcohol, and has a far lower boiling point than the corresponding alcohol.

Ethyl ether, or simply ether, is the familiar anesthetic. It is made by dehydrating two molecules of ethanol with concentrated H_2SO_4; hence the name sulfuric ether which Sherlock Holmes' Dr. Watson used for it. Similar intermolecular dehydration of glycol produces polyethers with chains of any desired length; they are valuable as solvents. Volatile ethers have pleasant odors. Note that vanillin is an ether as well as an aldehyde—and a phenol too, for that matter.

23.15. Amines

The replacement of the hydrogens in NH_3 by CH_3— groups produces successively methylamine, $CH_3 \cdot NH_2$ (a *primary* amine), dimethylamine, $(CH_3)_2 \cdot NH$ (a *secondary* amine), and trimethylamine, $(CH_3)_3N$ (a *tertiary* amine). The base strength increases in the same order. Tetramethyl-ammonium ion, $(CH_3)_4 \cdot N^+$ (containing quaternary nitrogen), can also be prepared; it is not a base at all. Neither, however, is it an acid, since there is no loose hydrogen. For the same reason, it cannot exhibit hydrogen bonding. Therefore its hydroxide is a true salt, the OH^- ion displaying its strong basic nature without interference from the cation, just as is true of KOH. In fact, $(CH_3)_4 \cdot N^+$ ion strongly resembles an outsized alkali metal ion.

Simple amines are not common outside the laboratory, except for methylamine, from decaying fish and seaweed; it is responsible for the "salt smell of the sea" so noticeable on many beaches but completely lacking out of sight of land. Complex amines occur everywhere. Most naturally occurring drugs are alkaloids, the name referring to the basic nitrogen that is present. Many hormones and vitamins and all enzymes are amino compounds. Amino acids are the building blocks of proteins.

The simplest amino acid is glycine, aminoacetic acid; its formula is conventionally written $NH_2 \cdot CH_2 \cdot COOH$. The formula indicates that it is a fairly good base at one end and a moderate acid at the other; but this is obviously impossible, for self-neutralization must occur. The proton is actually transferred from the carboxyl to the amino group and the formula is $^+NH_3 \cdot CH_2 \cdot COO^-$; in other words, an ammonium ion is substituted at one end and an acetate ion at the other. Glycine is amphoteric, losing a proton from the N in basic solution, adding one on the O in acid solution.

When a phenyl group, C_6H_5—, instead of a methyl group, CH_3—, replaces a hydrogen in NH_3, the resulting base, aniline, is formed. It is weaker instead of stronger than NH_3, because of the greater electronegativity of the phenyl group. Anilinium ion, $C_6H_5 \cdot NH_3^+$, is thus a considerably stronger acid than NH_4^+ ion. For historical reasons, organic chemists prefer to call salts of amines by such names as aniline hydrochloride, and to write their formulas in the style $C_6H_5NH_2 \cdot HCl$, rather than naming and formulating them as the substituted ammonium salts which they are. Aniline and its close relatives are used in the synthesis of innumerable dyes, drugs, and other widely used compounds.

These related compounds include many heterocyclic compounds in which a nitrogen atom with one unshared electron pair replaces a $=CH$— group in a conjugated system. Several such substitutions can occur in one ring.

23.16. Sugars

The bulk of the diet of human beings consists of three classes of foodstuffs—proteins for tissue building and repair, and fats and carbohydrates for energy. Proteins and fats were mentioned earlier in this chapter.

Carbohydrates are so called because, in addition to carbon, they contain hydrogen and oxygen in the proportion in which they occur in water, 2 : 1. Their systematic names end in *-ose*. The twenty-four carbohydrates whose formula is $C_6H_{12}O_6$ are called hexoses because of the six carbons in the molecule. Similarly, there are pentoses, heptoses, etc. A compound formed when two hexose molecules are linked together is called a dihexose. The most important and familiar carbohydrates are the hexoses, dihexoses, and polyhexoses. The first two are known as sugars. The most important polyhexoses, starch and cellulose, are discussed in the next chapter.

The names of individual sugars are based on their sources in nature, or occasionally on a property. Thus fructose refers to fruit, lactose to milk,

Fig. 23.6. Partially crystallized crude corn sugar being sliced into slabs, after which it is "aged" and shipped to be used in the rayon, brewing, tanning, and fermentation industries. (Courtesy, Corn Industries Research Foundation, Inc.)

and maltose to malt; glucose is derived from a word meaning sweet, and sucrose (common sugar) is based on the Arab word for sugar; the Arabs introduced sugar into Europe. Glucose is also called dextrose.

Glucose, the most important hexose, is present in grapes and many other fruits. It is prepared commercially—our output is over a billion pounds a year—by the hydrolysis of cornstarch.

$$(C_6H_{10}O_5)_n + nH_2O \xrightarrow[\text{pressure}]{\text{acid}} nC_6H_{12}O_6$$

The acid serves merely as a catalyst. In manufacturing the thick, moderately sweet corn syrup which is used in confectionery and as a table syrup, not all the starch is broken down completely into hexose units. Some remains as maltose (having two glucose units), and some as a mixture of moderate-sized polyhexoses called dextrin. The adhesive on postage stamps is pure dextrin. By hydrolyzing under more severe conditions, the starch can be converted almost completely into glucose. This concentrated solution (80 per cent glucose) is poured into molds where it solidifies; it is then sold as corn or "grape" sugar (Fig. 23.6). It is possible to crystallize pure dextrose monohydrate in needle-shaped white crystals. This product, about three-fifths as sweet as sugar, is sold under the trade name Dyno. In the Bergius process developed in Germany in 1935, glucose is produced by the hydrolysis of cellulose.

The most important of all sugars is sucrose, $C_{12}H_{22}O_{11}$. It is formed in plants and fruits by the elimination of water between a molecule of glucose and one of fructose, leaving them joined by an oxygen atom. In digestion it is hydrolyzed to the original hexoses, which are then absorbed into the blood stream. Millions of tons of such pure sucrose are prepared from the juices of sugar cane and sugar beets that it is impossible to determine its source.

Glucose   Fructose

The twenty-four isomeric hexoses are all very similar in structure, differing from each other only in the relative arrangement of the parts.

For this reason the structural formulas must be drawn in such a way as to suggest three dimensions. The above formula for glucose will be used as an example. The polygon represents a plane structure with a carbon atom at each corner except one, where there is an oxygen atom. The polygon is to be imagined as being horizontal; each solid line represents a valence bond projecting *upward* and outward from it, and each dotted line represent a valence bond projecting *downward* and outward. If the positions of the two ligands on any carbon atom in the ring, except the one to the right of the oxygen, are reversed, so that the bond which was pointing up is pointing down, and vice versa, a different sugar is formed. If the ring oxygen starts from the No. 1 carbon atom of the chain, as in glucose, there are 16 possible arrangements for the next four carbon atoms. If it starts from the No. 2 carbon atom, as in fructose, there are 8 possible arrangements for the next three carbon atoms. This accounts for the 24 known isomers, half of which are mirror images of the other half.

The hexoses have still further structural complications. Any hexose can be made to move back and forth between a six-member ring and a five-member ring, the ring oxygen remaining attached to the No. 1 or No. 2 carbon atom, but its other point of attachment shifting. Alternatively, when the oxygen breaks loose from the far end of the chain it may form a double bond with the first or second carbon atom; this results in a straight chain aldehyde, $CH_2OH \cdot CHOH \cdot CHOH \cdot CHOH \cdot CHOH \cdot CHO$, or a ketone, $CH_2OH \cdot CHOH \cdot CHOH \cdot CHOH \cdot CO \cdot CH_2OH$. When the ring is formed again the arrangement on the No. 1 or No. 2 carbon may be the same as it was before, but it may equally well be the reverse. All the changes described in this paragraph are considered to result simply in *forms* of the same hexose because of the ready interconvertibility of the forms. By proper variation of conditions or reagents, a given hexose can be separated in any one of its forms, but it exists in solution as an equilibrium mixture of all of them.

In a solution of a hexose, one or more of all the following active groupings are present: ether ($-O-$), primary alcohol ($-CH_2OH$), secondary alcohol ($-CHOH-$), and aldehyde ($-CHO-$) or ketone ($-CO-$). The laboratory researches and the logical deductions from them which elucidated all the hexose relationships and the relationship of each hexose to the others, constitute one of the most beautiful examples on record of man's applying his intelligence to "seeing" the invisible. Determining the structure of a natural product is one of the two typical problems of organic chemistry. Once the structure is known, solution of the other problem—how to synthesize the substance—becomes possible. Synthesis is now a cheaper and more reliable source of innumerable important materials than nature is.

QUESTIONS AND PROBLEMS

1. What characteristics of carbon permit the multiplicity of compounds it forms?
2. Account for the relatively low chemical reactivity of the hydrocarbons.
3. Which is more stable and more reactive, benzene or cyclohexane? How do you account for this?
4. Using line bond formulas, show all the possible isomeric hexanes, C_6H_{14}. What physical properties of these do you expect will vary?
5. How many monochlorobutane isomers, C_4H_9Cl, can you draw?
6. Draw the line bond formulas for a pentane, a pentene, a pentadiene, a pentyne.
7. Which of the compounds in question 6 are saturated? Which unsaturated? Give reasons for your answer.
8. In what way do the physical and chemical properties of a hydrocarbon change when oxygen is substituted for hydrogen in the molecule? What differences in the C—O bond compared to the C—H bond are responsible for this? Name other substituents comparable to oxygen that can cause such changes.

9. Explain the greater acidity of $Cl-\overset{\overset{\displaystyle H}{|}}{\underset{\underset{\displaystyle H}{|}}{C}}-\overset{\displaystyle O}{C}-OH$ compared to ordinary acetic acid on the basis of the inductive effect. How should $F_3C \cdot COOH$ compare with $Cl_3C \cdot COOH$ in strength?

10. Compare CO and CO_2 with respect to electronic structure, activity, properties, and uses.
11. What is the characteristic molecular structural unit of an alcohol? Write the structural formula of ethanol and describe two ways by which it is produced.
12. Show by means of equations how the ester forms when methanol reacts with acetic acid. What is the product? Which of the two molecules supplies the hydrogen and which the hydroxyl group for the water that forms?
13. Is an ester a salt? Defend your answer. Name some common esters and state their uses.
14. How many bonds are there between adjacent pairs of carbon atoms in benzene? Compare the hydrogens on benzene with those on saturated hydrocarbon chains or rings as far as activity is concerned.
15. Extend the reasoning used in question 14 to support the fact that phenols are more like acids than they are like alcohols.
16. Draw the structural formula of 1,2,3-trihydroxybenzene.
17. Give the names and structural formulas of the aldehydes, acids, and ethers derived from methanol, ethanol, propanol, glycol.

18. Compare the methyl amines to ammonia and ammonium ion.
19. What is unique about the chemical nature of simple amino acids? What is the important biochemical relationship of amino compounds to living organisms?
20. What is the basic characteristic of composition that distinguishes carbohydrates from other oxygen derivatives of the hydrocarbons?
21. Name some general classes of compounds that are carbohydrates.
22. How are sucrose and glucose related?
23. What active groups may be present in any one hexose?

24

Giant molecules

24.1. Non-Metals with a Coordination Number of 4

Carbon and the elements adjacent to it—boron, silicon, and nitrogen—have in common the ability to form four strong covalent bonds, tetrahedrally arranged. In all the saturated carbon compounds described in the preceding chapter, i.e., those in which there are no multiple bonds between neighboring carbon atoms, the molecules showed tetrahedral bonding. The same is true of nitrogen, when there are no multiple bonds. Probably because its kernel charge is only $+3$, boron, the first element in Group III, *can* form stable molecules in which it is only 3-coordinated.

$$\ddot{\underset{..}{F}}: \\ B:\ddot{\underset{..}{F}}: \\ :\ddot{\underset{..}{F}}:$$

is such a molecule. Since it has one empty orbital, the molecule is planar instead of being pyramidal like

$$:\overset{H}{\underset{..}{N}}:H,$$

or tetrahedral like

$$H:\overset{H}{\underset{..}{N}}:H^{+}.$$

But BF_3 and all other compounds of boron in which the element has a covalence of 3 are

Lewis acids of considerable strength. They readily accept a share in the electron pair offered by any base.

$$
\begin{array}{ccc}
& & \overset{\displaystyle ..}{:\!\overset{..}{F}\!:} \\[-2pt]
\overset{\displaystyle ..}{\underset{..}{\,\,:\!F\!:}} & & \overset{..}{:\!F\!:} \;\; \overset{..}{:\!F\!:} \\
B:\!\overset{..}{\underset{..}{F}}\!:^{-} + \;:\!\overset{..}{\underset{..}{F}}\!: \;\; \rightarrow \; :\!\overset{..}{\underset{..}{F}}\!:\!B:\!\overset{..}{\underset{..}{F}}\!:^{-} \\[-2pt]
\overset{\displaystyle ..}{\underset{..}{\,\,:\!F\!:}} & & \overset{..}{:\!F\!:} \\[-2pt]
& & \underset{..}{:\!F\!:}
\end{array}
$$

The resultant fluoborate ion, BF_4^-, is tetrahedral, as is any other boron molecule to which a fourth ligand is attached. Like carbon and nitrogen, boron can also display a coordination number of 3 by forming a double bond. Silicon is invariably tetrahedral; its kernel charge of $+4$ demands four electron pairs.

24.2. Coordination Number and Size of Molecule

Atoms which have a covalence of 1, like hydrogen and the halogens, can form only diatomic molecules. A covalence of 2 makes chains possible, as in the case of plastic sulfur. An atom with a higher covalence, all but two of whose valences have been satisfied with 1-covalent chain stoppers, may also form chains. The most notable example of this is the —CH_2— group studied in the preceding chapter. Three covalences distributed symmetrically in a plane make possible the formation of a sheet molecule of indefinite extent. The most familiar example of this is graphite, described in the next section. When four covalences are available, identical atoms can form a three-dimensional network in which every atom is held to each of its neighbors by covalent bonds so that an entire crystal constitutes a single giant molecule. Diamond (Section 24.4) is the most perfect example.

24.3. Graphite

Graphite is one of the two crystalline forms of carbon. Its density is 2.22. Its intense black color is familiar in very soft pencils, the "lead" of which is almost pure graphite. (In ancient times graphite was thought to be merely a softer, blacker form of lead; hence the name black lead, still used occasionally.) Its softness is not the softness of a plastic substance like butter; instead, graphite shears into thin flakes very readily. These flakes resist direct pressure but can be further sheared indefinitely. This combination of properties makes graphite an excellent lubricant that is used either dispersed in oil or water, or as a dry powder which can be blown into locks, etc. It has a considerable metallic luster and is a good conductor of electricity.

Graphite is mined in Mexico, Siberia, Austria, and Ceylon. Our own deposits are of minor importance. Synthetic graphite is made by volatilizing carbon in electric furnaces at about 4000° C. On condensing, the carbon crystallizes as graphite. Graphite electrodes, crucibles, and other such articles are indispensable in many electrical processes. Graphite is not attacked by dilute acids or by fused NaOH or fused Na_2SO_4—the latter dissolves amorphous carbon—but it reduces fused Na_2CO_3. It does not burn in chlorine, and it ignites in air at about 700° C. When protected from oxidation by a layer of silicon carbide 0.025 to 0.25 mm. thick (Section 24.11), graphite can be used hundreds of hours at 1500° C. or exposed indefinitely to boiling aqua regia.

The carbon atoms in a graphite crystal have been accurately located by x-ray methods. They are arranged in regular hexagons in flat parallel sheets. Each atom is bonded to each of its three neighbors in its plane by covalent bonds at an angle of 120°. The distance between planes is shown to scale in Fig. 24.1; it is much too large for any bond to form between atoms in different planes. Each sheet is thus a single molecule of giant size. Being perfectly flat and smooth, these sheet molecules slide over each other very easily; however, there is no tendency for them to break up

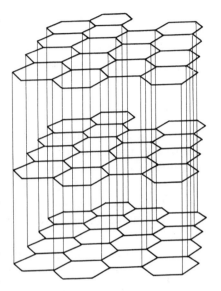

Fig. 24.1. Model of the graphite crystal showing its characteristic layer structure and the relatively greater distance between atoms in neighboring layers compared to the shorter distances between atoms in a given layer.

and be ground to pieces, because they are held together by actual chemical bonds.

The great distance between the sheet molecules is readily explained in terms of electronic structure. Every atom in one of these sheet molecules has a p orbital which lies outside the chemical bonds. The axis of this orbital is perpendicular to the plane of the sheet. The vertical lines in Fig. 24.1 represent half of these axes; the rest were omitted so that the diagram would not be too complicated. Each of these p orbitals overlaps those of its three neighbors above the plane and below the plane, forming an intercommunicating system that extends throughout the sheet. One electron from each atom is used in forming the three bonds that lie in the plane; the fourth enters the conjugated system above and below the plane. Each atom thus contributes one-third of an electron toward forming an additional bond with each of its three neighbors; hence the bond order in graphite is $1\frac{1}{3}$.

Thus both surfaces of each sheet molecule are covered with a cloud of electrons. The cloud above the lower sheet and the cloud below the upper sheet occupy the space between any two sheet molecules. This explains not only the distance between the sheet molecules and the readiness with which one slides over another, but also the electrical conductivity, which takes place entirely through the intercommunicating conjugated system of p orbitals.

24.4. Diamond

The other crystalline form of carbon is diamond. Its density is 3.51, over half as much greater than that of graphite. It is much harder than any other naturally occurring substance. The step between 9 (corundum) and 10 (diamond) on the Mohs scale, the mineralogical hardness scale, is actually greater than the sum of the steps from 1 (talc) to 9. Diamond has a much higher index of refraction than any other hard gem stone; it also excels these stones in dispersion. The high refractive index is responsible for the brilliance of a cut diamond; the high dispersion produces the notable display of colors. Diamond is a good conductor of heat, but does not conduct electricity. The name diamond comes from the Greek *adamas;* intermediate forms of the word are *adamant* and *diamaunt.*

Each atom in a diamond crystal is surrounded tetrahedrally by four other atoms. All the distances are identical—somewhat greater than the distance between adjacent atoms in a sheet of graphite, but far less than the distance between sheet molecules of graphite. This accounts for the greater density of diamond. The distance between each pair of atoms is the same as that between the carbon atoms in a molecule of C_2H_6 or any other *saturated* hydrocarbon. This, together with the fact that the neighbors of any carbon atom are arranged around it in the same way as the hydrogen atoms are in a molecule of CH_4, or the chlorine atoms in a molecule of CCl_4, indicates that the entire diamond crystal is held together by regular covalent bonds. Each carbon atom uses the four valence shell orbitals which featured so prominently in the preceding chapter. Thus diamond is a three-dimensional giant molecule, held together by single covalent bonds; these two facts account for its hardness. It does not conduct electricity because there is no intercommunicating conjugated bond system like those in graphite.

The diamonds that were known in ancient times were found in alluvial deposits in India and Borneo. Diamonds were discovered during placer gold mining activities in Brazil in 1670. The large fields discovered there in 1727 supplied most of the world supply of diamonds for the next century and a half. The original source of these alluvial diamonds has never been found. The great diamond mines near Kimberley, in South Africa, were discovered in 1867. These diamonds were found *in situ,* in cylindrical "pipes" of soft volcanic rock a few hundred feet in diameter which extend downward indefinitely. Some diamonds were mined from a similar formation in Arkansas, but there were too few to make mining them profitable.

Although the unit of weight for gem diamonds is the carat, equivalent to 200 mg., the total annual output of the African diamond mines is measured in tons. Most of it is useless as gems, but is of the highest value for industrial uses. Dark-colored opaque diamonds, known as boart and carbonado, are used in core drilling to check the extent and quality of mineral deposits; in lathe tools to true up abrasive wheels and to cut soft, tough metals which tend to tear under ordinary cutting tools; and in dies for drawing very fine wire, such as that used for filaments in tungsten lamps. These diamonds, of poor crystalline quality, are actually better for industrial purposes than gem stones because they are tough, whereas gem stones are rather brittle.

Heating a diamond to 1800° to 2000° C. in the absence of oxygen transforms it into graphite. When liquid or gaseous carbon crystallizes, it does so in the form of graphite unless the pressure is extremely high. Since carbon has a high boiling point, 4200° C., exceeded by only a few substances, it is extremely difficult to exert the necessary pressure of thousands of atmospheres upon liquid carbon. Hence attempts to synthesize diamonds were long unsuccessful. Several workers produced minute hard crystals they thought were diamonds, but more modern tests have shown that they were not. The actual synthesis of diamonds was finally accomplished by scientists of the General Electric Company in 1957. These diamonds are produced an ounce at a time and range up to coarse sand in size; they can be used for all industrial purposes that require diamonds of these sizes.

24.5. Linear Organic Giant Molecules

The two- and three-dimensional giant molecules formed by carbon were discussed before the linear molecules because the latter are much more complicated. In spite of the fact that a chain is a simpler geometric idea than a sheet or a three-dimensional network, linear giant molecules are less simple than the other type for three reasons. (1) Graphite and diamond are merely allotropic modifications of the element carbon. But any molecule consisting of a chain of carbon atoms must be a compound, with one or two chain stoppers—which cannot be carbon atoms—for each carbon atom in the chain; moreover, many different atoms or groups may serve as chain stoppers in the same molecule. (2) An —O— or —NH— group may replace a carbon atom at intervals along the chain. (3) A double or even a triple bond may be formed between pairs of carbon atoms every so often. Thus while there is only one graphite and only one diamond, there is no limit to the number of chain-type giant molecules. Furthermore, many of these chains can be cross-linked to any desired extent and thereby built into three-dimensional networks.

Many giant chain molecules, such as the hydrocarbons, rubber, gutta-percha, and chicle, exist in nature. In these the chains are linked through carbon-carbon bonds. Starch and cellulose chains consist of glucose rings linked together by oxygen atoms as glucose and fructose are linked in sucrose. The carbon atoms have —OH and other chain stoppers as well as —H. Proteins, including silk, have several kinds of chain stoppers, and there are —NH— connecting links at various intervals. Because of the complexity of many natural substances, the principles governing the formation and behavior of carbon chain molecules are best described in connection with synthetic materials.

24.6. Methods of Forming Long Chains

There are two general methods for linking small molecules together into a long chain— **polymerization** and **condensation.** Polymerization depends upon the existence of a double bond in the small unit, the *monomer.* Under proper conditions the double bond—we shall use ethylene, C_2H_4, as an example—will "open," one electron going to each

carbon atom: $\cdot \overset{\overset{\displaystyle H}{\cdot\cdot}}{\underset{\underset{\displaystyle H}{\cdot\cdot}}{C}} : \overset{\overset{\displaystyle H}{\cdot\cdot}}{\underset{\underset{\displaystyle H}{\cdot\cdot}}{C}} \cdot$. Each molecule forms an ordinary single bond

with its neighbor on either side; the resulting *polymer* has the same empirical formula, but its molecular weight is in the thousands. In our example, this polymer is called polyethylene.

Condensation, the second method for the formation of long molecules, involves the removal of two chain stoppers, one from each of two molecules; these are combined, forming a small molecule which escapes, and the two unstopped chains combine, doubling the length of the chain. This process can be repeated indefinitely. Not all chain stoppers are active enough to take part in condensation; —H usually is not, unless it is on a more electronegative atom such as N or O, or at least within the range of influence of such an atom. Nylon is made by condensing hexamethylene diamine with adipic acid. The reactive chain stopper on the first molecule is —H, that on the second is HO—; hence water is eliminated.

$$NH_2 \cdot CH_2 \cdot CH_2 \cdot CH_2 \cdot CH_2 \cdot CH_2 \cdot CH_2 \cdot N- \overset{H}{\underset{|}{}} \boxed{H + HO} -\overset{O}{\underset{\|}{C}} \cdot CH_2 \cdot CH_2 \cdot CH_2 \cdot CH_2 \cdot COOH \rightarrow$$

Hexamethylene diamine   **Adipic acid**

$$H_2O + NH_2(CH_2)_6NH \cdot CO(CH_2)_4COOH$$

Nylon monomer

But this product still has one of the active groups at one end of the molecule and the other active group at the other end; therefore any amount of further condensation can take place. The —CO·NH— linkage is called the **amide** (or **peptide**) **linkage.** The above product is called nylon monomer in accordance with trade custom. Actually, the nylon produced by further condensation is not a polymer of this substance, because more water is eliminated in each condensation.

24.7. Thermoplastic Materials

In the modern use of the term, a plastic is a substance that is *not* plastic to start with, but one that can be *made* plastic by heating and which, after cooling, will hold any shape into which it was forced while hot. By implication at least, a plastic is a relatively new, synthetic material; thus glass and the natural resins (rosin, shellac, damar, etc.) are not usually called plastics, although they fit the above definition. If the material can be softened by heating any number of times it is a thermoplastic. Thermoplastics are characterized by linear giant molecules. Carbon chains are very flexible because they can rotate freely around each single bond; hence the softening point of most thermoplastics is rather low. Ordinary polyethylene, for example, becomes soft below 100° C.

There are four chain stoppers in a molecule of ethylene, all of them H—. Substituting other chain stoppers for one or more of these hydrogens produces other thermoplastics which differ in physical and chemical properties both from polyethylene and from each other. Copolymers are formed by using various proportions of two different monomers. The possible variations are almost unlimited; a few of them are listed in Table 24.1.

TABLE 24.1. **Ethylene Derivatives Used in Thermoplastics**

Formula	Name	Name of Thermoplastic
$CH_2{=}CH_2$ (H, H / C=C / H, H)	Ethylene	Polyethylene
$CH_2{=}CH{-}O{-}C({=}O){-}CH_3$ (vinyl acetate structure)	Vinyl acetate	Polyvinyl acetate
		Copolymer = Vinylite
$CH_2{=}CHCl$ (H, H / C=C / H, Cl)	Vinyl chloride	Polyvinyl chloride
		Copolymer = Saran
$CH_2{=}CCl_2$ (H, Cl / C=C / H, Cl)	Vinylidene chloride	
$CF_2{=}CFCl$ (F, F / C=C / F, Cl)	Chlorotrifluoroethylene	Kel-F
$CF_2{=}CF_2$ (F, F / C=C / F, F)	Tetrafluoroethylene	Teflon
$CH_2{=}CH{-}C{\equiv}N$ (H, H / C=C / H, C≡N)	Acrylonitrile	Dynel; orlon
		Copolymer = Tyril
$CH_2{=}CH{-}C_6H_5$ (H, H / C=C / H, phenyl)	Styrene	Polystyrene; also part of copolymer in rubber
$CH_2{=}C(CH_3){-}C({=}O){-}O{-}CH_3$ (H, CH₃ / C=C / H, C(=O)—O—CH₃)	Methyl methacrylate	Lucite; Plexiglas
$CH_2{=}CH{-}CH_3$ (H, H / C=C / H, CH₃)	Propylene	Polypropylene; Pro-fax

Other long-chain thermoplastics are made by condensation. The formation of nylon was discussed in Section 24.6. In making Dacron, methanol, CH_3OH, is eliminated instead of water.

$$CH_3 \cdot O{-}\underset{\underset{O}{\parallel}}{C}{-}\langle\bigcirc\rangle{-}\underset{\overset{O}{\parallel}}{C}{-}O \cdot CH_3 \quad + \quad \underset{\overset{|}{H}}{O} \cdot CH_2 \cdot CH_2 \cdot \underset{\overset{|}{H}}{O} \rightarrow$$

Dimethyl terephthallate　　　　　**Ethylene glycol**

$$CH_3 \cdot O{-}\underset{\underset{O}{\parallel}}{C}{-}\langle\bigcirc\rangle{-}\underset{\overset{O}{\parallel}}{C}{-}\underset{\overset{|}{O}}{O}{-}CH_2 \cdot CH_2 \cdot \underset{\overset{|}{H}}{O} \quad + \quad CH_3OH$$

Dacron monomer

Like nylon monomer, Dacron monomer is reactive at both ends, and condensation can proceed indefinitely. The —CO·O— linkage is called the **ester linkage.** Nylon is a polyamide, Dacron a polyester. Other linkages used in chains include ureide, —NH·CO·NH—; methylene,

—CH₂—; ether, —O—; and polysulfide, $-S-\underset{\underset{S}{|}}{\overset{\overset{S}{|}}{S}}-$.

24.8.　Textile Fibers and Films

The molecules in a thermoplastic do not lie parallel, as in a crystal; they are not even straight. The tangled mass may be very strong in pieces of any considerable size; nylon, for example, makes excellent gears. But when hot liquid thermoplastic is squirted out of a spinneret to form a filament, its strength is disappointing. The filament is weak because only the portions of the molecules which run lengthwise of it can contribute to its tensile strength. This condition is remedied by forcing the liquid through a hole whose diameter is twice that of the desired filament, and winding the filament on a reel which is turning four times as fast as the liquid is being extruded. Drawing out the filament in this way, while it is still warm enough to be plastic, aligns the molecules so that they are parallel to the axis of the filament. The increase in strength that results is phenomenal. If the melted thermoplastic is extruded from a slit, a film is produced. Drawing this while still plastic strengthens it in the direction it is drawn but weakens it in the direction at right angles to that. Sheet glass is produced by a similar drawing process but contains too many three-dimensional molecules (Section 24.21) to acquire as effective an orientation.

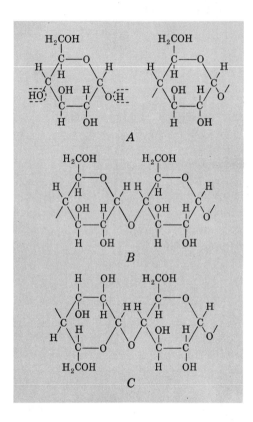

Fig. 24.2. The glucose molecule, $C_6H_{12}O_6$, and the $C_6H_{10}O_5$ unit (**A**) resulting from the condensation of glucose by the elimination of water as indicated by the dashed lines. The manner of linkage of the $C_6H_{10}O_5$ repeating units is shown in the starch molecule (**B**), and in the cellulose molecule (**C**).

All natural fibers are also characterized by giant chain molecules; in fact, they furnished the model upon which the artificial fibers were constructed. The animal fibers—spider webs, silk, and wool—are proteins. They consist of many different kinds of amino acid units that are connected by amide linkages. Other proteins that do not occur in natural fibers can be made into fibers by proper treatment. Thus fibers are manufactured commercially from casein (from milk) and from zein (from corn germ). A "silk" purse was once actually made from a sow's ear as a stunt.

The vegetable fibers—cotton, linen, ramie, hemp, etc.—are all composed of cellulose. Unlike the proteins, the units of cellulose are all the same $-C_6H_{10}O_5-$, the chains forming from glucose, $C_6H_{12}O_6$, by condensation, with the elimination of water. The repeating units in Fig. 24.2 are derived from glucose by the loss of an HO— group from one corner of the molecule and a proton from the —OH on the opposite corner. The repeating unit in starch is nearly the same as that in cellu-

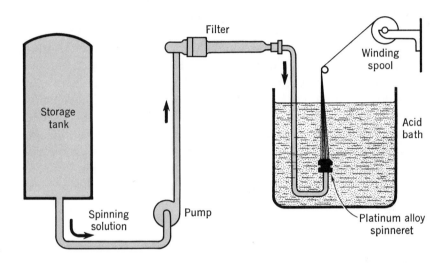

Fig. 24.3. Spinning process used in making viscose rayon.

lose, but the starch molecules are smaller, and 80 per cent of them are considerably branched because of condensation at the side chain, —OH.

Cellulose decomposes before reaching its melting point, so it is not thermoplastic in its natural state. However, each unit contains three reactive —OH groups which can be partially or completely converted into various esters, such as nitrate, acetate, and xanthate (dithiocarbonate, $-OCS_2^-$). These compounds can be "dissolved"—i.e., dispersed into syrupy colloidal liquids—by various processes and spun into filaments. The liquid from the spinneret is solidified by evaporation of the solvent (acetone in the case of cellulose acetate) or by a chemical bath which regenerates the insoluble cellulose (Fig. 24.3). Cellulose itself can be "dissolved" in solutions of certain metal salts. Vulcanized fiber is made by heating cellulose in concentrated zinc chloride, pressing the mixture into the desired shape, and removing the salt by washing. The dried product is so hard that it can be sawed like wood; it is used in making paper baskets, trunks, and even gears and washers.

The term rayon applies to regenerated cellulose fibers. Chardonnet, who invented rayon, made it first from cellulose nitrate which was denitrated after it was spun; he then made it from a dispersion in $Cu(NH_3)_4{}^{++}$ solution, which was spun into an acid bath that destroyed the copper complex ion. Nearly all rayon is now spun from viscose, a dispersion of cellulose xanthate in NaOH solution. Viscose is also the basis of cellophane. Cellulose acetate fiber is known by such trade names as Celanese but is frequently called simply acetate. Cellulose nitrate, or guncotton, is highly explosive. When plasticized with nitroglycerin it forms "gelatin" dynamite; when plasticized with ordinary solvents it is extruded through dies and cut into sticks or granules to form smokeless powder. Pyroxylin is a cellulose product that is only about 70 per cent nitrated; it is highly flammable but, unlike guncotton, is not sensitive to shock. It is used in some lacquers, including liquid nail polishes, and in collodion. Celluloid, the first synthetic plastic to be made, is prepared by plasticizing pyroxylin with camphor. It was formerly used as the base for photographic film, but has been replaced by cellulose acetate, which does not burn so readily.

24.9. Elastomers

Flexible chain molecules are naturally kinky. This is a matter of the law of probability. There is only one direction each bond can point in if the chain is to be fully extended; but there are an infinite number of other directions for a bond to point in, and all are more or less probable. When a textile fiber is being spun, the molecules are drawn out straight and parallel, and the fiber hardens while they are in that position. If a bit of the fiber is reheated just to the softening point it will shorten and thicken as the molecules kink up again; if the ends are held, a force will tend to pull them together. At a somewhat higher temperature, however, there is no such force; the molecules simply flow past each other and kink up. The ability to be stretched to several times the normal length and snap back when tension is released is an extremely valuable property. The temperature range in which it is shown differs for different molecules, but is never sufficiently wide. Raw natural rubber, for example, was satisfactory as a waterproof coating for raincoats in England, but in the United States it cracked in winter and melted in summer. Attempting to remedy this defect by mixing rubber with everything he could think of, Charles Goodyear in 1839 accidentally dropped onto a hot stove a piece which he had mixed with sulfur, and thereby discovered the process of **vulcanization.** (An independent investigator in England gave the process this name because in those days sulfur came from volcanoes.)

Eventually researchers discovered that rubber is a long-chain hydrocarbon and that vulcanization fastens the molecules together here and there, at odd intervals, by means of —S— links. These cross links are few enough to permit the molecules to be straightened a great deal by stretching, but prevent them from rekinking by flowing past each other. The desirable properties evident at room temperature remain at far higher and lower temperatures. When all these facts were understood, it became possible to impart rubberlike properties to a great array of linear high polymers that differ widely in chemical composition. The word **elastomer** has been coined as a name for materials of this type.

In order to be a good elastomer, a thermoplastic must be a viscous liquid at room temperature. Very smooth molecules, like those in polyethylene, fit together so tightly that they cannot flow at moderate temperatures. Very rough molecules, like those in cellulose, cannot flow past each other. A moderate number of "bumps" on a molecule keeps the chains from fitting too tightly together and hence permits flow. The same effect is produced by dispersing moderately large molecules of a plasticizer, such as dioctyl phthalate, $CH_3 \cdot (CH_2)_7 \cdot O \cdot CO \cdot C_6H_4 \cdot CO \cdot O \cdot (CH_2)_7 \cdot CH_3$, among smooth chains.

Most of the elastomers in use today may be regarded as derivatives of butadiene, $CH_2{=}CH \cdot CH{=}CH_2$. The intercommunicating conjugated double-bond system contains two electron pairs. When polymerization takes place, one electron goes to each end of the molecule and the other two go to the middle, where they form a double bond, thus: $-CH_2 \cdot CH{=}CH \cdot CH_2-$. These units add on indefinitely. The double bond which remains is the point of attack for the vulcanizing agent. The butadiene derivatives most commonly used in elastomers are shown in Table 24.2. Butadiene alone was tried by the Germans when their supply of natural rubber was shut off in World War I, but it was too smooth to make a good rubber. Instead, they made some 4 million tons of methyl rubber; although its properties were mediocre, it sufficed.

Two ideas made possible the immensely superior elastomers available today. One involved giving the long chains the optimum degree of roughness by copolymerizing butadiene with exactly the right amount of an

TABLE 24.2. **Some Butadiene Derivatives**

Formula	Name	Copolymer	Product
$CH_2{=}CH$ | $CH_2{=}CH$	Butadiene	Styrene Acrylonitrile Isobutylene	GR-S Buna-N Butyl rubber
$CH_2{=}CH$ | $CH_2{=}C\cdot CH_3$	Isoprene	None	Natural rubber, Natsyn, etc.
$CH_2{=}CH$ | $CH_2{=}C\cdot Cl$	Chloroprene	None	Neoprene, Duprene
$CH_2{=}C\cdot CH_3$ | $CH_2{=}C\cdot CH_3$	2,3-Dimethyl- butadiene	Butadiene	Methyl rubber

ethylene derivative (Table 24.1). The other involved emulsifying the hydrocarbon in soapy water in which a catalyst was dissolved. (The Germans used metallic sodium as a contact catalyst; hence the name Buna, from *bu*tadiene and *na*trium.) This made it possible to hold constant the extent of polymerization throughout the material and to stop it at any point.

Synthetic rubber research, although not attractive from a financial point of view during the depression of the thirties, was pursued by rubber companies which had the vision to foresee the possibility of war with Japan. With the aid of information from Germany, these new types of elastomers had gone through most of the laboratory stage of development by the time World War II broke out. Under ordinary circumstances it might have taken ten years to move these materials from the laboratory to full-scale commercial production. It is little short of a miracle that our chemists and chemical engineers were able to do this before our stockpile of natural rubber was exhausted. Furthermore, the scale of production actually achieved was sufficient to provide for our war needs, which were more than double our prewar requirements. After the war, research continued at an accelerated pace and led to great improvement in the quality of the elastomers. Isoprene became available at a moderate price for the first time; and catalysts were discovered that produced polymers which were all cis-, like natural rubber, instead of being a random intermingling of cis- and trans-. By 1957

Fig. 24.4. Part of a GR-S molecule as it might appear if flattened out into a plane. Every angle represents a carbon atom. At every point where three lines join, one hydrogen atom lies in the plane. Wherever two lines join, one hydrogen atom lies above and a second one below the plane. **a,** A butadiene unit in the cis-configuration, i.e., both continuations of the chain on the **same** side of the double bond. In the trans- configuration shown in **b,** the chain continuations lead in **opposite** directions from the double bond. At **c** is a styrene unit, the **copolymer** interlaced with butadiene in a ratio of 1:3. In natural rubber there is a CH_3- group instead of a hydrogen at one end of each double bond, and the configuration is entirely cis-. The cis- and trans- configurations are not interconvertible, for there is no rotation about a double bond.

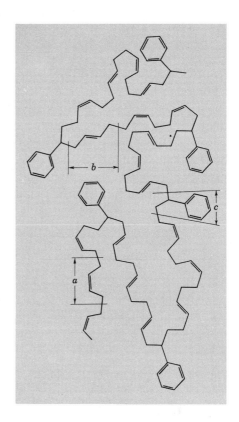

a true synthetic duplicate of natural rubber was being made.*

Rubber consumption in the United States expanded enormously after World War II. Instead of the 300,000 tons used before the war, our present consumption is more than double that amount, in addition to over 1 million tons of GR-S (Fig. 24.4). Our output of the various special types of rubber is not large in comparison with the above figures, but their special properties make these other types important. For example, neoprene and Buna-N are proof against oil and gasoline, and silicone rubber (Section 24.28) withstands high temperatures.

24.10. Thermosetting Resins

If enough sulfur is added to rubber and the mixture is heated, so many cross links will be formed between chains that the entire mass becomes

---

* The unit of isoprene which polymerizes by addition to identical units can be represented thus: $-CH_2-CH=C-CH_2-$. If all linkages between these units result in the $-CH_3$
$$\overset{\displaystyle |}{CH_3}$$
groups pointing in the same direction, the cis- polymer is formed. Should alternate $-CH_3$ groups in the resultant chain point in opposite directions, the trans- polymer is formed.

essentially a huge three-dimensional molecule. This material is called Ebonite, or hard rubber, and is used for bowling balls. In many long-chain polymers potentially reactive positions are scattered along the chain so that any desired degree of cross linking can be produced later. Thermosetting plastics are constructed in this way; after they have once been softened and forced into shape, they cannot be softened again. All plastics of this type have three-dimensional molecules and are plastic only while the molecules are of moderate size. The interlacing connec-

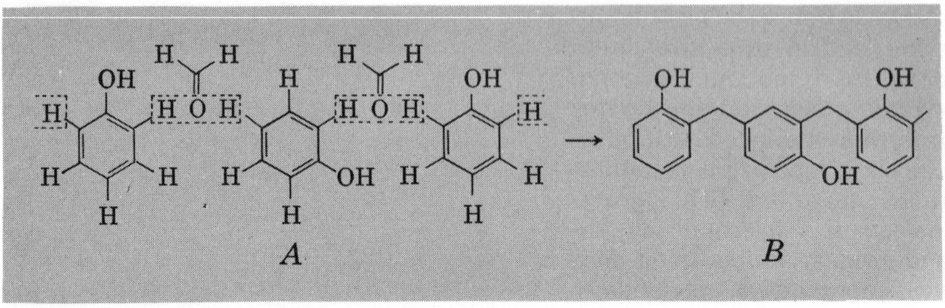

Fig. 24.5. Formation of Bakelite molding powder. **A,** The condensation reaction between formaldehyde, CH_2O, and phenol, C_6H_5OH, by the loss of water between them, results in the formation of the condensed molecule of molding powder shown in **B**. Hydrogens are implied in the latter product, as in Fig. 24.4.

tions grow rapidly in all directions at the molding temperature; hence by the time the object is removed from the mold it is to all intents and purposes a single molecule. Bakelite, which belongs to this class, is made by condensation, water being split off from between phenol and formaldehyde as the reaction proceeds (Fig. 24.5). The hydrogens from the phenol are those opposite or adjacent to the HO— group, forming a fusible chain resin. This material is powdered and mixed with more formaldehyde and a different catalyst. The powder is molded under a pressure of a ton or more per square inch at about 110° C. It melts, flows together, and then reacts further. This time a second hydrogen opposite or adjacent to the HO— group condenses with the O= of the formaldehyde; thus the tangled chains are linked together at every point of contact and the substance becomes a solid again, even while hot. Other thermosetting resins can be melted and injected into molds in which the final polymerization takes place. Injection molding resembles the die casting of metals.

There are other methods of establishing cross links in addition to those just described, most of them too complex chemically to be discussed here. We shall mention only the glyptal or alkyd resins, whose three-dimensional molecules result from continuous chain branching. This is achieved by the simple device of using glycerol, $CH_2OH \cdot CHOH \cdot CH_2OH$, instead of glycol, $CH_2OH \cdot CH_2OH$, in the formulation of a polyester resin.

24.11. Silicon and Silicon Carbide

Silicon is the second member of the carbon family. It would be expected to behave similarly to carbon and it actually does form crystals of the diamond type. But, although harder than glass, these crystals do not begin to approach diamond in hardness. This is the direct result of the greater radius of the silicon atom and its correspondingly lower electronegativity. Since its larger size precludes the formation of multiple bonds, silicon does not form the graphite type of crystal.

Silicon carbide, SiC, has the diamond type of crystal in which silicon and carbon atoms alternate. In hardness it is intermediate between silicon and diamond, i.e., very hard indeed. It is much harder than corundum, Al_2O_3; until very recently it was the hardest man-made substance. Curiously enough, instead of being the result of a logical prediction that a substance of that composition should have the desired properties, its discovery was completely accidental. In 1891, E. G. Acheson, a former assistant of Thomas A. Edison, was attempting to prepare corundum in an electric furnace. He noted that beautiful iridescent crystals formed when carbon vapor from the graphite electrodes reacted with silica, SiO_2, from the firebrick lining of the furnace. This was a case of true serendipity, for upon investigation Acheson found that he had made something better than what he was hoping to make. When analysis showed that the crystals contained carbon and were in fact silicon carbide, he coined the trade name Carborundum to suggest that its uses would be similar to those of corundum. It was this same Acheson, incidentally, who five years later invented the process by which synthetic graphite is made.

Carborundum is produced in furnaces 30 ft. long and 8 ft. square in cross section. Only the ends of the bed are permanent; the sides are built up as the charge is added. The charge consists of sand, SiO_2, coke, and sawdust, that are mixed with water and dextrin; the latter acts as a temporary binder. After the furnace is half filled with charge, a core of graphite blocks 6 in. on a side and 18 in. long is laid between the terminals. More charge is then added until the furnace is heaped high with it. When the current is turned on, arcs form at the contact points between the graphite blocks and the temperature increases rapidly. The sawdust burns out, leaving a porous mass. The reaction occurs at temperatures between 1620° and 2200° C.

$$\underline{SiO_2} + \underline{3C} \xrightarrow{\Delta} \underline{SiC} + \overline{2CO}$$

The CO burns at the top of the furnace. After the furnace has cooled, the SiC is dug out, crushed, washed, and graded. Material that has reacted incompletely is mixed with the next charge.

Silicon carbide is made into wheels and hones; applied to paper, it is used chiefly as an abrasive. It is, however, an excellent refractory material for furnaces, and is also used as a resistor in numerous electrical appliances.

24.12. Boron Nitride

Since the atomic number of boron is one unit less than that of carbon and two units less than that of nitrogen, the average number of electrons per atom in boron nitride, BN, is exactly the same as in diamond. Furthermore, both atoms are small, like carbon. These facts led to the expectation that when BN was synthesized it would show interesting resemblances to carbon. The first form of it that was produced proved to have the graphite structure. It is a refractory white solid that melts at 3000° C. under pressure. Like carbon, its vapor pressure reaches 1 atm. below its melting point. The lack of color, and particularly of metallic luster, indicates that the electrons in the conjugated system of p orbitals are not evenly distributed and mobile as in graphite; this is substantiated by the fact that BN is only a semiconductor of electricity. The p electrons are doubtless held much more closely to the nitrogen atoms, which are a whole unit above the boron atoms in electronegativity.

Many years passed before BN having the diamond type of crystal was made. This was done in 1957 by the General Electric group in the same apparatus they had used when they synthesized diamonds. The new cubic crystals were practically as hard as diamond; in fact, one of them scratched a diamond, just as one diamond can scratch another. Crushed crystals of BN can be used to cut and polish diamonds just as diamond dust is. This was a real triumph for logical deduction based on the electronic structure of substances.

24.13. Boron and Boron Carbide

Having only 3 valence electrons, boron must receive electrons from other elements if it is to form conventional valence octets. In the absence of sufficient or any electrons from such sources, boron has some peculiar characteristics. It is only quite recently that scientists have begun to understand some of its valence behavior. We saw in Section 24.1 that, when necessary, boron will develop a sextet of electrons in its valence shell instead of an octet. In this it behaves like Cu^+, Ag^+, and Be^{++}. Boron also forms bonds in which a single electron pair unites three atoms. In these cases the bond order is $\frac{1}{2}$, since normally two bonds would be needed to unite three atoms. There are even more complicated cases, with bond orders of $\frac{3}{4}$, etc. The theory that applies to bonds of order less than 1 is still very incomplete, and much too complex to present here. It is known, however, that this type of bonding is associated with coordination numbers that are higher than normal and with valence angles that are lower than normal. Molecules with this type of bonding tend to enclose space like a basket, bowl, or hollow ball.

In elemental boron the unit of structure is a group of twelve atoms arranged at the vertices of a regular icosahedron. In its own icosahedron each atom has five near neighbors with which it is linked. In addition, each boron forms a bond to a boron in another B_{12} group. Thus the complete crystal is another example of a three-dimensional giant molecule. The melting point of boron is 2300° C. and it is harder than Carborundum.

Boron carbide is even harder and more refractory than boron. It melts at 2450° C., and its hardness is estimated to be somewhat nearer to that of corundum than of diamond. In the carbide, the B_{12} groups characteristic of boron remain intact, but instead of neighboring B_{12} groups being linked together exclusively by boron—boron bonds as in the crystals of the element, 25 per cent of these linkages occur through carbon atom chains. The chain linkage consists of three carbon atoms, and in the boron carbide crystal there is one chain per B_{12} group. Thus the ratio of boron atoms to carbon atoms is B_4C, and hence this represents the empirical formula of the compound. The structure is more symmetrical and somewhat more compact than that of boron. The B_{12} groups alternate with C_3 groups in a sodium chloride type of arrangement.

B_4C is used for lapping tools and wire-drawing dies made of other hard carbides, and for cutting and polishing gems; it has replaced diamond dust in all these operations at one-hundredth the cost. When used in precision gauges (Fig. 24.6), B_4C may outlast other substances

Fig. 24.6. Various precision gauges with boron carbide tips and surfaces that enable them to resist wear and maintain accurate dimensions. (Courtesy, Norton Company.)

as much as a thousandfold. Other uses for which it offers similar advantages include linings for molds for grinding wheels, extrusion dies for coating welding rods, and nozzles for sandblasting (Fig. 24.7).

24.14. Quartz

The contrast between CO_2 and SiO_2 is startling when we consider only the fact that carbon and silicon are successive elements in the same family. As is well known, CO_2 is a gas; SiO_2, best known as quartz, melts above 1700° C. CO_2 is the actual molecular formula of carbon dioxide; SiO_2 is merely the empirical formula of silica, which is another example of a giant molecule. This difference is due to the same cause as the difference between O_2 and S_8 in molecular size, the reluctance of atoms of elements beyond the second period to form multiple bonds. As one silicon atom does not share two electron pairs with each of two oxygen atoms, it must share one pair with each of four oxygens. Each oxygen atom must then share electron pairs with two different silicons. One crystalline form of silica, cristobalite, has the structure of diamond except that an oxygen atom occurs at the mid-point of each bond. In the other two forms, tridymite and quartz, the silicon atoms also are tetrahedrally surrounded by oxygens; but tridymite has hexagonal symmetry, and in

quartz the tetrahedra are joined with a twist, producing right- and left-handed spirals.

Igneous rocks are about 12 per cent quartz. Most of it is in small crystals distributed through granite, but occasional veins of pure quartz are found. Only rarely does the quartz appear in well-formed transparent crystals. If colorless it is known as rock crystal. Violet quartz is amethyst; clear yellow quartz is called citrine or, improperly, topaz. The main source of large quartz crystals is Brazil. Slices cut from these have piezoelectric properties; that is, they become charged electrically in response to pressure. They are used to control the frequency in alternating-current generators. Unlike glass, SiO_2 is transparent to ultraviolet light; hence the prism for an ultraviolet spectrometer is cut from quartz. Because the industrial and scientific demand for quartz crystals exceeds the natural supply, they are now being produced synthetically. This cannot be done from a melt, the way synthetic rubies are made, because liquid silica is so viscous near its freezing point that it does not crystallize but remains an amorphous glass. Instead, a method is used which doubtless approximates that by which quartz crystals are formed in nature. SiO_2 is appreciably soluble in a superheated aqueous solution of Na_2CO_3, the more soluble the higher the temperature. If such a solution has broken quartz at the bottom and a seed crystal at the top where it is a little cooler, the seed will gradually grow. A month may be needed for a crystal of adequate size to grow.

Quartz has a hardness of 7 on the Mohs scale. No gem, however beautiful, can be considered a precious stone unless it is harder than that. A cut and polished amethyst or citrine is slowly dulled by the abrasive action of fine quartz particles—sand—in the dust on clothing, etc.; this is true even of semiprecious stones like tourmaline and zircon, which are slightly harder than quartz.

24.15. Amorphous Silica

Silica is a weakly acidic oxide. By melting it with Na_2CO_3 in various proportions, a water-soluble glass (water glass) is obtained. From solutions of the latter a number of sodium silicates can be prepared. The formation of the orthosilicate can be represented as follows:

$$SiO_2 + 2Na_2CO_3 \rightarrow Na_4SiO_4 + \overline{2CO_2}$$

SiO_4^{-4} ion is a very strong base, and can exist only in highly basic solutions or melts. If the solution is made slightly less alkaline, SiO_4^{-4} ions will pick up protons and condense into polysilicate ions by intermolecular loss of water, just as weak acids do. The first step in this process yields pyrosilicate ion, where two SiO_4 tetrahedra are linked by having one oxygen in common (Fig. 24.12).

$$2HSiO_4^{-3} \rightarrow Si_2O_7^{-6} + H_2O$$

Linking an indefinite number of tetrahedra in a chain gives the metasilicate ion, $(SiO_3)_n^{-2n}$, but these giant anions can expand in the second or third dimension just as well. When a soluble silicate is actually acidified, it soon sets to a gel. This gel is believed to be a tangled structure of endless polysilicic acid molecules.

$$
\begin{array}{ccc}
\text{H} & \text{H} & \text{H} \\
\ddot{\text{O}}\!: & :\ddot{\text{O}}: & :\ddot{\text{O}}: \\
:\ddot{\text{O}}:\text{Si}:\ddot{\text{O}}:\text{Si}:\ddot{\text{O}}:\text{Si} & & \text{etc.} \\
:\ddot{\text{O}}: & :\ddot{\text{O}}: & :\ddot{\text{O}}: \\
\text{H} & \text{H} & \text{H}
\end{array}
$$

Ions can move freely in the water which occupies the relatively large spaces between the fiberlike molecules of silicic acid. Diffusion removes the dissolved salts completely if the gel is crumbled and soaked in many changes of water. If the gel is dried, the acid itself is dehydrated to silica simultaneously with the evaporation of the free water. The material shrinks and becomes too hard for its shape to alter any further, long before the drying is completed. As a result, the particles, although glassy in appearance, actually have a submicroscopic spongelike structure which gives them an enormous surface area. Most of the silicon atoms in this surface have incomplete valence octets and are therefore surrounded by strong force fields which give the surface extraordinarily good sorbent powers. This dried material—called silica gel curiously enough, although it is no longer a gel—is an important commercial product that is used to remove moisture or vapors of volatile solvents from air. The sorbed material can be driven off by simple heating (and recovered if valuable), leaving the gel as good as new. A more porous or chalky type of gel can be made by using ferric chloride instead of hydrochloric acid. One of these chalky gels has been found to sorb benzene vapors to over 1.5 times its own weight. Airplane motors were kept free from rust on sea voyages during World War II by using silica gel to remove the water vapor from the air inside their sealed Pliofilm wrappers.

The silica glass mentioned in the preceding section is another important form of amorphous silica. Crystalline quartz expands with heat at different rates along different crystal axes, and shatters if heated suddenly. There is no order whatever in the arrangement of the molecules in a glass; they themselves are of many sizes. The substance is therefore *isotropic* in properties, i.e., the same in all directions. The coefficient of expansion of silica glass is so low that a test tube made of it can be plunged white-hot directly into water without breaking. Its softening point is far higher than that of ordinary glass; it is also much more resistant chemically, being attacked only by HF and alkali fusions. Silica glass made by the simple fusion of quartz is opaque because of the bubbles that are trapped in the viscous liquid. If transparency is desired, the molten quartz is placed in a high vacuum in which the bubbles expand until they rise to the surface and break. If the liquid is then cooled under pressure, any remaining gas is compressed to such a small volume that the glass is clear. Clear silica is used for the tubes of mercury arc lamps to permit the passage of the ultraviolet light, and in many other cases where transparency as well as resistance to heat and chemical attack is required.

The largest use of amorphous silica is in the form of kieselguhr, or diatomaceous earth, which consists of the skeletons of minute aquatic organisms called diatoms. The curious forms of these fragile particles prevent them from packing; a cubic foot of the powder weighs only 10 lb. and is mostly empty space. Nobel's invention of dynamite (which founded the fortune that supports the Nobel prizes) was based on the process of soaking nitroglycerin in kieselguhr. This made it less sensitive to shock and hence easier to handle. The purified material, under such trade names as Cellite, is mixed with suspensions which normally tend to clog filters. The filter cake thus formed is porous and filtration is speeded up. Careful treatment of diatomaceous earth with lime produces a calcium silicate powder with particles as small as 0.02 micron; it weighs only 6 lb. per cubic foot, and is the best heat-insulating material known today.

24.16. Packing of SiO_4^{-4} Tetrahedra

There is practically no difference in size between SiO_4^{-4}, PO_4^{-3}, SO_4^{--}, and ClO_4^- ions. This means that in each case the central atom with the positive oxidation number has drawn the four oxygen atoms toward it-

Fig. 24.8. An SiO_4^{-4} tetrahedron from above one vertex.

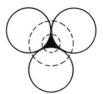

Fig. 24.9. An SiO_4^{-4} tetrahedron, looking directly at the base.

self until they are in contact with each other. This is substantiated by the fact that the distance between nuclei of adjacent oxygen atoms in a crystal of silicate is the same regardless of whether they are in the same SiO_4^{-4} ion or in different ones. In fact, the presence of metal cations nearly twice the size of Si^{+4} does not affect this distance. The cations simply fit into chinks between the close-packed oxygen atoms. Fig. 24.8 shows a SiO_4^{-4} ion viewed from directly above one vertex; the silicon atom is completely hidden by the top oxygen atom. In Fig. 24.9 the same group is inverted. The almost completely hidden oxygen atom beneath is indicated by the large broken circle; the shaded portion indicates the little part of the silicon atom (small broken circle) that can be seen through the opening between the three oxygen atoms.

Tetrahedra of oxygen atoms can be packed into a solid mass by having the layers alternate between being erect and inverted. Some erect SiO_4^{-4} ions are shown in Fig. 24.10; the broken circles represent the bottom layer of oxygen atoms, and a dot indicates the silicon atom in the center of the tetrahedra. Fig. 24.11 shows how the addition of an inverted SiO_4^{-4} ion fills both layers of oxygen atoms solidly. Al^{+3} ion is

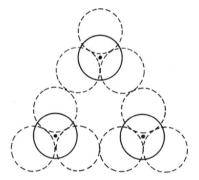

Fig. 24.10. Part of a sheet of SiO_4^{-4} ions, vertex up.

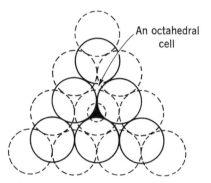

An octahedral cell

Fig. 24.11. Addition of an inverted SiO_4^{-4} ion fills vacancies in both layers of oxygens.

the only other third-period cation there is room for in a tetrahedral group of oxygens. There is, however, room for medium-sized cations in *octahedral* cells (Fig. 24.11, arrow), where the space between three oxygens on one layer falls above the space between three oxygens in the layer beneath. The bonds between Si^{+4} and its four surrounding oxygen atoms are strongly polar but still fundamentally covalent. This is not considered to be true of the ions with a lower charge in the larger octahedral cells.

Orthosilicate minerals are important constituents of many rocks. If all the cations are medium-sized divalent ones such as Mg^{++}, Fe^{++}, and Mn^{++}, the mineral is an olivine. Each SiO_4^{-4} ion must, of course, have two divalent cations, but they do not all need to be the same kind, nor is it common for them to be so. In the garnets half the positive charges are supplied by divalent cations like those just mentioned, and half by the somewhat smaller trivalent cations such as Al^{+3}, Cr^{+3}, and Fe^{+3}, in any combination. Electrical neutrality will also be achieved if there is one tetravalent cation for each anion. Zircon, $ZrSiO_4$, is such a mineral, but the Zr^{+4} ion is too large to fit into an octahedral cell. It changes the structure just described into a less symmetrical one in which the Zr^{+4} is 8-coordinated. Still another orthosilicate, cyanite, has the formula Al_2SiO_5. In it, each SiO_4^{-4} has one extra O^{--} arranged in the same close-packed structure shown in Fig. 24.11. In fact, a diagram of the silicons and oxygens in Al_2SiO_5 would look like Fig. 24.11, except that there would not be enough silicons to tie up all the oxygens.

24.17. Linking of SiO_4 Tetrahedra

Most silicate minerals have an excess rather than a deficiency of silicons. In this case some of the oxygens have to do double duty, i.e., be shared by two tetrahedra. The simplest example is the pyrosilicate ion, $Si_2O_7^{-6}$, shown in Fig. 24.12. It is found in thortveitite, $Sc_2Si_2O_7$. Just as this ion is formed by adding an SiO_3^{--} ion to one of the projecting oxygens of an SiO_4^{-4} ion, so a trisilicate can be formed by adding another SiO_3^{--} to one of the new oxygens, and so on indefinitely. The linear giant molecule thus formed is called the metasilicate ion. Its empirical formula is practically SiO_3^{--}. The metasilicate minerals are known as pyroxenes and are held together by cations between the parallel chains. The cations may be divalent (pure or mixed) or consist of equal numbers of monovalent and trivalent cations. Examples include $MgSiO_3$ (enstatite), $CaMg(SiO_3)_2$ (diopside), $NaAl(SiO_3)_2$ (jadeite), and $LiAl(SiO_3)_2$ (lepidolite).

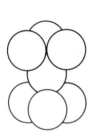

Fig. 24.12.
Pyrosilicate ion.

The amphiboles have a giant linear anion which may be thought of as composed of a pair of parallel metasilicate chains held together by shared oxygen atoms; this is shown diagrammatically in Fig. 24.13. The oxygen atoms in the upper layer (indicated by dots) form the vertices of SiO_4 tetrahedra; a silicon atom underlies each oxygen atom. One ring is formed for each $Si_4O_{11}^{-6}$ unit. The center of each ring is occupied by a completely independent molecule; it can be H_2O, O^{--}, OH^-, or F^-, all of these being practically the same size. When an OH^- ion occupies this spot, cations must furnish seven positive charges for each unit of the chain. A typical example is tremolite, $Ca_2Mg_5(Si_4O_{11})_2(OH)_2$. Another interesting mineral in the amphiboles is chrysotile, $(MgOH)_6Si_4O_{11} \cdot H_2O$. The H_2O molecule is in the ring, and the OH^- ions cover up the Mg^{++} ions so that each is in contact with only one silicate chain. These chains

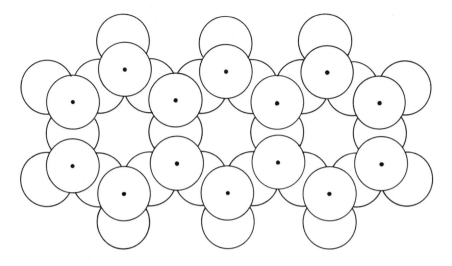

Fig. 24.13. Part of an $(Si_4O_{11})_n^{-6n}$ chain that occurs in amphiboles.

can therefore be readily separated into fibers so thin that they are flexible and hence can be woven into cloth. About 90 per cent of our asbestos is chrysotile; other amphiboles supply the rest.

24.18. Silicate Sheets

The system of hexagonal rings shown in Fig. 24.13 can be indefinitely extended sideways as well as lengthwise. This produces a giant sheet anion whose empirical formula is $Si_2O_5^{--}$. (Each ring consists of $\frac{1}{3}$ of each of six silicons, each with an unshared oxygen above or below it, and $\frac{1}{2}$ of each of the six shared oxygens; total, Si_2O_5.) As in the case of the amphiboles, each ring has a small independent molecule in its center, most commonly an OH^- ion. Silicate minerals constructed of these sheet anions can be flaked easily parallel to the sheets just as graphite can. Familiar examples include kaolin and talc. Kaolin is the major constituent of clay. The three shared oxygens of each $Si_2O_5^{--}$ group need only the addition of one more oxygen per ring (from the OH^- ion in the center) to form a solid sheet of oxygens. Since each $Si_2O_5^{--}$ group projects one unshared oxygen up into the next layer, that layer can be completed into a solid sheet by adding three more OH^- ions per ring. Between these two sheets there are four octahedral cells per ring. In kaolin, $Al_2Si_2O_5(OH)_4$, half of these cells are occupied by Al^{+3} ions. As was true for chrysotile, this unit has no charge. The ease with which these sheets can slide past each other gives clay and talc a greasy feeling. Talc is composed of neutral *double* sheets of $Si_2O_5OH^{-3}$, each pair held together by Mg^{++} ions. This is indicated by writing the formula $(Si_2O_5OH)Mg_3(Si_2O_5OH)$.

24.19. Aluminosilicates

In garnet, cyanite, jadeite, lepidolite, and kaolin—as well as in many other minerals not mentioned here—Al^{+3} ion occurs in an octahedral cell of oxygens. A cation in an octahedral cell is considered to be essentially a free ion. Occupying octahedral cells is typical metallic behavior, shown, for example, by all the divalent and trivalent ions of Sc, Ti, V, Cr, Mn, Fe, Co, and Ni, as well as by Li^+, Mg^{++}, and Al^{+3}. As long as the total number of such cations is sufficient to maintain electrical neutrality, they can replace each other at random without altering the essential structure of the mineral. This is known as the **principle of isomorphous replacement.** Most of the above ions are those of transition metals. Size is involved here. The ions of the heavier main-group elements in Groups I, II, and III are too large to occupy octahedral cells. They exhibit isomorphous replacement in larger cells—eight or twelve oxygens—in their own size groups. Be and B are small enough to occupy tetrahedral cells, in which they are covalently bonded.

As was mentioned in Section 24.16, Al^{+3} is at the same time the smallest ion found in octahedral cells and the largest that can fit into a tetrahedral cell without great distortion. It can therefore behave like both a metal ionically, and a non-metal covalently. This is in line with the well-known amphoteric behavior of $Al(OH)_3$. An aluminum atom that is in a tetrahedral cell of oxygen atoms bonds them together almost as strongly as a silicon atom does. It effectively takes the place of a silicon atom. Thus in all the giant molecules which have been described here in connection with silicon, aluminum can replace up to half the silicon. Since the atomic number of aluminum is one unit less than that of silicon, each such replacement makes the anion one unit more negative, and calls for one more cationic charge.

In many cases the extra cationic charges an aluminosilicate requires can result without any alteration in the original silicate structure. Sometimes this is done by replacing divalent by trivalent cations. For example, the replacement of one of the silicons in tremolite, $Ca_2Mg_5(Si_4O_{11}(OH))_2$, by aluminum can be compensated for by replacing one Mg^{++} by Al^{+3} or Fe^{+3}. The resulting product, $Ca_2Mg_4(Al,Fe)(AlSi_3O_{11}(OH))_2$, is hornblende, black grains of which are common in granite. The expression (Al,Fe) in the above formula means that either ion, or any mixture of them, may be present, but only in the proportion of one trivalent ion for each four Mg^{++} ions. Failure to realize that aluminum atoms in the formula for hornblende and many other aluminosilicates had two entirely different roles led to great confusion in the past. Until fairly recently, mineralogists completely neglected its non-metallic role. In the case of hornblende this meant that they formulated the anion as $Si_3O_{11}{}^{-10}$, and thus obscured the fact that its structure is the same as that of tremolite.

If one-fourth of the silicons in talc, $Mg_3Si_4O_{10}(OH)_2$, or the closely similar pyrophyllite, $Al_2Si_4O_{10}(OH)_2$, are replaced by aluminum, the previously neutral double sheet acquires one negative charge per $AlSi_3O_{10}$ unit. In the micas these charges are neutralized by a layer of alkali metal ions between each pair of double sheets. The attraction between the K^+ ions, for example, and the negatively charged double sheets keeps the latter from slipping over each other; hence mica is not a lubricant like talc. But the low charge and large size of the K^+ ions makes cleavage between the double sheets very easy, half the K^+ ions remaining with each sheet. When half the silicons are replaced by aluminum, the charge on the double sheets, which is twice as great as before, is neutralized by Ca^{++} ions between them; it becomes correspondingly more difficult for the sheets to separate from each other, and hence breakage is frequent. Micas of this type are known as brittle micas.

Sheet anions of the mica type can also be neutralized by alternate layers of $Mg_2Al(OH)_6{}^+$, resulting in the chlorites, or by an increase in the number of trivalent ions within the double sheets. Thus in vermiculite, Fe^{+3} as well as Mg^{++} and Fe^{++} ions are present in the double sheets; this is shown in the formula, $(Mg,Fe)_2Fe(AlSi_3O_{10})(OH)_2$, the last iron atom being trivalent. Curiously, these neutral double sheets are separated by sheets of water of crystallization (four H_2O per unit of the above formula). When a granule of vermiculite is heated, this water turns into steam and pushes the sheets apart. The grain expands, perhaps twentyfold, along the dimension perpendicular to the sheets; the resulting "little worm" gives the mineral its name. The laminae crinkle when they are forced apart, and remain separated even after the steam disappears. Expanded vermiculite is poured between walls to insulate houses; it is also used as packing in cases containing chemical reagents both to prevent breakage and to absorb corrosive liquids if breakage should nevertheless occur.

24.20. Three-Dimensional Aluminosilicate Anions

Silica itself, as we saw in Section 24.14, forms uncharged three-dimensional giant molecules. When some of the silicon atoms are replaced by aluminum, large positive ions of low charge must be introduced to restore electrical neutrality. Thus is formed an important series of rock-forming silicate minerals called feldspars.

If only one-quarter of the silicons are replaced, the cation will be Na^+ or K^+, as in orthoclase, $KAlSi_3O_8$, the most common of all the silicate minerals. Na^+ may replace up to half the K^+ without appreciably altering the crystalline structure. A series of $AlSi_3O_8^-$ feldspars, slightly lower in crystal symmetry than orthoclase, is called microcline when nearly pure $KAlSi_3O_8$; in anorthoclase up to 75 per cent Na^+ is substituted for K^+; in albite, between 90 and 100 per cent. Compositions between 75 and 90 per cent Na^+ do not exist.

If one-third of the silicon is replaced by aluminum, as in amphigene, $KAlSi_2O_6$, as many as 30 per cent of the K^+ ions may be replaced by half as many Ba^{++} ions. But if the number of aluminum and silicon atoms is equal, as in celsian, $BaAl_2Si_2O_8$, and anorthite, $CaAl_2Si_2O_8$, the ability of the structure to accommodate monovalent cations is low. Anorthite, however, has the same crystal symmetry as albite and forms solid solutions with it in all proportions. These solutions are known as plagioclase feldspars. Individual names—oligoclase, andesine, labradorite, bytownite—apply to solutions whose ranges of composition are arbitrarily set and are equal.

The anion structure of all these feldspars is fundamentally the structure of SiO_2 itself, although slightly deformed by the presence of the cations. In all of them the number of oxygens is twice the *sum* of the number of aluminums and silicons. Early attempts to interpret these minerals in terms of silicates led only to confusion. For example, $KAlSi_2O_6$ does *not* contain $(SiO_3^{--})_n$ chains, nor does $CaAl_2Si_2O_8$ contain discrete SiO_4^{-4} tetrahedra.

The feldspars have compact structures. Other aluminosilicates have three-dimensional giant anion structures with chambers large enough to contain such anions as Cl^-, SO_4^{--}, CO_3^{--}, S_2^{--}, and Se_2^{--}, and Te_2^{--}. Examples are sodalite, $Na_4Al_3Si_3O_{12}Cl$, and lapis lazuli, $(Na_4Al_3Si_3O_{12})_2S_2$. A pigment called ultramarine is prepared from artificial lapis lazuli.

The zeolites, another form of aluminosilicate, have three-dimensional giant anions with a spongelike structure. The channels are large enough to permit ion-bearing water to penetrate everywhere within a crystal. The zeolite cations can exchange with those in the solution. The equilibria which are set up strongly favor the retention of the most highly charged cations by the zeolite.

$$2NaAlSi_2O_6 \cdot H_2O + Ca^{++} \rightleftharpoons Ca(AlSi_2O_6 \cdot H_2O)_2 + 2Na^+$$

If water containing Ca^{++} or Mg^{++} ions (hard water) is allowed to seep through a bed of sodium zeolite granules, every divalent cation that wanders into one of the channels in the zeolite will be held there and will release an equivalent number of sodium ions into the moving water. The effluent will be soft water. After the water softener has exhausted its cation exchange power by replacing all its Na^+ by divalent or trivalent cations, the original zeolite can be regenerated by soaking the material in saturated NaCl brine. During this process any Ca^{++} ion, for example, which wanders out of the zeolite becomes lost in the swarm of Na^+ ions and never goes back. A synthetic silver zeolite was used in aviators' survival kits during World War II to produce potable water from sea water. The Ag^+ ions which were displaced from the zeolite by the Na^+ ions of the sea water precipitated the Cl^- ions from the water, leaving it largely de-ionized.

Note that the aluminosilicate anions of all the minerals described in this section have the general formula $((Al,Si)O_2)_n^{-a}$, a representing the number of aluminum atoms per unit. This is characteristic of silica itself and of all three-dimensional aluminosilicate giant anions, just as the ratio $((Al,Si)O_{2\frac{1}{2}})_n^{-(a+1)}$ characterizes a sheet anion, and SiO_3^{--} a single-chain anion.

24.21. Glasses

Crystalline minerals are formed from silicate melts when very slowly cooled; but when such liquids are extruded as lavas at the surface of the earth, they solidify before the large molecules have time to achieve the ordered arrangement necessary for crystal formation. The result is obsidian, or volcanic glass.

The difference between a crystalline solid and a glass is the difference between order and disorder. A liquid differs from a solid in that its molecules have no orderly arrangement. A liquid and a glass differ in that the molecules of the liquid have enough kinetic energy to move past each other, whereas those of a glass do not. This may be due to low temperature, i.e., low kinetic energy of the molecules, or to high intermolecular attraction. In a crystal, all the molecules are arranged similarly with respect to their neighbors, so if the temperature rises to the point at which one molecule can move around, all of them can; i.e., the crystal melts at a definite temperature. In a glass, in which different kinds of molecules are arranged in random fashion, a given temperature increase will enable some molecules to move, but not others. Each additional rise in temperature will free more molecules. Hence a glass gradually softens and becomes a viscous liquid; it has no definite melting point. It can well be thought of as a liquid which has been cooled until it is too viscous to flow.

Very viscous liquids are *elastic* and *brittle*. This is true both above and below the softening point. Glass which has been heated until it can be bent slowly will snap if bent with a jerk. Stiff taffy will, too. A very viscous solution of Na_2SiO_3 can be rolled into a ball which will bounce; it will shatter if bounced too hard, like a glass marble. A ball of "silly putty," a silicone (see Section 24.28), will bounce, shatter, or flow slowly into a puddle. Unvulcanized rubber flows when hot, bounces at room temperature, and breaks when cold.

Viscous liquids which stiffen into glasses instead of crystallizing tend to be formed when the molecules are large or so shaped that they fit together only with difficulty, and when a number of different kinds of molecules are present in a solution. Common examples include sugars, phosphoric acid, polyphosphates, polyborates, B_2S_3, SiO_2, and silicates. Solidified thermoplastic resins are also glasses.

24.22. Silicate Glasses

Silicate glasses are of so much more practical importance than other glasses that the word glass, used without qualification, definitely means a silicate glass. The first glass, the glazes on pottery, dates back to 3200 B.C. By about 2000 B.C. articles were being made entirely of glass, usually colored and opaque. The art of glass blowing was invented about 250 B.C., probably by the Phoenicians at Sidon, a great glass center. Caesar Augustus brought Egyptian glassworkers to Rome, and fine transparent glass was produced there until the fall of the Roman Empire. Byzantine glassmaking flourished from the sixth to the tenth century A.D., when it was superseded by the great Venetian glass industry. The use of glass in mirrors, the making of colored and enameled glass, and the art of cutting glass with diamond are contributions of the Venetian glassmakers. They also brought to its highest perfection the making of lace glass and *millefiori* glass. Window glass was being made in England in 1557. In about 1600 the Bohemians invented the art of engraving and cutting glass with a grinding wheel, and Prague gradually became the glass center of the world. However, glass was being made in many other countries. The first attempts to make glass in America occurred in 1608 when Dutch and Polish glass blowers were sent from London to Jamestown, Virginia, to make crude articles for the settlers. This enterprise was short-lived and was followed in 1621 with a second (unsuccessful) attempt, by Venetian workmen, to inaugurate the industry in America. In 1645 a centralized glass industry was finally established in the Dutch settlement of New Amsterdam.

Silica, being a non-metallic oxide, is a weak acid, but its non-volatility enables it to displace other acidic oxides from molten salts. Glassmakers take advantage of this fact in preparing silicates for glasses. The most commonly used reactions take place at temperatures in the vicinity of 1400° C.; they include:

$$Na_2CO_3 + SiO_2 \rightarrow Na_2SiO_3 + \overline{CO_2}$$

$$CaCO_3 + SiO_2 \rightarrow CaSiO_3 + \overline{CO_2}$$

$$Na_2SO_4 + SiO_2 \rightarrow Na_2SiO_3 + \overline{SO_3}$$

Silicates can also be made by direct reaction between SiO_2 and metal oxides. The above equations show the formation of metasilicates; however, all commercial glasses contain more SiO_2 than is indicated here. This means that the silicate anions are more complicated than the simple chain of the metasilicates. As a result, they have higher melting points, a lower coefficient of expansion with heat (and correspondingly greater resistance to breaking when heated), and lowered solubility in water and other chemicals. A common $Si : O$ ratio is $1 : 2\frac{3}{4}$. Although this corresponds to the double chain $Si_4O_{11}{}^{-6}$ shown in Fig. 24.13, silicate glass actually contains many different silicate anions, some simpler and some more complex than the double chain.

Other cations can be used instead of Na^+ and Ca^{++}; and aluminum, boron, phosphorus, and other non-metals may replace part of the silicon. These changes in composition affect all the properties mentioned in the preceding paragraph, and also two very important optical properties—index of refraction, and color.

Glasses of the $Si_4O_{11}{}^{-6}$ type are easy to work, but are easily scratched, broken by heat, and attacked by chemicals. They are used for special purposes in which these poor qualities are unimportant. One example is lead glass, in which a high index of refraction is obtained by replacing most of the Ca^{++} with Pb^{++}. Lead glass is used for certain lenses, for cut glass and costume jewelry (in which use it is known as paste), and for incandescent light bulbs. Its low melting point and long working range are of advantage in the latter use. Green bottle glass, another example, is an otherwise ordinary lime-soda glass in which a third of the silicon has been replaced by aluminum and which has a high Fe^{++} content. The Fe^{++} is responsible for the green color, and the aluminum makes it tougher. White glass requires the considerably more expensive iron-free glass sand; hence green bottle glass has the further advantage of low cost.

Lime-soda glass, which exceeds all other glass in tonnage output, is used for containers and windows. In the latter use the SiO_2 content is increased to resist weathering. Ordinary window glass has a Si : O ratio of $1 : 2\frac{2}{3}$; for plate glass the ratio is $1 : 2\frac{1}{2}$. The latter corresponds to the ratio in sheet molecules, but both chain and three-dimensional anions are present. The melting point can be lowered by replacing up to half the Ca^{++} with Mg^{++}. The presence of some Fe^{++} is unavoidable; its green color is apparent when you look into the edge of a sheet of window glass. This color is much more objectionable in the thicker plate glass, particularly that used for mirrors, through whose glass the light must pass twice; a woman using such a mirror would be tempted to put on too much color. This situation is remedied by adding a little MnO_2, pyrolusite (Gr., *pyro*, fire; *louein*, to wash).

$$2Fe^{++} + MnO_2 \rightarrow 2Fe^{+3} + Mn^{++} + 2O^{--}$$

The yellow color of the Fe^{+3} is complementary to the violet of the Mn(IV), which is added in slight excess. Together they produce a neutral gray. The color of the Mn^{++} is negligible.

24.23. Borosilicate Glasses

Ordinary glass is unsatisfactory for chemical containers and apparatus for three reasons. It has such a high coefficient of thermal expansion that it shatters if heated or cooled rapidly; it softens below the temperature required for many chemical reactions; and it is too easily attacked by many chemicals. The third disadvantage is not so obvious as the first two but is easily demonstrated. Thus, solutions stored in ordinary glass bottles always give a strong flame test for sodium. If broken window glass is ground with distilled water in a mortar, enough sodium silicate will dissolve in a few moments to color phenolphthalein a strong pink.

Improving the glass used for chemical purposes has been a gradual process. The first step was to raise the melting point by substituting K^+ for Na^+. In the Bohemian or hard glass thus produced, only the softening point was improved. Decreased solubility was imparted to Jena resistance glass by lowering the alkali metal content and replacing Ca^{++} largely with Ba^{++} and Zn^{++}. The accompanying increase in the SiO_2 content raised the softening point. The addition of Al_2O_3 and some B_2O_3 increased the mechanical strength sufficiently so that beakers and other vessels could be made fairly thin and so withstand reasonably rapid heating. Extreme care in using such articles was required, however; innumerable students pushed stirring rods through the bottom of Jena test tubes, or broke the mouth of the test tube while inserting a stopper. Jena glass was the standard chemical glass before World War I.

In 1917 the Corning Glass Works developed Pyrex glass which not only met the emergency caused by the stoppage of imports from Austria, but surpassed the Jena product in every way. It is now in universal use in laboratories and has invaded the kitchen and the factory.

Pyrex is a borosilicate glass in which the $(B + Si) : O$ ratio is only $1 : 2.01$. This means that the anions are almost entirely three-dimensional, and accounts for the high softening point. An oxygen-fed blast lamp is necessary to work Pyrex, but the coefficient of expansion is so low that the glass can be put directly into the flame of a Bunsen burner, and into the blast flame after only a very short preliminary heating. Just as replacing some of the $Si(IV)$ in the quartz structure by $Al(III)$ produces the anionic structure of feldspar, so the use of $B(III)$ produces a structure which is negatively charged although otherwise similar to that of SiO_2. The necessary cations are furnished entirely by Na^+ and K^+. Borosilicate glass is very resistant to chemical attack. Its low rate of expansion when heated enables the manufacture of apparatus thick enough to be very strong without danger of cracking when heat is applied. An even more resistant glass called Vycor is made from Pyrex glass by long treatment with concentrated HNO_3, which removes nearly all the Na^+ and K^+ and most of the $B(III)$. This is done after the glass has been shaped into the desired objects. The slightly porous glass is then heated until it becomes clear again, shrinking about 10 per cent in the process. It contains about 96 per cent SiO_2 and is almost like quartz glass in properties but is much cheaper.

24.24. Optical Glasses

The interesting property in optical glasses is the index of refraction for light of various colors. These glasses are traditionally divided into two classes, *crown* and *flint*. Crown glass is characterized by a relatively high weight percent SiO_2 content and more Na^+ than K^+. Flint glass has more K^+ than Na^+, and from one-third to two-thirds of the total weight may be Pb^{++}. In barium flint glass, one-sixth to one-half the weight may be Ba^{++} and Zn^{++} instead of lead. Crown glass also contains smaller quantities of Ba^{++}, in place of the Ca^{++} present in ordinary lime glass. There is little or no Ca^{++} in optical glasses. Their boron content may approach

Fig. 24.14. The largest solid piece of glass ever cast by man looked much like a huge cake of ice after cooling. This 200-in. telescope mirror disk is large enough for more than 100 men to stand upon it. The circular opening in the center, 40 in. in diameter, is for the passage of light rays. Supporting the disk is the bottom of the great mold mounted on the carriage of the 60-ton locomotive hoist which moved it from the annealing kiln. The disk was poured at Corning, New York, on December 2, 1934; its dimensions as poured were 200 in. in diameter, 27 in. thick, 20 tons in weight, 218 sq. ft. surface area. (Courtesy, Corning Glass Works.)

that of Pyrex (3.7 per cent B) or be less. The range in refractive indices (for sodium light) is from 1.5 for ordinary crown to nearly 1.9 for the densest flint. The latter is above the value for most precious stones, but still far below the 2.41 of diamond.

24.25. Colored Glass and Glazes

Much of the glass produced is intentionally colored for decorative purposes. This includes not only all-glass objects, but glazes for ceramic ware and baked enamels for metals. Glazes and enamels are made by pouring melted glass of the proper composition into water, forming an easily pulverized frit. This is ground to a powder, made into a paste, and applied to the object. The object is then fired, and the glaze or enamel melts and again becomes a glass.

Glass is colored in two ways: by dissolving in it metal oxides which will supply metal ions of the desired color, or by dispersing in it colloidal particles of some material that will not dissolve. Metal ions used

Fig. 24.15. The completed ceramic mold for the 200-in. disk with cores in position. The large central core produced the 40-in. hole required in the center of the disk. The remaining system of cores produced the ribbed structure of the disk. (Courtesy, Corning Glass Works.)

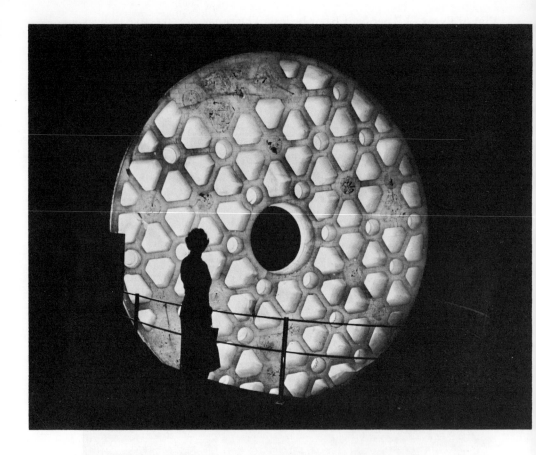

Fig. 24.16. The 200-in. telescope disk, showing the geometrically cored pattern on its under side. These hollows and ribs of glass lighten the weight of the 20-ton disk and provide a means of supporting it in the telescope. (Courtesy, Corning Glass Works.)

for coloring include Cr^{+3} and Fe^{++} for green, Cu^{++} and Co^{++} for blue, and Mn(IV) for violet. Tiny opaque particles dispersed in glass produce reds and yellows just as the red and yellow of the sunset are produced by dust particles in the air; that is, they scatter light of short wave lengths, permitting the longer waves to come through. Gold, selenium, and Cu_2O are easily dispersed in particles about 0.6 micron in diameter—too small to be seen, but able to scatter all except red light, which has a wave length ranging from 0.65 to 0.80 micron. Thus only red light is transmitted. Selenium can be dispersed in 0.5-micron particles, as can carbon. Either selenium or carbon permits green and yellow light as well as red to be transmitted.

All these colored glasses are transparent. Opaque glass is produced by having the insoluble particles a micron or more in diameter. For white glass fluorspar, CaF_2, cryolite, Na_3AlF_6, or SnO_2 or $Ca_3(PO_4)_2$ can be used. Like ordinary black ink, black glass is colored by a mixture of strong complementary colors; light transmitted by one is absorbed by the other. Ordinary glass transmits the visible spectrum and infrared (heat) but is opaque to ultraviolet. Special glasses also transmit ultraviolet. A glass can be made which is opaque to infrared rays but transmits all the visible spectrum except a little of the red portion. Similarly, a glass can be made which is transparent to ultraviolet (black light), but almost completely opaque to visible light. Glass containing neodymium ion, Nd^{+3}, is used in glassblowers' goggles; it screens out the brilliant yellow sodium flame almost completely, but is otherwise transparent.

24.26. Ceramics

The making of ceramics—brick, tile, pottery, and porcelain—is obviously connected with the glass industry because of the frequent use of glazes on such objects. There is also a less obvious but more fundamental relationship; the infinitesimal particles of clay from which all ceramics are made are held together by varying quantities of glass that is produced during the firing process. Pure clay is mainly kaolin, $Al_2Si_2O_5(OH)_4$ (Section 24.18). The kaolin dehydrates at the temperature of the kiln, but the residue does not melt. However, the clay always contains traces of fusible impurities which melt to a glass that cements the particles together where they come in contact. This cementing process, which is called **sintering,** imparts to products the porosity characteristic of common brick, terra cotta, or earthenware. A glaze may be applied and the article fired to seal the surface. Or the clay may be mixed initially with enough fusible material so that the glass produced on firing will fill all the voids. These ceramic materials are said to be *vitrified.* If the material is porous, the product is called earthenware. When ground feldspar is mixed with the clay, it melts on firing and produces a vitrified body known as porcelain. The red color of common brick and primitive pottery is due to the Fe_2O_3 in common clay. For white china, iron-free china clay must be used.

24.27. Portland Cement

A paste of $Ca(OH)_2$ and water, mixed with sand, has been used as mortar for millennia. Lime mortar hardens by simple drying (although there is some conversion to $CaCO_3$ over a long period of years); therefore it never hardens if kept wet. Eventually someone discovered that if volcanic ash like that which buried Pompeii was used instead of sand, a hydraulic cement was produced which hardened even under water. The Carthaginians used this in a 70-mile aqueduct that is still in existence. The Romans not only used hydraulic cement in mortar to hold cut stones together, but mixed it with sand and crushed rock to make concrete, which they cast in forms as is done today. The mausoleum of Emperor Hadrian, built in A.D. 138, was actually made of reinforced concrete. During medieval times several buildings were erected above it, and the entire structure is now known as the Castle of St. Angelo (Fig. 24.17).

In 1756 an English engineer, John Smeaton, was faced with the task of making a suitable foundation for a lighthouse. He discovered that a calcined mixture of a certain limestone and clay could be ground into a powder which produced a much better hydraulic cement than that used by the Romans. Because blocks made of this cement resembled the famous Portland building stone that originated in England, it was called Portland cement. It was first manufactured on a commercial scale by William Aspdin of Leeds in 1824.

Modern Portland cement is made in enormous cylindrical kilns that may be as much as 420 ft. long and are inclined at a slight angle to the horizontal. A finely powdered mixture of the proper composition is fed in at the upper end, and a great blast of flame from oil, gas, or powdered coal is blown in at the lower end. By the time the slow rotation of the kiln has brought the mixture to the lower end, all the CO_2 and water has been driven off and the mixture is in a state of incipient fusion. On cooling, it solidifies into small nodules of clinker. The clinker is ground to a fine powder, mixed with as much as 3 per cent of gypsum to retard setting, and then stored in great silos until sold.

The Al : Si : Ca ratio for the feed mixture for a cement kiln should be about 1 : 2 : 4. In many localities different rocks are in close proximity and can produce such a mixture by being blended in proper proportions; consequently cement is manufactured almost everywhere. In this country clay is commonly replaced by shale formed by the consolidation of clay and silt. In some cases an argillaceous or clay-bearing limestone called cement rock can be used without admixture.

In the first flush of the "concrete age" at the beginning of this century, a large number of enthusiasts decided to get rich by making cement. Plants were built in 33 states at a capital expenditure of over 700 million dollars. The 151 of them still in operation during World War II had an annual capacity of 240 million barrels; but in 1942, the peak year of war construction, only 182 million barrels were required. (A barrel contains 376 lb. of cement.) In 1944 production had dropped to 30 per cent of capacity, but the end of the war brought a building boom that consumed all the stock on hand and required large increases in capacity. The production in 1959 was 340 million barrels.

The cations in all the several kinds of crystals in cement clinker are mainly Ca^{++}; the anions are SiO_4^{-4}, O^{--}, and aluminate ions in which the

Fig. 24.17. Castle of St. Angelo in Rome, built in 138 **A.D.** The structure is reinforced concrete. (Courtesy, Portland Cement Assoc.)

Al : O ratio ranges from 1 : 2⅓ to 1 : 3; the latter corresponds to a polyaluminate chain of the metasilicate type. Apparently there are no aluminosilicates, for the silicate and aluminate ions are found in separate crystals. The substance present in the largest amount is called tricalcium silicate. It is actually an oxide-silicate double salt, Ca_3SiO_4O, the calcium analogue of cyanite, Al_2SiO_4O (Section 24.16). The substitution of three large Ca^{++} ions for two small Al^{+3} ions in the cyanite lattice results in a weaker structure and makes it subject to attack by water.

$$Ca_3SiO_5 + 2H_2O \rightarrow 2Ca(OH)_2 + CaSiO_3$$

The aluminates also react with water.

$$Ca_3(AlO_3)_2 + 6H_2O \rightarrow 3Ca(OH)_2 + 2Al(OH)_3$$

The products are insoluble and precipitate as a gel from which crystals gradually form. The initial set, which occurs in about three hours, is produced by felted needles of $Ca(OH)_2$ in the gel. The reactions may take as long as a month to go to completion, the cement eventually taking up about 20 per cent of its own weight of water. The heat given out during the process is sufficient to dry the mixture before the reaction is complete, even though a 100 to 200 per cent excess of water is used, unless the mixture is kept covered or wetted from time to time. An elaborate cooling system was built into Hoover Dam to carry away the heat from the interior so the cement would set in a reasonable time. On the other hand, the production of heat is an advantage in cold-weather construction. If the extra cost is justified, a high-aluminum cement is available that in twenty-four hours acquires a tensile strength equal to that attained by ordinary cement in four weeks.

24.28. Silicones

The electronegativity of silicon is only 1.8, whereas that of carbon is 2.5. Si—Si bonds are therefore weaker than C—C bonds. By the same token silicon reacts more energetically with oxygen than carbon does. Silane, SiH_4, disilane, $SiH_3 \cdot SiH_3$, and trisilane, $SiH_3 \cdot SiH_2 \cdot SiH_3$, have been prepared but are not very stable thermally; they ignite on contact with air. They hydrolyze vigorously with the slightest trace of water, liberating hydrogen.

$$Si_2H_6 + 6H_2O \rightarrow 2H_2SiO_3 + 7H_2$$

Hence there are no hydrosilicon plastics.

The hardness and inertness of silicate minerals prove how strong the Si—O bond is. A silicon atom which is bonded to two oxygen atoms has only a quarter share instead of a half share of each bonding pair; i.e., the bond is 50 per cent ionic. This loss of electrons makes it higher than normal in electronegativity; accordingly such an atom can form a strong bond with carbon. These facts are the basis of an industry that had its inception during World War II, the manufacture of a whole new series of compounds called **silicones**. The silicones are compounds whose molecules are chains consisting of *alternate* silicon and oxygen atoms. Each silicon regularly has two CH_3—groups as chain stoppers.

Elemental silicon which has been alloyed with a little copper as a catalyst reacts readily with methyl chloride, CH_3Cl. In effect, the molecule breaks into two fragments, a chlorine atom, $: \ddot{C}l \cdot$, and a methyl

radical, $H : \overset{\overset{\displaystyle H}{\cdot\cdot}}{\underset{\cdot\cdot}{\underset{\displaystyle H}{C}}} \cdot$, both of which unite with silicon, $\cdot \overset{\displaystyle \cdot}{Si} \cdot$; this is repeated

and dimethylsilicon dichloride is formed: $Cl—\overset{\overset{\displaystyle CH_3}{|}}{\underset{\underset{\displaystyle CH_3}{|}}{Si}}—Cl$. The Si—C bonds

are fairly stable, but the Si—Cl bonds undergo hydrolysis like any other non-metal halide. In hydrolysis the chlorines are replaced with —OH groups; the HCl escapes. Condensation sets in immediately, with elimination of water between —OH groups on adjacent molecules.

$$HO—\overset{\overset{\displaystyle CH_3}{|}}{\underset{\underset{\displaystyle CH_3}{|}}{Si}}—\overline{OH \quad H}O—\overset{\overset{\displaystyle CH_3}{|}}{\underset{\underset{\displaystyle CH_3}{|}}{Si}}—OH$$

By regulating the conditions the condensation may be made to produce rings of various sizes or chains of any desired length; thousands of molecular units in one chain are usual.* Furthermore, by using a chosen proportion of methylsilicon trichloride, any desired number of cross links can be produced between chains. Products having the physical properties of oils, rubbers, and resins can be thus produced. Chemically,

---

* The empirical formulas approximate $(CH_3)_2SiO$. The similarity of this to the formula for acetone, a *ketone*, $CH_3 \cdot CO \cdot CH_3$ or $(CH_3)_2CO$, is responsible for the name silicone.

they are much more stable against both heat and oxygen than the corresponding carbon compounds.

Because of their wartime inception, the original uses of the silicones were military in nature. As has been the case with many military developments of new products, additional benefits have been derived from subsequent civilian use.

The waterproofing of various electrical components and insulators was of prime necessity for high-altitude aircraft. For example, the surface of porcelain is covered with a tightly adsorbed layer of water molecules. This water reacts readily with the vapor of dimethylsilicon dichloride, and is thus replaced by a monomolecular silicone layer that adheres just as tightly. The outer surface of this new layer, being composed of methyl groups, is similar to the surface of a piece of paraffin or a layer of oil, and is equally water-repellent. The radios of high-altitude bombers used to be put out of operation on their return to sea level by the condensation of a conducting film of water on the cold porcelain cores of certain coils which shorted the coils. Treating the porcelain as just described eliminated this trouble.

Silicone rubber gaskets, replacing asbestos ones, made big naval searchlights airtight against the intrusion of moist sea air which had been corroding the reflectors. Ordinary rubber melted in the heat of the searchlight and could not be used.

Silicone liquids in the hydraulic systems of planes retained satisfactory viscosity at temperatures so low that standard hydraulic fluid became stiff, and so hot that the regular liquid became water-thin and leaked out.

Silicone varnishes are such excellent insulators and so heat-resistant that insulating wiring with them enabled motors to work under overloads that would have set fire to the insulation formerly used. Our big bombers would be overloaded beyond successful operation with their multitude of remote-control electric motors had not silicone insulation halved the size of the motor.

A whole new field of chemistry and technology, civilian as well as military, has been opened up by the development of silicones.

24.29 Boron Hydrides (Boranes)

Since boron is only a trifle higher in electronegativity (2.0) than silicon, what was said in the preceding section about the instability and reactivity of silicon hydrides applies almost equally to boron hydrides, or boranes. These properties made early research on the boranes incredibly difficult, while at the same time the peculiar valence behavior of boron (Section 24.13) made correct theoretical interpretation almost impossible. This was obviously a field of "pure science" from which nothing of practical value could conceivably come. And yet certain borane-hydrocarbon derivatives have been found to have superfuel qualities suitable for certain rockets and jets. The drawbacks of the boranes as substances for experiment have proved to be among their most valuable qualities. The extreme flammability keeps jet engines from disastrous flame-outs at extreme altitudes. The weakness of their bonds means that an unusually large amount of energy is set free when boranes react with oxygen. Some metals have as high a heat of combustion, per gram atom, but not per gram, because they have far higher atomic weights than boron. A further disadvantage of the metals is that their combustion products have far higher molecular weights than those of the boranes, which means lower exhaust velocity and decreased efficiency. Decaborane, $B_{10}H_{14}$, is actually almost as efficient, from the standpoint of pounds of fuel needed per second to maintain a given thrust, as liquid hydrogen is, and it is far easier to store and to handle. It is about 50 per cent more efficient than ordinary jet fuel.

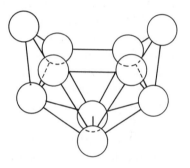

Fig. 24.18. The boron atoms in $B_{10}H_{14}$.

The molecule of $B_{10}H_{14}$ is closely related structurally to the element boron. Imagine that one icosahedral B_{12} unit is removed from a crystal of boron. If two adjacent boron atoms are now removed from this molecule, a hollow, basket-shaped B_{10} structure remains (Fig. 24.18). One hydrogen atom is attached to each boron atom to make up for the latter's separation from a neighboring B_{12} group. Four more hydrogen atoms are attached around the edge of the "basket" to satisfy the valence bonds directed toward the two boron atoms that were removed. Each of these hydrogens on the edge is attached to two boron atoms by a *single* electron pair, in one of the curious three-atom bonds so characteristic of boron (Section 24.13).

The structures of other boranes—B_2H_6, B_4H_{10}, B_5H_9, B_5H_{11}, etc.— are similarly related to an icosahedral unit of the giant molecule of elemental boron. Researchers were almost completely baffled until this fact was recognized.

24.30. Metal Borides

The tendency of a non-metal atom to form a monatomic anion by gaining enough electrons to complete its valence octet lessens, as we have seen, as the electronegativity decreases. At the same time the tendency to complete the octet by forming covalent bonds increases. Thus fluorine exists almost entirely as F^- ion; O^{--} ion is common; N^{-3} ion is rare; and the true monatomic carbide ion, C^{-4}, is found only in Be_2C and Al_4C_3. (Other metal "carbides" contain covalently bonded groups of carbon atoms such as the acetylide ion, $: C : : : C :^{--}$, in CaC_2.) Hence it is natural to find that boride ion does not exist. Indeed, for an atom whose electronegativity is 2.0 to gain complete possession of *five* more electrons would seem obviously impossible.

Nevertheless, many metal borides exist. Borides of perhaps most of the metals up through uranium have been prepared, usually by direct union of the elements at high temperatures, or by using the metal to reduce B_2O_3 or a boron trihalide. Although many of the borides have simple empirical formulas such as M_2B, MB, and MB_2, their properties are those of giant molecules, not simple salts. For example, many of them melt above 1500° C.—a chromium boride mixture melts at 2800° C.—and have excellent resistance to thermal shock and chemical attack. The refractory borides are very hard, even at high temperatures, which suggests their possible use for rocket exhaust orifices.

That the giant molecule explanation is correct has been proved by King and Kanda at Syracuse University. Magnesium boride had been reported to have the formula Mg_3B_2 on no better grounds than that the formula of the nitride is Mg_3N_2, and both boron and nitrogen can be trivalent. This boride formula was suspect on two grounds. (1) There was no analysis of a pure compound to support it; and (2) it was not valid from the standpoint of the modern electronic theory of valence, for a B^{-3} ion would have only 6 valence electrons. King and his co-workers proved that no such compound as Mg_3B_2 exists; instead they found MgB_2, MgB_4, MgB_6, and a fourth which is probably MgB_{12}. X-ray investigations showed these compounds to be composed of giant sheet anions of covalently bonded boron atoms with layers of Mg^{++} ions between them. The bonding of the boron atoms to each other is closely related to the bonding in elemental boron. The $(B_{12}^{--})_n$ anion is probably a sheet of B_{12} icosahedra; the others would seem to be sheets that are half or a third or a sixth that thickness respectively.

Alkaline earth borides, MB_6, are successfully attacked by oxidizing acids, fused alkalies, and peroxides, but borides of metals with higher valences are more resistant. Tantalum boride, for example, is soluble in a mixture of HNO_3 and HF but resists aqua regia. Boron itself is only a semiconductor; but some borides, such as those of titanium, zirconium, and vanadium, are better electrical conductors than the parent metals. Small molecules that contain B—B bonds are powerful reducing agents. Thus $H_4B_2O_4$, a monobasic acid of unknown structure, reacts rapidly in alkaline solution, liberating hydrogen.

$$2H_2O + H_4B_2O_4 + 2OH^- \rightarrow 2B(OH)_4^- + \overline{H_2}$$

24.31. Other Boron Compounds

The plane triangular molecules formed by three-coordinated boron were mentioned in Section 24.1. All the halides, BX_3, exist. BF_3 is an important Lewis acid catalyst in the petroleum industry. Pure boron is prepared by heating a mixture of BBr_3 and hydrogen or the decomposition of BI_3 gas in contact with a hot tungsten filament. Boron esters have the formula $B(OR)_3$, where R is a hydrocarbon group. They are volatile liquids. Methyl borate, $B(OCH_3)_3$, the most volatile of the esters, is produced in making a common test for borates; the green color of the flame that appears when it burns is characteristic of boron compounds.

$$H_3BO_3 + 3CH_3OH \rightarrow \overline{B(OCH_3)_3} + 3H_2O$$

Boron trialkyls, BR_3, are of little interest at present.

Since all the compounds mentioned thus far in this section are gases or volatile liquids, the fact that boric acid, $B(OH)_3$, is a non-volatile solid requires explanation. This is found in the occurrence of hydrogen bonding, a phenomenon which accounts for numerous cases of abnormally low volatility or high melting point. Fig. 24.19 shows how this occurs. In the planar BO_3 group each oxygen atom has an unshared electron pair which makes a 120° angle with the bonds to boron and to hydrogen, as indicated by the short lines in the figure. This puts them in exactly the right position to attract the hydrogen atoms on the adjoining molecules. As a result, boric acid has a giant sheet molecule structure resembling that of graphite. The expected lubricating properties can readily be demonstrated by sprinkling a little powdered H_3BO_3 on a dance floor. H_3BO_3 is a weak acid, a mild antiseptic, and a poison. Boric acid solution used by mistake instead of boiled water in babies' formulas has caused some deaths.

Although a number of reactions should and apparently do produce borine, BH_3, it cannot be obtained, because if not simultaneously used up in some other reaction it instantly dimerizes to diborane, B_2H_6.

The compounds of 4-coordinated boron made by adding a base to any of the triangular compounds are perfectly normal tetrahedral molecules. They can, however, revert to the triangular compounds by losing the weakest base of the four that are present; this is not necessarily the last one added. A great number of mixed compounds can be obtained by alternate additions and losses.

The most important tetrahedral boron molecule is borohydride ion, BH_4^-. It is made by displacing weaker bases from boron with the very

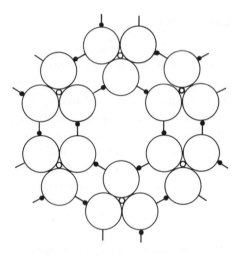

Fig. 24.19. Part of a sheet of H_3BO_3. Large circles represent oxygen, small open circles boron, very small solid circles hydrogen. $- =$ hydrogen bond.

strong base hydride ion, H^-. The covalent bonding makes it just enough weaker than H^- ion as a reducing agent for it to be selective in its reducing action on organic compounds. $NaBH_4$, unknown before World War II, has within the last few years had a tonnage output. Tetrahedral boron compounds are usually named as derivatives of borohydride ion; e.g., $HB(OCH_3)_3^-$ is called trimethoxyborohydride ion. Ions containing F^- or OH^- that are attached to boron are exceptions.

Fluoborate ion, BF_4^-, is identical in shape, size, and charge to ClO_4^- ion and shows the expected chemical similarities. Not only are fluoborates regularly isomorphous with perchlorates, but BF_4^- ion apparently is as weak a base as ClO_4^- ion. It forms salts whose cations are so acid that they react with any base of appreciable strength, such as nitrosyl ion, NO^+. Even its first hydrolysis product, hydroxyfluoborate ion,

BF_3OH^-, which should be a stronger base, forms a stable hydronium salt. Further hydrolysis produces dihydroxyfluoborate ion, $BF_2(OH)_2^-$, trihydroxyfluoborate ion, $BF(OH)_3^-$, and orthoborate ion, $B(OH)_4^-$, which are successively stronger bases. $B(OH)_4^-$ is as strong a base as NH_3. Its formula is regularly written $H_2BO_3^-$ because the formula of dry boric acid is H_3BO_3; this, however, takes up any base and becomes tetrahedral. A water solution of boric acid probably contains $H_2OB(OH)_3$. In alkaline solutions $B(OH)_4^-$ ion is in equilibrium with a small amount of triborate ion, $B_3O_6^{-3}$, and a trace of a dimer of the latter ion.

So far as they have been investigated, the crystalline borates seem to be analogous to the silicates in containing discrete, chain, and sheet anions. However, the chain and sheet anions are based on the triangular borate ion, BO_3^{-3}, rather than on tetrahedra, The discrete anions include BO_3^{-3}, $B_2O_5^{-4}$ (pyroborate, which consists of two BO_3 triangles that share a single oxygen atom), and $B_3O_6^{-3}$ (Fig. 24.20). Calcium metaborate $Ca(BO_2)_2$, contains infinite chains of these triangles, but $NaBO_2$ is actually the triborate, $Na_3B_3O_6$. The tetraborate ion, $B_4O_7^{--}$, is thought to be a double chain analogous to amphibole, but this has not been proved.

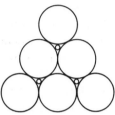

Fig. 24.20. Triborate ion, a plane triangle.

The decahydrate of sodium tetraborate, $Na_2B_4O_7 \cdot 10H_2O$, is called borax; it is the most important boron compound. It was relatively scarce until deposits of colemanite, $Ca_2B_6O_{11} \cdot 5H_2O$, were discovered in Death Valley in 1880. This mineral, from which borax is easily prepared, was drawn by 20-mule-team caravans 165 miles to the nearest railroad. Borax is now obtained chiefly from the salts of Searles Lake, in connection with the production of KCl, but deposits of kernite, $Na_2B_4O_7 \cdot 4H_2O$, also mined in California, are another source. Borax is used as a moderate base, particularly where its antiseptic action is desired. The anhydrous salt is used in making vitreous enamels, glazes, and glass, and as a flux in brazing. It is the starting material for the manufacture of all other boron compounds.

QUESTIONS AND PROBLEMS

1. Compare the conditions under which tetrahedral bonding takes place in the case of carbon, boron, nitrogen, and silicon.

2. Why can crystals of boron, carbon, and silicon be considered giant molecules? Are all crystals giant molecules?

3. Using suitable illustrations, distinguish between the following: monomer—polymer; condensation—polymerization.

4. In which of the above do chain stoppers play an important role?

5. Name some natural and synthetic plastics. What are some of the important linkage groups that are used to form giant chains in synthetic plastics?

6. Do you consider that cotton and wool fibers are giant molecules? Defend your answer.

7. List as many substances as you can, from which rayon could be manufactured.

8. What is an elastomer? Name some natural and some synthetic ones.

9. Is a monomer with one double bond suitable for forming an elastomer? Give reasons for your answer.

10. Distinguish between thermosetting and thermoplastic polymers.

11. In what respects is Carborundum similar to diamond and boron nitride? Similar to diamond and graphite?

12. What is the characteristic geometric disposition of silicon and oxygen atoms in SiO_2, SiO_4^{-4}, SiO_3^{--}, and $Si_2O_7^{-6}$?

13. How can silica be dissolved? What valuable product is thus formed? Name some other useful applications and properties of silica.

14. Where in interlinked SiO_4 tetrahedra are isomorphous cations replaced? Why is this possible?

15. Which element can partially substitute for silicon in SiO_4 tetrahedra? In each substitution, what happens to the charge on the anion? How can this be compensated?

16. How do you account for the fibrous quality of asbestos and the sheet quality of mica?

17. List the general formulas of the aluminosilicate three-dimensional anions, and the sheet anion.

18. Contrast the melting of a glass with that of a crystal. How do you account for this? What common substances can be classified as glasses?

19. What chemical property of silica permits its use in the manufacture of glass (silicates)? Give a chemical equation for this.

20. What part does the Si : O ratio in giant molecular anions play in controlling various physical properties of glass?

21. What chemical evidence indicates that the covalent bonds between silicon and hydrogen are relatively weak in silicon hydride molecules? Explain how the ability of silicon to form covalent bonds is increased if highly electronegative groups are added.

22. What is a silicone? Name some outstanding properties and applications of the silicones.

23. Illustrate by means of chemical equations (a) the hydrolysis of dimethylsilicon dichloride; (b) the condensation of dimethylsilicon dihydroxide.

24. Describe and illustrate some of the peculiar valence characteristics of boron.

25. Name some of the known boron-hydrogen molecules and give their formulas. What are some of their important properties and uses?

26. Why does hydrogen bonding affect the physical properties of substances in which it occurs? What are the requirements for its presence?

27. Why does H_3BO_3 have a planar structure and BH_4^- a tetrahedral structure? Name other boron molecules whose structures should be similar to these.

25

The heavier elements in Group III

25.1. The Main-Family Elements

All the elements in Group III have odd atomic numbers, wherefore it is to be expected that they will be relatively scarce. Aluminum, surprisingly enough, makes up 8.13 per cent of the earth's crust. Although it is the third most abundant element, it is only one-third as abundant as silicon; however, it is four times as abundant as magnesium. The heavier elements in the group are relatively scarce, each being present to the extent of only 10^{-3} to 10^{-5} per cent. There is little likelihood that any of them will become familiar because they are not common like aluminum nor do they occur in concentrated deposits like boron. Table 25.1 lists some of the properties of these elements.

The valence shells of boron and aluminum contain 2 s electrons and 1 p electron. The other four elements in the main family have only 2 s electrons in the valence shell; the third valence electron is a d electron in the shell directly below the regular valence shell. They are therefore **transition elements.** However, this d electron has so nearly the same energy as the outer s electrons that the s electrons cannot be

TABLE 25.1. **Properties of Main-Family Elements in Group III**

Name	Boron	Alu-minum	Scan-dium	Yt-trium	Lan-thanum	Acti-nium
Symbol	B	Al	Sc	Y	La	Ac
Atomic number	5	13	21	39	57	89
Atomic weight	10.82	26.98	44.96	88.92	138.92	227
Density, g./ml.	2.33	2.70	2.5	5.51	6.194	
Melting point, °C.	2300	660	1200	1490	826	
Boiling point, °C.	2550	2057	2400	2500	1800	
Electronegativity	2.0	1.5	1.3	1.2	1.2	1.1
Radius of M^{+3} ion, A.	0.20	0.50	0.81	0.96	1.06	1.11

removed without removing the d electron. All the elements listed in Table 25.1 have a valence of $+3$, and all the ions are of the inert gas type.

25.2. The Subgroup Elements

The subgroup elements—gallium, indium, and thallium—are also scarce and hence unfamiliar. Gallium was the first of the elements predicted by Mendeleev to be discovered. (Scandium, in the main family of Group III, was the second; and germanium, whose atomic number is next after that of gallium, was the third.) Table 25.2 lists some of the properties of the elements in this subgroup; boron and aluminum are included for purposes of comparison. With the exception of boron, these elements are characterized by the long temperature range in which they remain a liquid; that for gallium is the longest known. Gallium melts at 29.780° C. but supercools; hence it is often liquid at room temperature.

TABLE 25.2. **Properties of Subgroup Elements in Group III (Boron and aluminum included for comparison)**

Name	Boron	Aluminum	Gallium	Indium	Thallium
Symbol	B	Al	Ga	In	Tl
Atomic number	5	13	31	49	81
Atomic weight	10.82	26.98	69.72	114.82	204.39
Density, g./ml.	2.33	2.70	5.927	7.293	11.85
Melting point, °C.	2300	660	30	156	304
Boiling point, °C.	2550	2057	1983	2000	1457
Electronegativity	2.0	1.5	1.6	1.7	1.8
Radius of M^{+3} ion, A.	0.20	0.50	0.62	0.81	0.95

25.3. Main Family vs. Subgroup

The main-family and subgroup assignments in the two preceding sections are reversed in many chemistry texts. There are two reasons for this. In the first place, as was said above, the scandium subgroup—scandium, yttrium, lanthanum, and actinium—are transition elements since they have 1 d electron in the shell next to the outside shell; and *most* transition elements actually are subgroup elements. Physicists are not interested in chemical properties and therefore tend to arrange their periodic tables so that regularities in atomic structure will be brought out clearly. To the chemist the terms subgroup element and transition element should not be exactly synonymous. The subgroup classification is based on the structure of the ion, not of the element. A main-group element is one which forms ions of the inert gas type; a subgroup element does not. In this respect, scandium and titanium are main-group elements even though they are transition elements. Zinc and gallium are not transition elements, but form ions with 10 d electrons in their surface; therefore they are definitely subgroup elements.

The second reason for confusing the main- and sub-group character of these elements is based on chemistry, namely, on the fact that the gallium subgroup—gallium, indium, and thallium—resemble aluminum in being amphoteric, whereas scandium is only slightly so, yttrium is not amphoteric, and $La(OH)_3$ is a strong enough base to turn blue litmus red. Rightly understood, however, these facts provide excellent arguments for the opposite point of view.

The electronegativities of main-family elements decrease downward; this is not the case with subgroup elements. Its electronegativity of 2.0 makes boron a border-line non-metal. Elements with only slightly lower electronegativities are amphoteric metals. Aluminum, half a unit lower than boron, is down toward the bottom of these metals. Hence it is to be expected that the heavier metals in the main family will *not* be amphoteric, and that those in the subgroup will be. This is exactly what we find. The resemblance of the gallium subgroup to aluminum is a further example of a previously stated rule to the effect that any ion with d electrons in its surface behaves chemically as though it were smaller in size than it actually is. The first example we cited was the resemblance of Zn^{++} ion to Mg^{++}. We also pointed out that the ions of a subgroup element with a variable valence resemble whatever smaller ion in the main family that has the same valence, even if it is in a different group. Thus Fe^{++} is like Mg^{++}, and Fe^{+3} like Al^{+3}.

25.4. The f Transitions

Potassium at the beginning of the fourth period of the periodic table marks the start of a new electron shell just as the lighter alkali metals did in the first three periods. In this case, however, the new or fourth shell is begun while the shell beneath it, the third, is incomplete. There are five empty d orbitals in it. After the $4s$ orbital has been filled (Ca), electrons begin to enter these $3d$ orbitals. Thus scandium marks the beginning of a d transition. This d transition is characterized by a long series of elements that can form divalent cations which are generally very similar, although the electronegativity increases moderately from 1.3 to 1.8.

The fifth period, commencing with rubidium, follows the pattern of the fourth exactly, even though the fourth shell is still incompletely filled, having seven empty f orbitals as well as five empty d orbitals (Fig. 3.11). Yttrium marks the beginning of a second d transition. Thus, beginning with cesium in the sixth period, there are not merely empty d orbitals in the fifth shell, but the f orbitals in the fourth shell are still empty (Fig. 3.11). There is no theoretical way of predicting which of these empty orbitals will fill first, or how completely it will be filled before the other starts to fill.

Actually lanthanum is exactly analogous to yttrium, showing that it has begun a third d transition; but the next fourteen elements also form trivalent ions all of which are extremely similar to La^{+3} and Y^{+3}. This is obviously an f transition. The fifteenth element, hafnium, is like zirconium, a typical Group IV transition element; so the third d transition resumes after the completion of the f transition. It is this behavior that is shown in Fig. 3.11 by having the ascending (dashed) line graze the $5d$ circle on its way from the $6s$ to the $4f$ circle, which denotes the addition of a $5d$ electron before any $4f$ electrons are added. Then, after the 14 $4f$ electrons are added, the remaining 9 d electrons are added to the $5d$ orbitals. This pattern starts to repeat itself at the beginning of the seventh period; actinium begins a d transition which is interrupted at the next element, cerium, by a second f transition. However, there are just enough elements to finish the second f transition, so the fourth d transition is never resumed.

The single d electron in the next to the outer shell of scandium and its congeners is always lost along with the s electrons in the outer shell; so the $+3$ valence is characteristic of this group. It will be remembered that all of the d transition elements except those of Group III show the characteristic $+2$ valence in spite of the fact that in a number of them one of the outer electrons has dropped down into a d orbital. There is a similar irregularity in the electron structure of the *f* transition elements. In many of them the single *d* electron of lanthanum has dropped down into an *f* orbital, but in most cases the energy difference responsible for this is so small that it has no chemical effect. All of these elements, therefore, form +3 ions. These trivalent cations resemble each other much more closely than do the divalent cations of the *d* transition elements because the former all have the same outer shell—i.e., the inert gas type of octet that is characteristic of the ions of main-family elements—successive *f* electrons being added to the shell *beneath*. Divalent cations of the *d* transition elements, as we saw earlier, differ from each other in the number of *d* electrons in their *surface*.

25.5. The Lanthanides

The elements in the first *f* transition are called lanthanides because of their strong resemblance to lanthanum. Since the *f* electrons apparently affect only the colors and the magnetic susceptibilities of the ions, and not their chemical properties, it would be impossible to separate them from each other were it not for the slight decrease in size which accompanies the increase in atomic number. This contraction is shown in Table 25.3; scandium, yttrium, lanthanum, and actinium are included at appropriate places for comparison.

The increase of fourteen units in atomic number, without a new shell being started, results in a total contraction of 0.21 A. This is sufficient to overlap the radius of Y^{+3} ion; but the Lu^{+3}, the smallest lanthanide ion, is still significantly larger than Sc^{+3} ion. The lanthanide contraction has a marked influence on the size of the elements that follow the lanthanides in the periodic table. Thus hafnium (at. no. 72) is nearly the same size as zirconium, the preceding element in its family.

25.6. Chemical Properties of the Lanthanides

Each step in the lanthanide contraction produces a slight increase in electronegativity. Exactly the same thing happens throughout a *d* transition, but there the increase in electronegativity due to the decrease in size merges with and is overshadowed by the increase due to the additional *d* electron in the surface of the ion. The lanthanides provide the first opportunity to observe the effects of an increase in electronegativity along with an increase in charge density. One effect is a steady decrease in the solubility and basic strength of the hydroxides. Similarly, there are regular small changes in the solubilities of their salts with various anions,

TABLE 25.3. **The Lanthanide Contraction**

Element	Symbol	Atomic Number	Atomic Weight	Radius of M^{+3} Ion, A
Actinium	Ac	89	227	1.11
Lanthanum	La	57	138.92	1.06
Cerium	Ce	58	140.13	1.03
Praseodymium	Pr	59	140.92	1.01
Neodymium	Nd	60	144.27	1.00
Promethium	Pm	61	147[a]	
Yttrium	Y	39	88.92	0.96
Samarium	Sm	62	150.35	0.96
Europium	Eu	63	152.0	0.95
Gadolinium	Gd	64	157.26	0.94
Terbium	Tb	65	158.93	0.92
Dysprosium	Dy	66	162.51	0.91
Holmium	Ho	67	164.94	0.89
Erbium	Er	68	167.27	0.88
Thulium	Tm	69	168.94	0.87
Ytterbium	Yb	70	173.04	0.86
Lutecium	Lu	71	174.99	0.85
Scandium	Sc	21	44.96	0.81

[a] Most stable artificial isotope; not found in nature.

some becoming more soluble, others less. The ability to form complex ions increases.

These changes are produced mainly by the decrease in size, which increases the charge density at the surface of the ion. That the f electrons have little to do with the chemical properties is proved by the fact that yttrium, which has no f electrons, is almost indistinguishable chemically from the lanthanides between which it appears in Table 25.3.

Separating one lanthanide from the others in a moderately pure state once involved thousands of tedious fractional crystallizations of first one salt, then another. Several of them had never been separated in any appreciable quantity by that method. Very recently the ion-exchange method was used; and as a result, salts of most of these elements are now available in commercial quantities, and in a purer state than ever before.

When a solution containing a mixture of all the lanthanide cations is poured into the top of a tall column of cation exchange material, all the trivalent ions exchange immediately with univalent ions—e.g., H^+—in the top portion of the exchange material, just as is the case in water softening (Section 15.15). A solution of a complexing agent such as ammonium citrate is then passed slowly down the column. This establishes a series of equilibria between the lanthanide ions which are bonded on the column, and complexes of the same ions which are carried in the solution. The ions leave the solid and form complexes and the complexes dissociate and allow the freed cation to be picked up by the ion exchanger an almost infinite number of times. It is always the smallest ions that are held longest by the downward-moving solution and released most quickly from the solid. If the column is long enough, all the Lu^{+3} ions will emerge from the bottom before any of the Yb^{+3} ions do; then come the Yb^{+3} ions, and so on, in order of increasing size.

25.7. "Anomalous" Lanthanide Valences

The $+3$ oxidation state of the lanthanides is so characteristic of them that there was a tendency to consider other oxidation states which a few of them display as "anomalous." Actually, they are to be expected from the electron structures involved and from analogies with the d transition elements.

The most notable of these extra valences is $+4$ which cerium, the first f transition element, can show. It is possible to remove the single f electron from cerium because it is the least electronegative of the lanthanides. It is not easy to remove the f electron from Ce^{+3} ion. The simple hydrated Ce^{+4} ion which can be present in solutions of $Ce(ClO_4)_4$ is a stronger oxidizing agent than MnO_4^-. In solutions of the sulfate and nitrate, $Ce(IV)$ is more or less complexed with the anion but is still an extremely strong oxidizing agent that is valuable in analytical chemistry. $Pr(IV)$ exists in the strongly covalent oxide; and $Pr(V)$, which would have the La^{+3} and Ce^{+4} structure, has been reported, but its existence is doubtful.

It was pointed out (Section 17.15) that the electronic structures of Mn^{++}, Fe^{+3}, and metallic chromium commonly have 5 unpaired d electrons in the third shell. In the case of Mn^{++} and Fe^{+3} the ions are exceptionally stable, since Mn^{++} is harder to oxidize and Fe^{+3} harder to reduce than would be expected. Both metallic copper and chromium have electron structures with single s electrons in the valence shell.

Cu . . . . _ _ _ _

Cr . . . . _ _ _ _

In both cases, an s electron can be regarded as having shifted into a d orbital in order to complete the electron pairings (in copper) and the filling of d orbitals (in chromium) with 1 electron each. The lanthanides provide evidence that half-filled and filled f subshells (Gd and Lu respectively) have similar extra stability. We might expect all of the lanthanides which have no d electrons to have a possible valence of $+2$. This has not yet been demonstrated for praseodymium. The $+2$ valence does not acquire appreciable stability until samarium, with only one vacant f orbital, is reached. Eu^{++}, with a half-filled f shell, has long been known. Further evidence of the extra stability of the Gd^{+3} structure is furnished by the existence of Tb(IV), which is isoelectronic with it. Similarly, in the second half of the f transition series, the $+2$ valence first makes its appearance in thulium, with one half-filled f orbital. Yb^{++}, with the f shell full, is reasonably stable.

25.8. The Rare Earths

The term earth may be defined in the chemical sense as a metallic oxide that is almost or completely non-basic. (Cf. the *alkaline* earth metals, Group IIA.) When prepared by being precipitated from solution and dried at a moderate temperature, alumina, Al_2O_3, is a typical earth. Names ending in *-a* were given to many earths before the corresponding metal was known; later the metals were named from the earths by changing the *-a* to *-um*.

In 1794 the chemist Gadolin, who lived in the village of Ytterby not far from Stockholm in Scandinavia (called Thule by the Romans), was analyzing some rare minerals. Instead of alumina and silica, the common earths, he separated a new earth which he called yttria. Its history illustrates the difficulties and confusion which workers in this specialized field had to face. In 1842 Gadolin's yttria was broken down into three new portions; they were called yttria, erbia, and terbia, all based on the village name, Ytterby. In 1878 another earth was separated from yttria; this was called ytterbia. Thirty years later, Urbain, in Paris (Lutetia), made still another separation; he retained the name ytterbia for the major portion and named the other portion lutetia. In 1911, Urbain believed that he had separated an oxide of a still heavier element from lutetia and he named it celtium. Later he announced that x-ray spectra identified celtium as element 72 which was as yet undiscovered; however, he was mistaken in regard to both the separation and the spectra. Lutetia contains no heavier element. Ten years later, after work on the theory of transitions had proceeded, Coster in Copenhagen (its Latin name is Hafnia) realized that element 72 could not possibly be a rare earth metal but had to belong in Group IV. He promptly found it in zirconium compounds, in concentrations ranging from 1 to 20 per cent and averaging 5 per cent. Hafnium had escaped notice in supposedly pure zirconium compounds because of the almost identical radius of Zr(IV) and Hf(IV), a result of the lanthanide contraction.

The names of other rare earths indicate similar troubles. Thus lanthana (from the Greek meaning to lie hidden) was found *hidden* in ceria, named in 1803 after the asteroid Ceres which was discovered in 1801. Another rare earth was called didymia (Gr., *didymos,* twin) because it seemed to be almost a *twin* of lanthana. In 1879 didymia was broken down into two portions, the name didymia being retained for one, and the other one being named samaria. In 1885 this didymia was itself broken down into praseodymia (green twin) and neodymia (new twin). Dysprosium means "hard to speak to."

The term rare earth metals is a broader term than lanthanides. It is also an older term, for it definitely includes yttrium—the reasons for this should by now be obvious—and sometimes it has been made to include scandium, although the latter is separated from the others easily enough. Some chemists speak of lanthanum and the lanthanides, limiting the latter to the f transition elements; but it is more usual to include all fifteen elements. In both the long and the short forms of the periodic table all the lanthanides are customarily indicated as belonging in the lanthanum square.

25.9. Uses of the Rare Earths

Monazite sand, the only commercial source of the rare earth metals, is found in many states in this country, as well as in Brazil and India, among other countries. The monazite ore is separated from the sand magnetically. The magnetic properties of the unpaired f electrons make this possible if the magnetic field is sufficiently strong. Monazite is mainly $LaPO_4$ and $CePO_4$, but contains around 10 per cent of thorium, probably as the silicate, and small amounts of zircon, $ZrSiO_4$, and ilmenite, $FeTiO_3$. The phosphate portion also contains smaller quantities of the ions of the other rare earth metals.

Both thorium and cerium are easily separated from the mixture by virtue of the fact that cerium can be oxidized to the $+4$ state—the stable valence state that thorium exhibits. The two elements themselves are easily separated after the cerium is reduced back to its normal $+3$ state. The incandescent gas mantles used in gasoline pressure lanterns are made of thoria, ThO_2, with about 1 per cent ceria, Ce_2O_3.

Carl Auer von Welsbach, who worked with the rare earths almost a century ago, invented this once widely used lighting device after discovering that adding this small amount of ceria increased a hundredfold the amount of light produced when the compound was held in a Bunsen burner flame. CeF_3 is used in the carbon electrodes of flaming arc lights to change the color from blue to white and increase the intensity. Ceria is used to fine-polish lenses; it gives glass a golden-yellow color when added to the mix.

The cerium that remains after the relatively small amount required for the above purposes, is the major ingredient (50 to 75 per cent), along with a mixture of the accompanying rare earth metals and a little iron, of misch metal. Since all the rare earth metals are much more active than aluminum—they approach the alkaline earth metals in this respect— misch metal is an excellent deoxidizer for various metals, and can be used as a getter in vacuum tubes. Its most familiar use, however, is for the so-called "flints" for cigarette lighters and the lighters used to ignite oxyacetylene torches. The hot sparks given off when the material is abraded are burning specks of cerium.

Large amounts of unseparated rare earths were stockpiled for years, awaiting uses which might develop if a practicable method of separating them were found. Ion exchange has provided this method; the uses will undoubtedly follow. However, two uses were sufficiently unique to warrant purification of small amounts of individual elements even with the old methods. Glass-blowers' goggles have lenses of neodymium glass to eliminate the blinding glare of sodium light from the hot glass. When ordinary d transition ions are used to color glass, wide ranges of wave lengths are absorbed. The wave lengths of all the offending orange-yellow light from sodium range from 5890 A. to 5896 A.; but in screening it out with cobalt glass, for example, all the green, yellow, orange, and most of the red are absorbed. This includes all the light to which the eye is most sensitive. The lanthanide ions, on the other hand, have very narrow and very sharp absorption bands, because the unpaired electrons that are responsible for them are the f electrons inside the atom and hence shielded from external disturbances. One of the absorption bands of neodymium ranges from 5650 A. to 5950 A.; it neatly eliminates the sodium wave lengths, but few others. The only other absorption band of importance, from 5000 A. to 5400 A., cuts out the green; the transmitted light is a light pink.

In the second use, $Gd_2(SO_4)_3 \cdot 8H_2O$ has been used for producing temperatures within 0.01° of absolute zero. Because of its 7 unpaired f electrons, Gd^{+3} ion is strongly affected by a magnetic field. A tube of the salt was surrounded by liquid helium which was boiling under reduced pressure. When as much heat energy as possible had been carried off, a strong magnetic field was applied. The magnetization of the Gd^{+3} ions released heat, and this too was carried away by the helium. When the magnetic field was removed, the demagnetization of the Gd^{+3} ions absorbed as much heat as their magnetization had released; in fact, nearly all the remaining heat energy in the salt was used up.

25.10. The Actinides

The planet Uranus was discovered in 1781; it was farther away from the sun than any of the six already known planets. Eight years later Klaproth discovered a new element whose atomic weight was nearly thirty units greater than that of bismuth, the heaviest element known at that time. The name uranium was a natural. Thorium was discovered in 1828. No other actinide was discovered until the end of the century, when extremely minute traces of actinium and protactinium were found, barely enough to indicate that they could have valences of $+3$ and $+5$.

The lanthanides presented an insoluble problem to Mendeleev; he made no attempt to include such of them as he knew about in his periodic table. Thorium and uranium, he thought, presented no problem at all; their respective valences of $+4$ and $+6$ and their high atomic weights placed them at the bottom of Groups IV and VI respectively. There they stayed until the transuranium elements were artificially prepared during and after World War II.

In 1921 Charles R. Bury, of the University College of Wales, proved that the elements with atomic numbers 57 through 71 all belonged in the lanthanum square, and he suggested that thorium and uranium were members of a similar actinide series. The idea of a parallel series was rejected by chemists who were not impressed by Bury's theoretical reasoning, on the grounds that all the members should form trivalent ions. But if elements 89 to 92 were not f transition elements, they had to belong to a d transition. As such, they should have a valence of $+2$ which should become increasingly stable until the end of the transition at element 98; it should be in Group IIB. Furthermore, elements 93 and 94 should have oxidation numbers of $+7$ and $+8$ respectively, like rhenium and osmium. None of these conditions proved to be true. On the contrary, the $+3$ valence becomes more and more stable as the atomic number increases, and the series continues on past 98 without a break. Now no shadow of a doubt remains; all the known elements, with atomic numbers from 89 on up, are f transition elements and belong in the actinium square in the periodic table.

25.11. Thorium and Uranium

Although its $+4$ valence naturally led the early chemists to assign thorium to Group IV, its behavior is quite different from that of titanium, zirconium, and hafnium, the actual Group IVB elements. Because of its relatively low electronegativity, thorium forms the ion Th^{+4}, whereas the IVB elements form covalent compounds. $ThCl_4$ is a true salt; it dissolves in water as ions, without undergoing serious hydrolysis. The same is true of the sulfate and nitrate; on the other hand, such compounds of the IVB elements are hydrolyzed—e.g., to the zirconyl ion, ZrO^{++}—even in concentrated acid.

Thoria, ThO_2, is one of the most refractory oxides known; crucibles of it can stand temperatures up to 2300° C. Its use in gas mantles was mentioned above. Tungsten filaments alloyed with a little thorium are used as cathodes in vacuum tubes because they emit more electrons at a given temperature than pure tungsten does. Thorium is a possible source of nuclear energy. Like all elements with atomic numbers above 82, it is radioactive.

Uranium occurs mainly as pitchblende, except in Colorado, where carnotite is found. In pitchblende, U_3O_8, one-third of the uranium is in the $+4$ state and two-thirds in the $+6$ state. As is commonly the case when two valences of the same metal are present, pitchblende is jet-black. Yellow carnotite is mainly potassium uranyl vanadate, $KUO_2VO_4 \cdot 1\frac{1}{2}H_2O$. Ignition of uranyl carbonate, obtained from this source, forms U_3O_8. In 1959 we produced 17,000 tons of U_3O_8.

Uranium has positive valences of 3, 4, 5, and 6, the latter being the most common. UF_6 sublimes at 56° C.; the resulting gas is treated in the vast installation at Oak Ridge. The fissionable isotope ^{235}U is separated in small quantities from the ordinary isotope ^{238}U by taking advantage of the slightly greater diffusion rate of $^{235}UF_6$. Uranic acid, H_2UO_4, or uranyl hydroxide, $UO_2(OH)_2$—the same substance—is apparently amphoteric in an unusual way. Ordinary amphoteric substances are hydrated hydroxides which gain or lose protons, —OH groups becoming H_2O— groups, and vice versa. The above compound, however, apparently loses either protons to bases, forming uranate ion, UO_4^{--}, or OH^- ions to acids, forming uranyl ion, UO_2^{++}. The formula UO_2^{++} seems to be the actual formula, and not a conventionally "dehydrated" formula for $U(OH)_4^{++}$. The oxygen-uranium distance is shorter than normal, and it has been suggested that f orbitals are concerned in some way with the bonding. If so, the compound would be unique in that respect. However, the UO_2^{++} ion is unique among the -yl compounds in that it can exist as an independent cation in solution, whereas the others exist only in covalent compounds—e.g., insoluble antimonyl chloride, SbOCl, and liquid chromyl chloride, CrO_2Cl_2. Sodium uranate, or uranium yellow, is used for painting porcelain and for making yellow glass that has a greenish fluorescence. When people speak of "uranium" salts, they usually refer to uranyl salts. $UO_2(NO_3)_2 \cdot 6H_2O$ is the salt that is commonly available in laboratories; it is used as a red-brown "toner" for photographic prints.

25.12. Chemical Properties of the Subgroup Elements

Gallium, indium, and thallium, like boron and aluminum, have 2 s electrons and 1 p electron in their valence shells, but differ from the two light elements in that the shell below contains 10 d electrons. The effect of d electrons on electronegativity has already been discussed. The electronegativities of these subgroup elements increase slightly with increasing atomic weight and are larger than those of aluminum and the rest of the main group. Gallium and indium are accordingly less active than aluminum; indium is not attacked by air or boiling water, and has been used as a flash plate on silver to prevent tarnishing. Thallium would be the least active of the group if, as is true of the others, its only stable valence was $+3$. But the p electron in the valence shell of thallium can be removed rather easily; this leaves it with the inert pair of s electrons. (This loss of p electrons from thallium, lead, and bismuth, and the retention of the s electrons, was described in Section 19.9.)

The trivalent ions have increasingly strong covalent tendencies. Ga^{+3} and In^{+3} can replace Al^{+3} in alums; all the ions that do this—the trivalent ions of Ti, V, Cr, Mn, Fe, Co, Rh, and Ir are the others—are larger than Al^{+3}, but are of the non-inert gas type and behave as though they were smaller than they really are. Sc^{+3}, a rare gas type of ion that is practically the same size as In^{+3}, does not form alums. Tl^{+3} ion is too large to form alums even though it has 10 d electrons in its surface. Tl^+ ion forms alums, but replaces the K^+ ion, not the Al^{+3}. All the oxyacid salts of Tl^+ are isomorphous with the corresponding K^+ salts. As was mentioned in Section 10.9, the thallous halides resemble the corresponding silver halides in solubility. The inert pair of s electrons in the valence shell increases the size of the ion to 1.49 A.; hence the d electrons beneath have no effect on difficultly polarizable ions like NO_3^-, SO_4^{--}, ClO_4^-, and F^-.

But they can still lower the solubility of TlCl, TlBr, and TlI by causing some degree of covalent bonding with the more easily polarizable anions in those crystals.

QUESTIONS AND PROBLEMS

1. How do the ions of the main family in Group III differ structurally from those of the subgroup family in Group III?

2. Discuss the differences in trend and behavior in main groups and subgroups.

3. Do similarity of properties and characteristics of ions necessarily mean that they belong to the same periodic group? Give some examples in your answer.

4. Distinguish between a d transition and an f transition. How often does the latter occur in the periodic table? What is each of the series called that this transition affects? What is the characteristic valence of the f transition elements?

5. Distinguish between the electronic structure of d and f transition ions.

6. What is meant by the lanthanide contraction? What is its significance for elements with larger atomic numbers than the lanthanides have?

7. What are some of the valences, other than $+3$, that certain f transition elements display? Indicate why some of these are logical.

26

Nuclear transformations

26.1. Transmutation of Elements

To the alchemists of the Middle Ages it seemed perfectly reasonable that lead might be "purified" into silver or silver ennobled into gold, by proper treatment. If black brittle galena could be "turned into" gray soft lead, why not dull lead into beautiful silver? To them the term element indicated one of the "principles" from whose combination in various proportions they imagined that all substances could be obtained. These "principles" were originally Aristotle's four—earth, air, fire, and water. Later they were the *tria prima*—salt, sulfur, and mercury—which embodied the principles of earthiness, flammability, and metallicity.

Early in the sixteenth century Paracelsus stated that the true aim of alchemy should be the preparation of medicines, not gold. The study of substances during the next century or so led to the discovery that while most substances could be decomposed into simpler substances, there were some that could not. In 1661 Robert Boyle, the first real chemist, concluded that these undecomposable substances were that way by nature, and that all other substances were composed of combinations of a relatively small number of these elements. "I mean by elements," he wrote, "certain primitive and simple, or perfectly unmingled bodies; which not being made of other bodies or of one another, are the ingredients of which all those perfectly mixed bodies are immediately compounded, and into which they are ultimately resolved."

Boyle's statement was eventually simplified; accordingly an element was defined as a substance which cannot be decomposed by any chemical means. In 1896, however, Becquerel discovered radioactivity; and the work of the Curies and others showed that radioactivity actually does involve the transmutation of the elements. (Unfortunately, it seems, the transmutations end with lead, instead of leading from it.) The phrase "by any chemical means," which had been included in the definition more or less by accident, proved to be the salvation of the definition. Radioactive changes, it appeared, could very well be excluded from the category of chemical changes on two grounds. In the first place, these changes were not subject to human control. Changes in temperature, pressure, or state of chemical combination of the radioactive element had no effect. Each radioactive transformation goes on inexorably at its own individual rate regardless of anything. In the second place, the amount of energy involved in radioactivity was of an entirely different order of magnitude from that involved in chemical changes—a million or more times as great, in fact. Hence during the present century the accent has been on the word chemical whenever the early definition of element is mentioned.

Radioactivity supplied the tool which enabled Rutherford to prove that the mass of atoms is concentrated almost entirely in their nuclei, each nucleus peculiar to a particular element and each surrounded by a relatively large cloud of electrons that are identical in all atoms. Moseley's discovery of the atomic number in 1913, coupled with Soddy's work on the nature of isotopes, furnished the remaining facts that were needed to frame a modern definition of an element. Today an element is defined as consisting of all atoms which have the same nuclear charge, or atomic number.

Hence transmutation of one element into another involves a nuclear change, whereas chemical changes affect only some of the outer electrons.

26.2. The Nucleus

We have seen that the nucleus of an atom is composed of protons and, in every case except the light isotope of hydrogen, of neutrons. The laws governing the interactions of these particles are barely beginning to be understood, so no attempt will be made to discuss them here. However, certain empirical facts will be noted. For light elements the number of neutrons tends to be equal to the number of protons. Not until neon is there an isotope of an appreciable abundance in which the number of neutrons exceeds the number of protons by 2. As the atomic number increases, the excess of neutrons over protons tends to increase gradually. $^{36}_{16}S$ is the first nucleus in which the excess of neutrons is greater than 2; $^{58}_{29}Cu$ is the last in which there is no excess of neutrons. Eventually in the heaviest elements, the ratio of neutrons to protons slightly exceeds 1.5 : 1.

There is a sharp alternation between more and less abundant species as the atomic number increases. Almost without exception, elements with even atomic numbers are more abundant than their odd-numbered neighbors. They also have more isotopes (tin has 10); the majority of odd-numbered elements consist of but one stable (non-radioactive) isotope, and none of these elements has more than two. Accompanying this odd and even alternation is a general tendency for the heavier elements to be less abundant.

There is an even stronger tendency for the nucleus to contain an even number of neutrons. Thus the mass number (neutrons + protons) is odd for practically all elements with odd atomic numbers, and even for all but a few of the others.

26.3. Unstable Nuclei

Nuclei are unstable if (1) the neutron-to-proton ratio is too high for the atomic number; (2) the neutron-to-proton ratio is too low for the atomic number; (3) the atomic number is above 82; (4) there are more than 126 neutrons; or (5) there is a stable isobar, i.e., a nucleus with an identical number of neutrons + protons, whose atomic number differs by only one unit.

All stable nuclei occur in nature; without exception, all nuclei which have been made artificially are unstable unless they are identical with already known natural nuclei. Unstable nuclei also occur in nature, but only if their rate of decay is very slow, or if they are continually produced by the decay of long-lived nuclei or the action of cosmic rays. Apparently the process of creation of elements was such as to produce all conceivable types of nuclei, of which only the more stable ones have survived.

Unstable nuclei become stable nuclei at rates which differ for each species but which have one feature in common. In all cases the number of nuclei which change per second is proportional to the number of such nuclei present, and only to this; specifically, as mentioned before, it does not depend upon temperature or state of chemical combination. Therefore, in view of this proportionality, the number of nuclei that change per second in any sample of material will decrease as the number of unchanged atoms decreases. Theoretically this means that for all the nuclei in any given sample to change would take an infinite time. But the time required for *half* the nuclei to change is finite, and inversely proportional to the characteristic proportionality constant of the rate of change. This period of time, called the **half-life,** is used to identify unstable isotopes. The half-lives which have been measured range from 10^{-7} second to 10^{14} years. For comparison, apparently the earth was created about 5×10^{9} years ago.

26.4. Radioactivity

Whenever an unstable nucleus becomes a more stable one, energy is released. Particles may or may not be emitted. If they are, they are emitted with tremendous energy. The velocities range from a few thousand miles per second for the heavier particles up to 95 per cent of the velocity of light for the lightest particles in the most energetic changes. When a particle is shot out from a nucleus it is often accompanied by a flash of invisible "light" of very high frequency and correspondingly high energy. In some cases the flash of light may take place without the emission of a particle. Some of this light is identical with ordinary x-rays; the rest, of even higher vibration frequency and greater energy, is called gamma (γ) radiation. Very energetic light quanta are so like particles in their behavior that they are commonly referred to as **photons.**

The emission of photons or material particles by nuclei is called **radioactivity.** The nuclei that radiate them are said to undergo **radioactive decay.** The kind of radiation emitted is dependent upon the instability of the particular nucleus.

In the most common form of radioactive decay there are too many neutrons for the number of protons that are present. This might be remedied by the emission of a neutron. Actually, however, neutrons are emitted only when the nucleus is in a high state of agitation as the result of an artificially induced transmutation such as will be described shortly. Unless the neutron is emitted within a microsecond or so of the time when the nucleus was formed, stabilization will be attained in a different way. That is, one of the excess neutrons will be converted into a proton and an electron, and the electron will be ejected at high velocity as a beta (β) ray. An interesting example of a beta change is provided by the decay of ^{14}C which is used in the radioactive-carbon dating of archaeological objects. ^{14}C has a relatively short half-life of 5100 years. There would be no measurable amount of ^{14}C in existence if the supply were not continually replenished by the action of cosmic rays on the N_2 in the atmosphere. All living things are in equilibrium with atmospheric CO_2, and since ^{14}C is evenly distributed in the CO_2 in the atmosphere, all contain the same proportion of ^{14}C; but as soon as they die, the intake of ^{14}C from the atmosphere ceases. The ^{14}C in the organism continues to decay according to the reaction:

$$^{14}_{6}C \rightarrow {}^{14}_{7}N + e^-$$

If the nucleus contains too few neutrons for the number of protons in it, the reverse changes takes place, as with $_{47}Ag^{106}$.

$$^{106}_{47}Ag \rightarrow {}^{106}_{46}Pd + e^+$$

The positive counterpart of the electron in the above equation is called a **positron.** Positrons were discovered by C. D. Anderson of the California Institute of Technology in 1932. The life of a positron is always terminated in a small fraction of a second by one of the following reactions:

$$\text{Positron} + \text{Electron} \rightleftharpoons \text{Gamma rays}$$

$$\text{Positron} + \text{Neutron} \rightleftharpoons \text{Proton} + \text{Energy}$$

The positron is thought not to be a constituent of matter but to be formed at the moment of its ejection from a nucleus by the reverse of the second reaction immediately above. The energy is not necessarily radiant energy; it may be potential energy from force fields within a nucleus, or kinetic energy from a colliding high-velocity particle. Similarly it is believed that the electrons of beta rays are not part of the nucleus from which they are ejected, but are created at that moment by means of the reversible reaction:

$$\text{Neutron} + \text{Energy} \rightleftharpoons \text{Proton} + \text{Electron}$$

In a few cases, all of them involving synthetic radioisotopes, a deficiency of neutrons is remedied by the capture of an electron from an inner shell by the nucleus. As a result, one of the protons in the nucleus becomes a neutron, the reaction being the reverse of that in the last equation above. After the capture of this electron, an outer orbital electron falls into the vacant orbital, and a characteristic x-ray photon is radiated. $_{26}^{55}$Fe decays in this manner.

$$e^- + {}_{26}^{55}\text{Fe} \rightarrow {}_{25}^{55}\text{Mn}$$

If a nucleus is too large for stability, it may eject an alpha (α) particle, $_2^4$He; and the resulting nucleus, if still too large, may eject another alpha particle, and so on. $_{92}^{238}$U, the heaviest nucleus existing in nature in appreciable quantities, has to lose eight alpha particles before it reaches stability as $_{82}^{206}$Pb. Since protons and neutrons are lost in equal numbers by the emission of alpha particles, the neutron-to-proton ratio increases gradually and must be readjusted occasionally by beta changes. These alpha and beta changes are illustrated by the first three steps in the decay of the common isotope of uranium.

$$_{92}^{238}\text{U} \rightarrow {}_{90}^{234}\text{Th} + {}_2^4\text{He}$$
$$_{90}^{234}\text{Th} \rightarrow {}_{91}^{234}\text{Pa} + e^-$$
$$_{91}^{234}\text{Pa} \rightarrow {}_{92}^{234}\text{U} + e^-$$

26.5. Radioactive Series

If the total number of protons and neutrons in a heavy nucleus is divisible by 4, the corresponding number—the **mass number**—of every nucleus produced from it by successive alpha changes must also be divisible by 4. This is true, regardless of any intervening beta changes. Similarly, if when the mass number of the parent nucleus is divided by 4 there is a remainder of 1, there must be a remainder of 1 when the mass numbers of all the daughter nuclei are divided by 4. Thus there are four independent radioactive decay series among the natural heavy elements.

The four disintegration series are named for the heaviest member that was known at the time of discovery. The thorium ($4n$) series begins with $_{90}^{232}$Th, which has a half-life of 1.39×10^{10} years. This means that more than three-quarters of the thorium originally formed is still in existence. The final member of this series is $_{82}^{208}$Pb. The ($4n + 1$) series is not found in nature, for none of its members have long enough half-lives to have persisted in detectable quantities for five billion years. However, it is the source of the only long-lived isotope of bismuth, $_{83}^{209}$Bi. It is called the neptunium series after $_{93}^{237}$Np, the first member of the series to be synthesized, and the most stable member, with a half-life of 2.25×10^6 years. Several higher members have since been prepared. The first radioactive decay series to be discovered is the uranium ($4n + 2$) series, discovered by the Curies. The parent is $^{238}_{92}U$, with a half-life of 4.51×10^9 years; 46 per cent of the amount originally formed is still in existence. The actinium ($4n + 3$) series begins with the fissile isotope of uranium, $^{235}_{92}U$; its half-life is 7.07×10^8 years. Originally half as plentiful as $^{238}_{92}U$, only 1/90 of it now remains; this amounts to 0.71 per cent of the natural isotopic mixture. Like all series except the neptunium, the actinium series also ends in an isotope of lead.

None of the relatively short-lived isotopes which are produced as intermediate decay products in these series are leftovers from the earth's original supply. Like ^{14}C, they are continually replenished, though from earthly not cosmic sources. Their quantities represent a special sort of equilibrium, an equilibrium between rate of formation and rate of decay, just as the earth's population of any living species represents an equilibrium between the birth and death rates. In any mixture which has remained undisturbed long enough to attain this **radioactive equilibrium,** such as a piece of uranium ore, the amount of any of these short-lived radioactive intermediate isotopes in the radioactive decay mixture—e.g., radium—is a definite fraction of the amount of the long-lived parent—in this case, uranium—that is present.

The work done by the Curies, Lord Rutherford, Soddy, Fajans, and others around the turn of the century resulted in the identification of some forty isotopes in the naturally occurring disintegration series and the working out of the relationships between them. This was done without any knowledge of the relation between nuclear charge and chemical properties, or even, indeed, of the existence of a nucleus, and in spite of the generally accepted idea that the most fundamental property of an atom was weight. The achievements of these workers were truly remarkable and provided much of the foundation of our present knowledge about the structure of atoms.

Anyone who reads the fascinating story of their work will note the almost completely unfamiliar names for the various isotopes. Since some sort of designation was necessary as each new isotope was described, in the absence of any knowledge as to the element involved it was usually assigned a name that indicated in some way its relationship to the parent element. Thus the $4n$ series includes thoron, mesothorium 1 and 2, and thorium A, B, C, C′, C″, and D. In the $4n + 2$ series there are uranium I, II, X_1, X_2, and Z, ionium, and radium A, B, C, C′, C″, D, E, E″, F, and G. The $4n + 3$ series contains actino-uranium, uranium Y, actinon, radio-actinium, and actinium A, B, C, C', C'', D, K, X, and Y. Some of these names are still used occasionally.

26.6. Effects of Radiation

Extremely energetic radiation, whether of particles or photons, can break chemical bonds. In some cases this is desirable. Thus thermoplastics are irradiated to produce a controlled amount of cross linking, for whenever a hydrogen atom is broken off of a carbon atom in one chain, the carbon atom displaces a hydrogen atom from a neighboring chain and forms a C—C bond. This process, which is the equivalent of vulcanization, hardens the plastic and raises its softening point.

Any living cell can be destroyed by a sufficient dose of radiation. Some of the early workers with radioactive materials suffered deep and severe burns before this fact was discovered. Because cancer cells are more susceptible to radiation than normal cells, radioactive materials have proved valuable in cancer therapy. The use of radiation in the sterilization of foods is being studied, but at present it apparently imparts more off-flavors than sterilizing by heat does.

Radiation is measured in units called **roentgens,** in honor of the discoverer of x-rays. The absorption of 1000 roentgens by the human body results in almost certain death within thirty days; with half that quantity, there is a 50-50 chance for survival. In the H-bomb explosion off Bikini in 1956, twenty-three Japanese fishermen received about 200 roentgens. Three years later one of them died, presumably but not certainly because of exposure. The others were in good health and back at work. An unexpected shift in the wind exposed the sixty-four inhabitants of Rongelap to 175 roentgens. Although they experienced various unpleasant symptoms, the entire group had recovered completely six months later. In view of these experiences, the generally accepted safety limit of 10 roentgens per year seems reasonably conservative.

When luminous watch dials first went on the market, the girls who painted them with radium kept shaping their brushes in their mouths, contrary to instructions. The Ra^{++} ion thus absorbed was carried to and retained in their bones because of the family resemblance to Ca^{++}. A number of these girls eventually developed bone cancer, presumably as the result. The incidence of leukemia, or blood cancer, among radiologists is several times the normal incidence. It has been suggested, but not proved, that even small amounts of radiation increase the likelihood of this disease developing. It is known that radiation can produce genetic mutations. For all these reasons, it is well worth while for all of us to consider the amounts of radiation to which we are exposed from various sources, including radioactive fall-out from nuclear explosions.

26.7. Radiation from Our Environment

Uranium and its decay products are present almost everywhere in minute but measurable quantities. The amount which through geologic accident has been concentrated into ore that can be mined is a tiny fraction of the whole. The same is true with regard to thorium. It is estimated that the average igneous rock contains 4 g. of uranium and 11.5 g. of thorium per metric ton. Ra^{++} ion from rocks and soil is present in all ground water, along with its more abundant relative, Ca^{++} ion.

The thorium and uranium series are not the only source of radioactivity in our surroundings, although they are the largest natural source. Seven lighter elements have one long-lived radioactive isotope: $^{40}_{19}K$, $^{87}_{37}Rb$, $^{115}_{49}In$, $^{150}_{60}Nd$, $^{152}_{62}Sm$, $^{176}_{71}Lu$, and $^{187}_{75}Re$. Of these, $^{152}_{62}Sm$ emits alpha rays; the others emit beta rays. In addition, two short-lived isotopes are maintained at a low concentration by cosmic rays: $^{3}_{1}H$, frequently called tritium, and $^{14}_{6}C$. None of these elements are parents of long decay chains. The product of the radioactive change is a familiar stable isotope in all cases except $^{150}_{60}Nd$; the latter produces $^{150}_{61}Pm$. Although it has no stable isotope, prometheum has not been isolated in sufficient quantity so that we can determine what becomes of it. Because of the way our bodies concentrate potassium, by far the most important of these seven isotopes is $^{40}_{19}K$, 0.011 per cent of which is the radioactive isotope. The much shorter half-life of $^{14}_{6}C$ compared with that of $^{40}_{19}K$ (5×10^3 years and 1.8×10^9 years respectively) means that its specific rate of decay is 3×10^6 times as great, but it is so scarce that it accounts for only 3 per cent of the body's radioactivity. The radioactivity from the above sources to which we are exposed amounts to about 0.12 roentgen a year.

Cosmic rays are another source, the dosage from them varying from 0.035 roentgen at sea level to 0.05 roentgen at an altitude of 1 mile—e.g., Denver—and to considerably greater amounts at some of the higher altitudes such as Peru and Tibet. Our houses constitute a further source—only 0.01 roentgen for a wooden house, but 0.04 for a brick one. A wrist watch with a luminous dial can contribute 0.03 roentgen; a single chest x-ray, 0.10. The present level of radiation due to radioactive fall-out from nuclear explosions is 0.003 roentgen per year. It is estimated that if nuclear tests were continued at the rate prior to the cessation of the

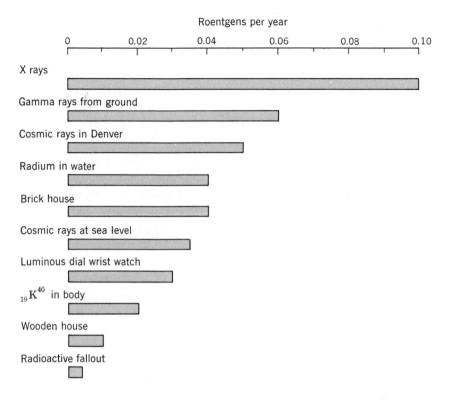

Fig. 26.1. Radiation absorbed by the average individual from various sources, in roentgens per year.

test program, this amount would level off at about 0.015 roentgen. The total amount of radiation a resident of the United States is likely to receive in a year may range anywhere from 0.17 roentgen to 0.36 roentgen, and more if he needs frequent x-rays. As Fig. 26.1 makes clear, the amount due to radioactive fall-out is small compared to the difference between that involved in living at sea level or in the mountains, or in a brick house instead of a wooden house, and negligible compared to that resulting from the incautious use of x-rays.

About 10 per cent of all the mutations which occur naturally in our genes are caused by radiation. (The rest are caused by heat and chemicals.) The nuclear explosions have increased our exposure to radiation by about 1 per cent, and therefore the number of mutations by about 0.1 per cent. Most gene mutations are harmful, and some are lethal, but some are beneficial. It is the preservation of the beneficial mutations that is the basis of all evolution, including that of man.

26.8. Nuclear Synthesis

The artificial production of new nuclei is accomplished by adding a particle to an existing nucleus. The most important particle for this purpose is the neutron because a nucleus does not repel an approaching neutron. These transmutations may be produced by neutrons of all velocities, from thermal (on the order of 1 mile per second) up to those evolved in nuclear explosions, which may be 10^3 times as rapid. Nuclei differ widely from each other in readiness to absorb neutrons. Thus zirconium, which is used as a construction material in nuclear reactors because of its low absorption of neutrons, must first be freed from hafnium on account of the latter's high absorption. Cadmium, with a particularly high rate of neutron absorption, is used to control nuclear reactors; graphite, particularly low in this respect, is used to slow fast neutrons down. Some nuclei absorb slow neutrons more readily than fast ones; for other nuclei, the reverse is true. The result of the absorption of neutrons may be different in the two cases. Thus absorption of a fast neutron by $^{238}_{92}U$ produces fission, whereas absorption of a slow neutron starts the decay chain:

$$^{238}_{92}U + ^{1}_{0}n \rightarrow ^{239}_{92}U \xrightarrow[23.5 \text{ min.}]{\beta-} ^{239}_{93}Np \xrightarrow[2.3 \text{ days}]{\beta-} ^{239}_{94}Pu$$

This series illustrates the fact that although the absorption of a neutron may have no immediate effect on the charge on the nucleus, it may result in the formation of elements with higher atomic numbers. The reverse may also be true, as in the natural production of ^{14}C from nitrogen. The impact of a cosmic ray neutron on $^{14}_{7}N$ causes it to emit a proton, and $^{14}_{6}C$ is formed. In other cases the absorption of a neutron results in the emission of an alpha particle, or of *two* neutrons. All natural nuclei except $^{4}_{2}He$ have been transmuted by means of neutrons.

Charged particles can also be used to bombard nuclei and form heavier nuclei with a higher charge. The particles most commonly used are protons, $^{1}_{1}H$, deuterons, $^{2}_{1}H$, and alpha particles, $^{4}_{2}He$; but heavier ones up to $^{16}_{8}O$ have also been used. The latter was used in the synthesis of fermium; the reaction is:

$$^{238}_{92}U + ^{16}_{8}O \rightarrow ^{250}_{100}Fm + 4 ^{1}_{0}n$$

Because of the repulsion between like charges, these reactions require high energies and are relatively inefficient with all but the lightest nuclei. The reaction:

$$^{4}_{2}He + ^{9}_{4}Be \rightarrow ^{12}_{6}C + ^{1}_{0}n$$

is a convenient small source of neutrons. The alpha particles are provided by radon. Nuclear reactors in which fission is taking place by chain reaction (Section 26.10) provide an unlimited source of neutrons.

The energies of particles from naturally radioactive isotopes range between 4 and 8 Mev. (One million electron volts per atom is equal to 2.31 $\times$ 10^7 kcal./mole. The energies of chemical reactions are rarely more than 2 $\times$ 10^2 kcal./mole.) These energies are sufficient to produce reactions involving light nuclei; but for the transuranium elements, energies in the billion-electron-volt (Bev) range are needed. These are provided by **particle accelerators** (atom smashers) of fantastic size and cost. The particle may move in a straight line down an evacuated tube that may be miles in length, or make millions of revolutions in a circular path under the control of great magnets, energy increments being imparted to it by radar waves or successive applications of powerful electric fields. The names of these machines are too numerous even to list; most of them end in -*tron*, e.g., cyclotron.

26.9. The Transuranium Elements

The chemistry of the transuranium elements was discussed in Chapter 25 in connection with the actinide group to which they all belong. The transuranium elements are the members of the actinide series from atomic numbers 93 to 103 inclusive. Plutonium is prepared in quantity from uranium by the reaction shown in Section 26.8. The reaction produces other isotopes as well, since more than one neutron may be absorbed; as many as 15 neutrons are absorbed in the formation of $^{254}_{100}$Fm from $^{239}_{94}$Pu. Because $^{241}_{94}$Pu has a half-life of 2.5 $\times$ 10^4 years, it can be stored for use as a nuclear explosive, but the heaviest elements in this series have very short half-lives. Only a few *atoms* of some of them have been prepared, being recognized by their disintegration energies as they decomposed.

The names of these new elements are of some interest, and in discussing them a comparison with the corresponding lanthanides is convenient. In the accompanying tabulation the atomic number is given below each element; the last line indicates the number of f electrons.

La	Ce	Pr	Nd	Pm	Sm	Eu	Gd	Tb	Dy	Ho	Er	Tm	Yb	Lu
57	58	59	60	61	62	63	64	65	66	67	68	69	70	71

Ac	Th	Pa	U	Np	Pu	Am	Cm	Bk	Cf	Es	Fm	Md	No	Lw(?)
89	90	91	92	93	94	95	96	97	98	99	100	101	102	103

0	1	2	3	4	5	6	7	8	9	10	11	12	13	14

Elements 93 and 94, the two next beyond uranium, were named neptunium and plutonium after Neptune and Pluto, the two planets beyond Uranus that were discovered in 1846 and 1930 respectively. The next two actinides were named by analogy with the corresponding lanthanides. Americium is an obvious counter to europium. Curium honors the Curies, who laid the groundwork for work on the radioactive elements (all the actinides are radioactive), just as gadolinium honors Gadolin for his work on the rare earths. Similarly, berkelium and californium commemorate the place where most of the transuranium elements were made, just as terbium, erbium, and ytterbium commemorate Ytterby, and holmium Stockholm. Einsteinium was so named in honor of Einstein for his famous equation relating mass and energy. Element 100 was called fermium after Fermi, who was in charge of the construction of the first nuclear reactor. Mendelevium received its name because the transuranium elements contributed so much to our understanding of Mendeleev's periodic system. Nobelium was so called because part of the work on these elements was done in the Nobel Institute. For element 103, prepared at Berkeley in 1960, the name lawrencium, symbol Lw, has been suggested in honor of Lawrence, builder of the first cyclotron and director of the Radiation Laboratory. It had not yet been officially adopted as this book went to press. If element 104 is ever prepared it will be in Group IV.

26.10. Fission

If sufficient energy is released when a particle enters a nucleus, the nucleus breaks into two roughly equal parts. This is called **fission.** Large numbers of light fragments corresponding to a decrease of up to 30 units in mass number and of up to 14 units in charge may also be produced. This is called **spallation.** Spalling occurs only when the bombarding particles are highly energetic. Thermal neutrons are adequate to cause fission in ^{235}U; they are neutrons which have the same kinetic energy as any other molecule at room temperature. Fission has been produced in many different elements by neutrons, protons, deuterons, alpha particles, and even gamma rays; it also occurs spontaneously in some isotopes. At the present time the neutron-induced fission of isotopes of thorium, uranium, and plutonium is of the greatest interest.

When a heavy atom undergoes fission, the lighter nuclei thus produced have the same neutron-to-proton ratio as the original nucleus, but this ratio is too high to be stable for the fission products with their lowered atomic numbers. At the instant of fission, while the new nuclei are still highly excited, they may emit neutrons. Thus $^{235}_{92}$U emits an average of $2\frac{1}{2}$ neutrons. Each of these can in turn cause fission in another atom; hence a branching chain reaction is initiated. Unless the neutrons either escape to the outside as fast as they are formed or are absorbed in non-fissile nuclei, within an inconceivably short time the whole mass reacts and a nuclear explosion takes place.

The nuclei of atoms present a very small target for neutrons to hit. A relatively large mass of natural uranium would be required to prevent the escape of neutrons produced by the spontaneous fission of a $^{235}_{92}$U nucleus in its interior. The size of this **critical mass** can be brought to within practical limits by the use of moderators. A **moderator** is a substance that has light, stable nuclei which deflect and at the same time slow down most neutrons that strike them. This not only diminishes the rate at which the neutrons escape, but increases the rate of fission of $^{235}_{92}$U, which fissions with thermal neutrons but not with fast ones. Graphite and deuterium oxide (heavy water) are regularly used as moderators. The size of the critical mass can be decreased still further by using uranium which has been enriched with $^{235}_{92}$U.

26.11. Power from Fission

Great as the energy from radioactivity is, compared with that from chemical reactions, the energy released by nuclear fission is far greater. For $^{235}_{92}$U it is some 200 Mev per atom. The fission of 1 g. of it produces as much heat as the combustion of *1500 tons* of coal. This offers hope to a power-hungry world in a period of diminishing fossil fuel reserves. It also raises difficult problems for chemists.

The first problem confronting chemists is extracting uranium economically from its low-grade ores. Great progress has been made here, but much more is needed. The second problem concerns the discovery and preparation of construction materials which will withstand the severe conditions in a nuclear reactor. Such materials must resist not merely ordinary corrosion and high temperatures, but terrific neutron bombardment. Zirconium and titanium have proved to be outstanding in this respect. The third chemical task involves the heat transfer medium. Water is at a disadvantage because its vapor pressure is extremely high at temperatures that are high enough for thermodynamic efficiency. Repairing leaks in a violently radioactive reactor is far from simple; and sodium, sodium-potassium alloy, and high-boiling organic liquids are being tried out. There is also the problem of salvaging the fuel elements. These become unusable long before the uranium supply is exhausted, because of the accumulation of fission products, some of which are avid neutron absorbers. The large number of elements involved makes the chemistry of the purification process very complex. Finally there is the problem of disposing of the radioactive wastes.

All these problems involving chemistry contribute to the cost of nuclear power. Another important factor in regard to cost is the fantastic precautions required on account of the tremendous amount of radioactivity involved. All told, nuclear power is definitely not cheap power at present. The United States, which is blessed with an abundant fuel supply, is wise in not building numerous large power plants that will necessarily operate at a loss, but instead concentrating on experimental work which will doubtless render obsolete all the installations planned at present. The situation is of course different in countries in which fuel is scarce or of poor quality, or has to be transported long distances. The British believe that for them the use of nuclear power is now economical.

26.12.   Metals Used in Reactors

Some of the metals used in nuclear reactors are familiar. Aluminum and magnesium, for example, are used to contain the fuel elements because of their low absorption of neutrons and correspondingly low induced radioactivity. However, magnesium is of far greater importance in the thermal reduction of the less familiar metals. The major reason why many if not most of the reactor metals are unfamiliar is not their scarcity so much as the difficulty of preparation. They may be too active to be reduced by means of carbon, or they may form carbides. Although aluminothermy, i.e., the Thermit process, is frequently useful with such metals, the **Kroll process** is the method of choice at present. This process, only recently developed on a large scale, involves the reduction of volatile metal halides by one of the very active metals. The production of titanium from $TiCl_4$ by this process consumed over 12,000 tons of magnesium and 18,000 tons of sodium in 1957. Thousands of tons of uranium of an extremely high purity have been produced by reducing UF_4 with magnesium. Zirconium, hafnium, and beryllium are also produced on a smaller but rapidly increasing scale.

The use of sodium as a coolant was mentioned in the preceding section. Sodium-potassium alloy, also mentioned there, has the advantage of being liquid at room temperature. If sodium vapor is brought into contact with molten KCl in a distillation column packed with stainless-steel rings, sodium-potassium alloy or pure potassium can be made to distill out under the proper conditions.

Titanium, a metal with outstanding resistance to high temperature oxidation, is about as strong as steel and less than 60 per cent as heavy. In 1950, a titanium industry could scarcely be said to exist; production of a piece that weighed several pounds was a technical achievement, and the total output was 75 tons. Six years later, 6000-lb. ingots were being rolled, and total production in 1957 was over 17,000 tons. Since 1957 titanium production has fallen sharply because of business recessions coupled with military cutbacks in jet plane production. This is reflected in the 5000-ton output in 1959; most of this went into military aircraft but part was used in nuclear reactors.

Zirconium is an even newer metal than titanium. Its commercial production began in 1953, when a single company manufactured 75 tons. In 1958 the output was more than 3000 tons, and the price had dropped from $12.50 to $7 per pound for the reactor grade (low hafnium content). It is hoped that the price can be lowered to $3.50 per pound when the supply becomes sufficient for the commercial demand. The tendency of zirconium to capture neutrons is 82 per cent as great as that of aluminum, but only 6 per cent that of stainless steel. It also surpasses aluminum in ability to retain its strength at moderately high temperatures. Of even greater importance is its outstanding resistance to corrosion by heat-transfer media, such as water or fused sodium, above 260° C. Zirconium was used in the piping and other components of the nuclear-powered submarine *Nautilus*. It is also used as a cladding material to prevent a reaction occurring between graphite and liquid sodium. In the 100,000-kw. reactor recently put into operation at Shippingport, Pennsylvania, 110 lb. of enriched uranium was alloyed with zirconium, rolled into thin plates $2\frac{1}{2}$ in. wide and 6 ft. long, and cladded with pure zirconium. These were stacked a fraction of an inch apart and welded into boxlike units which were assembled into a core. Twelve tons of natural uranium in the form of U_3O_8 were compressed into pellets the size of an eraser on a pencil. These were loaded into 95,000 tubes of zirconium 10 in. in diameter. After being welded shut to prevent the escape of fission products, these tubes were assembled in long bundles; spacers welded in place permitted water to circulate around each tube and formed a jacket around the core. In this reactor, water under a pressure of 1 ton p.s.i. is both the moderator and the heat-transfer fluid.

The Atomic Energy Commission bought 350 lb. of niobium in 1955 at $98 per pound. In 1958 it bought 30 tons at prices as low as $55 per pound. Niobium is suitable for cladding cores of fast reactors, for it surpasses zirconium, molybdenum, and vanadium in resisting heat and corrosion. It is low in neutron absorption; fuel plates for one experimental

5000-kw. reactor contain 250 lb. of niobium in the form of an alloy which is 1 per cent niobium, 5 per cent zirconium, and 94 per cent uranium. Like vanadium, the preceding element in Group VB, niobium has for some time been used as an alloying agent in steel. It is particularly effective in preventing the precipitation of carbides in stainless steels between 400° and 800° C. As much as 20,000 tons of such steels could be used annually in nuclear energy equipment alone by 1962, it has been estimated. Niobium alloys are being developed which it is hoped will permit an increase of 250° C. in the operating temperature of jet engines, with resulting considerable greater efficiency. A new chemical process for producing niobium oxide from its ores involves a liquid-liquid separation process and may lower the price of the metal to $10 or $12 a pound.

In 1958 the Atomic Energy Commission contracted for an annual supply of beryllium amounting to 25 tons per year for several years. Beryllium is light (its density is two-thirds that of aluminum) and strong, and has a high melting point, 1350° C. It slows down high-energy neutrons and reflects thermal neutrons with little loss by absorption. Its prospective use in nuclear reactors is much greater than its older uses.

Beryllium has a unique use as "windows" in x-ray tubes; for this use its low atomic number is responsible. The absorption of x-rays by materials through which they pass is proportional to the atomic numbers of all the atoms encountered. Beryllium is therefore much more transparent to x-rays than glass is. Its major and indispensible use, however, has been as a beryllium-copper alloy in springs such as those used for the indicating hands of airplane instruments. A mere 1 or 2 per cent of beryllium produces an astonishing change in the properties of copper. The alloy has a temper like steel and is corrosion-resistant. Most important, its fatigue resistance surpasses that of steel about as much as steel does copper in this respect. When any piece of metal is bent back and forth a sufficient number of times, cracks form along the lines of the crystal grains and presently, even when no more force is applied than it has withstood many times before, it breaks "from fatigue." The almost infinite fatigue resistance of the beryllium alloy makes it ideal for use in places where it is subjected to continuous heavy vibration, as in airplanes. Its cost of $20 a pound is unimportant here but limits its use in tools, where its non-sparking quality makes it valuable when there is danger of igniting explosive gases.

Beryllium is extracted from its ore by treatment with H_2SO_4. Pure beryl, $Be_3Al_2Si_6O_{18}$, contains about 5 per cent beryllium. $Be(OH)_2$ is precipitated from the purified sulfate solution by NaOH (not excess, for $Be(OH)_2$ is amphoteric), and redissolved in HF. The metal is obtained from the BeF_2 by the Kroll process, using magnesium.

26.13. The Source of Nuclear Energy

At the beginning of this book we said, in connection with the law of the conservation of mass, that $E = mc^2$, Einstein's famous equation relating mass and energy, predicted that no detectable loss of weight should accompany the evolution of energy in chemical reactions. On the other hand, the weight losses accompanying radioactive changes should be easily measurable, since 1 Mev corresponds to slightly more than 0.001 atomic weight unit (1 a.w.u. = 931 Mev). For example, the weight of $^{206}_{82}$Pb plus that of the eight alpha particles and six electrons that were emitted during its formation from $_{92}$U^{238} totals 0.04 unit less than the weight of the parent atom. This weight loss is exactly accounted for by the weight equivalent of all the energy produced during the process.

Careful determination of the weight of 148 of the 283 naturally occurring nuclear species shows that it is always less than that of the protons and neutrons of which they are composed. These losses in weight represent the amounts of energy produced during their formation. Since these same amounts of energy would have to be supplied in order to dissociate nuclei into their original components, they are commonly called **binding energies.** In Fig. 26.2 the binding energy *per nuclear particle,* obtained by dividing the total binding energy for each nucleus by its mass number, is plotted against the mass number. To illustrate the correlation between mass and binding energy we consider the formation of deuterium, $^2_1$H, by the addition of a neutron to ordinary hydrogen. $^1_1$H. The exact masses of these are respectively 2.01474, 1.00898, and 1.00814. Thus:

$$^1_1\text{H} \quad + \quad ^1_0 n \quad \rightarrow \quad ^2_1\text{H}$$
$$1.00814 \qquad 1.00898 \qquad 2.01474$$

Note that the sum of the masses of the components of deuterium (1.00814 + 1.00898) is 2.01712, which is greater than the mass of deuterium by 0.00238. Thus a loss of mass amounting to 0.00238 a.w.u. occurs when a proton and a neutron are combined in a nucleus to form deuterium. This loss in mass appears in the form of a larger binding energy per particle in the deuterium nucleus. The energy equivalent of this mass is given by:

$$0.00238 \times 931 = 2.21 \text{ Mev}$$

Thus 2.21 Mev is the binding energy of the deuterium nucleus, which consists of two nuclear particles. Therefore the binding energy per nuclear particle in deuterium is one-half of 2.21 Mev, or 1.11 Mev. Note that this is the value given for a nuclear particle for deuterium in Fig. 26.2.

As mass numbers of isotopes increase, the binding energy per particle increases until a broad maximum is reached in the vicinity of iron. Through the range of this maximum the binding energy per particle is about 8.7 Mev. Beyond this maximum the binding energies gradually

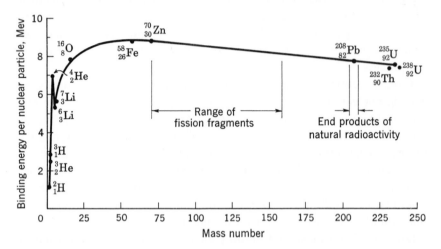

Fig. 26.2. Binding energy of naturally occurring nuclei. Many of the binding energies fall slightly above and below the curve, as is shown in the case of a few examples.

fall off to a minimum of about 7.5 Mev. The decrease in binding energy is associated with the greater instability of the atomic nuclei. This results from the gradual increase of the neutron-to-proton ratio in the isotopes with large mass numbers.

None of the elements that have a mass number greater than 70 (zinc) are present to the extent of 0.01 per cent in the igneous rocks of the earth's surface, although these rocks contain 5 per cent of iron. The core of the earth is believed to consist very largely of iron. These facts are associated with the greater stability of the elements in the vicinity of iron. Less stable atomic species with mass numbers greater than 210, such as thorium and uranium, readily emit alpha particles, $_2^4$He, during radioactive decay. It can be seen from Fig. 26.2 that the binding energy in the alpha particle is greater than that in any other simple combination of neutrons and protons for species in the vicinity of the alpha particle. In view of the abundance of protons and neutrons in the nuclei of the very heavy unstable atoms it is perfectly feasible that these nuclei should emit alpha particles in the process of reaching a more stable state. Since the mass number of the resultant nucleus shifts downward, the binding energy increases as the maximum of the curve is approached. This requires an additional loss in mass beyond that due to particle loss, since the increased binding energy must be obtained from the conversion of mass into energy.

Very few radioactive nuclei emit neutrons in order to become more stable. Fig. 26.2 shows that a large amount of energy would be required to overcome the binding energy of a neutron (or proton) in the unstable heavy nuclei. It was pointed out in Section 26.4 that neutron-rich nuclei emit neutrons only at the instant of formation and while in a state of high excitation. Instead, the neutron excess is more readily diminished by the emission of beta particles, e^-, from the nucleus as a beta ray. Beta particles, which are electrons, originate from the neutrons in the nucleus. Thus if the neutron, an electrically neutral particle, emits an electron, the residual particle must be positively charged and have a mass virtually that of the original neutron. This is, of course, the proton. In effect, beta particle emission diminishes the number of neutrons while simultaneously the proton number increases. This results in a greater proton-neutron ratio in the nucleus which is more favorable for stability.

In the fission process the newly generated isotopes from uranium range in mass number between 70 and 160. The most abundant fission fragments have mass numbers in the vicinity of 95 and 140. The fission fragments are unstable, neutron-rich, and radioactive. They usually emit beta particles along with gamma rays. Occasionally neutrons are emitted by them, since, when the fragments are created, they are in a state of high excitation because of the enormous energy released suddenly by the fission process. In the mass number range of the fission fragments (70 to 160) the binding energy per particle in stable nuclei is about 8.5 Mev, whereas for $^{235}_{92}U$ it is 7.6 Mev. Thus, when the uranium atom fissions into fragments, the energy liberated is:

$$235(8.5 - 7.6) \cong 212 \text{ Mev.}$$

26.14. Fusion

In Fig. 26.2 it can readily be seen that the binding energy in ^4_2He is significantly greater than that of the elements preceding and following this isotope, e.g., ^1_1H and ^7_3Li. The conversion of these elements into

$^4_2$He is called **fusion**. Fusion would result in a mass loss and as a consequence the equivalent in energy would be created. It is interesting to note that the increase in binding energy per particle in the fusion reaction:

$$4^1_1H \rightarrow \ ^4_2He + Energy$$
$$4(1.00814) \quad 4.00387$$

is approximately six times greater than that for the fission process (1.1 to 7 Mev in contrast to 7.6 to 8.5 Mev). The mass loss for the reaction results in an energy equivalent of about 27 Mev per helium atom formed. This can be calculated by the method used in the preceding section. The two neutrons in the helium nucleus arise from the capture of 2 orbital electrons which convert the nuclear protons into neutrons.

The fusion of light nuclei takes place only at fantastically high temperatures measured in tens or hundreds of millions of degrees centigrade. Such reactions occur in the sun. Although a series of reactions accounts for the tremendous evolution of energy by the sun, the end result is in essence the fusion of hydrogen into helium. About 1/15,000 of the sun's mass is converted into energy in this way in a billion years.

Neither the series of fusion reactions of the sun nor the highly improbable four-body collision of $^1_1$H to form helium appears to be practicable for use on earth. However, two-body collisions are highly probable and a fusion reaction involving this simpler binary collision process is possible. This can occur at a sufficiently high temperature between two deuterons, $^2_1$H, or between hydrogen and tritium, $^3_1$H.

$$2^2_1H \rightarrow \ ^4_2He$$
$$^1_1H + \ ^3_1H \rightarrow \ ^4_2He$$

Edward Teller, a University of California physicist who is often referred to in the popular press as "the father of the hydrogen bomb," had computed that the necessary velocity (temperature) would be available within the explosion of a fission bomb. The correctness of his computation was demonstrated in November, 1952, when a fission-fusion device was exploded by the United States for the first time. The awesome devastating force of this bomb was evident from the fact that the Pacific islet that was the site of the explosion was wiped off the face of the earth. The heavy hydrogen in which the fission bomb "trigger" was immersed was kept liquid by refrigerating machinery; so the whole device was more like a factory than a bomb. The first *fusion bomb* was set off by the Russians in August, 1953, using lithium instead of hydrogen. It is possible that our H-bombs are now using lithium deuteride. Fusion bombs are called thermonuclear devices because the reaction is initiated by the heat of a nuclear explosion.

There is hope that the fusion of deuterium to form helium may be tamed for use as a source of power. This is far from being as "simple" as controlling the fission reaction, for the fusion reaction must be carried out under high pressure at a temperature far above the decomposition point of any chemical compound. Obviously no material substance can be used for the reaction chamber. The only possibility seems to be the use of electromagnetic force fields. Neutral atoms cannot exist at the temperatures involved; only atomic nuclei and completely free electrons are possible. These charged particles can be constricted into a narrow column by a magnetic field, the temperature being raised by an electric field that drives them violently past each other in opposite directions. In our present state of knowledge these conditions have not been attained. The best we have been able to do is to create and maintain a temperature of 5 to 10 million degrees for a millisecond or so, or around 100 million degrees for a microsecond. No one can predict with certainty that the problem will ever be solved. If it is, it will forever put an end to worries about a fuel shortage. There is enough $_1^2 H$ in the ocean to supply all of mankind's conceivable energy needs for far longer than the time that has elapsed since man made his appearance on earth.

QUESTIONS AND PROBLEMS

1. Distinguish between chemical change and transmutation.
2. How do isotopic distribution and the neutron : proton ratio vary with atomic number?
3. Distinguish between a stable and an unstable isotope.
4. What factors are related to the instability of nuclei?
5. How is the rate of the radioactive decay of these nuclei measured? Can this rate be changed? Explain.
6. What over-all changes occur during radioactive decay?
7. What particles are ejected by nuclei with too many protons? With too many neutrons? What is the relationship between the atomic number of the atom produced and that of the original atom for each of these changes?
8. Supply the missing numbers and/or symbols for the following hypothetical decay reactions. The original isotope in each case is X.

$$_8^{18}X \rightarrow \quad + e^-$$
$$_{86}^{224}X \rightarrow \quad + _2^4He$$
$$_{50}^{115}X \rightarrow _{49}^{115}Y +$$

9. What are some sources of radiation man is exposed to in his normal environment? Which of these involve the greatest dosage? What is the estimated "safe" annual dosage for human beings?

10. What is artificial radioactivity? How can it be realized in the laboratory?

11. Why are neutrons used in fission reactions? Are all elements fissionable? Explain. What is the source of energy from a fission reaction?

12. Relative to nuclear energy, what is meant by critical mass? Moderator? Thermal neutrons? Fast neutrons? Spallation?

13. How many Mev of energy are liberated by the conversion of 0.1 of an atomic weight unit of mass into energy?

14. What is meant by nuclear binding energy? Is the mass of a nucleus equal to, greater than, or less than the mass sum of its components? Explain.

15. Distinguish between atomic fission and fusion.

Appendix

TABLE A.1. Conversions

Multiply	By	To Obtain
Atmospheres	76.0	Centimeters of mercury
Atmospheres	29.92	Inches of mercury
Atmospheres	14.7	Pounds per square inch
British thermal units	0.252	Kilogram-Calories
Centimeters	0.3937	Inches
Cubic centimeters	1×10^{-6}	Cubic meters
Cubic centimeters	1×10^{-3}	Liters
Cubic centimeters	1.057×10^{-3}	Quarts
Cubic centimeters	3.531×10^{-5}	Cubic feet
Cubic feet	1728.	Cubic inches
Cubic feet	28.32	Liters
Cubic feet	29.92	Quarts
Cubic inches	16.39	Cubic centimeters
Feet	30.48	Centimeters
Gallons	3785.	Cubic centimeters
Gallons	3.785	Liters
Grains (troy)	0.0648	Grams
Grains (troy)	2.0833×10^{-3}	Ounces (troy)
Grains per gallon	17.12	Parts per million
Grams	980.7	Dynes
Grams	2.205×10^{-3}	Pounds
Horsepower	0.7457	Kilowatts
Inches	2.54	Centimeters
Kilograms	2.205	Pounds
Kilometers	3281.	Feet
Kilometers	0.6214	Miles
Liters	61.02	Cubic inches
Liters	1.0567	Quarts
Liters	0.2642	Gallons
Meters	39.37	Inches
Microns	1×10^{-6}	Meters
Miles	5280.	Feet
Pounds	453.6	Grams
Square centimeters	0.155	Square inches
Square feet	929.	Square centimeters
Square inches	6.452	Square centimeters
Watt-Hours	3.415	British thermal units
Watt-Hours	1×10^{-3}	Kilowatt-Hours

TABLE A.2. Water Vapor Pressure At Various Temperatures

° C.	Pressure, mm.	° C.	Pressure, mm.	° C.	Pressure, mm.
0	4.6	21	18.6	30	31.8
5	6.5	22	19.8	40	55.3
10	9.2	23	21.0	50	92.5
15	12.8	24	22.4	60	149.4
16	13.6	25	23.8	70	233.7
17	14.5	26	25.2	80	355.1
18	15.5	27	26.7	90	525.8
19	16.5	28	28.3	100	760
20	17.5	29	30.0		

TABLE A.3. The Complete Electronegativity Scale[a]

																	H 2.1
Li 1.0	Be 1.5											B 2.0	C 2.5	N 3.0	O 3.5	F 4.0	
Na 0.9	Mg 1.2											Al 1.5	Si 1.8	P 2.1	S 2.5	Cl 3.0	
K 0.8	Ca 1.0	Sc 1.3	Ti 1.5	V 1.6	Cr 1.6	Mn 1.5	Fe 1.8	Co 1.8	Ni 1.8	Cu 1.9	Zn 1.6	Ga 1.6	Ge 1.8	As 2.0	Se 2.4	Br 2.8	
Rb 0.8	Sr 1.0	Y 1.2	Zr 1.4	Nb 1.6	Mo 1.8	Tc 1.9	Ru 2.2	Rh 2.2	Pd 2.2	Ag 1.9	Cd 1.7	In 1.7	Sn 1.8	Sb 1.9	Te 2.1	I 2.5	
Cs 0.7	Ba 0.9	La—Lu 1.1–1.2	Hf 1.3	Ta 1.5	W 1.7	Re 1.9	Os 2.2	Ir 2.2	Pt 2.2	Au 2.4	Hg 1.9	Tl 1.8	Pb 1.8	Bi 1.9	Po 2.0	At 2.2	
Fr 0.7	Ra 0.9	Ac 1.1	Th 1.3	Pa 1.5	U 1.7	Np—No 1.3											

[a] The values given in the table refer to the common oxidation states of the elements. For some elements, variation of the electronegativity with oxidation number is observed; for example, Fe^{II} 1.8, Fe^{III} 1.9; Cu^{I} 1.9; Cu^{II} 2.0; Sn^{II} 1.8, Sn^{IV} 1.9. For other elements, see W. Gordy and W. J. O. Thomas, *J. Chem. Phys.*, 24:439 (1956).

SOURCE: Reprinted with permission from Linus Pauling, *The Nature of the Chemical Bond*, 3rd ed., Cornell University Press, 1960.

TABLE A.4. Solubility—Product Constants

Anion	Equilibrium Equation	K_{sp}
Arsenate	$Ag_3AsO_4 \rightleftharpoons 3Ag^+ + AsO_4^{-3}$	1.0×10^{-22}
Bromide	$AgBr \rightleftharpoons Ag^+ + Br^-$	4.0×10^{-13}
Carbonate	$BaCO_3 \rightleftharpoons Ba^{++} + CO_3^{--}$	8.0×10^{-9}
	$CaCO_3 \rightleftharpoons Ca^{++} + CO_3^{--}$	8.5×10^{-9}
	$MgCO_3 \rightleftharpoons Mg^{++} + CO_3^{--}$	4.0×10^{-5}
Chloride	$AgCl \rightleftharpoons Ag^+ + Cl^-$	1.6×10^{-10}
	$Hg_2Cl_2 \rightleftharpoons Hg_2^{++} + 2Cl^-$	2.0×10^{-18}
	$PbCl_2 \rightleftharpoons Pb^{++} + 2Cl^-$	1.6×10^{-5}
Chromate	$BaCrO_4 \rightleftharpoons Ba^{++} + CrO_4^{--}$	2.4×10^{-10}
	$CaCrO_4 \rightleftharpoons Ca^{++} + CrO_4^{--}$	2.5×10^{-3}
	$PbCrO_4 \rightleftharpoons Pb^{++} + CrO_4^{--}$	1.8×10^{-14}
Hydroxide	$Al(OH)_3 \rightleftharpoons Al^{+3} + 3OH^-$	5.0×10^{-33}
	$Co(OH)_2 \rightleftharpoons Co^{++} + 2OH^-$	2.5×10^{-16}
	$Co(OH)_3 \rightleftharpoons Co^{+3} + 3OH^-$	3×10^{-17}
	$Cr(OH)_3 \rightleftharpoons Cr^{+3} + 3OH^-$	6.7×10^{-31}
	$Fe(OH)_3 \rightleftharpoons Fe^{+3} + 3OH^-$	6×10^{-38}
	$Mg(OH)_2 \rightleftharpoons Mg^{++} + 2OH^-$	1.4×10^{-11}
	$Mn(OH)_2 \rightleftharpoons Mn^{++} + 2OH^-$	2.0×10^{-13}
	$Ni(OH)_2 \rightleftharpoons Ni^{++} + 2OH^-$	1.6×10^{-16}
	$Zn(OH)_2 \rightleftharpoons Zn^{++} + 2OH^-$	5.0×10^{-17}
Oxalate	$BaC_2O_4 \rightleftharpoons Ba^{++} + C_2O_4^{--}$	1.5×10^{-7}
	$CaC_2O_4 \rightleftharpoons Ca^{++} + C_2O_4^{--}$	1.3×10^{-9}
	$MgC_2O_4 \rightleftharpoons Mg^{++} + C_2O_4^{--}$	8.6×10^{-5}
Phosphate	$Ca_3(PO_4)_2 \rightleftharpoons 3Ca^{++} + 2PO_4^{-3}$	1.0×10^{-25}
	$MgNH_4PO_4 \rightleftharpoons Mg^{++} + NH_4^+ + PO_4^{-3}$	2.6×10^{-13}
Sulfate	$BaSO_4 \rightleftharpoons Ba^{++} + SO_4^{--}$	1.5×10^{-9}
	$PbSO_4 \rightleftharpoons Pb^{++} + SO_4^{--}$	1.3×10^{-8}
Sulfide	$Ag_2S \rightleftharpoons 2Ag^+ + S^{--}$	5.5×10^{-51}
	$As_2S_3 \rightleftharpoons 2As^{+3} + 3S^{--}$	4.0×10^{-29}
	$Bi_2S_3 \rightleftharpoons 2Bi^{+3} + 3S^{--}$	1.6×10^{-72}
	$CdS \rightleftharpoons Cd^{++} + S^{--}$	1.4×10^{-28}
	$CoS(\alpha) \rightleftharpoons Co^{++} + S^{--}$	5.0×10^{-22} (freshly formed)
	$CoS(\beta) \rightleftharpoons Co^{++} + S^{--}$	2.0×10^{-27} (after standing)

TABLE A.4. *Continued*

Anion	Equilibrium Equation	K_{sp}
Sulfide	$CuS \rightleftharpoons Cu^{++} + S^{--}$	4.0×10^{-38}
	$FeS \rightleftharpoons Fe^{++} + S^{--}$	4.0×10^{-19}
	$HgS \rightleftharpoons Hg^{++} + S^{--}$	2.0×10^{-54}
	$MnS \rightleftharpoons Mn^{++} + S^{--}$	7.0×10^{-16}
	$PbS \rightleftharpoons Pb^{++} + S^{--}$	2.0×10^{-29}
	$SnS \rightleftharpoons Sn^{++} + S^{--}$	1.0×10^{-26}
	$ZnS \rightleftharpoons Zn^{++} + S^{--}$	1.2×10^{-23}

TABLE A.5. **Ionization Constants**

Compound	Equilibrium Equation	Ionization Constant
Water	$H_2O + H_2O \rightleftharpoons H_3O^+ + OH^-$	$K_w = 1.0 \times 10^{-14}$
Acids		
Acetic	$HC_2H_3O_2 + H_2O \rightleftharpoons H_3O^+ + C_2H_3O_2$	$K_{ion} = 1.8 \times 10^{-5}$
Arsenic	$H_3AsO_4 + H_2O \rightleftharpoons H_3O^+ + H_2AsO_4^-$	$K_1 = 5.6 \times 10^{-3}$
	$H_2AsO_4^- + H_2O^- \rightleftharpoons H_3O^+ + HAsO_4^-$	$K_2 = 1.7 \times 10^{-7}$
	$HAsO_4^{--} + H_2O \rightleftharpoons H_3O^+ + AsO_4^{-3}$	$K_3 = 3.0 \times 10^{-12}$
Arsenious	$H_3AsO_3 + H_2O \rightleftharpoons H_3O^+ + H_2AsO_3^-$	$K_1 = 6.0 \times 10^{-10}$
Carbonic	$H_2CO_3 + H_2O \rightleftharpoons H_3O^+ + HCO_3^-$	$K_1 = 4.3 \times 10^{-7}$
	$HCO_3^- + H_2O \rightleftharpoons H_3O^+ + CO_3^{--}$	$K_2 = 4.4 \times 10^{-11}$
Hydrosulfuric	$H_2S + H_2O \rightleftharpoons H_3O^+ + HS^-$	$K_1 = 9.1 \times 10^{-8}$
	$HS^- + H_2O \rightleftharpoons H_3O^+ + S^{--}$	$K_2 = 1.2 \times 10^{-15}$
Sulfuric	$H_2SO_4 + H_2O \rightleftharpoons H_3O^+ + HSO_4^-$	$K_1 = $ large
	$HSO_4^- + H_2O \rightleftharpoons H_3O^+ + SO_4$	$K_2 = 2.0 \times 10^{-2}$
Sulfurous	$H_2SO_3 + H_2O \rightleftharpoons H_3O^+ + HSO_3^-$	$K_1 = 1.5 \times 10^{-2}$
	$HSO_3^- + H_2O \rightleftharpoons H_3O^+ + SO_3^{--}$	$K_2 = 6.0 \times 10^{-8}$
Bases		
Ammonia	$NH_3 + H_2O \rightleftharpoons NH_4^+ + OH^-$	$K_{ion} = 1.8 \times 10^{-5}$

TABLE A.6. Four-Place Logarithms

N	0	1	2	3	4	5	6	7	8	9
10	0000	0043	0086	0128	0170	0212	0253	0294	0334	0374
11	0414	0453	0492	0531	0569	0607	0645	0682	0719	0755
12	0792	0828	0864	0899	0934	0969	1004	1038	1072	1106
13	1139	1173	1206	1239	1271	1303	1335	1367	1399	1430
14	1461	1492	1523	1553	1584	1614	1644	1673	1703	1732
15	1761	1790	1818	1847	1875	1903	1931	1959	1987	2014
16	2041	2068	2095	2122	2148	2175	2201	2227	2253	2279
17	2304	2330	2355	2380	2405	2430	2455	2480	2504	2529
18	2553	2577	2601	2625	2648	2672	2695	2718	2742	2765
19	2788	2810	2833	2856	2878	2900	2923	2945	2967	2989
20	3010	3032	3054	3075	3096	3118	3139	3160	3181	3201
21	3222	3243	3263	3284	3304	3324	3345	3365	3385	3404
22	3424	3444	3464	3483	3502	3522	3541	3560	3579	3598
23	3617	3636	3655	3674	3692	3711	3729	3747	3766	3784
24	3802	3820	3838	3856	3874	3892	3909	3927	3945	3962
25	3979	3997	4014	4031	4048	4065	4082	4099	4116	4133
26	4150	4166	4183	4200	4216	4232	4249	4265	4281	4298
27	4314	4330	4346	4362	4378	4393	4409	4425	4440	4456
28	4472	4487	4502	4518	4533	4548	4564	4579	4594	4609
29	4624	4639	4654	4669	4683	4698	4713	4728	4742	4757
30	4771	4786	4800	4814	4829	4843	4857	4871	4886	4900
31	4914	4928	4942	4955	4969	4983	4997	5011	5024	5038
32	5051	5065	5079	5092	5105	5119	5132	5145	5159	5172
33	5185	5198	5211	5224	5237	5250	5263	5276	5289	5302
34	5315	5328	5340	5353	5366	5378	5391	5403	5416	5428
35	5441	5453	5465	5478	5490	5502	5514	5527	5539	5551
36	5563	5575	5587	5599	5611	5623	5635	5647	5658	5670
37	5682	5694	5705	5717	5729	5740	5752	5763	5775	5786
38	5798	5809	5821	5832	5843	5855	5866	5877	5888	5899
39	5911	5922	5933	5944	5955	5966	5977	5988	5999	6010
40	6021	6031	6042	6053	6064	6075	6085	6096	6107	6117
41	6128	6138	6149	6160	6170	6180	6191	6201	6212	6222
42	6232	6243	6253	6263	6274	6284	6294	6304	6314	6325
43	6335	6345	6355	6365	6375	6385	6395	6405	6415	6425
44	6435	6444	6454	6464	6474	6484	6493	6503	6513	6522
45	6532	6542	6551	6561	6571	6580	6590	6599	6609	6618
46	6628	6637	6646	6656	6665	6675	6684	6693	6702	6712
47	6721	6730	6739	6749	6758	6767	6776	6785	6694	6803
48	6812	6821	6830	6839	6848	6857	6866	6875	6884	6893
49	6902	6911	6920	6928	6937	6946	6955	6964	6972	6981
50	6990	6998	7007	7016	7024	7033	7042	7050	7059	7067
51	7076	7084	7093	7101	7110	7118	7126	7135	7143	7152
52	7160	7168	7177	7185	7193	7202	7210	7218	7226	7235
53	7243	7251	7259	7267	7275	7284	7292	7300	7308	7316
54	7324	7332	7340	7348	7356	7364	7372	7380	7388	7396

N	0	1	2	3	4	5	6	7	8	9
55	7404	7412	7419	7427	7435	7443	7451	7459	7466	7474
56	7482	7490	7497	7505	7513	7520	7528	7536	7543	7551
57	7559	7566	7574	7582	7589	7597	7604	7612	7619	7627
58	7634	7642	7649	7657	7664	7672	7679	7686	7694	7701
59	7709	7716	7723	7731	7738	7745	7752	7760	7767	7774
60	7782	7789	7796	7803	7810	7818	7825	7832	7839	7846
61	7853	7860	7868	7875	7882	7889	7896	7903	7910	7917
62	7924	7931	7938	7945	7952	7959	7966	7973	7980	7987
63	7993	8000	8007	8014	8021	8028	8035	8041	8048	8055
64	8062	8069	8075	8082	8089	8096	8102	8109	8116	8122
65	8129	8136	8142	8149	8156	8162	8169	8176	8182	8189
66	8195	8202	8209	8215	8222	8228	8235	8241	8248	8254
67	8261	8267	8274	8280	8287	8293	8299	8306	8312	8319
68	8325	8331	8338	8344	8351	8357	8363	8370	8376	8382
69	8388	8395	8401	8407	8414	8420	8426	8432	8439	8445
70	8451	8457	8463	8470	8476	8482	8488	8494	8500	8506
71	8513	8519	8525	8531	8537	8543	8549	8555	8561	8567
72	8573	8579	8585	8591	8597	8603	8609	8615	8621	8627
73	8633	8639	8645	8651	8657	8663	8669	8675	8681	8686
74	8692	8698	8704	8710	8716	8722	8727	8733	8739	8745
75	8751	8756	8762	8768	8774	8779	8785	8791	8797	8802
76	8808	8814	8820	8825	8831	8837	8842	8848	8854	8859
77	8865	8871	8876	8882	8887	8893	8899	8904	8910	8915
78	8921	8927	8932	8938	8943	8949	8954	8960	8965	8971
79	8976	8982	8987	8993	8998	9004	9009	9015	9020	9025
80	9031	9036	9042	9047	9053	9058	9063	9069	9074	9079
81	9085	9090	9096	9101	9106	9112	9117	9122	9128	9133
82	9138	9143	9149	9154	9159	9165	9170	9175	9180	9186
83	9191	9196	9201	9206	9212	9217	9222	9227	9232	9238
84	9243	9248	9253	9258	9263	9269	9274	9279	9284	9289
85	9294	9299	9304	9309	9315	9320	9325	9330	9335	9340
86	9345	9350	9355	9360	9365	9370	9375	9380	9385	9390
87	9395	9400	9405	9410	9415	9420	9425	9430	9435	9440
88	9445	9450	9455	9460	9465	9469	9474	9479	9484	9489
89	9494	9499	9504	9509	9513	9518	9523	9528	9533	9538
90	9542	9547	9552	9557	9562	9566	9571	9576	9581	9586
91	9590	9595	9600	9605	9609	9614	9619	9624	9628	9633
92	9638	9643	9647	9652	9657	9661	9666	9671	9675	9680
93	9685	9689	9694	9699	9703	9708	9713	9717	9722	9727
94	9731	9736	9741	9745	9750	9754	9759	9763	9768	9773
95	9777	9782	9786	9791	9795	9800	9805	9809	9814	9818
96	9823	9827	9832	9836	9841	9845	9850	9854	9859	9863
97	9868	9872	9877	9881	9886	9890	9894	9899	9903	9908
98	9912	9917	9921	9926	9930	9934	9939	9943	9948	9952
99	9956	9961	9965	9969	9974	9978	9983	9987	9991	9996

Index

Aqua regia, 257
Argon, electronic structure, 61
Arsenic, analysis, 570–572
    arsenic acid, 561, 572–573
    arsenites, 562
    arsine, 558–560
        Gutzeit test, 559
        Marsh test, 559–560
    chloride, 560
    oxide, 559, 560–563
    preparation, 563
    properties, 563–564
    silver arsenate, 573
    sulfides, 566–568, 572
    thio-anions, 568, 572
    uses, 565
Astatine, 234
Atom, 41, 44, 51
    electronic structure, 57–68
        electron orbitals, 60–66
        energy levels (shells), 58–60
        stable configurations, 67–68
Atomic, hydrogen, 151, 154
    torch, 154
    kernels, 77
        of halogen elements, 245
    number, 51
        and periodic table, 69
        determination of, 53
    volume, variation with atomic number, 479–480
    weight, 37, 55
        approximate experimental values, 161
        from equivalent weights, 160
Avogadro's law, 35
Avogadro's number, 37

Baking powder, 419–420
Balard, 198
Barium, analysis, 431–434
    carbide, 412
    carbonate, 425, 432
        case hardening of steels, 498
    chromate, 433
    hydride, 412, 415
    nitride, 412
    oxide, 412, 414
    peroxide, 415
    production, 407
    sulfate, 271, 305, 348, 405, 425
    thermite process, 393
        See also Alkaline earth metals
Base, 88
    Brønsted, 237
    conjugate, 237–238, 247, 280
    formation from oxides, 131
    in buffer mixtures, 371–372
    indicators, 369
    ionic equilibrium in water, 363–364
    non-aqueous, 403–404

Base (Continued)
    pH values, 366
    titration with acid, 188
Basic anhydride, 133
Basic salts, 261, 569
Battery, see Voltaic cell
Bauxite, 390
    Bayer purification process, 445
Becquerel, Henri, 715
Beryllium, 405
    amphoterism, 441
    nuclear synthesis, 724
    production, 730
    properties and uses, 730
Beta ray, 48
    in radioactive decay, 718
    nuclear synthesis, 724
Bismuth, analysis, 571, 574
    basic salts, 569–570
    bismuthic acid and bismuthate ion, 562
    bismuthine, 558–559
    chloride, 561, 569
    complex anions, 567
    hydroxide, 562, 570, 574
    nitrate, 567, 569–570
    oxides, 562–563
    preparation, 563
    properties, 563–564
    sulfides, 567
    uses, 565
Bleaching, powder, 261
    with chlorine, 224
    with sulfur dioxide, 287
    wood pulp, 224, 262, 264
Bohr, Niels, 51, 57
    energy levels and spectra, 58, 61
Boiling point, 14, 190
    concentration effects in solutions, 190–192
    constant-boiling mixtures, 235–236
Bond, 84
    conjugated, 624–626, 652
    coordinate covalent, 88
    covalent, 86
    fractional order, 667
    hydrogen, 164
    ionic character, 86
    multiple, 91, 316, 624
    non-polar, 85
    pi, 91
    polar, 85
    sigma, 91
Boron, boranes, 127, 692
    properties, 693
    structure, 693
    borates: calcium and sodium, 697
    sources, 697
    boric acid, 695
    properties, 695
    structure, 695–696

Fluorine (*Continued*)
fluorocarbons, 226
ionic character of covalent bonds, 202
oxidizing ability, 201–202
physical properties, 197
production, 198–200
source, 198
uses, 202–204
    See also Halogens
Fluoro-complexes, 248–249
Fluorspar, 198
preparation of hydrogen fluoride, 238
Flux, 256
in metallurgy, 390
soldering, 472
steel production, 495
Formula (chemical), 98
and oxidation numbers, 105
common, 99
electronic, 81, 85, 99
empirical, 100, 108
experimental determination of, 106
molecular, 99, 108
percentage composition, 106
structural, 99
weight, 109
relation to equivalent weight, 159
use in solution concentrations, 181–
183
Frasch process, 272–273
Freezing point, 13
of solutions, 190–192
Fundamental units of matter, 44
Fusion (nuclear), 733–735

Gadolinium, sulfate, 709
for attainment of low temperatures,
709–710
Galvani, L., 610
Galvanic cell, 598
    See also Voltaic cell
Gas, critical pressure and temperature, 32
density, 35
ideal and real, 27
inert, 68, 78
intermolecular attraction, 27
kinetic theory of, 14–16
laws: Avogadro, 35
Boyle (P-V), 16–18
Charles (V-T), 18
combination (PVT), 22
Dalton (partial pressures), 23–25
deviations, 26
Gay-Lussac: combining volumes, 36;
(P-T), 20
Graham (diffusion), 35
Henry (solubility), 179
liquefaction of, 29–33, 122
molecular volume, 26

Gas (*Continued*)
molecular weight, 37–39
pressure, 15
refrigerant, 33
solutions of, in liquids, 179
van der Waal's equation, 27
Gay-Lussac, J., gas laws, 20, 36
sulfur, 271
Geiger counter, 68
Gems, natural, 457
oriental (corundum), 457
synthetic, 457
Giant molecules, 563, 649
linear (chain) form: condensation, 654,
657, 659, 664, 691
elastomers: rubber, 660–663; vulcanization, 661
organic molecules, 654–660
polymerization, 654
silicate anions, 674–675
silicones, 691–692
sulfur, 275
sheet form: boric acid, 695–696
borides, 694
graphite, 651
organic molecules, 657, 660
phosphorus, 340
silicate anions, 675–677
three-dimensional form, aluminosilicate
anions, 677–679
boron, 667
diamond, 652
quartz, 668, 670
thermosetting plastics, 663–665
Gold, alloys, 584
history, 578
metallurgy: anion complexes, 583
cyanide process, 582–583
occurrence, 582
properties and uses, 583–586
Gold(I), complex anions, 587
electronic structure, 587
Gold(III), complex halo- ions, 595
electronic structure, 592
fluoride, 595
hydroxide, 595
Goodyear, Charles, vulcanization of rubber, 661
Gram, atomic heat capacity, 162
use in calculating approximate atomic
weights, 162
equivalent weight, 157
use in chemical calculations, 160
molecular volume, 37, 112
molecular weight, 37, 109
calculation of, 38, 109
relation to gram equivalent weight,
158
Group (periodic), 72

Mordant, aluminum hydroxide, 456–457
  chromium(III) hydroxide, 464
  tin(IV) oxide, 546
Mortar, cement, 687–690
  plaster of Paris, 424–425
Mosely, H. G. J., 53
Muriatic acid, 235
        See also Hydrogen chloride

Neptunium, 720
  nuclear synthesis, 724
Neutron, 45
  isotopes, 54
  properties, 50
  use in nuclear synthesis, 724
Nickel, alnico magnet, 512
  carbonyl, 518
    structure, 522–523
  history, 518
  Nicad storage battery, 615–616
  occurrence, 518
  production, 518–519
  trends of 3d transition elements, 479–482
  uses and alloys, 519
Nickel(II), analysis, 524–527
  complexes: amine, 520
    covalent, 520–521
    hydrate, 520
    magnetic susceptibility, 520
  dimethylglyoxime, 520–521
  hydroxide, 520–521
  nitrate, 521–522
  oxide, 522
  sulfate, 520
  sulfide, 524–525
Nickel(III), arsenide, 521–522
  oxide, 512, 521–522
Nickel(IV), 510–511
  arsenide, 521
  oxide, 522
Niobium, use in nuclear reactors, 729–730
Nitrate ion, analysis, 337–338
  properties, 336
  structure and bonding, 335–336
Nitration, 303, 333
Nitric acid, production: Ostwald process,
        326, 330–331
    saltpeter, 330
  properties, 331–333
  uses, 331–333
Nitride ion, properties, 317
Nitrite ion, complexing ability, 337
  properties and uses, 337–338
  structure and bonding, 337
Nitrogen, family, 314
  fixation processes: arc, 318
    cyanamide, 318
    Haber, 319

Nitrogen (*Continued*)
  molecular structure and bonding, 316
  oxides: dinitrogen tetroxide, 317
    nitric, 296, 317, 318, 330–331
    nitrogen dioxide, 296, 317, 331
    nitrogen pentoxide, 317
    nitrogen trioxide, 317, 338
    nitrous, 317, 329
  preparation, 315
  properties, 315–318
  trichloride, 265, 317
  trifluoride, 223, 318
Nitronium ion, 303, 333
Nitrosyl, chloride, 331–332
  ion: formation of mixed complexes, 523–524
  sulfuric acid, 296–297
Nitrous acid, 337–338
Nobel, Alfred, 334
Nomenclature, 101
  ions, 102
  acids, 104
Normality, 183
  relation to molarity, 183
  volume relationships, 187
Nuclear, binding energy, 731–733
  fission, 57, 727
  fusion, 56, 733–735
  reactors, 724–725
    construction materials, 728–730
    critical mass, 727
    moderator, 727
  synthesis, 724
Nucleus, atomic, 51
  isotopes, 54
  symbols, 54
  unstable, 716–717
        See also Isotopes

Occlusion, of hydrogen by metals, 151
Octet (valence), 86
  expansion, 231
Orbit, 58
Orbital, 60
  classes, 61–62
    electron capacities, 62
  energy, 63
    variation with atomic number, 65
  filling of orbitals and electron shells, 64–68, 72
  molecular, 83, 91
  relation to periodic table, 69–73
  wave function, 60
Ore, 388–393
  concentration, 389
  pyrometallurgical treatment, 389–392
Organic chemistry, acids: acetic, 640
    adipic, 641, 655

Phosphorus (*Continued*)
  hydrides, phosphine and diphosphine,
    341
  matches, 343
  metallic modification, 563–564
  molecular structure and bonding, 339–
    340
  oxides, pent- and tri-, 342–343
  oxy-acids, 345–347
  phosphates, uses, 347–348
  physical properties, 339–341
  production, 338–339
  sulfides, penta- and sesqui-, 343
Photography, development, 589
  fixing, 589–590
  latent image, 589
  photochemical reactions, 588
Photons, 717
Physical properties, 6
Pigments, cadmium selenide and sulfide,
  533
  chromium, 466–467
  iron, 501–504
  lead, 466–467, 553–554
Planck, Max, 57
Plutonium, fission, 726
  nuclear synthesis, 724–725
Polar molecule, 86
  hydrogen fluoride, 201, 235
  water, 164, 170
Polarizability, and color of ions, 505
  and tendency to form covalent bonds,
    246, 248, 481–482
  effect on lattice energy, 251
  halide ions, 245
  of ligands and magnetic susceptibility of
    complex ions, 504
  sulfide ion, 281
Polonium, 270, 310
Polybasic (polyprotic) acids, 267, 280, 304,
  345
  equilibrium constants, 361–363
  hydrated cations, 440
Polymers, *see* Giant molecules
Polymorphism, of metals, 382–384
Polysulfides, 283–284
Positron, 718
Potassium, acid fluoride, 198–199
  alloy coolant for reactors, 727–728
  analysis, 431–434
  bromide, 229
  carbonate, 399, 417, 420
  chloride, 424
  fluoride, 199
  hydroxide, 415, 416
  nitrate, 329, 336
  production, 400–401
  properties, 398–399, 402, 404
  source, 399–400

Potassium (*Continued*)
  sulfate, 424
    alum, 458
  superoxide, 404, 415
  uses, 400
    See also Alkali metals
Pressure, 13, 15
  critical, 32
  effect on: boiling point, 190
    solubility of gases in liquids, 179
    volume of gases, 16
  standard, 23
  vapor, 25, 31, 190
Priestley, Joseph, 119
Proton, 45
  hydration, 236
  properties, 48
  transfer, 87, 221, 236–238
    See also Atom; Atomic number
Pyrites, 271, 285, 510

Qualitative analysis, anions: borate,
  695
  nitrate, 337
  phosphate, 346
  sulfate, 309
  sulfide, 309
  sulfite, 309
  the halides, 253–255
  thiosulfate, 309
  cations: group I, 591–592
    group II, 570–575
    group III, aluminum subgroup, 474–
      476; nickel subgroup, 524–527
    group IV, 431–434
    separation of analytical groups, 281–
      283, 430–431
Quantum, of radiant energy, 588

Radioactivity, 715
  artificial, 724–725
  decay reactions, 718–719
  equilibrium, 720
  half-life, 717
  natural, 720
  radiation effects, 721–723
    intensity, 721
    sources, 722–723
  series 719–721
Radium, 721–722
Raoult's law, 191–192
Rare earth metals, discovery, 707–708
  ion exchange purification, 394–395
  uses, 708–710
    See also Lanthanides
Reaction, addition, 226, 302
  chain, 225
  dismutation, 262–263
  displacement, 226

Silver (*Continued*)
nitrate, 586–587
occurrence, 511, 582
Parkes process, 549
perchlorate, 587
permanganate, 587
properties and uses, 583–585
sulfate, 586–587
sulfide, 585, 589
Sintering, 445, 687
Slag, 421
in metallurgy of iron and steel, 490–491, 493–496
Smelting, 389–390
Soap, chemical properties, 426
emulsifying action, 426
Soddy, F., 715, 720
Sodium, amide, 401, 403
analysis, 431–434
antimonate, 562
antimonite, 562
azide, 401
bicarbonate, 417–419
carbonate, 417–419
Solvay process, 417–418
water softening, 427
chloride: crystal lattice, 204, 206, 250
electrolysis: fused, 204–208; solutions, 208–210
chromate, 466
coolant in reactors, 727–728
cyanide, 401
ethylate, 403
fluoaluminate, 198, 256
hydride, 401, 404
hydroxide, 415–416
electrolytic production, 208–212
hypochlorite, 260
metaphosphate, 430
nitrate, 330, 332, 336
nitride, 401
peroxide, 121, 262, 401, 404
phosphate, 345, 348
pyrosulfite, 590
silicate (glass), 682–685
stearate (soap), 426
sulfate, 305, 423–424
alum, 458
sulfide, 280, 423
thiosulfate, 589
See also Alkali metals
Solids, 6, 12, 30
diffusion, 31
expansion, 31
melting point, 190
vapor pressure, 190
Solubility product, 372–376
Solute, 169
crystallization process, 173

Solute (*Continued*)
dissolving process, 172
gaseous, 179
immiscible liquid, 177
in alloys, 387–388
liquid, 177
miscible liquid, 177
Solution, 168
boiling points, 190–192
colloidal, 177–179
concentration expressions, 181–185
concentration-volume calculations, 186–190
constant boiling, 235–236
dissolution action, 171
heat of, 176
Henry's law, 179
ideal, 191
ion clusters, 173
melting points, 190–192
miscible and immiscible, 177, 233
Raoult's law, 191–192
rate of, 175
saturated, 175, 180
solid, in alloys, 387–388
solubility, 175
solute, 169
solvent, 169
strong and weak acids in, 174
supersaturated, 176, 180
vapor pressure of, 191
Solvent, 169
immiscible liquid, 177, 233
in alloys, 387–388
miscible liquid, 177
non-polar, 170
polar, 170, 246
vapor pressure, 190
Spallation, in nuclear reactions, 726
Specific gravity, lead storage battery, 613–615
of solutions, 184–185
relationship to density, 184
Specific heat, 29
B.t.u., 30
calorie, 30
use in calculating approximate atomic weights, 161–163
Spectograph, mass, 48, 49, 56
Spectroscope 57, 435
Spectrum, 57, 435
absorption, 92, 435–436
emission, 436
Spinels, 457
aluminum-: cobalt, 512
magnesium, 457
chromium-: cobalt, 512
iron, 460
cobalt-cobalt, 512

Waterglass, 670
Wave length, diffraction effects, 94
  relation to: crystal structure, 93
    energy levels of atoms, 57–59
    molecular structure, 92
  spectroscope, 57–58
  x-ray and atomic number, 53
Werner complexes, 516–517
Wilson cloud chamber, 49
Wood pulp, Kraft process, 423

X-rays, 53
  diffraction, 93–96
  wave length relation to atomic number,
    53

Yield point, 12
Yttrium, 701

Zeolite, 427, 444, 678–679
Zinc, amphoteric behavior, 441–442
  analysis, 474–476

Zinc (*Continued*)
  bright plating of, 532
  chloride, 472–473
  dithionite, 474
  ions: electronic structure and properties
    of Zn^{++}, 471
    positive and negative complexes, 442,
      471–472
  ore (roasting), 392
  phosphate, 474
  preparation of hydrogen, 148, 150, 470
  production, 468–470
  properties and uses, 470–471
  sources, 468
  stearate, 474
  sulfate, 468–469, 473
  sulfide, 281, 425, 468
Zirconium, production, 728–729
  silicate, 708
  use in nuclear reactors, 724, 727
  zirconyl ion, 711
Zone refining, 395

Set in Monophoto and Fotosetter Times Roman

Format by Frances Tilley

Published by Harper & Brothers, New York